Algebra and Trigonometry

Algebra and Trigonometry

Bernard J. Rice
Jerry D. Strange

University of Dayton

Prindle, Weber & Schmidt, Incorporated
Boston, Massachusetts

Printed in the United States of America
Second printing: July 1977

Library of Congress Cataloging in Publication Data

Rice, Bernard J
    Algebra and trigonometry.

    Includes index.   1. Algebra.   2. Trigonometry.   I. Strange
Jerry D., joint author.   II. Title.
QA154.2.R5   512'.13   76-58894
ISBN 0-87150-228-3

Cover photograph by Robert Mann

Technical art by PIP, Inc. Photographs on the chapter opening pages by Robert Mann.
Text design by Deborah Schneider in collaboration with the PWS production staff.
Composed in Times Roman and Univers by Santype International, Ltd. Printed and
bound by Halliday Lithograph Corporation.

Preface

Besides being a prerequisite subject for the study of calculus and other more advanced mathematics courses, algebra is also a subject that is essential to the understanding of the quantitative nature of our world. While most modern elementary mathematics books at the college level speak to the prerequisite role of algebra, few relate to the student's need to identify mathematical concepts with familiar physical problems. In this book we have attempted to overcome this shortcoming. In writing this book we have followed current pedagogy and made the functional concept the central theme while simultaneously stressing the utilitarian aspects of mathematics by including problems stated in the context of some real world situation.

The material presented in this book presupposes some capability in algebraic manipulation, obtained either in high school or in a post-high school elementary algebra course. However, topics such as special products, factoring, exponents, and radicals are presented in the text. Set notation is used only in a way familiar to students with the most meager background in algebra. Heavy emphasis is placed on graphing throughout the book.

Because repetition is an important part of the learning process, we have included an abundant supply of graded problems in each exercise set, over 3300 in all. There are also over 400 worked examples. Many of these problems and examples are stated in the terminology of some application so that the student will feel comfortable with mathematics as a tool. Each chapter concludes with two chapter tests to give the student some clue as to what his expected level of comprehension should be. One test emphasizes concepts; the other emphasizes manipulative skills. The answers to the odd-numbered exercise problems are included in the back of the book.

A large variety of topics are covered in the book to allow the individual instructor sufficient latitude to meet the needs of a particular course. Certain sections can be omitted without loss of continuity. In some cases, sections have been marked as optional to aid the instructor in preparing a course outline. The first two chapters, which may be used to equalize the skill levels of the students, review the fundamentals of the number line and the basic algebraic laws.

Chapter 3, a thorough discussion of functions, includes an introduction to functions defined by different rules on different intervals, with particular emphasis on the absolute value function. The concluding section on inverses and composite functions may be omitted or delayed until needed in Chapter 8.

Chapters 4 and 5 consider linear equations and systems of equations with an introduction to the use of matrices and determinants. Systems of equations are solved graphically, thus giving emphasis to the use of the coordinate plane and absolute values. A brief discussion of the application of two variable linear inequalities to linear programming is an optional topic.

Quadratic equations and functions are reviewed in Chapter 6 along with a complete discussion of the method of sign diagrams to solve inequalities. This method is the most appropriate since it extends to higher order and rational inequalities. The discussion in Chapter 7 of polynomial functions includes several optional sections on synthetic division and its corollary, the method of nested multiplications.

Exponential and logarithmic functions are considered in Chapter 8. The functional nature of exponents and logarithms is emphasized while the computational aspects are given a minor role since hand calculators are so readily available.

The initial development of trigonometry in Chapter 9 is in terms of the right triangle definitions since it is our belief that trigonometry is best learned and almost always remembered with this approach. In Chapter 10 the extension of the domain of the trigonometric functions to angles in standard position in the Cartesian plane is followed by a derivation of the law of cosines and law of sines. Applications where solutions to triangles are important are included in these chapters.

Chapters 11 and 12 are devoted to the modern analytical aspects of trigonometry and related nontriangular applications. For those who wish to particularly emphasize graphing and precalculus trigonometry, many of the applications of Chapters 9 and 10 may be omitted or shortened without losing continuity.

The important ideas of vectors and complex numbers are the subject of Chapter 13. These are two of the most important subjects that a student will need in science and engineering related disciplines. The text concludes with a chapter on finite mathematics and an introductory chapter on analytic geometry. These chapters give an added flexibility to the book and allow an individual instructor to adjust to the different needs of the students.

Algebra and Trigonometry was revised several times in manuscript form and reviewed at various stages since its conception. We wish to single out the following who assisted us with their comments:

Richard J. Easton (Indiana State University, Terre Haute)
Douglas Hall (Michigan State University)
George A. Huff (Kansas State University)
Richard W. Marshall (Eastern Michigan University)
Anthony A. Patricelli (Northeastern Illinois University)
Kenneth A. Rager (Metropolitan State College)
David J. Shannon (University of Kentucky)
Albert W. Zechmann (University of Nebraska, Lincoln)

We wish also to thank Mr. John Martindale who encouraged us to undertake the task of writing this text and Mr. Locke Macdonald for his valuable assistance in finalizing the manuscript.

BERNARD J. RICE

JERRY D. STRANGE

University of Dayton

February 1977

The lion is used in this book to indicate the end of a solution to an example (or the end of an example if no solution follows).

Contents

8
Exponential and
Logarithmic Functions

9
Right Triangle
Trigonometry

Contents

Appendix

1
Some
Fundamental Ideas

1.1
The Language of
Mathematics

In this section we briefly introduce two "languages" used throughout this book and throughout much of mathematics. Both are abbreviations or abstractions that enable us to write mathematical relationships with a minimum of effort.

Algebraic Language

Algebraic language refers to the use of symbols to describe relations between numbers. Without it, many mathematically related problems would be solvable by only a few relatively intelligent people; with it, most of us can solve otherwise difficult problems. Historically, the use of symbols to represent relationships is considered to be one of the great accomplishments of mankind. As you move through this book, you will learn how to use algebraic language to abbreviate and symbolize relationships between numbers. As a general rule, the idea is to let symbols, such as letters of the alphabet, stand for the unknown number(s) and then try to write the desired relationship in terms of these symbols. Some examples follow.

(1)　If we allow w to represent the width of a rectangle, l its length, and A its area, then the fact that "the area of the rectangle is the product of the length and the width" is written as $A = l \cdot w$.

(2)　If you have to pay 8 percent tax on the cost of a car, then by letting x represent the cost of the car, the tax you pay is written $.08x$.

(3)　The distance traveled in miles, d, is equal to the product of the speed in miles per hour, denoted by v, and the time in hours, t. Symbolically, we have $d = vt$.

(4)　The sum of two numbers is 12. If x is one of the numbers, $12 - x$ is the other.

(5)　By letting x be the units digit of a number and y the tens digit, we can write the value of the number as $10y + x$.

(6)　If x represents a number, then $x + 4$ represents the number that is 4 greater than x; $5x$ represents the number 5 times x; and $5x + 4$ represents the number 4 greater than 5 times x.

The foregoing examples show how algebraic language can be used to represent an English expression in an abstract, symbolic form. In abstract form the given expression can be studied independently of the sentence itself. Further, in the abstract setting seemingly dissimilar problems often turn out to be mathematically identical.

Set Language

Set language is used to describe a collection or aggregate of objects. The individual objects of a set, called **elements** of a set, are said to be **members** of the set. Notationally, capital letters denote sets and lowercase letters characterize the elements in the set. The symbol $\in$ means "is a member of." Thus, $a \in A$ means that a is an element in set A.

Sets are described either by telling all the elements that are in the set, such as $\{1, 3, 5, 7, 9\}$, or by giving some property of membership, such as, "the set of odd numbers between 0 and 10." A special notation, called **set builder notation**, is sometimes used to give the property of membership of a set. Using this notation, we list the **variable** and then indicate the property of membership. For example, the set $\{1, 3, 5, 7, 9\}$ can also be denoted by

$$\{x \mid x \text{ is an odd number between 0 and 10}\}$$

It reads, "The set of all x such that x is an odd number between 0 and 10."

A set with no elements, called the **empty** or **null** set, is denoted by $\varnothing$. A set is said to be **finite** if all the members of the set can be enumerated; otherwise, it is called **infinite**.

Example 1.1   Use set language to describe

(a) A, the set of counting numbers between 2 and 5,

(b) B, the set of counting numbers between 2 and 3,

(c) N, the set of counting numbers.

Solution

(a) $A = \{x \mid x \text{ is a counting number between 2 and 5}\}$. Since this is a finite set, we can also write it as $A = \{3, 4\}$. Both descriptions are correct.

(b) $B = \varnothing$ since there are no counting numbers between 2 and 3.

(c) $N = \{x \mid x \text{ is a counting number}\}$. This set cannot be enumerated since the set is infinite.

Two sets, M and N, are said to be **equal** if they have exactly the same elements. We write $M = N$ to describe this equality. For example, the set $M = \{1, 3, 5, 7, 9\}$ and the set $N = \{x \mid x \text{ is an odd number between 0 and 10}\}$ are equal. The set $A = \{1, 2, 3\}$ and the set $B = \{a, b, c\}$ are *not* equal even though they have the same number of elements. The equality of two sets is not always as obvious as those stated so far. For example, can you tell if the set $\{2\}$ is equal to the set $\{x \mid 3x + 2 = 8\}$?

The order of the elements in a set does not affect its equality. Thus, $\{a, b\} = \{b, a\}$.

If M is the set $\{1, 2, 3, 4, 5\}$ and N is the set $\{1, 3, 5\}$, then N is called a **subset** of M because every member of N is also a member of M. We write $N \subseteq M$. If $N \subseteq M$, but $N \neq M$, then N is a **proper** subset of M; this is denoted $N \subset M$.

Example 1.2   List all the subsets of $\{1, 2, 3\}$. Which are proper?

Solution   The subsets are $\{1, 2, 3\}$, $\{1, 2\}$, $\{1, 3\}$, $\{2, 3\}$, $\{1\}$, $\{2\}$, $\{3\}$, $\varnothing$. All except the first are proper subsets.

Most discussions focus attention on a *fixed* set of objects. If all the sets to be discussed are subsets of this one set, we call it the **universal** set, or simply the universe, and denote it by U. Generally, the universal set is established from the discussion and may vary from situation to situation. Changing the universal set can very well result in a different "answer" to a given problem.

Example 1.3   Determine the subset of even counting numbers if the universal set is

(a) $U_1 = \{2, 3, 4, 5, 6, 7\}$,

(b) $U_2 = \{1, 3, 5, 7\}$.

Solution   Let E be the set of even counting numbers. Then

(a) $E_1 = \{2, 4, 6\}$,

(b) $E_2 = \varnothing$ since there are no even counting numbers in U_2.

The **complement** of a set A, denoted by $\bar{A}$, is the set of elements in U that are *not* in the set A. For instance, in Example 1.3 the complements of E_1 and E_2 are

$$\bar{E}_1 = \{3, 5, 7\}   \text{and}   \bar{E}_2 = \{1, 3, 5, 7\}$$

Notice in each case that $\bar{E}_1$ and $\bar{E}_2$ depend upon the universal set.

There are two fundamental methods of forming new sets from old ones. The following definition gives the rules of formation.

Definition

- The **union** of two sets A and B, denoted by $A \cup B$, is the set $\{x \mid x \in A \text{ or } x \in B\}$.
- The **intersection** of two sets A and B, denoted by $A \cap B$, is the set $\{x \mid x \in A \text{ and } x \in B\}$.

In words, $A \cup B$ is the combined set of elements that are in A, in B, or in both A and B. See Figure 1.1. The intersection is the set of elements common to A and B. See Figure 1.2

Example 1.4   Let $A = \{a, b, c, d, e\}$ and $B = \{d, e, f\}$. Find $A \cup B$ and $A \cap B$.

Solution $A \cup B = \{a, b, c, d, e, f\}$ and $A \cap B = \{d, e\}$.

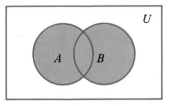

Figure 1.1   A ∪ B is the shaded area.

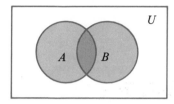

Figure 1.2   A ∩ B is the darker shaded area.

If two sets *A* and *B* have no elements in common, they are said to be **disjoint**. The notation is $A \cap B = \emptyset$. Two disjoint sets appear in Figure 1.3.

When unions and intersections of more than two sets are considered, many interesting relationships can be established. Some of these appear in the exercises at the end of this section.

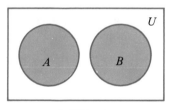

Figure 1.3   A ∩ B = φ

Exercises for
Section 1.1

Express each of the following sentences, or parts thereof, in algebraic symbols.

1.   The area of a triangle is equal to one-half the product of the base times the height.

2.   The area of a circle is equal to the product of π times the square of the radius.

3.   The perimeter of a square is 4 times the side length.

4.   The perimeter of a triangle is the sum of the length of the sides.

5.   Acceleration is equal to the velocity divided by the time.

6.   Voltage is equal to the current in the circuit times the resistance of the circuit.

7.   A number that is 8 less than another number.

8.   A number 3 times the square of another number.

9.   A number 5 times the sum of another number plus 3.

10. A number 3 more than 5 times another number.

11. Twenty percent of the amount by which a number exceeds 12,000.

12. The sum of two numbers divided by 2.

13. The average of three numbers.

14. The portion of a job done in one day if it takes x days to do the entire job.

15. Interest equals principal times rate.

16. The product of the sum and difference of two numbers.

17. Twice the sum of two numbers.

18. The area of a triangle whose base is twice the height.

19. The surface area of a cube.

20. The volume of a rectangular box.

21. Let A be the set $\{1, 2, 3, 4\}$. Which of the following statements are true and which are false? Give reasons.

(a) $2 \in A$ (b) $5 \in A$ (c) $\pi \in A$

(d) $\varnothing \in A$ (e) $\varnothing \subseteq A$ (f) $A \in A$

(g) $A \subseteq A$ (h) $A \in \{a, \varnothing\}$ (i) $\{2, 3, 1, 4\} \neq A$

22. Determine all subsets of the set $\{5, 6, 7, 8\}$.

23. Use set builder notation to describe the following sets.

(a) The set of people whose ages are equal to or greater than 40.

(b) The set of air conditioned cars in the city of New York.

(c) The set of people who own color TV sets in the United States.

24. Which of the following sets are infinite and which are finite?

(a) The number of men who have walked on the moon.

(b) The number of people who have walked on the earth.

(c) The fractions with denominator 2.

(d) The grains of sand in the world.

(e) The points on the head of a penny.

25. Suppose the universal set is given by $U = \{1, 2, 3, 4, 5, 6, 7, 8, 9, 10\}$.

(a) Find the subset of even numbers.

(b) Find the subset containing numbers larger than 5.

(c) Find the complement of the set $\{2, 3, 4\}$.

26. Repeat Exercise 25 with $U = \{1, 2, 3, 4, 5\}$.

Let $A = \{1, 2, 3, 5, 7, 8\}$, $B = \{1, 3, 6, 8\}$, and $C = \{2, 3, 4, 5\}$. Form the statements in Exercises 27–35.

27. $A \cup B$ **28.** $A \cup C$

29. $A \cap B$ **30.** $A \cap C$

31. $(A \cup B) \cap (A \cup C)$ **32.** $A \cup (B \cup C)$

     1 Some Fundamental Ideas

33. $A \cap (B \cup C)$ **34.** $(A \cup B) \cup C$

35. $(A \cap B) \cup C$

Which of the statements in Exercises 36–41 are true? Explain your answer.

36. $\{x \mid x + 2 = 2\} = \emptyset$

37. $\{x \mid 3x - 1 = 2x + 3\} = \{4\}$

38. $\{x \mid x^2 = 4\} = \{x \mid x^2 - 4 = 0\}$

39. $\{x \mid 2x + 7 = x - 2\} = \{x \mid 3x + 5 = 2x + 4\}$

40. $\{1, 3\} \subseteq \{x \mid x^2 - 3x + 2 = 0\}$

41. $\{2\} \subseteq \{x \mid x^2 = 4\}$

42. Is the number of elements in the union of two sets A and B equal to the number of elements in A plus the number of elements in B? Explain.

1.2
Number Systems

In almost all applications of mathematics numbers are used to represent physical situations or to describe problems in an analytic manner. Certainly, without numbers and man's ability to use them with mathematics, science would never have advanced to its present state.

Man first encountered numbers in counting. Counting led to the development of the set of counting numbers, or as they are also called, the **natural numbers,** or *positive integers.* They are denoted by

$$N = \{1, 2, 3, 4, 5, \ldots\}$$

The dots indicate that the set is infinite. The set of natural numbers is used for all applications related to counting. It is with the natural numbers that you initially learn to perform the fundamental arithmetic operations of addition, subtraction, multiplication, and division.

The set of positive integers, however, is insufficient for many purposes. This insufficiency occurs for two fundamental reasons: (1) the desire for numbers to represent the result of subtracting a larger number from a smaller one, such as $3 - 4$; and (2) the desire for numbers to give the result of dividing a smaller number by a larger one, such as $3 \div 4$.

In order to satisfy the first of these needs, mathematicians developed the *negative integers*

$$N^- = \{-1, -2, -3, \ldots\}$$

Together with the positive integers and the element 0, they comprise the set of **integers.** The set of integers can be denoted by

$$I = N \cup \{0\} \cup N^-$$

To express the ratio of two integers, the set of **rational numbers**, Q is needed. Technically, a number is a rational number *if it can be expressed as the ratio of two integers, the second being nonzero*. The first of these numbers is called the *numerator* and the second, the *denominator* of the rational number. The ratio is usually called a *fraction*. Each integer can be thought of as a rational number since each integer n can be written as $n/1$. Hence, $I \subseteq Q$. More exactly, I is a proper subset of Q since certain fractions such as $\frac{1}{2}$ are obviously not integers. (See Figure 1.4.)

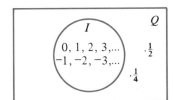

Figure 1.4

Rational numbers can also be written in *decimal form*. This decimal representation takes one of two forms:

(1) A finite number of places is needed after the decimal point, for example,

$$\frac{1}{2} = 0.5, \qquad \frac{25}{4} = 6.25, \qquad \frac{19}{8} = 2.375$$

In this case, the decimal is said to *terminate*.

(2) Infinitely many decimal places are necessary, but a block of digits continually repeats itself. Such a decimal is called *infinite repeating*; for example,

$$\frac{1}{6} = 0.166666 \ldots \qquad \frac{11}{7} = 1.571428571428 \ldots$$

Instead of the three dots, a bar is often placed over the repeating block, so that $\frac{1}{6} = 0.1\overline{6}$ and $\frac{11}{7} = 1.\overline{571428}$. The bar identifies the block of digits that repeats infinitely often.

To convert a fraction to its decimal representation, simply carry out the long division process. The process will always give either a terminating decimal or an infinite repeating decimal. Conversely, to convert a terminating decimal to a fraction, merely write the number over an appropriate power of 10; for example,

$$3.17 = \frac{317}{100}$$

The next example demonstrates the conversion of an infinite repeating decimal to fractional form.

1 Some Fundamental Ideas

Example 1.5   Express the decimal $4.7\overline{82}$ in fractional form.

Solution   Let $N = 4.78282\ldots$ Multiply this number by a power of 10 equal to the number of digits in the repeating block. In this case two digits appear in the repeating block, so multiply by 100 to get

$$100N = 478.28282\ldots$$

Subtracting N from $100N$,

$$99N = 473.5$$

Therefore,

$$N = \frac{473.5}{99} = \frac{4735}{990} = \frac{947}{198}$$

It is possible to show that there is no rational number whose square is 2. To solve problems of this type mathematicians invented the **irrational** numbers. Irrational numbers may be thought of in either of the following ways:

(1)   As numbers that *cannot* be expressed as the ratio of two integers.

(2)   As numbers whose decimal representation is *not* terminating and *not* infinite repeating; for example, $0.1001000100001\ldots$ A more famous irrational number, is the number π.

In general, the process of finding a decimal representation for an irrational number is quite difficult since it is normally impossible to establish any kind of coherent pattern. Most often in applied work some sort of approximation is employed. Decimal approximations are tabulated for most irrational numbers used in applications; for instance, $\pi = 3.14159\ldots$, $e = 2.718\ldots$, $\sqrt{2} = 1.414\ldots$ Thus, each of these irrational numbers can be approximated by rational numbers to any degree of accuracy desired. The set of all irrational numbers together with the set of rational numbers comprises a set called the set of **real numbers**, R. Rational numbers and irrational numbers form mutually exclusive sets; that is, the set of rational numbers contains no irrational numbers and, conversely, the set of irrational numbers contains no rational numbers. Figure 1.5 graphically displays the "hierarchy" of the real number system.

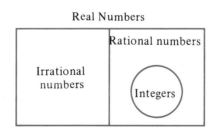

Real Numbers

Figure 1.5

You should be aware of the various kinds of numbers and how they fit into the hierarchy of the real number system. For instance, the number 3 is at the same time a natural number, an integer, a rational number, and a real number; $\frac{1}{2}$ is *both* rational and real, but not an integer or an irrational number; and π is *both* an irrational number and real, but not an integer or a rational number.

The value of a real number independent of its sign is called the **absolute value** of the number and is denoted by a pair of vertical lines around the number. For example, $|3| = 3$, $|-2| = 2$, $|0| = 0$. The absolute value of a number is always positive or zero.

In most of this book and in most of calculus, you will use the set of real numbers exclusively. However, at times you will want to use the square root of a negative number. We define the number i to be that number which, when squared, is equal to -1; that is, $i^2 = -1$. The number i is called a *pure imaginary number*.

The set of imaginary numbers is of the form bi, where b is a real number. When an imaginary number is added to a real number, a **complex number** is obtained. Thus, a complex number takes the form $a + bi$, where both a and b are themselves real. Algebraically, the complex numbers are manipulated as real expressions except that $i^2 = -1$. We take a closer look at complex numbers in the chapter called "Vectors and Complex Numbers."

1.3
The Real Line

The real numbers can be represented geometrically by associating each element of R with a point on a straight line. This association between real numbers on the one hand and points on the other is crucial to the easy use and description of many algebraic problems. In forming this association, the line is called the **real number line**, or simply the number line. The number line helps in "visualizing" the number system.

Begin by choosing an arbitrary point 0 on the line l, calling it the *origin*. (See Figure 1.6.) With the point 0 we associate the real number 0. Then select

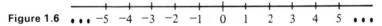

Figure 1.6 ••• -5 -4 -3 -2 -1 0 1 2 3 4 5 •••

any other point to the right of 0 and with it associate the real number 1. The line segment determined by the origin and the point corresponding to 1 is called a *unit distance*. Proceeding from 0, we may lay off 2 units, 3 units, 4 units, etc. and in each case associate the numbers 2, 3, 4 with the points so determined. In this way the entire set of natural numbers is associated with equispaced points on the line. Similarly, measure off unit distances to the left to make an association of points with the negative integers. In either case, **the absolute value of the number corresponds to its distance from the origin.**

The appearance of the number line will alter with a change in the unit distance but the procedure remains the same. Figure 1.7 shows another number

Figure 1.7 ••• −2 −1 0 1 2 •••

line with a different unit distance. Although the scale has been expanded, the same numbers are represented.

To locate rational numbers on the number line, divide the unit distance into appropriate parts with a corresponding labeling of the points. For example, if the unit distance is divided into thirds, each of the points is labeled as shown in Figure 1.8.

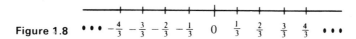

Figure 1.8 ••• $-\frac{4}{3}$ $-\frac{3}{3}$ $-\frac{2}{3}$ $-\frac{1}{3}$ 0 $\frac{1}{3}$ $\frac{2}{3}$ $\frac{3}{3}$ $\frac{4}{3}$ •••

In locating rational numbers that are represented in decimal form, always divide the unit distance by a power of 10. For example, the tenths are divided by making hundredths and hundredths by making thousandths, as shown in Figure 1.9.

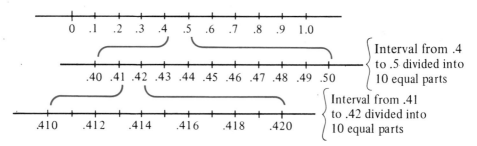

Figure 1.9

When points on the number line are associated with real numbers, the number is called the **coordinate** of the point and the point is called the **graph** of the number. For emphasis, points corresponding to integers are referred to as *integral points*, points corresponding to rational numbers as *rational points*, and points corresponding to irrational numbers as *irrational points*. In precise language, we say the point represents the real number. However, the two concepts are customarily used interchangeably; that is, we say "the point 2" instead of "the point whose coordinate is 2."

Example 1.6   Locate the points 1.4 and 1.43 on a number line.

Solution   Locate 1.4 by subdividing the portion between 1 and 2 into ten equal parts. Locate 1.43 by subdividing the portion between 1.4 and 1.5 into ten equal parts. See Figure 1.10.   ✦

1.3 The Real Line

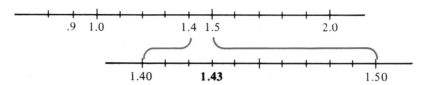

Figure 1.10

1.4
Intervals

In saying that the real numbers are **ordered**, we mean that given any two distinct real numbers a and b, one of the two is larger. The fact that a is greater than b is denoted by $a > b$ and defined by

$a > b$,   if $a - b$ **is positive.**

We can also write

$a < b$,   which is read "a is less than b."

$a \geq b$,   which is read "a is greater than or equal to b."

$a \leq b$,   which is read "a is less than or equal to b."

The symbols $>$ and $<$ are inequality symbols. From the definition of the ordering of the real numbers, 0 is less than every positive number and greater than every negative number. Further, every negative number is less than every positive number; for example, $-1000 < 0.0001$.

The notation $a \geq b$ includes the possibility that $a = b$ as well as $a > b$. A similar statement applies to the notation $a \leq b$.

The number line gives an easy and interesting geometric interpretation of ordering. A real number a is greater than b if the point corresponding to the number a is to the right of the point corresponding to b. See Figure 1.11.

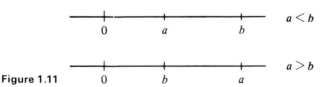

Figure 1.11

A subset of the real numbers between two real numbers is called an **interval**.

Definition

An **open interval**, denoted by (a, b), is the set of real numbers $\{x \mid a < x < b\}$.

The double inequality notation, $a < x < b$, is the shorthand way of writing $\{x \mid a < x\} \cap \{x \mid x < b\}$. We read it "$x$ is greater than a and less than b." Hence, the notation (a, b) presumes $a < b$, for it would be meaningless otherwise.

Definition

A **closed interval**, denoted by $[a, b]$, is the set of real numbers $\{x \mid a \le x \le b\}$.

The points corresponding to a and b are called *endpoints* of the interval. Thus, the distinction between an open and a closed interval is the exclusion or inclusion of the endpoints. Graphically, an endpoint to be included in the intervals is represented by a closed dot. Otherwise an open dot is used. See Figure 1.12.

Open Interval (a, b) Closed Interval $[a, b]$

Figure 1.12

If only one of the endpoints is included, the interval is called *half-open*. See Figure 1.13.

Figure 1.13   Half-open interval $(a, b]$

Open, closed, and half-open intervals are called bounded sets in the sense that there is a number M such that if x is in the interval, $|x| < M$. Any set that is not bounded is said to be **unbounded**. For example, the set $\{x \mid x \ge 0\}$ is unbounded. See Figure 1.14. A slight extension of interval and double inequality notation describes this kind of set. The symbol $-\infty$ means that there is no finite lower point for the interval, while the symbol ∞ means that there is no finite upper point.* Thus, the set of points shown in Figure 1.14 is

Figure 1.14   Unbounded interval $[0, \infty)$

denoted by $[0, \infty)$ or by $0 \le x < \infty$. The unbounded interval shown in Figure 1.15 is the set $\{x \mid x \le 2\}$. Using interval notation it is denoted by $(-\infty, 2]$ or, with double inequalities, $-\infty < x \le 2$.

Figure 1.15   Unbounded interval $(-\infty, 2]$

* The symbol ∞ is read "infinity."

1.4 Intervals

13

More general sets of numbers can be written using unions and intersections of bounded and unbounded intervals. Examples 1.7 and 1.8 illustrate this notation.

Example 1.7 Using set notation, describe the set A of real numbers shown in Figure 1.16.

Figure 1.16 -3 -1 0 2 7

Solution The set A of real numbers consists of the three intervals $x < -3$, $-1 < x \leq 2$, and $x > 7$. In set notation,

$$A = \{x \mid x < -3\} \cup \{x \mid -1 < x \leq 2\} \cup \{x \mid x > 7\}$$

Example 1.8 Sketch the set of real numbers given by

$$\{x \mid x < 4\} \cap \{x \mid x > -10\} \cap \{x \mid -1 < x < 8\}$$

Solution Figure 1.17 shows the three sets. The intersection is obviously the interval $(-1, 4)$.

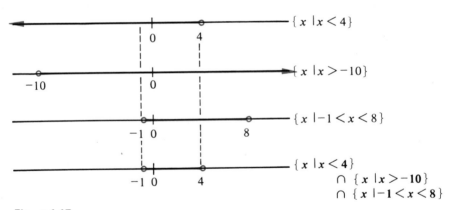

Figure 1.17

The inequalities $|x| < b$ and $|x| > b$ both describe sets of real numbers that can be represented by intervals on the real line. The inequality $|x| < b$ describes the set $\{x \mid -b < x < b\}$ and is a representation of the interval $(-b, b)$. In a like manner, $|x| > b$ describes the union $\{x \mid x > b\} \cup \{x \mid x < -b\}$, which is the union of the intervals $(-\infty, -b)$ and (b, ∞). Figure 1.18 pictures these two special sets of real numbers. Chapter 4 expands the discussion of inequalities involving absolute values.

14   1 Some Fundamental Ideas

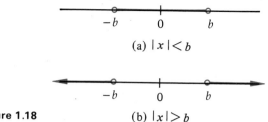

Figure 1.18

(a) $|x| < b$

(b) $|x| > b$

Exercises for
Sections 1.2 through 1.4

1. Find the decimal representation of: (a) $\frac{1}{7}$; (b) $\frac{22}{7}$; (c) $\frac{3}{8}$; (d) $\frac{6}{11}$

Express Exercises 2–5 in fractional form.

2. 2.43   3. $2.\overline{43}$ 4. 9.724724724 ...   5. $9.\overline{9}$

6. Find an approximation, good to three decimal places, valid for the real number whose square is 3.

7. Locate the rational number -1.67 on the number line.

8. Locate the rational number 2.43 on the number line.

Sketch the graph of the intervals in Exercises 9-25

9. $(-2, 3)$ 10. $[-2, 3]$

11. $(-\infty, 0]$ 12. $[1, \infty)$

13. $(-\infty, \infty)$ 14. $(-3, 3]$

15. $[2, 3]$ 16. $[\frac{1}{4}, \frac{1}{2})$

17. $(-1, 3)$ 18. $[-3, -1]$

19. $[-5, 0)$ 20. $(0, 1) \cup (\frac{1}{2}, 1)$

21. $(2, 3) \cap (3, \infty)$ 22. $(-\infty, -3) \cup (3, \infty)$

23. $(-3, 5) \cap [4, 7)$ 24.   Complement of $(-3, 3)$

25. $(2, \infty) \cap (3, \infty)$

Use interval notation to represent each of the sets in Exercises 26–30.

26. $\{x \,|\, 1 < x < 3\}$ 27. $\{y \,|\, y \geq 0\}$ 28. $\{x \,|\, x < -2\}$

29. $\{x \,|\, x \leq 4\}$ 30. $\{t \,|\, -2 < t \leq 1\}$

31.   Is $(a, b) \subset [a, b]$? Explain.

32.   Which of the sets of real numbers in Exercises 26 through 30 are bounded and which are unbounded?

33.   Compute: (a) $|-5|$; (b) $|6 - 9|$; (c) $6 + |-9|$.

1.4 Intervals

Describe the sets in Exercises 34–37 using interval notation and then sketch each graph.

34. $|x| \leq 6$ **35.** $|x| < 1.5$ **36.** $|x| > 7$ **37.** $|x| \geq 4$

Describe the intervals in Exercises 38–41 using absolute value notation.

38. $(-5, 5)$ **39.** $(-10, 10)$

40. $(-\infty, -3) \cup (3, \infty)$ **41.** $(-\infty, -1] \cup [1, \infty)$

42. What is wrong with describing the set $\{x \mid |x| > a\}$ with the notation $-a > x > a$?

43. By example show that $|x| + |y| \neq |x + y|$.

Answer the following statements true or false and give reasons for the answers.

44. The union of two intervals is an interval.

45. The intersection of two intervals is a nonempty interval.

46. The intersection of two bounded sets of real numbers is bounded.

47. The intersection of two unbounded sets of real numbers is unbounded.

48. An interval that is not open is closed.

49. The number $-x$ is always negative.

50. The number π is an irrational number.

51. An integer is a rational number.

1.5
Arithmetic Review

Addition, subtraction, multiplication, and division of positive integers are easy. Since these operations are somewhat more difficult for negative numbers and rational numbers, we take this opportunity to review them.

Confusion usually arises when working with negative numbers because the negative sign designates both the operation of subtraction and signed numbers—an unfortunate situation, but one with which you must learn to cope.

Signed Numbers

The sum of two real numbers with like signs is the sum of the absolute values of the two numbers preceded by their common sign. For example,

$$(+3) + (+5) = +(3 + 5) = +8 \quad \text{and} \quad (-5) + (-7) = -(5 + 7)$$
$$= -12$$

To add two real numbers with unlike signs, subtract the smaller absolute value from the larger and affix the sign of the one with the larger absolute value.

Thus,

$$(-4) + (+9) = +(9 - 4) = +5 \quad \text{and} \quad (-8) + (+2) = -(8 - 2)$$
$$= -6$$

To subtract two real numbers, change the sign of the one being subtracted and then follow the rules for addition. For example,

$$(+4) - (+9) = (+4) + (-9) = -(9 - 4) = -5$$

and

$$(-3) - (-7) = (-3) + (+7) = +(7 - 3) = +4$$

To multiply (or divide) two real numbers, multiply (or divide) their absolute values. If both numbers have the same sign, the product (or quotient) is positive. If the numbers have unlike signs, the product (or quotient) is negative.

$$(+7)(-6) = -(7 \cdot 6) = -42$$
$$(-2)(-3) = +(2 \cdot 3) = +6$$
$$\frac{(+5)}{(-9)} = -\left(\frac{5}{9}\right) = -\frac{5}{9}$$

Rational Numbers

The fractions $\frac{3}{4}$, $\frac{15}{20}$, and $\frac{120}{160}$ represent the same rational number. However, of the three forms, we prefer the representation $\frac{3}{4}$ because it is the simplest. A fraction is in *simplest form* if the numerator and the denominator contain no common integer factors except 1.

A basic rule of arithmetic states that *if both numerator and denominator are multiplied or divided by the same nonzero number, the value of the fraction is unchanged.* As a result of this rule, fractions can always be reduced to simplest form.

Example 1.9

(a)   The fraction $\frac{15}{20}$ is reduced to simplest form by noting that

$$\frac{15}{20} = \frac{3 \cdot 5}{4 \cdot 5} = \frac{3}{4}$$

(b)   The simplest form of $\frac{63}{27}$ is $\frac{7}{3}$.

Multiplying fractions is easy. The rule is to multiply numerators and multiply denominators.

Example 1.10

(a) $\quad \dfrac{2}{3} \cdot \dfrac{5}{7} = \dfrac{10}{21}$

(b) $\quad \dfrac{-5}{2} \cdot \dfrac{21}{8} = \dfrac{-105}{16} = -\dfrac{105}{16}$

In dividing fractions, the rule is to invert the fraction in the denominator and then follow the rule for multiplication.

Example 1.11

(a) $\quad \dfrac{\frac{5}{4}}{\frac{6}{7}} = \dfrac{5}{4} \cdot \dfrac{7}{6} = \dfrac{35}{24}$

(b) $\quad \dfrac{\frac{3}{2}}{5} = \dfrac{3}{2} \cdot \dfrac{1}{5} = \dfrac{3}{10}$

To obtain the sum of two fractions having the same denominator, add the respective numerators and divide this sum by the common denominator. For example,

$$\frac{1}{5} + \frac{7}{5} - \frac{2}{5} = \frac{1 + 7 - 2}{5} = \frac{6}{5}$$

When the fractions to be added have different denominators, use the basic principle of fractions to obtain common denominators before summing the fractions. Thus, to add the fractions $\frac{2}{3}$ and $\frac{7}{6}$, multiply $\frac{2}{3}$ by $\frac{2}{2}$ to get $\frac{4}{6}$. The sum of the two fractions is then

$$\frac{2}{3} + \frac{7}{6} = \frac{2 \cdot 2}{3 \cdot 2} + \frac{7}{6}$$

$$= \frac{4}{6} + \frac{7}{6}$$

$$= \frac{4 + 7}{6} = \frac{11}{6}$$

As another illustration of this rule, consider the following sum:

$$\frac{2}{5} + \frac{3}{4} - \frac{1}{10}$$

We desire to convert these fractions to equivalent fractions having a common denominator. While any number that is divisible by each of the given denominators will work as a common denominator, we prefer to use the smallest number that has this property. Thus, the **lowest common denominator (LCD)** of the given fraction is 20. We obtain the desired equivalent fractions as follows:

$$\frac{2}{5} + \frac{3}{4} - \frac{1}{10} = \frac{2}{5} \cdot \frac{4}{4} + \frac{3}{4} \cdot \frac{5}{5} - \frac{1}{10} \cdot \frac{2}{2}$$

$$= \frac{8}{20} + \frac{15}{20} - \frac{2}{20}$$

$$= \frac{8 + 15 - 2}{20} = \frac{21}{20}$$

Exercises for
Section 1.5

Write the statements in Exercises 1–16 as a single real number.

1. $(+5) + (-6)$ **2.** $5 - (-7)$ **3.** $-3 + 7$

4. $-15 - (+3)$ **5.** $-9 - (-3)$ **6.** $-10 - 6 + 20$

7. $(16)(-3)(9)$ **8.** $(-3)(-2)(-6)$ **9.** $4(5 - 7)$

10. $5 + (-4) - (3 - 4)$ **11.** $-2 - (7 - 10)(5)$ **12.** $-(-3)(5)$

13. $-[2 + 3(6 - 8)][4 - (5 + 2)]$

14. $[3 - (6 + 1)][-2 - (-5)]$

15. $[-(-2) - (4 - 6)][3 + (7 - 3)]$

16. $[3 - 7(5 - 6)][-3(-2 - 5(-4))][-6 + (5 - 7)]$

Write the expressions in Exercises 17–40 as a single rational number in lowest terms.

17. $\frac{2}{3} \cdot \frac{5}{7}$ **18.** $\frac{4}{6} \cdot \frac{7}{15}$

19. $\left(\frac{150}{200}\right)\left(\frac{9}{27}\right)$ **20.** $\left(\frac{25}{65}\right)\left(\frac{36}{24}\right)$

21. $\frac{\frac{3}{5}}{\frac{7}{6}}$ **22.** $\frac{\frac{15}{60}}{\frac{19}{38}}$

23. $\frac{1}{6} + \frac{1}{2}$ **24.** $\frac{16}{24} - \frac{17}{6}$

25. $\frac{3}{4} - \frac{5}{3}$ **26.** $7 - \frac{2}{5}$

27. $2 - \frac{1}{3} + \frac{1}{2}$ **28.** $\frac{17}{3} + \frac{29}{5}$

29. $3\left(\frac{5}{8} - \frac{3}{4}\right)$ **30.** $21\left(\frac{1}{6} + \frac{1}{3} + 1\right)$

31. $\frac{1}{2}\left(\frac{1}{2} - 1\right)$ **32.** $\frac{3}{4}\left(\frac{2}{3} - \frac{7}{8} - \frac{1}{12}\right)$

33. $\left(\dfrac{2}{3} - \dfrac{1}{2}\right)\left(\dfrac{2}{3} + \dfrac{1}{2}\right)$ **34.** $\left(\dfrac{5}{4} + \dfrac{1}{3}\right)\left(\dfrac{7}{6} - 2\right)$

35. $\dfrac{2 - \frac{1}{3}}{\frac{3}{2}}$ **36.** $\dfrac{\frac{2}{5} - \frac{1}{7}}{\frac{1}{2}}$

37. $\dfrac{\frac{9}{16} - \frac{3}{4}}{\frac{1}{2} - \frac{7}{8}}$ **38.** $\dfrac{3 - \frac{4}{3} + \frac{3}{2}}{\frac{9}{4} - \frac{5}{6}}$

39. $\dfrac{1 + \dfrac{1}{\frac{1}{2} + \frac{3}{4}}}{1 - \dfrac{2}{1 - \frac{3}{2}}}$ **40.** $\dfrac{\frac{3}{2} + \dfrac{1}{\frac{3}{2} + \frac{2}{3}}}{15 - \frac{17}{6}}$

Test 1 for Chapter 1

1. Answer true or false.

   (a) The sets $\{a, b\}$ and $\{c, d\}$ are equal.

   (b) For every set A, $A \cap \bar{A} = \varnothing$.

   (c) Every rational number is real.

   (d) Every real number is either positive or negative.

   (e) For every two sets A and B, $A \cap B \subseteq A \cup B$.

   (f) A number may be rational and irrational.

   (g) The absolute value of $-\sqrt{3}$ is $\sqrt{3}$.

   (h) Irrational numbers are formed by taking the ratio of two rational numbers.

   (i) $0 \div m = 0$ if $m \neq 0$.

   (j) The intersection of two open intervals is always an open interval or the empty set.

2. Express $32.6\overline{45}$ as a ratio of two integers.

3. Locate $\sqrt{10}$ on the number line between rational numbers a and b such that $a - b \leq .01$.

4. Graph the following set on the number line and then represent it first with interval notation and then with a double inequality: $[-3, 7) \cap [2, 9)$.

5. Repeat Problem 4 using the set $\{x \mid x > 2\}$.

6. Simplify: (a) $(\frac{1}{2} - \frac{7}{8})/\frac{2}{5}$; (b) $7 - (2 - (3 - 4))$.

7. Let $A = \{1, 2, 3, 4\}$, $B = \{1, 3, 5, 7, 9\}$, and the universal set $U = \{1, 2, 3, 4, 5, 6, 7, 8, 9, 10\}$. (a) Find $A \cup B$. (b) Find $A \cap B$. (c) Find $\overline{(A \cup B)}$. (d) Find $\bar{A} \cup \bar{B}$.

Test 2 for Chapter 1

   1. Use algebraic symbols to express a number 12 less than 5 times the number.

   2. Write all subsets of $\{5, 6, 10\}$.

   3. If $U = \{2, 3, 5, 8, 15\}$, find the complement of $A = \{3, 8\}$.

4. Given $A = \{1, 2, 3\}$ and $B = \{2, 3, 7, 9\}$, find: (a) $A \cup B$; (b) $A \cap B$.

5. Sketch the graph of: (a) $(-2, 5)$; (b) $[-1, \infty)$; (c) $(0, \infty) \cap (-\infty, 4]$.

6. Write $|x| < 2$ using interval notation and then sketch the graph.

7. Express $3.\overline{12}$ in fractional form.

8. Answer true or false.

(a) A rational number is also an integer.

(b) An irrational number can be expressed as an infinite repeating decimal.

(c) $\{x \mid 2x - 3 = 0\} = \{\frac{3}{2}\}$

(d) $I \cap Q \subseteq I$

(e) $-15 > -3$

9. Evaluate: $[-3 + 2(4 - 7)][6 - 3(-7)]$.

10. Evaluate: $\dfrac{3 + \frac{1}{2} - \frac{1}{5}}{\frac{2}{3} - \frac{5}{4}}$.

2
Basic
Algebra

2.1
The Rules of
Algebra

The two basic operations performed with any two real numbers are addition and multiplication. This section reviews the laws that govern these operations. You should familiarize yourself with these laws and practice using them until they become second nature.

If x, y, and z represent real numbers, the rules that govern addition and multiplication are:

- **Commutative Law of Addition:** $x + y = y + x$
  For example, $5 + \sqrt{2} = \sqrt{2} + 5$.
- **Commutative Law of Multiplication:** $x \cdot y = y \cdot x$
  For example, $2 \cdot \sqrt{7} = \sqrt{7} \cdot 2$.
- **Associative Law of Addition:** $(x + y) + z = x + (y + z)$
  For example, $(7 + 3) + 5 = 7 + (3 + 5)$.
- **Associative Law of Multiplication:** $x(yz) = (xy)z$
  For example, $\sqrt{2}(7 \cdot \pi) = (\sqrt{2} \cdot 7)\pi$.
- **Distributive Law of Multiplication over Addition:** $x(y + z) = xy + xz$
  For example, $\sqrt{2}(\pi + 7) = \sqrt{2} \cdot \pi + \sqrt{2} \cdot 7$.

An algebraic expression written as a product of simpler algebraic expressions is said to be in *factored form*. The individual expressions are called the *factors*. An algebraic expression written without factors is said to be in *expanded form*.

Example 2.1

(a) The algebraic expression $x^3 - yx^2 - xy^2 + y^3$ is in expanded form. One of its factored forms is $(x - y)(x^2 - y^2)$; another is $(x - y)^2(x + y)$.

(b) The expression $5a^2(c - 3a^3b)$ is in a factored form. The expanded form of the same expression is $5a^2c - 15a^5b$

Mathematics books at all levels expect you to know the process of expressing algebraic expressions in either a factored form or its equivalent expanded form. The next three examples show how to expand a product using the distributive law.

Example 2.2   Expand $3x(x + 2y - 4z)$.

Solution   Using the distributive law,

$$3x(x + 2y - 4z) = 3x^2 + 6xy - 12xz$$

Example 2.3   Expand the product $(x - y)(x^3 - y)$.

   Solution $(x - y)(x^3 - y) = x(x^3 - y) - y(x^3 - y) = x^4 - xy - yx^3 + y^2$ 🐦

In general, to form the product of two algebraic expressions, multiply one of them by each term of the other and collect similar terms.

Example 2.4   Expand $(x^2 + 5x - 3)(x^3 - x^2 - 7)$.

   Solution   Applying the distributive law,

$$
\begin{aligned}
(x^2 + 5x - 3)(x^3 - x^2 - 7) &= (x^2 + 5x - 3)x^3 + (x^2 + 5x - 3)(-x^2) \\
&\quad + (x^2 + 5x - 3)(-7) \\
&= x^5 + 5x^4 - 3x^3 - x^4 - 5x^3 + 3x^2 \\
&\quad - 7x^2 - 35x + 21 \\
&= x^5 + 4x^4 - 8x^3 - 4x^2 - 35x + 21
\end{aligned}
$$
🐦

Certain products occur so frequently in algebraic expressions that learning the equivalent expanded form is advantageous. The following list contains some of these *special products* in factored and expanded form. The validity of each of these expansions is easily checked using the fundamental rules.

(1) $(x + y)^2 = x^2 + 2xy + y^2$
(2) $(x - y)^2 = x^2 - 2xy + y^2$
(3) $(x + y)(x - y) = x^2 - y^2$
(4) $(x + y)^3 = x^3 + 3x^2y + 3xy^2 + y^3$
(5) $(x - y)^3 = x^3 - 3x^2y + 3xy^2 - y^3$
(6) $(x + y)(x^2 - xy + y^2) = x^3 + y^3$
(7) $(x - y)(x^2 + xy + y^2) = x^3 - y^3$

Example 2.5   Expand $(x - 7)(x + 7)$.

   Solution   Using (3) from above,

$$(x - 7)(x + 7) = x^2 - 7^2 = x^2 - 49$$
🐦

Example 2.6   Find the square of $(3z + 5)$.

24   2 Basic Algebra

Solution Letting $x = 3z$ and $y = 5$ in (1),

$$(3z + 5)^2 = (3z)^2 + 2(3z)(5) + (5)^2$$
$$= 9z^2 + 30z + 25$$

Example 2.7 Expand $(2x - 3y)^3$.

Solution Using (5),

$$(2x - 3y)^3 = (2x)^3 - 3(2x)^2(3y) + 3(2x)(3y)^2 - (3y)^3$$
$$= 8x^3 - 36x^2y + 54xy^2 - 27y^3$$

An algebraic expression involving the sum or difference of two terms is called a *binomial*. The product of two binomials follows a pattern that can be identified by expanding the general product $(ax + by)(cx + dy)$. Thus,

$$(ax + by)(cx + dy) = ax(cx + dy) + by(cx + dy)$$
$$= acx^2 + adxy + bcxy + bdy^2$$
$$(ax + by)(cx + dy) = acx^2 + (ad + bc)xy + bdy^2$$

Since two general binomials were used in this expansion, the result can be applied to the product of *any* two binomials. The final form of the expansion has the following structure:

- The first term is the product of the two first terms of the given binomials.
- The middle term is the sum of the products obtained by multiplying the first term in each binomial by the second term in the other.
- The third term is the product of the two second terms of the given binomials.

Example 2.8 Expand $(2x + 3)(5x - 4)$.

Solution

$$10x^2 \qquad -12$$
$$(2x + 3) \quad (5x - 4)$$
$$15x$$
$$-8x$$

Referring to the diagram,

$$(2x + 3)(5x - 4) = 10x^2 + 7x - 12$$

2.1 The Rules of Algebra

Exercises for
Section 2.1

Use the distributive law to expand the products in Exercises 1 through 20.

1. $x^2(x^3 + 2)$
2. $(x^2 + 3x - 5)x^3$
3. $x^3(x^2 - 5x)$
4. $x^9(x^3 + x^5)$
5. $(x + 2y)(x - 2y)$
6. $(x - 1)(x^2 - 1)$
7. $(x^2 - 1)(x^2 + 1)$
8. $(x + 3)(x^2 - 2x + 5)$
9. $(x^3 - x^2 + x - 1)(x - 1)$
10. $(x^2 - y)^2$
11. $(xy + 1)(xy - 1)$
12. $(x^2 + 1)(x^2 - 2)$
13. $(x + y^2)^3$
14. $(2x + 4)^2(3x - 2)$
15. $(x + y)(x - y)(x^2 - y)$
16. $(x^2 - y)(x - y^2)$
17. $(x + y + z)^2$
18. $(x + y)^2(x^2 - y^2)$
19. $(3x + 4y - z)(2x - 3y)$
20. $(x^2 + 2x - 3)^2(x + 3)$

Use the table of special products for assistance in expanding the following products.

21. $(x + 4)^2$
22. $(x - 2)^2$
23. $(x + 15)^2$
24. $(a - 9)^2$
25. $(b + 12)(b - 12)$
26. $(y + 7)(y - 7)$
27. $(2x + 5)^2$
28. $(3a + 2)^2$
29. $(9y - 2)^2$
30. $(2x + 3)(2x - 3)$
31. $(4x + 5)(4x - 5)$
32. $(7x + 9)(7x - 9)$
33. $(x + 2)^3$
34. $(x - 4)^3$
35. $(5a + b)^3$
36. $(4x + 3)^3$
37. $(2x - 5)^3$
38. $(a + 3b)^3$
39. $(x + 2)(x^2 - 2x + 4)$
40. $(x^2 - 5x + 25)(x + 5)$
41. $(x - 3)(x^2 - 3x + 9)$
42. $(x + 1)(x^2 - x + 1)$
43. $(2x + 1)(4x^2 - 2x + 1)$
44. $(3x - 2)(9x^2 - 6x + 4)$

Use the general rule for expanding the product of two binomials in the following exercises.

45. $(x + 5)(x + 9)$
46. $(y + 3)(y + 7)$
47. $(2x - 8)(3x + 5)$
48. $(x - 4)(3x + 9)$
49. $(2y + 5)(y + 2)$
50. $(8x - 3)(3x - 2)$
51. $(2x - 3y)(x + 4y)$
52. $(6m + 1)(7m - 3)$
53. $(12x - 5)(3x - 8)$
54. $(x + 2y)(5x - 4y)$

2.2
Factoring

Expanding a product is usually easy since it is a straightforward application of the distributive property or some well-known formula. Factoring, on the other hand, requires much more ingenuity. To some extent this ingenuity depends upon knowing the special product formulas listed in the previous section.

Example 2.9   Factor $6x^5 + 12x^2 - 2x$.

Solution   Each term contains $2x$ as a factor; therefore,

$$6x^5 + 12x^2 - 2x = 2x(3x^4 + 6x - 1)$$

Example 2.10   Factor $9x^2 + 24x + 16$.

Solution   Observe that $9x^2 = (3x)^2$ and $16 = 4^2$. Now, since $24x = 2(3x)(4)$, we conclude that the desired factored form is

$$9x^2 + 24x + 16 = (3x + 4)^2$$

Example 2.11   Factor $9x^2 - 25y^2$.

Solution   Since the expression is the difference of two perfect squares, we conclude that

$$9x^2 - 25y^2 = (3x - 5y)(3x + 5y)$$

Example 2.12   Factor $2x^2 - x - 1$.

Solution   If this expression can be factored, it will be of the form $(ax + b)(cx + d)$. This means that the product ac must equal 2 and the product of bd must equal -1. Hence, the only possibilities are $(2x - 1)(x + 1)$ and $(2x + 1)(x - 1)$. The second form is the correct one since the sum of the products obtained by multiplying the first term of each binomial by the second term of the other must equal $-x$. Thus, $(2x)(-1) + (x)(1) = -2x + x = -x$, which is the given middle term.

Example 2.13   Factor $5x^2 + 13x - 6$.

Solution   As in the previous example, if the expression can be factored, it will be of the form $(ax + b)(cx + d)$. Since the factors of 5 are ± 5 and ± 1 and those of -6 are ± 6, ± 1, ± 2, and ± 3, the following are possible factors for the given expression.

$$(5x + 6)(x - 1)$$
$$(5x - 6)(x + 1)$$
$$(5x + 1)(x - 6)$$
$$(5x - 1)(x + 6)$$
$$(5x + 2)(x - 3)$$
$$(5x - 2)(x + 3) \quad \leftarrow \text{correct factored form}$$
$$(5x + 3)(x - 2)$$
$$(5x - 3)(x + 2)$$

The correct factors are those that yield a middle term of $13x$ when expanded. Thus, $(5x - 2)(x + 3)$ are the correct factors.

Example 2.14   Factor $x^3 + 27$.

Solution   Recalling that $(x + y)(x^2 - xy + y^2) = x^3 + y^3$ and observing that $x^3 + 27 = x^3 + 3^3$, we can write

$$x^3 + 27 = (x + 3)(x^2 - 3x + 9)$$

Exercises for
Section 2.2

Factor the expressions in Exercises 1–51.

1.	$3x^3 - 5x^2 + 15x$	**2.**	$x^{10} + 16x^5$
3.	$13y^7 - 27y^3$	**4.**	$y^2 + 14y + 49$
5.	$z^2 - 24z + 144$	**6.**	$x^2 + 50x + 625$
7.	$9x^2 + 6x + 1$	**8.**	$25x^2 - 10x + 1$
9.	$\frac{1}{4}x^2 + x + 1$	**10.**	$x^2 - 25$
11.	$x^2 - 169$	**12.**	$x^2 - 400$
13.	$4m^2 - 64$	**14.**	$9y^2 - 25$
15.	$x^2 - 4y^2$	**16.**	$16x^2 - 25y^2$
17.	$\frac{1}{4}x^2 - \frac{1}{9}$	**18.**	$\frac{4}{9}x^2 - \frac{1}{25}$
19.	$9x^2 + 12x + 4$	**20.**	$25x^2 - 30x + 9$
21.	$\frac{1}{9}x^2 + \frac{2}{9}x + \frac{1}{9}$	**22.**	$x^2 - x - 6$
23.	$x^2 - x - 12$	**24.**	$a^2 - a - 2$
25.	$y^2 + 13y + 42$	**26.**	$m^2 + m - 42$
27.	$x^2 - 3x - 54$	**28.**	$b^2 - 4b - 21$
29.	$2x^2 + 7x + 3$	**30.**	$2x^2 + 5x + 3$

31. $5x^2 - 28x + 15$ **32.** $5y^2 - 3y - 2$

33. $6m^2 - 11m + 5$ **34.** $6h^2 + 29h - 5$

35. $3x^2 + 4xy - 15y^2$ **36.** $x^2 - xy - 12y^2$

37. $3x^2 - 4xy - 4y^2$ **38.** $12a^2 + 13ab - 35b^2$

39. $8x^2 - 20xy + 8y^2$ **40.** $x^3 - 27$

41. $x^3 + 64$ **42.** $y^3 - 125$

43. $8x^3 + 1$ **44.** $27y^3 - 8$

45. $a^3 + \frac{1}{8}$ **46.** $x^3 + 6x^2 + 12x + 8$

47. $y^3 - 9y^2 + 27y - 27$ **48.** $a^3 - 6a^2b + 12ab^2 - 8b^3$

49. $8x^3 + 12x^2 + 6x + 1$ **50.** $8x^3 - 24x^2 + 24x - 8$

51. $27x^3 + 54x^2 + 36x + 8$

2.3
Fractional
Expressions

A basic principle of fractions states that *if both the numerator and the denominator of a fraction are multiplied or divided by the same nonzero quantity, the value of the fraction is unchanged.* This principle, stated previously for arithmetic fractions, is restated here for emphasis. Using this principal, it is easy to see that

$$\frac{-a}{b} = \frac{a}{-b} = -\frac{a}{b}$$

An algebraic expression is in simplest form when the numerator and the denominator have no common factors. To reduce a fraction to its simplest form, write the numerator and the denominator in factored form and then divide each by every factor common to both.

Example 2.15 Reduce $(x^2 + 3x + 2)/(x^2 - 1)$ to its simplest form.

Solution Factoring, we have

$$\frac{x^2 + 3x + 2}{x^2 - 1} = \frac{(x + 2)(x + 1)}{(x - 1)(x + 1)}$$

Dividing the numerator and the denominator by $x + 1$ gives

$$\frac{x + 2}{x - 1}$$

as the simplest form of the given fraction. Because the factor $x + 1$ has, in effect, been cancelled, the above operation is sometimes referred to as *cancellation* of terms.

Multiplication and Division of Algebraic Fractions

The product of two fractions is defined as the product of the two numerators divided by the product of the two denominators. Thus, if a/b and c/d are the given fractions,

$$\frac{a}{b} \cdot \frac{c}{d} = \frac{a \cdot c}{b \cdot d} = \frac{ac}{bd}$$

Of course, any common factors in the numerator and the denominator of the product should be cancelled.

Example 2.16   Evaluate:

$$\frac{3(x^2 - y^2)}{x^2 + x - 6} \cdot \frac{x^2 + 3x}{x + y}$$

Solution

$$\frac{3(x^2 - y^2)}{x^2 + x - 6} \cdot \frac{x^2 + 3x}{x + y} = \frac{3\cancel{(x + y)}(x - y)}{(x - 2)\cancel{(x + 3)}} \cdot \frac{x\cancel{(x + 3)}}{\cancel{x + y}} = \frac{3x(x - y)}{x - 2}$$

Example 2.17   Evaluate:

$$\frac{3x^2 y^3}{5a^4} \cdot \frac{15a^3}{16x^5 y^5} \cdot \frac{xy}{a^2}$$

Solution

$$\frac{3x^2 y^3}{5a^4} \cdot \frac{15a^3}{16x^5 y^5} \cdot \frac{xy}{a^2} = \frac{45a^3 x^3 y^4}{80a^6 x^5 y^5} = \frac{9}{16a^3 x^2 y}$$

The method for evaluating the quotient of two fractions learned in arithmetic, is to invert the denominator fraction and then follow the rules of multiplication. This same rule is followed for the division of two algebraic fractions.

Example 2.18   Evaluate:

$$\frac{x^2 - 3x - 4}{x^2 - 1} \div \frac{x^2 - 16}{x - 1}$$

Solution

$$\frac{x^2 - 3x - 4}{x^2 - 1} \div \frac{x^2 - 16}{x - 1} = \frac{x^2 - 3x - 4}{x^2 - 1} \cdot \frac{x - 1}{x^2 - 16}$$

$$= \frac{(x - 4)(x + 1)}{(x + 1)(x - 1)} \cdot \frac{x - 1}{(x + 4)(x - 4)}$$

$$= \frac{1}{x + 4}$$

Addition and Subtraction of Fractions

The operation of summing algebraic fractions is analogous to the operation learned for summing arithmetic fractions. For convenience, the general procedure for adding fractions follows in outline form.

(1) Factor the numerator and the denominator of each fraction.

(2) Reduce to lowest terms any fractions not already in this form.

(3) Find the lowest common denominator (LCD).

(4) Multiply the numerator and the denominator of each fraction by the quotient obtained by dividing the specific denominator into the LCD.

(5) Add the numerators of the fractions and place over the LCD.

(6) Reduce the resulting fraction to lowest terms.

Example 2.19   Simplify: $\dfrac{x}{x + 1} - \dfrac{x}{x - 2}$.

Solution   The LCD is $(x + 1)(x - 2)$. Thus,

$$\frac{x}{x + 1} - \frac{x}{x - 2} = \frac{x(x - 2)}{(x + 1)(x - 2)} - \frac{x(x + 1)}{(x - 2)(x + 1)}$$

$$= \frac{x(x - 2) - x(x + 1)}{(x + 1)(x - 2)}$$

$$= \frac{x^2 - 2x - x^2 - x}{(x + 1)(x - 2)}$$

$$= \frac{-3x}{(x + 1)(x - 2)}$$

Example 2.20   Simplify:

$$\frac{2a}{3b^2c^2} - \frac{3b}{5a^2c^5} - \frac{c}{2ab^3}$$

2.3 Fractional Expressions

31

Solution The LCD is $30a^2b^3c^5$; therefore, multiply the numerator and the denominator of the first fraction by $10a^2bc^3$, of the second by $6b^3$, and of the third by $15ac^5$.

$$\frac{2a}{3b^2c^2} - \frac{3b}{5a^2c^5} - \frac{c}{2ab^3} = \frac{2a}{3b^2c^2} \cdot \frac{10a^2bc^3}{10a^2bc^3} - \frac{3b}{5a^2c^5} \cdot \frac{6b^3}{6b^3}$$

$$- \frac{c}{2ab^3} \cdot \frac{15ac^5}{15ac^5}$$

$$= \frac{20a^3bc^3}{30a^2b^3c^5} - \frac{18b^4}{30a^2b^3c^5} - \frac{15ac^6}{30a^2b^3c^5}$$

$$= \frac{20a^3bc^3 - 18b^4 - 15ac^6}{30a^2b^3c^5}$$

Example 2.21   Simplify:

$$\frac{a-4}{a^2-7a+12} + \frac{5}{a^2-9} - \frac{3a-6}{a^2+a-6}$$

Solution   Factor the denominator before finding the LCD. Thus, the given fractions can be written as

$$\frac{a-4}{(a-3)(a-4)} + \frac{5}{(a+3)(a-3)} - \frac{3(a-2)}{(a-2)(a+3)}$$

$$= \frac{1}{a-3} + \frac{5}{(a+3)(a-3)} - \frac{3}{a+3}$$

From this we see that a^2-9 is the LCD. Therefore,

$$\frac{1}{a-3} \cdot \frac{a+3}{a+3} + \frac{5}{(a+3)(a-3)} - \frac{3}{a+3} \cdot \frac{a-3}{a-3}$$

$$= \frac{a+3}{a^2-9} + \frac{5}{a^2-9} - \frac{3a-9}{a^2-9}$$

$$= \frac{(a+3)+5-(3a-9)}{a^2-9}$$

$$= \frac{a+3+5-3a+9}{a^2-9} = \frac{-2a+17}{a^2-9}$$

Example 2.22   Simplify the following fraction.

$$\frac{3 - \dfrac{x+3y}{x+y}}{1 + \dfrac{y}{x-y}}$$

Solution   Before performing the division, combine the fractions in the numerator and the denominator. The numerator becomes

$$\frac{3(x+y)-(x+3y)}{x+y} = \frac{2x}{x+y}$$

The denominator becomes

$$\frac{(x - y) + y}{x - y} = \frac{x}{x - y}$$

Thus, the original fraction may be written

$$\frac{3 - \dfrac{x + 3y}{x + y}}{1 + \dfrac{y}{x - y}} = \frac{\dfrac{2x}{x + y}}{\dfrac{x}{x - y}} = \frac{2x}{x + y} \cdot \frac{x - y}{x} = \frac{2(x - y)}{x + y}$$

Exercises for Section 2.3

Perform the indicated multiplications and divisions in Exercises 1–24.

1. $\dfrac{b}{3a} \cdot \dfrac{5c}{4ab^3}$

2. $\dfrac{x^2 y}{5xy^2} \cdot \dfrac{3xy^2}{x^3 y^5}$

3. $\dfrac{3x}{4y^3} \div \dfrac{9x^4}{2y}$

4. $\dfrac{xyz}{5x^2 y^3 z} \div \dfrac{4}{25x^3 y^2 z^2}$

5. $\dfrac{9b^2}{4c^3} \cdot \dfrac{24ac^2}{18b^5} \div \dfrac{c}{2a^3 b}$

6. $\dfrac{3x + 6}{x + 3} \cdot \dfrac{x^2 + 3x}{5x + 10}$

7. $\dfrac{x^2 + x - 6}{x^2 - 9} \cdot \dfrac{x^2 - 6x + 9}{2x - 4}$

8. $\dfrac{2x^2 + 11x + 15}{x^2 + 2x - 3} \cdot \dfrac{x^2 - x}{4x^2 + 20x + 25}$

9. $\dfrac{4xy^2}{4x^2 - 9} \div \dfrac{10x^2 y}{6x + 9}$

10. $\dfrac{15ab^2}{a^2 + a - 12} \div \dfrac{25a^2 b}{a - 3}$

11. $\dfrac{x^2 - xy}{y(x + y)} \cdot \dfrac{x^2 + xy}{y(x - y)} \div \dfrac{x^2 - x}{xy - 2y}$

12. $\dfrac{xy^2 + xy}{x^2 - 4} \cdot \dfrac{x^2 - 2x}{y^2 + y} \div \dfrac{x}{y(x + 2)}$

13. $\dfrac{2y^2 + 11y + 5}{2y^2 + 7y + 6} \div \dfrac{y^2 + 4y - 5}{2y^2 + y - 3}$

14. $\dfrac{6m^2 + m - 1}{2m^2 + 5m + 2} \div \dfrac{3m^2 - 7m + 2}{m^2 - m - 6}$

15. $\dfrac{2x^2 + x - 3}{3x^2 + 10x - 8} \cdot \dfrac{3x^2 - 2x}{x^2 - 1} \div \dfrac{x + 6}{x^2 + 5x + 4}$

16. $\dfrac{2x^2 + 3x - 9}{6x^2 - 7x + 2} \cdot \dfrac{3x - 2}{4x^2 - 8x + 3} \div \dfrac{x^2 + 3x}{2x^2 + 13x - 7}$

17. $\dfrac{(s-2)s-3}{s-2} \div \dfrac{s^2-9}{(s+1)(s-2)}$

18. $\dfrac{x(x+3)+2}{x+5} \cdot \dfrac{x(x+3)+5(x+3)}{x^2+5x+6}$

19. $\dfrac{ax+ay+bx+by}{ax-ay+bx-by} \div \dfrac{x+y}{x-y}$

20. $\dfrac{x(x-2)-3(x-2)}{x^2-4} \cdot \dfrac{x+2}{x(x-3)+(x-3)}$

21. $\dfrac{2y^2-5y-3}{y-4} \div \left[\dfrac{(y-3)^2}{y^2-16} \cdot \dfrac{1}{3-y}\right]$

22. $\dfrac{x^5+x^4-x-1}{x-1} \div \dfrac{x+1}{2x}$

23. $\dfrac{a^2+300a+20,000}{1600-a^2} \cdot \dfrac{a^2+360a-16,000}{2a+400}$

24. $\dfrac{(2x+3)x+1}{(2x+3)(x-1)} \cdot \dfrac{(x+1)x-2}{x(x+1)+2(x+1)}$

Perform the indicated additions and subtractions in Exercises 25–54.

25. $\dfrac{2}{b}+\dfrac{1}{c}-\dfrac{3}{a}$

26. $\dfrac{a}{bc}-\dfrac{b}{ac}$

27. $\dfrac{2}{3s}-\dfrac{1}{t}+\dfrac{4}{12st}$

28. $\dfrac{1}{x^2}-\dfrac{1}{y^2}$

29. $\dfrac{3}{xy^2}+\dfrac{2}{x}-\dfrac{3}{y}$

30. $\dfrac{s+1}{s}+\dfrac{s}{2}-\dfrac{1}{s}$

31. $\dfrac{3}{x+1}+\dfrac{2}{x-3}$

32. $\dfrac{5}{x+3}-\dfrac{3}{x-2}$

33. $\dfrac{x}{x-5}+\dfrac{2}{x+3}$

34. $\dfrac{3x}{2x+3}+\dfrac{x}{x-2}$

35. $\dfrac{3}{x}-\dfrac{2}{x+2}-\dfrac{1}{x(x+2)}$

36. $\dfrac{x-y}{x}+\dfrac{y}{x+y}+\dfrac{y^2}{x^2+xy}$

37. $\dfrac{2}{a}+\dfrac{3}{2a+3}-\dfrac{2}{a(2a+3)}$

38. $\dfrac{5}{2x-1}+\dfrac{x}{4x^2-1}-\dfrac{7}{2x+1}$

39. $4-\dfrac{9x-16}{3x+4}$

40. $x+\dfrac{4-x^2}{x-3}$

41. $\dfrac{2}{p}+\dfrac{2}{p^2+2p+1}-\dfrac{1}{p+1}$

42. $\dfrac{xy}{x-y}+\dfrac{x^2}{y-x}+x$

43. $\dfrac{1}{(x+3)(x-2)}+\dfrac{1}{(x+1)(x+3)}-\dfrac{1}{(x+1)(x-2)}$

44. $\dfrac{3}{x(x+2)}-\dfrac{1}{(x+2)(x-1)}+\dfrac{4}{x(x-1)}$

45. $\dfrac{5x+6}{x^2+x-6}+\dfrac{x+1}{x^2-4x+4}-\dfrac{x^2}{x^3-2x^2}$

46. $\dfrac{2-k}{k^2+k-6}+\dfrac{5}{k^2-9}-\dfrac{4-k}{k^2-5k+6}$

47. $\dfrac{x+2}{(x-5)x+6}+\dfrac{x+2}{(x-7)x+12}+\dfrac{1-x}{(6-x)x-8}$

48. $\dfrac{x}{(x-3)(x+2)}-\dfrac{2x}{x^2+6x+9}+\dfrac{x}{x^2-9}$

49. $\dfrac{x-\dfrac{1}{x}}{1-\dfrac{1}{x}}$

50. $\dfrac{1-\dfrac{3}{x}+\dfrac{2}{x^2}}{\dfrac{1}{x}-\dfrac{2}{x^2}}$

51. $\dfrac{\dfrac{2}{x-1}-x-2}{1-x+\dfrac{2}{x+2}}$

52. $\dfrac{\dfrac{1}{x}+\dfrac{2}{x+1}-x}{1-\dfrac{1}{x^2+2x+1}}$

53. $\dfrac{\dfrac{x}{x-4}+\dfrac{1}{x-1}}{\dfrac{x}{x-1}+\dfrac{2}{x-3}}$

54. $\dfrac{x^2-4y^2}{1-\dfrac{2x+y}{x-y}}$

55. An exothermal process is one that releases heat. In calculating how much heat is released by a new process, a chemist encounters the expression

$$\frac{1}{3}+\frac{2}{4t}-\frac{5}{2t^3}$$

Combine the terms and simplify.

56. In calculating the center of gravity of a certain concrete beam, the difference

$$\frac{1}{x}-\frac{1}{x(2x+1)}$$

is encountered. Simplify this expression.

57. A marketing student encounters the expression

$$\frac{3}{s^2+s}+\frac{2}{s^2+4s+3}$$

while analyzing past trends in the sales of a certain product. Simplify this expression.

2.3 Fractional Expressions

35

2.4
Exponents

In your previous work in mathematics you undoubtedly have had the opportunity to use exponential notation. Initially, exponents are considered to be shorthand for repeated multiplication of the same quantity; that is, for n, a positive integer, and x, any real number,

$$x^n = \underbrace{x \cdot x \cdot x \cdot x \cdot \cdots \cdot x}_{n \text{ times}}$$

The positive integer n is called the **exponent**, or the *power* of x, and x is called the *base*. For example,

$$\left(\frac{1}{3}\right)^2 = \left(\frac{1}{3}\right)\left(\frac{1}{3}\right) = \frac{1}{9}$$
$$(-3)^4 = (-3)(-3)(-3)(-3) = 81$$

More generally encountered are expressions of the form ax^n, where a is a real number called the *coefficient*. Take care to note the difference between ax^n and $(ax)^n$. In the first case x is raised to the nth power and then multiplied by a; in the second case the entire quantity ax is raised to the nth power. For example,

$$5(2)^3 = 5 \cdot 8 = 40, \text{ but } (5 \cdot 2)^3 = 1000$$

Several more or less basic rules govern the manipulations with exponents. These **rules of exponents** are given here in symbolic form.

Rule 1 $(a^n)(a^m) = a^{m+n}$

The reason for this is straightforward if we examine what is meant by exponential notation. For

$$(a^n)(a^m) = \underbrace{(x \cdot x \cdot x \cdot x \cdot \cdots \cdot x)}_{n \text{ times}}\underbrace{(x \cdot x \cdot x \cdot \cdots \cdot x)}_{m \text{ times}}$$

Since the total number of factors is $m + n$, this is equal to a^{m+n}.

Rule 2 $(a^m)^n = a^{mn}$

The proof follows directly from the definition of the exponent itself and from Rule 1.

$$(a^m)^n = \underbrace{(a^m)(a^m)(a^m) \cdots \cdot (a^m)}_{n \text{ times}}$$

$$= a^{\overbrace{m+m+m+ \cdots +m}}$$

$$= a^{mn}$$

Rule 3 $(ab)^n = a^n b^n$

$\left(\dfrac{a}{b}\right)^n = \dfrac{a^n}{b^n}$

Rule 4 $\dfrac{a^m}{a^n} = a^{m-n}$, if $m > n$

$= \dfrac{1}{a^{n-m}}$, if $n > m$

$= 1$, if $n = m$

Rules 3 and 4 can be verified with relative ease, so the verifications are not included. Working through the following examples will help make clear the application of these rules.

Example 2.23
(a) $x^3 \cdot x^4 = x^{3+4} = x^7$

(b) $y^5 \cdot y = y^{5+1} = y^6$

Example 2.24
(a) $(2^3)^2 = 2^6 = 2 \cdot 2 \cdot 2 \cdot 2 \cdot 2 \cdot 2 = 64$

(b) $(a^5)^4 = a^{20}$

Example 2.25
(a) $(5xy)^3 = 5^3 x^3 y^3 = 125 x^3 y^3$

(b) $\left(\dfrac{a}{b}\right)^4 = \dfrac{a^4}{b^4}$

Example 2.26
(a) $\dfrac{a^5}{a^3} = a^{5-3} = a^2$

(b) $\dfrac{2x^3 y^2}{xy^5} = \dfrac{2(x^{3-1})}{y^{5-2}} = \dfrac{2x^2}{y^3}$

2.4 Exponents

Exponential notation and the corresponding rules of manipulation are extended to include zero and negative integers. To give meaning to a^0, we note that since $a/a = 1$ and also $a/a = a^{1-1} = a^0$, it is convenient to define

$$a^0 = 1, \qquad a \neq 0$$

By a^{-n}, n a positive integer, we mean

$$a^{-n} = \frac{1}{a^n}, \qquad a \neq 0$$

This follows from

$$\frac{1}{a^n} = \frac{a^0}{a^n} = a^{0-n} = a^{-n}$$

Example 2.27   Simplify:

$$\frac{xy^{-2}}{3xb^{-3}}$$

Solution   Eliminating the negative exponents first,

$$\frac{xy^{-2}}{3xb^{-3}} = \frac{x \cdot \dfrac{1}{y^2}}{3x \dfrac{1}{b^3}} = \frac{\dfrac{1}{y^2}}{\dfrac{3}{b^3}} = \frac{1}{y^2} \cdot \frac{b^3}{3} = \frac{b^3}{3y^2}$$

Example 2.28   Simplify:

$$\frac{x^0 + y^0}{(x+y)^0}$$

Solution

$$\frac{x^0 + y^0}{(x+y)^0} = \frac{1+1}{1} = \frac{2}{1} = 2$$

Example 2.29   Simplify: $x^{-2} - y^{-3}$.

Solution

$$x^{-2} - y^{-3} = \frac{1}{x^2} - \frac{1}{y^3} = \frac{y^3}{x^2 y^3} - \frac{x^2}{x^2 y^3} = \frac{y^3 - x^2}{x^2 y^3}$$

Example 2.30   Simplify:

$$\frac{x^{-1} + y^{-1}}{(x+y)^{-1}}$$

Solution

$$\frac{x^{-1} + y^{-1}}{(x+y)^{-1}} = \frac{\dfrac{1}{x} + \dfrac{1}{y}}{\dfrac{1}{x+y}} = \frac{\dfrac{y+x}{xy}}{\dfrac{1}{x+y}} = \frac{x+y}{xy} \cdot \frac{x+y}{1} = \frac{(x+y)^2}{xy}$$

Scientists must often express positive real numbers in an abbreviated manner, which has come to be known as *scientific notation,* or the *scientific form* of a real number. To use the scientific form, express the real number as the product of a number between 1 and 10 and a power of 10. That is, if x is a positive real number, then the scientific form for x is

$$x = m \cdot 10^c$$

where m is between 1 and 10 and c is an integer.

Scientific notation is especially valuable for either very large or very small numbers. For example, the number 0.000000000000000000000053 represents the weight of an oxygen molecule. In scientific form this value is equal to 5.3×10^{-23} since the decimal point is moved to the right by 23 places to obtain the number 5.3 between 1 and 10.

Example 2.31 Write the numbers 5278, 37,910,000, 0.000172, and 0.24 in scientific notation.

Solution

$$5278 = 5.278 \times 10^3$$
$$37{,}910{,}000 = 3.791 \times 10^7$$
$$0.000172 = 1.72 \times 10^{-4}$$
$$0.24 = 2.4 \times 10^{-1}$$

The use of scientific notation has become even more commonplace with the general availability of the small scientific calculators. Most of the "slide rule" calculators have a button that the user can push to display the numbers in scientific notation. The number between 1 and 10 occurs with the usual 8-to-10-digit accuracy. To the right appears a two-digit number for the exponent. Hence, such a calculator can handle any number between 10^{-100} and 10^{100}.

Exercises for
Section 2.4

In Exercises 1–20 carry out the indicated computation to simplify the expression.

1. 4^3
2. -4^4
3. $(-4)^4$
4. $4^0(4^2)$
5. a^2/a^4
6. a^4/a^2

2.4 Exponents

7. $3(5^0)$ **8.** $(x^2/y^3)^4$ **9.** $(a/bx)^3$

10. $(-\frac{3}{2})^3$ **11.** $(-2)^{-3}$ **12.** $(2x^2)^3/3x^4$

13. $(\frac{2}{3})^{-1}$ **14.** $(\frac{1}{3})^{-1}(3^{-1})^{-3}$ **15.** $((6^2)^0)^{-1}$

16. $(x/y)^{-1}$ **17.** $(x+y)^{-1}$ **18.** $x^{-1} \cdot y^{-1}$

19. $(x+y)^0$ **20.** $x^0 + y^0$

In Exercises 21–30 eliminate negative exponents and simplify.

21. $(x^2 + x^{-1})^{-1}$ **22.** $(3x^{-2} + y^2)^0$

23. $(x^{-1} + y)^{-1}$ **24.** $\dfrac{a^0 + b^0}{(a^{-1} + b^{-1})^{-1}}$

25. $\dfrac{(ab)^{-1}}{a^{-1} + b^{-1}}$ **26.** $(a^{-2} + y^{-2})$

27. $((2^{-2})^{-2})^{-2}$ **28.** $((3^{-1})^{-1})^{-1}$

29. $\dfrac{(x+2)(x-3)^{-1} + (x-1)(x+4)^{-1}}{(x-3)^{-1} - (x+4)^{-1}}$

30. $x(x+1)^{-2} - (x+3)(x+1)^{-3}$

Write Exercises 31–36 in scientific notation.

31. 8,234,400,000   **32.** 93,002

33. 0.000000000052   **34.** .00786

35. 46 followed by 38 zeros   **36.** 53 followed by 13 zeros

Write Exercises 37–42 without scientific notation.

37. 3.4852×10^9 **38.** 1.423×10^{19}

39. 9.385×10^{-7} **40.** 8.99×10^{-11}

41. 2.222×10^{-2} **42.** 7.003×10^{-20}

43. The speed of light is approximately 30,000,000,000 cm/sec. Write this number in scientific notation.

44. A television rating service estimates that 28,500,000 people watch a particular program. Write this number in scientific notation.

45. An economist estimates that 1.5×10^6 people will be unemployed next year. Write this number without scientific notation.

Answer true or false in Exercises 46–53. Give reasons.

46. The sum of two rational numbers is rational.

47. $(x+y)^{-1} = x^{-1} + y^{-1}$

48. $(2x)^3 = 8x^3$

49. For any nonzero x, $(x^2)^3 = x^{2^3}$.

50. $\dfrac{1}{x+y} = \dfrac{1}{x} + \dfrac{1}{y}, \ x \neq 0, \ y \neq 0$

51. $\dfrac{x+a}{y+a} = \dfrac{x}{y}$

52. $\dfrac{x+y}{w} = \dfrac{x}{w} + \dfrac{y}{w}, \ w \neq 0$

53. $\dfrac{w}{x+y} = \dfrac{w}{x} + \dfrac{w}{y}, \ x \neq 0, \ y \neq 0, \ x+y \neq 0$

2.5
Radicals and
Fractional Exponents

We describe the statement $5^2 = 25$ by saying that 25 is the square of 5 or that 5 is the square root of 25. Similarly, -2 is the cube root of -8, since $(-2)^3 = -8$. In general,

Definition

If r is a real number and n is a positive integer such that $r^n = a$, then r is called an **nth root of a.**

The following observation arises from the definition of an nth root of a real number: *the nth root of a number is not unique.* For example, both 5 and -5 are square roots of 25. To avoid this kind of redundancy, we usually agree to use one root, called the **principal root**. The principal nth root of a number a is denoted by

$$\sqrt[n]{a}$$

The symbol $\sqrt{}$ is called the *radical sign* and n, the *index* of the radical. The meaning attached to $\sqrt[n]{a}$ depends upon the values of a and n and is governed by the definition of the principal nth root.

Definition

- If n is even and $a > 0$, then $\sqrt[n]{a}$ is the positive nth root.
- If n is odd and $a < 0$, then $\sqrt[n]{a}$ is the negative nth root.
- If n is odd and $a > 0$, then $\sqrt[n]{a}$ is the positive nth root.

The principal root, for n even and $a < 0$, cannot be defined at this time, but note that *for the square root of a negative number, the principal root is given by* $\sqrt{a} = i\sqrt{|a|}, \ a < 0.$

Example 2.32   Find the principal root of: (a) $\sqrt[4]{81}$; (b) $\sqrt[5]{-32}$; (c) $\sqrt{-25}$.

Solution

(a) $\sqrt[4]{81} = 3$, not ± 3

(b) $\sqrt[5]{-32} = -2$

(c) $\sqrt{-25} = 5i$

Since $\sqrt[n]{a} = r$ means $r^n = a$, it follows that

$$(\sqrt[n]{a})^n = a$$

For example, $(\sqrt[3]{5.14})^3 = 5.14$. Also, since a principal square root is a unique number, we can write $\sqrt{a^2} = |a|$. Thus, $\sqrt{(-2)^2} = 2$, not -2.

The following rules are useful in working with radical expressions.

Rule 1 $\sqrt[n]{a}\,\sqrt[n]{b} = \sqrt[n]{ab}$

Rule 2 $\dfrac{\sqrt[n]{a}}{\sqrt[n]{b}} = \sqrt[n]{\dfrac{a}{b}}$

These two rules tell how to multiply or divide numbers taken to the same root. No corresponding rule exists for combining radicals by addition.

Example 2.33   Simplify: $\sqrt{16x^3y^6}$; that is, remove any perfect square roots.

Solution $\sqrt{16x^3y^6} = \sqrt{16}\,\sqrt{x^3}\,\sqrt{y^6} = 4xy^3\sqrt{x}$

Example 2.34   Simplify: $\sqrt[3]{-16x^5}$.

Solution $\sqrt[3]{-16x^5} = \sqrt[3]{(-8x^3)(2x^2)} = \sqrt[3]{-8x^3}\,\sqrt[3]{2x^2} = -2x\sqrt[3]{2x^2}$

Example 2.35   Simplify: $\sqrt{2}\sqrt{3}$ and $\sqrt{\frac{1}{9}}$.

Solution $\sqrt{2}\sqrt{3} = \sqrt{2 \cdot 3} = \sqrt{6}$ and $\sqrt{\dfrac{1}{9}} = \dfrac{\sqrt{1}}{\sqrt{9}} = \dfrac{1}{3}$

Example 2.36   Simplify: (a) $\sqrt{8} + \sqrt{18}$; (b) $\sqrt{2} + \sqrt{12}$.

Solution

(a) $\sqrt{8} + \sqrt{18} = \sqrt{4}\sqrt{2} + \sqrt{9}\sqrt{2} = 2\sqrt{2} + 3\sqrt{2} = 5\sqrt{2}$

(b) $\sqrt{2} + \sqrt{12} = \sqrt{2} + \sqrt{4}\sqrt{3} = \sqrt{2} + 2\sqrt{3}$

When radicals occur in the denominator of a fraction, we consider eliminating them a "simplification" and call the process **rationalization** of the denominator. The next example shows the technique.

Example 2.37   Rationalize the denominator to simplify each expression.

(a) $\dfrac{1}{\sqrt{3}}$ (b) $\dfrac{x}{\sqrt{x+y}}$

Solution

(a) $\dfrac{1}{\sqrt{3}} = \dfrac{1}{\sqrt{3}} \cdot \dfrac{\sqrt{3}}{\sqrt{3}} = \dfrac{\sqrt{3}}{3}$

(b) $\dfrac{x}{\sqrt{x+y}} = \dfrac{x}{\sqrt{x+y}} \cdot \dfrac{\sqrt{x+y}}{\sqrt{x+y}} = \dfrac{x\sqrt{x+y}}{x+y}$

Example 2.38   Write $1/(2\sqrt{x} + \sqrt{y})$ as a fraction with a rational denominator.

Solution   To rationalize the given fraction, use the fact that $(\sqrt{x})^2 = x$ and the special product $(a + b)(a - b) = a^2 - b^2$ to write

$$\dfrac{1}{2\sqrt{x} + \sqrt{y}} = \dfrac{1}{2\sqrt{x} + \sqrt{y}} \cdot \dfrac{2\sqrt{x} - \sqrt{y}}{2\sqrt{x} - \sqrt{y}} = \dfrac{2\sqrt{x} - \sqrt{y}}{4x - y}$$

Fractional Exponents

We now extend the definition of exponential notation to include fractional exponents. Assuming that the laws of exponents are valid for fractions, we interpret expressions of the form $a^{1/n}$ such that

$$(a^{1/n})^n = a^{n/n} = a$$

Consequently, $a^{1/n}$ is defined as a number whose nth power is a. It then follows that

$$a^{1/n} = \sqrt[n]{a}$$

Similarly, if the fraction p/q is in lowest terms, $a^{p/q}$ is interpreted as

$$a^{p/q} = (a^{1/q})^p = (a^p)^{1/q}$$

and hence $a^{p/q}$ is defined as

$$a^{p/q} = \sqrt[q]{a^p} = (\sqrt[q]{a})^p$$

Example 2.39 $\sqrt[5]{y^2} = (y^2)^{1/5} = y^{2/5}$

Example 2.40   Simplify: $(-8)^{2/3}(9)^{-3/2}$.

Solution

$$(-8)^{2/3}(9)^{-3/2} = [(-8)^{1/3}]^2[(9^{1/2})]^{-3} = (-2)^2(3)^{-3} = \frac{(-2)^2}{3^3} = \frac{4}{27}$$

Example 2.41   Simplify:

$$\left[\frac{3x^{2/3}}{y^{5/2}}\right]^3\left[\frac{7y^{1/6}}{5x^{5/6}}\right]^{-1}$$

Solution

$$\left[\frac{3x^{2/3}}{y^{5/2}}\right]^3\left[\frac{7y^{1/6}}{5x^{5/6}}\right]^{-1} = \frac{27x^2}{y^{15/2}} \cdot \frac{5x^{5/6}}{7y^{1/6}} = \frac{135x^{17/6}}{7y^{23/3}}$$

In passing, note that the exponent concept can be extended further to include irrational numbers so that the rules of exponents hold for all real exponents. Such a development is beyond the scope of this text but we shall use the result when necessary. For example, the number $3^{\sqrt{2}}$ may be approximated as close as desired by using rational approximations to $\sqrt{2}$. Calculations of this type usually work best with a hand calculator that has an "exp" button. Then we may make the following approximations to $3^{\sqrt{2}}$. $3^1 = 3$, $3^{1.4} = 4.655$, $3^{1.41} = 4.706$, $3^{1.414} = 4.727 \ldots$ Continue these approximations to obtain any desired degree of accuracy; for example, to 9 decimal places $3^{\sqrt{2}} = 4.728804388$. Chapter 8 explores this subject in greater detail.

Exercises for
Section 2.5

Write Exercises 1–8 in fractional exponent form.

1. $\sqrt[3]{x}$ **2.** $\sqrt{a}$ **3.** $\sqrt[4]{x/y}$ **4.** $\sqrt{x\sqrt{x\sqrt{x}}}$

5. $\sqrt[3]{x^2}$ **6.** $\sqrt{x} + \sqrt{y}$ **7.** $\sqrt[4]{x\sqrt{x\sqrt[3]{x}}}$ **8.** $\sqrt{5x\sqrt[3]{x}}$

Write Exercises 9–14 in radical form.

9. $x^{3/5}$ **10.** $x^{3/4}$ **11.** $(a^{3/2})^{1/4}$

12. $\dfrac{1}{x^{-1/2}}$ **13.** $(a+b)^{1/3}$ **14.** $x + y^{1/2}$

Simplify the expressions in Exercises 15–22.

15. $\sqrt{125}$ **16.** $\sqrt[4]{16}$ **17.** $\sqrt{25x^4y^6}$

18. $\sqrt[3]{x^5y^7}$ **19.** $\sqrt[3]{3x^2}\sqrt[3]{9y}$ **20.** $\dfrac{\sqrt{4x^3}}{\sqrt{3x^5}}$

21. $\sqrt[4]{\sqrt[3]{16}}$ **22.** $\sqrt{a^2+b^2}$

Write Exercises 23–32 as a fraction with a rational denominator.

23. $\dfrac{1}{\sqrt{5}}$

24. $\sqrt{3/2}$

25. $\sqrt{\dfrac{x}{x+y}}$

26. $\dfrac{x+y}{\sqrt{xy}}$

27. $\dfrac{1}{\sqrt{3}+\sqrt{5}}$

28. $\dfrac{2}{\sqrt{2}-\sqrt{7}}$

29. $\dfrac{x}{\sqrt{x}+\sqrt{y}}$

30. $\dfrac{\sqrt{x}}{\sqrt{x}-3\sqrt{y}}$

31. $\dfrac{\sqrt{a}+\sqrt{b}}{\sqrt{a}-\sqrt{b}}$

32. $\dfrac{1}{\sqrt[3]{x}+\sqrt[3]{y}}$

Simplify the expressions in Exercises 33–53. Write all answers using positive exponents when exponents are required.

33. $(64)^{1/2}$ **34.** $(64)^{2/3}$ **35.** $(81)^{3/4}$ **36.** $8^{-5/3}$

37. $(32)^{-3/5}$ **38.** $(-125)^{1/3}$ **39.** $x^{1/2}x^{2/3}$ **40.** $a^{1/4}a^{1/3}$

41. $y^{4/3}y^{-1/2}$ **42.** $x^{3/8}x^{1/4}$

43. $(125a^3b^9)^{1/3}$ **44.** $(9x^4y^{10})^{1/2}$

45. $(9x^{2/3})^{1/2}$ **46.** $(16a^{-8/9}b^{4/3})^{3/4}$

47. $2x^{-1/2}+3y^{-1/2}$ **48.** $x^{1/2}-x^{-1/2}$

49. $(a^{1/2}+b^{1/2})^2$ **50.** $(a^{1/2}+b^{1/2})(a^{1/2}-b^{1/2})$

51. $(y^{1/2}+y^{-1/2})^2$ **52.** $x^{1/2}y+x^{-1/2}$

53. $(x+3)(x-2)^{-1/2}+(x-2)^{1/2}$

In the expressions in Exercises 54–59 perform the indicated operations and express the answer in simplest form.

54. $\sqrt{32}-\sqrt{18}$ **55.** $\sqrt{27}+5\sqrt{12}$ **56.** $\sqrt[3]{-16}+\sqrt[3]{128}$

57. $\sqrt{125}+3\sqrt{45}-2\sqrt{20}$ **58.** $\sqrt{x^3y}-\sqrt{x^5y^3}$ **59.** $\sqrt{\dfrac{1}{2}}+\sqrt{\dfrac{9}{2}}$

60. Under what circumstances is
     (a) $\sqrt{x}>x$ (b) $\sqrt{x}=x$ (c) $\sqrt{x}<x$

61. Can you find real numbers a and b such that

$$\frac{1}{a}+\frac{1}{b}=\frac{2}{a+b}$$

Using a hand calculator with an "exp" button, approximate the numbers in Exercises 62–66 by using rational number approximations to the given irrational numbers.

62. $2^{\sqrt{3}}$ **63.** $8^{\sqrt{8}}$ **64.** $\pi^{\sqrt{2}}$ **65.** π^π **66.** $(\sqrt{2})^\pi$

Answer true or false for Exercises 67–70. If false, give a counterexample.

67. $\sqrt{x+y}=\sqrt{x}+\sqrt{y}$ **68.** $\sqrt{xy}=\sqrt{x}\cdot\sqrt{y}$

69. $\sqrt{16}=\pm4$ **70.** $\sqrt{x^2}=x$

2.6
Manipulative
Skills

These first two chapters reviewed those skills necessary for any subsequent mathematics course. In addition to learning the concepts, you must also cultivate manipulative skills. These skills are dependent not only upon knowing the governing algebraic rule, but also upon intangibles such as precision, carefulness, and experience in "knowing what to do next."

You have probably had many occasions in which you have made careless or inadvertent errors. In mathematics examples of such errors might be writing a number illegibly, omitting signs, leaving out necessary parentheses, or writing the exponent of a number as a coefficient. Such "trivial" mistakes can be very important in some of the mathematically related disciplines. Computer programmers soon find out that the manner in which a computer responds to the omission of a right parenthesis is far from minor. The computer will unhesitatingly reject the entire program for such a "trivial" error. Likewise, failure to clearly distinguish between $(3x)^2$ and $3x^2$ or to change the sign of every term when removing signs from expressions such as $-(x^2 - 4xy + y^2)$ might cause your bridge to collapse if you are a civil engineer. Perhaps these examples seem dramatic, but carelessness and imprecision *can* be costly. As you progress in mathematics, you must know the laws of real numbers and be very careful when applying them. The following exercise set shows some of the "trivial" errors that have occurred on exam papers. See if you can spot them.

Exercises for
Section 2.6

Tell in precisely which manner the mathematical statements in Exercises 1–21 are incorrect.

1. $2x^2 = 4x^2$

2. $(3x)^2 = 3x^2$

3. $-(2x - 1) = -2x - 1$

4. $-(x^2 - 5x - 6) = -x^2 - 5x - 6$

5. $\dfrac{1}{2} + \dfrac{3}{4} = \dfrac{4}{6}$

6. $\dfrac{2}{6} - \dfrac{1}{2} = \dfrac{1}{4}$

7. $\dfrac{x + 2}{x} = x + \dfrac{2}{x}$

8. $(x + y)^2 = x^2 + y^2$

9. $(x^{-1} + y^{-1})^{-1} = x + y$

10. $\sqrt{x + y} = \sqrt{x} + \sqrt{y}$

11. $(x^3 + x^2) = x^2(x + x^2)$

12. $(\sqrt{x} + \sqrt{y})^2 = x + y$

13. $\dfrac{1}{x + y} = \dfrac{1}{x} + \dfrac{1}{y}$

14. $\sqrt{2x} = \sqrt{2}\,x$

15. $(-x)^2 = -x^2$

16. $\dfrac{2}{x^2 + 2x + 1} = \dfrac{1}{x^2 + x + 1}$

17. $(x^2)^3 = x^5$

18. $x^2 \cdot x^6 = x^{12}$

19. $x + x = x^2$

20. $4^{1/2} = \dfrac{1}{2}$

21. $\dfrac{3(5x + 2)}{x^2 + 5x + 2} = \dfrac{3}{x^2}$

Test 1 for Chapter 2

Answer true or false for Exercises 1–10.

1. An exponent of -2 means to take the square root.

2. $(\sqrt{x + y})^2 = x + y$ for real numbers x and y.

3. $(2^3)^2 = 2^{(3^2)}$

4. $(x + 4)^3 = x^3 + 4^3$

5. $\dfrac{x + y}{x} = 1 + \dfrac{y}{x}$

6. $\dfrac{x^2 - y^2}{x^2 + y^2} = \dfrac{1 - \dfrac{x^2}{y^2}}{1 + \dfrac{y^2}{x^2}}$

7. $a \div (b + c) = (a \div b) + (a \div c)$

8. $\sqrt{4} = \pm 2$

9. $-4x^2 = 16x^2$

10. $\dfrac{x/y}{z} = \dfrac{x}{y/z}$

11. Eliminate negative exponents and simplify: $(x^{-1} + y^{-1})(x^{-1} - y^{-1})$.

12. Divide $x^5 + 3x^4 + 2x^3$ by $x + 2$.

13. Multiply $x^3 + x^2 - 5x + 2$ by $x^2 - 3x - 3$.

14. Factor $x^2 - 9x + 14$.

15. (a) Write in scientific notation: 762,500. (b) Write without scientific notation: 4.23×10^{-5}.

16. Simplify:

$$\dfrac{1 - \dfrac{6}{x} + \dfrac{5}{x^2}}{\dfrac{1}{x} - \dfrac{5}{x^2}}$$

Test 2 for Chapter 2

1. Express in scientific notation: (a) 5,375,000; (b) 0.000139.

2. Simplify: (a) $\sqrt[3]{128x^4 y^{12}}$; (b) $x^{2/3} x^{-1/2}$.

3. Rationalize: $\dfrac{x + 5}{\sqrt{x - 3}}$.

4. Write $(x + 2y)(x^3 - 5y^2 + 2)$ in expanded form.

5. Write $x^2 - 6x + 9$ in factored form.

6. Write $6x^2 + 7x - 3$ in factored form.

Perform the indicated operations in Exercises 7–10, and write in simplest form.

7. $\dfrac{x^2 - 3x + 2}{3x - x^2} \div \dfrac{x^2 + 2x - 8}{x - 3}$

8. $\dfrac{2}{ab} + \dfrac{3}{ac^2} - \dfrac{5}{b^3c}$

9. $3 + \dfrac{5}{x + 1} - \dfrac{x}{x^2 - 2x - 3}$

10. $\dfrac{(xy)^{-2}}{x^{-2} - y^{-2}} + x^{-2}$

3
The Idea of
a Function

3.1

The Cartesian
Coordinate System

We pointed out in Section 1.1, that the set $\{a, b\}$ and the set $\{b, a\}$ are considered equal; that is, the order in which the elements are written is inconsequential. At times, however, the order of the elements in a set becomes important, particularly for sets of two elements. Such two-element ordered sets are called **ordered pairs** and are denoted by (a, b). In this case a is called the *first element* and b, the *second element* of the ordered pair. Recall that the notation (a, b) also designates the open interval on the real line between a and b. Usually the context will tell if an ordered pair or an open interval is being described.

Two ordered pairs are equal when they consist of the same pair of elements listed in precisely the same order. Thus, the ordered pair $(3, 2)$ is not equal to $(2, 3)$.

Many discussions in mathematics require that we deal with sets of ordered pairs of numbers. The following is a fundamental way in which ordered pairs arise from the use of sets. Let A and B be sets of elements. Then we can form ordered pairs by selecting elements from A as first elements and elements from B as second elements. $A \times B$ denotes the set of *all* possible ordered pairs formed from A and B in this manner. This set is called the **Cartesian product** of A and B after René Descartes, the first person to systematically use ordered pairs of numbers to advantage.

Note that the formation of the Cartesian product of A and B differs from formation of unions and intersections in that elements of the Cartesian product $A \times B$ are not elements of either A or B. Cartesian products of sets are not limited to ordered pairs of numbers either in concept or in their usefulness.

Example 3.1   Suppose that you can buy a car with interior colors red, black, or green, and exterior colors either tan or white. Use the concept of a Cartesian product to describe all the possibilities.

Solution   Let $I = \{r, b, g\}$ represent the set of interior colors and $E = \{t, w\}$, the set of exterior colors. Then the Cartesian product $I \times E$ represents all the combinations.

$$I \times E = \{(r, t), (b, t), (g, t), (r, w), (b, w), (g, w)\}$$

Example 3.2   Let $A = \{a, b\}$ and $B = \{1, 2\}$. Find $A \times B$ and $B \times A$.

Solution

$$A \times B = \{(a, 1), (a, 2), (b, 1), (b, 2)\}$$
$$B \times A = \{(1, a), (1, b), (2, a), (2, b)\}$$

3 The Idea of a Function

Example 3.2 shows that the order in which the Cartesian product is taken is important; that is, $A \times B \neq B \times A$. However, the number of elements in the two sets is always the same and is equal to the product of the number of elements in A and the number of elements in B. Elementary school teachers often use the Cartesian product to describe the concept of multiplication of natural numbers. For example, to show that $3 \cdot 2 = 6$, we select any set of three elements, say $A = \{a, b, c\}$ and any set of two elements, say $B = \{c, d\}$. Then

$$A \times B = \{(a, c), (a, d), (b, c), (b, d), (c, c), (c, d)\}$$

which has six elements and thereby shows the intended multiplication fact.

Just as we form a correspondence between real numbers and points on a line, so also do we associate ordered pairs of numbers with points in a plane. Any one of several approaches could accomplish this association, but the most commonly used approach is called the **rectangular coordinate system** or, just as popularly, the **Cartesian coordinate system**. To construct such a system, first draw a pair of mutually perpendicular number lines to intersect at zero on each line, as is shown in Figure 3.1.

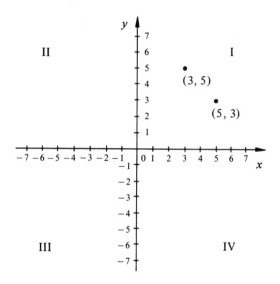

Figure 3.1

Normally the horizontal line is called the x-axis, the vertical line the y-axis, and their intersection the origin. Considered together, the two axes are called the coordinate axes. As you can see, the coordinate axes divide the plane into four zones, or **quadrants**. The upper right quadrant is called the first quadrant and the others are numbered consecutively in a counterclockwise direction as in Figure 3.1. The coordinate axes are not considered to be in any quadrant.

To locate points in the plane, use the origin as a reference point and lay off a suitable scale on each of the coordinate axes. The displacement of a point in the plane to the right or left of the y-axis is called the **x-coordinate**, or **abscissa**, of the point, and is denoted by x. Values of x measured to the right of the y-axis are considered to be *positive* and to the left, *negative*. The displacement of a point in the plane above or below the x-axis is called the **y-coordinate**, or **ordinate**, of the point, and is denoted by y. Values of y above the x-axis are considered to be *positive* and below the x-axis, *negative*. Considered together, the abscissa and the ordinate of a point are called the **coordinates** of the point. The coordinates of a point are conventionally written in parentheses, with the abscissa written first and separated from the ordinate by a comma; that is, (x, y).

We see that a point (x, y) lies

- in quadrant I if both coordinates are positive,
- in quadrant II if the x-coordinate is negative and the y-coordinate is positive,
- in quadrant III if both coordinates are negative,
- in quadrant IV if the x-coordinate is positive and the y-coordinate is negative.

Since the first number represents the horizontal displacement and the second the vertical displacement, we see the significance of order. For example, the ordered pair $(3, 5)$ represents a point that is displaced 3 units to the right of the origin and 5 units above it, while the ordered pair $(5, 3)$ represents a point that is 5 units to the right and 3 units up. The association of points in the plane with ordered pairs of real numbers is an obvious extension of a similar idea on the real line.

To be precise, we should always distinguish between the point and the ordered pair; however, it is common practice to blur the distinction and say "the point (x, y)" instead of "the point whose coordinate is (x, y)."

Employment of the rectangular coordinate system establishes a one-to-one correspondence between the points in a plane and all possible ordered pairs of real numbers (x, y); that is, each point in the plane can be described by a unique ordered pair of numbers (x, y) and each ordered pair of numbers (x, y) can be represented by a unique point in the plane called the **graph** of the ordered pair. You may have noticed that the rectangular plane is a graphical representation of the Cartesian product $R \times R$; that is, the set of real numbers with itself. (A gold star if you did!)

Example 3.3 Locate the points $P(-1, 2)$, $Q(2, 3)$, $R(-3, -4)$, $S(3, -5)$, and $T(\pi, 0)$ in the plane.

Solution

$P(-1, 2)$ is in quadrant II because the x-coordinate is negative and the y-coordinate is positive.

$Q(2, 3)$ is in quadrant I because both coordinates are positive.

$R(-3, -4)$ is in quadrant III because both coordinates are negative.

$S(3, -5)$ is in quadrant IV because the x-coordinate is positive and the y-coordinate is negative.

$T(\pi, 0)$ is not in any quadrant, but lies on the positive x-axis.

The points are plotted in Figure 3.2.

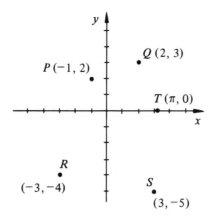

Figure 3.2

In plotting an entire *set* of ordered pairs, the corresponding set of points in the plane is called the *graph* of the set.

Example 3.4   Graph the set $A \times B$ if $A = \{1, -1\}$ and $B = \{1, 2, 3\}$.

Solution   The set $A \times B = \{(1, 1), (1, 2), (1, 3), (-1, 1), (-1, 2), (-1, 3)\}$. The set of corresponding points is shown in Figure 3.3.

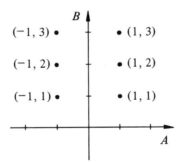

Figure 3.3

Example 3.5   Graph the set of points whose abscissas are greater than -1 and whose ordinates are less than or equal to 4.

Solution   In set notation we describe this set as

$$\{(x, y) \mid x > -1 \quad \text{and} \quad y \leq 4\}$$

The shaded region in Figure 3.4 is the graph of the set. The solid line is part of the region, whereas the broken line is not.

3.1 The Cartesian Coordinate System   53

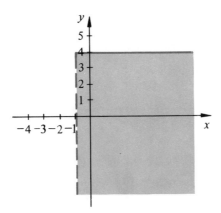

Figure 3.4

3.2
The Distance
between Two Points

Consider two points P_1 and P_2 on the x-axis as shown in Figure 3.5.

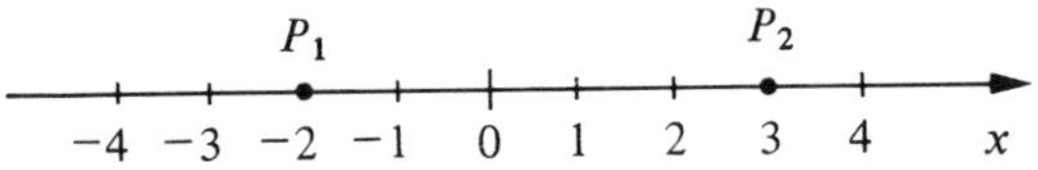

Figure 3.5

The distance between these two points can be found by counting the number of units between them, or algebraically, by subtraction. To be sure that the numerical quantity obtained in the computation of horizontal distance will be positive, we define it to be the absolute value of the difference between P_1 and P_2. Thus*

$$\overline{P_1 P_2} = |P_1 - P_2|$$

Computing the distance in Figure 3.5, we have

$$\overline{P_1 P_2} = |-2 - 3| = |-5| = 5$$

A similar scheme is followed if the points lie on the y-axis.

Now consider two points $P_1(x_1, y_1)$ and $P_2(x_2, y_2)$ that determine a slant line, as shown in Figure 3.6. Draw a line through P_1 parallel to the x-axis and a line through P_2 parallel to the y-axis. These two lines intersect at the point $M(x_2, y_1)$. Hence, by the Pythagorean theorem,

$$(3.1) \qquad (\overline{P_1 P_2})^2 = (\overline{P_1 M})^2 + (\overline{M P_2})^2$$

---

* In general, $P_1 P_2$ refers to the line segment connecting a point P_1 to a point P_2, while $\overline{P_1 P_2}$ denotes the *length* of that line segment.

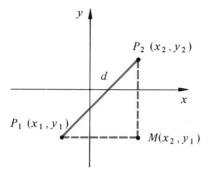

Figure 3.6

We see from Figure 3.6 that $\overline{P_1 M}$ is the horizontal distance between P_1 and P_2. Therefore, the distance $\overline{P_1 M}$ is given by

$$\overline{P_1 M} = |x_2 - x_1|$$

Likewise, the vertical distance $\overline{MP_2}$ is given by

$$\overline{MP_2} = |y_2 - y_1|$$

Making these substitutions into equation (3.1) and denoting $\overline{P_1 P_2}$ by d,

$$d^2 = (x_2 - x_1)^2 + (y_2 - y_1)^2$$

(3.2) $$d = \sqrt{(x_2 - x_1)^2 + (y_2 - y_1)^2}$$

Equation (3.2) is called the **distance formula** and is used to find the distance between two points in the plane directly from the coordinates of the points. The order in which the two points are labeled is immaterial since

$$(x_2 - x_1)^2 = (x_1 - x_2)^2 \quad \text{and} \quad (y_2 - y_1)^2 = (y_1 - y_2)^2$$

Example 3.6   Find the distance between $(-3, -6)$ and $(5, -2)$. (See Figure 3.7.)

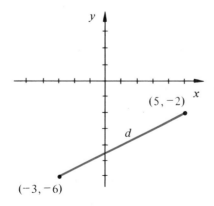

Figure 3.7 $(-3, -6)$

3.2 The Distance between Two Points

Solution   Let $(x_1, y_1) = (-3, -6)$ and $(x_2, y_2) = (5, -2)$. Substituting these values into the formula,

$$d = \sqrt{(x_2 - x_1)^2 + (y_2 - y_1)^2}$$
$$= \sqrt{[5 - (-3)]^2 + [-2 - (-6)]^2}$$
$$= \sqrt{64 + 16} = \sqrt{80} = 4\sqrt{5}$$

Notice the inclusion of the numerical sign of each number in the substitution of values into the distance formula.

Example 3.7   Find the distance between $(2, 5)$ and $(2, -1)$.

Solution   In this case the two given points lie on a vertical line since they have the same abscissa. (See Figure 3.8.) The distance between the two points, therefore, can be found directly.

$$d = |5 - (-1)| = |5 + 1| = 6 \text{ units}$$

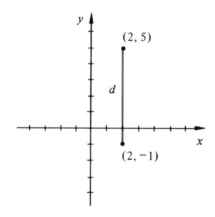

Figure 3.8

The distance can also be found from the distance formula. Letting $(x_1, y_1) = (2, 5)$ and $(x_2, y_2) = (2, -1)$,

$$d = \sqrt{(2 - 2)^2 + (-1 - 5)^2} = \sqrt{36} = 6 \text{ units}$$

Exercises for
Sections 3.1 and 3.2

Plot the ordered pairs in Exercises 1–6.

1. $(3, 2)$ 2. $(4, 6)$ 3. $(-2, \frac{1}{2})$

4. $(-6, -5)$ 5. $(\frac{1}{4}, \frac{1}{2})$ 6. $(-2.5, 1.7)$

7. In which two quadrants do the points have positive abscissas?

8. In which two quadrants do the points have negative ordinates?

9. In which quadrant are both the abscissa and ordinate negative?

10. In which quadrants is the ratio y/x negative?

11. What is the ordinate of a point on the x-axis?

3 The Idea of a Function

Plot the pairs of points in Exercises 12–19 and find the distance between the points.

12. (1, 2), (5, 4)   **13.** (0, 4), (−1, 3)

14. (−1, 5), (−1, −6)   **15.** $(\frac{1}{2}, \frac{1}{2})$, $(\frac{1}{2}, -\frac{3}{4})$

16. (−5, 3), (2, −1)   **17.** (0.5, 1.6), (6.2, 7.5)

18. (−3, 4), (0, 4)   **19.** (2, −6), $(-\sqrt{3}, -3)$

Find the graph $A \times B$ for the sets in Exercises 20–22.

20. $A = \{1\}$, $B = \{0\}$ **21.** $A = \{1\}$, $B = \{-1, 1\}$

22. $A = \{1\}$, $B = \varnothing$ **23.** $A = \{0, 2\}$, $B = \{0, 1, 2\}$

24. $A = \{1, 2\}$, $B = \{1, 2, 3\}$

25. The point $(x, 3)$ is 4 units from $(5,1)$. Find x.

26. Find the distance between the points $(\sqrt{x}, \sqrt{y})$ and $(-\sqrt{x}, -\sqrt{y})$.

27. Find the distance between the points (x, y) and $(-x, y)$.

28. Find the distance between the points (x, y) and $(x, -y)$.

29. Find the point on the x-axis that is equidistant from $(0, -1)$ and $(3, 2)$.

Graph the sets of points in Exercises 30–37.

30. $\{(x, y) \mid y > 0\}$ **31.** $\{(x, y) \mid x = 0\}$

32. $\{(x, y) \mid x > 0\}$ **33.** $\{(x, y) \mid y = 2\}$

34. $\{(x, y) \mid x > -1 \text{ and } y > 0\}$ **35.** $\{(x, y) \mid x = y\}$

36. $\{(x, y) \mid x > 0, y > 0\} \cap \{(x, y) \mid x < 1, y < 1\}$

37. $\{(x, y) \mid x > -1, y < -1\} \cap \{(x, y) \mid x \le -1, y \ge -1\}$

3.3
Variation

Most applications of mathematics concern the relationship of one quantity to another; for example, how the acceleration of an object is related to the force causing the acceleration, or how the profit of a company is related to manpower. This chapter shows how relations of this sort can be made explicit through the formulation of the concept of "function." Here are two relations that can be expressed by formulas.

Example 3.8   The formula for the area of a circle is $A = \pi r^2$, where r is the radius of the circle and π is a **constant**. We call π an absolute constant because it represents the same number (3.14159 ...) in all discussions. The value of r can take on any value during a discussion, so we call it a **variable**. Notice also that A is written as a *dependent* variable since its value depends upon that of r. If we write $r = \sqrt{A/\pi}$, then r is written as the dependent variable. 🐿

Example 3.9   In converting temperature from degrees Celsius to degrees Fahrenheit the formula $F = (\frac{9}{5})C + 32$ is used. Both F and C are variables in this formula; the numerical values $\frac{9}{5}$ and 32 are constants. 🐿

In practice, many applied problems are solved by establishing some simple proportion or ratio between the variables.

Example 3.10   A model airplane for use in wind tunnel tests is built to a scale of $\frac{1}{4}$ inch to 1 foot. What is the wing span of the model if the actual airplane has a wing span of 50 feet?

Solution   Establish a proportion using S_M, S_A, W_M, and W_A to represent the respective values of the model scale, the actual scale, the model wing dimension, and the actual wing dimension. Thus,

$$\frac{S_M}{S_A} = \frac{W_M}{W_A}$$

Note that in supplying the known values $S_M = \frac{1}{4}''$, $S_A = 1'$, and $W_A = 50'$, the appropriate units are maintained.

$$\frac{\frac{1}{4}''}{1'} = \frac{W_M}{50'}$$

$$W_M(1') = \frac{1}{4}''(50')$$

$$W_M = 12.5'' \quad \text{(wing span of wind tunnel model)}$$ 🐿

This example used the simple idea of a ratio or proportion to establish a desired relation. If the ratio of two variables is always a constant, then the two variables are said to **vary directly**.

Definition
The variable y is said to vary directly as x if $y = kx$, where k is the *constant of direct proportionality*.

Given that two variables are related by direct variation, then a knowledge of the value of the variables in but one case will give the formula of y in terms of x for all cases.

Example 3.11   Newton's law of motion says that the acceleration a of an object is directly proportional to the force F applied to it. Suppose that an object is accelerated 10 m/sec^2

by a force of 5 newtons. What acceleration will the same object experience if a force of 20 newtons is applied?

Solution   Symbolically, Newton's law is written $a = k \cdot F$. Since $a = 10$ when $F = 5$, we have that $10 = k \cdot 5$, or $k = 2$. Hence, the general formula is $a = 2F$. In particular, if $F = 20$, then $a = 2 \cdot 20 = 40$ m/sec^2.

Another important kind of variation, called **inverse variation**, occurs when the *product* of the variables is a constant.

Definition

The variable y is said to vary inversely as x if $y = k/x$, where k is the *constant of inverse proportionality.*

In direct variation the two variables increase (or decrease) together. But in inverse variation an increase in one variable means a decrease in the other.

By considering the values of x and y as determining ordered pairs, a picture of direct and inverse variation can be drawn on a Cartesian coordinate system. Figure 3.9 shows typical cases of direct variation $(y = kx)$ and inverse variation $(y = k/x)$.

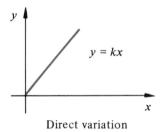

Direct variation

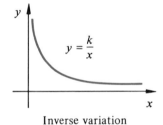

Inverse variation

Figure 3.9

Example 3.12   In chemistry Boyle's law states: *If the temperature of a gas is constant then the product of the volume V and the applied pressure P are constant.* Suppose that the volume of a gas is 100 in.^{3} when the pressure is 20 psi. What is the volume when the pressure is 14.7 psi?

Solution   Boyle's law states that $V = k(1/P)$. Hence, if $V = 100$ when $P = 20$, we have

$$100 = k\left(\frac{1}{20}\right)$$

or $k = 20(100) = 2000$

Boyle's law for this gas is then

$$V = (2000)\frac{1}{P}$$

Substituting $P = 14.7$ psi into this formula yields

$$V = \frac{2000}{14.7} = 136 \text{ in.}^3$$

The preceding examples indicate variation in which one quantity is dependent on another. With cases in which the variation is in terms of either the product or the quotient of two other quantities, the first quantity is said to vary *jointly* as the others. The words "directly" and "inversely" describe the relations between the variables, as the following example makes clear.

Example 3.13   The ACE Light Bulb Company finds that the price P of each light bulb it produces should vary directly as the cost C of material and inversely as the square root of the number produced n. If materials cost $2000 to produce 40,000 light bulbs priced at $.30, how much should the company charge for a new bulb if $1500 of material will make 10,000 bulbs?

Solution   The relationship among P, C, and n may be written

$$P = k\frac{C}{\sqrt{n}}$$

The condition $P = .30$, $C = 2000$, and $n = 40,000$ yields

$$.30 = k\frac{2000}{\sqrt{40,000}} = \frac{2000k}{200} = 10k$$

Solving for k, we have

$$k = .03$$

Thus, the price is given by

$$P = \frac{.03C}{\sqrt{n}}$$

Substituting $C = 1500$ and $n = 10,000$,

$$P = \frac{.03(1500)}{\sqrt{10,000}} = .45$$

Hence, the company should charge $.45 for each of these bulbs.

Exercises for
Section 3.3

1. A road map employs a scale of 1 in. = 20 mi. How far is Cincinnati from Cleveland if the map distance measures 12.6 in.?

2. In a blueprint scale 1 in. = 5 ft. What are the dimensions of a room that measures 9 in. by 7 in. on the blueprint?

3. The ratio of sodium to chlorine in common table salt is approximately 5/3. Find the approximate amount of each element in a salt compound weighing 100 lb.

4. A sample revealed that on a certain day, for every 1000 baseballs manufactured, 20 were defective. If 15,250 were manufactured on that day, how many were defective?

5. A piece of wire 8 ft long is to be cut so that the parts are in the ratio of 5 to 4. How many inches should each part be?

6. A saloon keeper advertises 18-oz steins of beer for 40¢, while the neighborhood grocer advertises a case of 24 12-oz cans for $6.10. Which is the better buy and why?

7. A punch press applies a force of 20,000 lb to a piece of metal with an area of 50 in.^{2}. What is the ratio of force to area?

8. The *acceleration* of an object is equal to the ratio of the applied force, f, to the mass, m, of the object. What is the acceleration if $f = 12$ and $m = 5$?

9. The *slope* of an inclined plane is the ratio of the vertical rise to the corresponding horizontal run. What is the slope of an incline having a vertical rise of 15 ft for a horizontal run of 100 ft?

10. The *density* of an object is the ratio of the object's weight to its volume. What is the density of an object having a volume of 25 cu in. and a weight of 75 lb?

11. If y varies directly as x and if $y = 5$ when $x = 10$, find the value of y when $x = 12$.

12. If r varies directly as the square of t and if $r = 3$ when $t = 4$, find the value of r when $t = 5$.

13. If z varies inversely as t and if $z = 4$ when $t = \frac{1}{2}$, find the value of z when $t = 2$.

14. If y varies inversely as the square root of x and if $y = 2$ when $x = 9$, find the value of y when $x = 4$.

15. When an object falls from rest, its velocity varies directly as the time of fall. Find the velocity of an object 2 sec after release if it has a velocity of 96 ft/sec at the end of 3 sec.

16. Hooke's law states that the force required to stretch a spring is directly proportional to the elongation of the spring. If a 5-lb force stretches the spring 1.5 in., how much force is required to stretch it 2.0 in.?

17. The unit cost to produce a monthly magazine varies inversely as the square root of the circulation. If it costs 40¢ per unit when the circulation is 200,000, what will it cost if the production jumps to 400,000?

18. The distance an object falls from rest varies directly as the square of the elapsed time. If an object fell 64 ft in 2 sec, how far had it fallen at the end of $\frac{1}{2}$ sec?

19. The intensity of light varies inversely as the square of the distance from the source. If the intensity 5 ft from a light is 4 foot-candles, what is the intensity 10 ft from the light?

20. The law of gravitation attraction states that the gravitational force between two objects varies inversely as the square of the distance between them. If the gravitation force between two objects is 150 lb when they are 200 mi apart, what is the gravitational force between them when they are 50 mi apart?

21. The power in a resistive circuit varies jointly as the resistance and the square of the current. If the power in a 50-ohm resistor is 50 watts when the current is 0.5 amp, what is the power when the current is 1.0 amp?

22. The cost of labor varies jointly as the number of workers and the number of days they work. If three men work 5 days for $1500, how many days must 5 men work to earn $1500?

23. Ohm's law states that the electric current in a circuit varies directly as the voltage and inversely as the resistance. Given that the current in a 20-ohm resistor is 0.5 amp when a voltage of 6 v is applied, what is current in the resistor when the applied voltage is 12 v?

24. The volume of a gas varies directly as the temperature and inversely as the pressure. Find a formula relating volume, temperature, and pressure. Suppose that the volume is 100 cu in. when $T = 200°$ Celsius and the pressure is 50 lb/sq in. Find the volume when the temperature is 300° Celsius and the pressure is 100 lb/sq in.

25. The cost of publishing a pamphlet is $2000 plus an amount varying directly with the number of copies published. If 1000 copies of the pamphlet cost $2200, how much will it cost to publish 1500 copies?

26. The number of gallons of gasoline used by an automobile traveling at a constant speed is directly proportional to the number of miles traveled, while the number of miles traveled is in turn directly proportional to the number of hours spent driving. Can you conclude that the number of gallons used is directly proportional to the time driven?

27. If y is directly proportional to t and if x is directly proportional to t, what can you say about

(a) xy (b) $\dfrac{x}{y}$ (c) $x + y$

28. Kepler's third law states that the time in which a planet revolves about the Sun varies directly as the 3/2 power of the maximum radius of its orbit. Using 93 million miles as the maximum radius of the Earth's orbit and 142 million miles as the maximum radius of Mars' orbit, in how many days will Mars make one revolution about the Sun?

3.4
The Functional
Relation

Perhaps the most important concept in all of mathematics is pairing numbers. Pairing frequently occurs very naturally without any emphasis on the underlying pairing. For example, in the preceding section you learned that direct variation means that for any value of x, a value of y is obtained from the equation $y = kx$. Thus, in direct variation a natural and unique set of pairs

(x, y) is formed. From the perspective of the pairing idea we say that a particular value of x is paired with one and only one value of y. The following definition formalizes this concept.

Definition   If the relationship between two variables, x and y, is such that there is exactly one value of y for each value of x, then we say that **y is a function of x**. The letter x stands for the independent variable and the letter y, for the dependent variable.

The definition of a function requires that for each x there corresponds exactly one value of y. This idea, in conjunction with the idea of an ordered pair, gives rise to another interpretation of the word "function" in terms of sets.

Alternate Definition   A function is a set of ordered pairs $\{(x, y)\}$ such that no two ordered pairs have the same first element.

For example, the set $\{(2, 3), (-1, 4), (0, -5), (3, 4)\}$ is a function, but the set $\{(-3, 4), (2, 5), (2, -6), (9, 7)\}$ is not because in the second set the ordered pairs $(2, 5)$ and $(2, -6)$ have the same first element.

Functions are frequently defined by using some formula or expression involving x and y. The following remarks should help to clarify the important points of the definition of a function as it relates to the use of formulas.

- A formula such as $y = \pm\sqrt{x}$ does not give a functional relationship since two values of y correspond to each value of x. However, each of the formulas $y = \sqrt{x}$ and $y = -\sqrt{x}$ taken separately *does* define a function.

- The definition does not require that the value of the dependent variable change when the independent variable changes, but only that the dependent variable have a unique value corresponding to each value of the independent variable. Thus, $y = 5$ is a function, since y has the unique value 5 for any value of the independent variable. However, $x = 5$ is not a function because many (in fact, infinitely many) values of y correspond to the value $x = 5$.

- We are not saying that expressions such as $y = \pm\sqrt{x}$ and $x = 5$ do not occur or are unimportant. These formulas simply do not describe functions. Instead, they describe a broader concept called a *relation*.

Example 3.14   The expression $y = 3x^2 + 5$ defines a function. The following table lists some of the corresponding ordered pairs.

x	0	-1	$+1$	-2	$+2$	-3	$+3$
y	5	8	8	17	17	32	32

Note that only one value of y is obtained for each value of x.

Example 3.15   The expression y is greater than $x(y > x)$ does not define a function because there are many values of y for each x.

Although the functional relationship between two variables is usually given by a formula, it may be given in other ways. For instance, let A denote the set of letters $\{a, b, c\}$ and let B denote the set of numbers $\{5, 2, 4, \sqrt{6}, 12\}$. Suppose a rule is given that assigns a to 5, b to $\sqrt{6}$, c to 4. Figure 3.10 diagrams this situation.

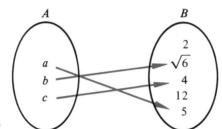

Figure 3.10

Then the rule, together with the sets A and B, is said to be a function from A to B. The set A is called the *domain* of the function. All elements of B that are assigned by the rule to some member of A are called the *range* of the function, that is the set $\{5, 4, \sqrt{6}\}$. This terminology applies to all functions.

Definitions

The **domain** of a function is the set of all values that may be taken on by the independent variable.

The **range** of a function is the corresponding set of values taken on by the dependent variable.

The domain and the range of a function are usually sets of numbers, but as Figure 3.10 illustrates the domain and/or range may be sets which contain no numbers.

Keep in mind that while a functional relationship may be given in a variety of forms, it must never assign more than one range element to the same domain element. Figure 3.11 does not describe a function because c is mapped onto the two different elements, 5 and 6.

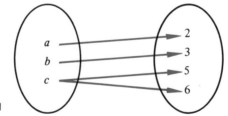

Figure 3.11

3 The Idea of a Function

Single letters or symbols customarily denote functions; for instance, f, g, h, ϕ. If x is an element of the domain of a function f, the corresponding element of the range is denoted by $y = f(x)$. Thus, from Figure 3.10, $f(a) = 5$, $f(b) = \sqrt{6}$, and $f(c) = 4$. The notation $f(x)$ reads "f of x" or "f at x," meaning the (range) *value* of the function for a particular x. Note that $f(x)$ does *not* mean the product of f times x.

The following analogy may be useful in clarifying the concept of a function. We can compare a function, f, to a machine that has an input and an output. (See Figure 3.12.) When an element, x, enters the machine, it is formed

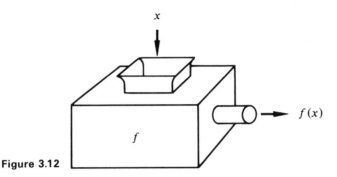

Figure 3.12

by the machine (function) into a new element, $f(x)$. The set of elements that can be put into the machine represents the domain of the function and the output represents the range.

Example 3.16   An ice vending machine will dispense a 8 # bag of crushed ice for 45¢, a 10 # bag of cubes for 65¢, and a 20 # block for 70¢. This machine represents a function because a unique output exists for each input, as illustrated in Figure 3.13. This function can be described by the set $\{(45, 8), (65, 10), (70, 20)\}$, where the first number gives the cost and the second the weight.

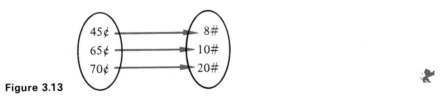

Figure 3.13

While there is a tendency to use the letter f to name a function, any other letter or symbol will suffice. In practice it is frequently necessary to use different functional names to avoid confusion. For instance, $v_1 = f(t)$ and $v_2 = g(t)$ might indicate that the atomic velocities of two particles p_1 and p_2 are different functions of time. Had either f or g symbolized both functional names, the distinction between the velocity functions would not be obvious. The worth of function notation lies in its flexibility.

3.4 The Functional Relation   65

The function f may or may not have a definite mathematical expression describing the rule of correspondence. If, however, such a specific expression is available, functional notation offers a convenient way of indicating numbers in the range. To find a number in the range that is associated with any number in the domain, merely replace the letter x wherever it appears in the expression for $f(x)$ by the number from the domain.

Example 3.17   Find the value of the function $f(x) = x^2 + 3x$ at $x = 2$.

Solution   We denote the value of $f(x)$ at $x = 2$ by $f(2)$. To find $f(2)$, substitute 2 for x in $x^2 + 3x$; that is,

$$f(2) = (2)^2 + 3(2) = 10$$

It is sometimes helpful to think of x as representing a blank so that the functional notation tells us what to put in the blank. The function in Example 3.17 could be written

$$f(\ ) = (\ )^2 + 3(\ )$$

Then, for example,

$$f(a^2) = (a^2)^2 + 3(a^2) = a^4 + 3a^2$$

Example 3.18   Calculus frequently requires the calculation of the "difference quotient" of a function, which is defined by

$$\Delta f = \frac{f(a + h) - f(a)}{h}$$

Find the difference quotient if $f(x) = 1/x$.

Solution   Here $f(a + h) = 1/(a + h)$ and $f(a) = 1/a$. Therefore,

$$\Delta f = \frac{\dfrac{1}{a + h} - \dfrac{1}{a}}{h} = \frac{1}{h}\left(\frac{a - (a + h)}{a(a + h)}\right) = \frac{-1}{a(a + h)}$$

When the rule of correspondence is given by a formula, the domain and the range are often not specifically mentioned. If not otherwise stated, think of the domain as including all those real numbers for which the expression itself is real. The range is then the corresponding set of functional values. For example, the function whose rule is given by $f(x) = \sqrt{x}$ has a domain of all non-negative real numbers, since $\sqrt{x}$ is an imaginary number if x is negative. The range is also the non-negative real numbers since $\sqrt{x}$ always yields a non-negative number. On the other hand, the function $f(x) = x^2$ has a domain of all real numbers (the value of x has no limitations), but all the range values are non-negative reals since any number squared cannot be negative. In general, the determination of the domain and range is left to you. Typically, the domain values are limited by the occurrence of the variable inside a radical or in a denominator.

The dependent variable may be a function of two or more independent variables. For example, the formula for the area of a triangle is $A = \frac{1}{2}bh$, where b is the length of the base and h is the altitude. Thus, the area of a triangle is a function of *both* the base and the altitude of the triangle. This idea could be noted in general by using functional notation and writing $A = F(b, h)$. In the same way, if we want to indicate that the acceleration a of a body is a function of force f and mass m we could write

$$a = G(f, m)$$

Functions of the type $y = f(x)$ are called functions of *one* variable; functions of real type $z = f(x, y)$ are called functions of *two* variables.

Exercises for
Section 3.4

Which of the expressions in Exercises 1–6 define functions? (Assume that y is dependent on x.)

1. $y = 2x + 5$ 2. $y = x^2$ 3. $y = 10$

4. $y < 3x$ 5. $y = \sqrt[3]{x}$ 6. $y^2 = x^3$

Which of the sets in Exercises 7–12 define functions?

7. $\{(1, 2), (1, 3), (2, 4), (3, 7)\}$ 8. $\{(2, 3), (7, 9), (8, 3)\}$

9. $\{(x, y) \,|\, y = 5x + 1\}$ 10. $\{(s, t) \,|\, s = 1/t\}$

11. $\{(x, y) \,|\, y = \pm\sqrt{x}\}$ 12. $\{(x, y) \,|\, y = x^{1/2}\}$

13. Which of the diagrams define functions?

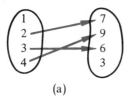   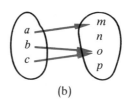   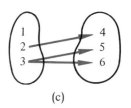

      (a)   (b)   (c)

Find the domain and the range of each of the real valued functions in Exercises 14–28.

14. $f(x) = 2x$ 15. $g(x) = 4 - 3x$

16. $h(t) = 3t^2 + 5$ 17. $F(x) = \sqrt{x}$

18. $G(x) = 1/x^2$ 19. $y = x^{1/3}$

3.4 The Functional Relation

20. $\{(1, 2), (3, 5), (7, 1), (12, -2)\}$ **21.** $f(x) = \sqrt{-x}$

22. $f(x) = \sqrt{-x^2}$ **23.** $f(x) = \sqrt{x-1}$

24. $f(x) = \sqrt{1-x}$ **25.** $f(x) = \dfrac{\sqrt{x}}{x-1}$

26. $f(x) = \sqrt{x^2}$ **27.** $f(x) = \dfrac{x}{x^2-1}$

28. $f(x) = \dfrac{1}{\sqrt{x^2-1}}$

29. Suppose that the function f has the rule $f(x) = 3x + 1$. Compute the following:

(a) $f(3)$ (b) $f(\pi)$ (c) $f(z)$ (d) $f(x-h)$

(e) The element in the domain that maps onto 10

(f) The range of the function

(g) $f(f(3))$

(h) $f(f(f(0)))$

(i) The difference quotient of f

30. Suppose that the function G has the rule $G(t) = t^2 - 2t + 1$. Compute the following:

(a) $G(2)$ (b) $G(-1)$ (c) $G(x^2)$

(d) $G(x-h)$ (e) $G(\sqrt{t})$ (f) $G(G(0))$

(g) The difference quotient of G

31. Suppose that the function H is defined by the set $\{(2, 3), (5, 9), (7, -3)\}$. Compute the following:

(a) $H(2)$ (b) $H(7)$

(c) $H(3)$ (d) The range of H

(e) The domain of H (f) Compare $H(2+5)$ to $H(2) + H(5)$.

Compute the difference quotient for the functions in Exercises 32–37.

32. $f(x) = x$ **33.** $f(x) = x^2$ **34.** $f(x) = 2$

35. $f(x) = \dfrac{1}{x^2}$ **36.** $f(x) = \dfrac{1}{x+1}$ **37.** $f(x) = \pi^2$

38. Suppose that y is directly proportional to x, that is, $y = f(x) = kx$.

(a) Compute $f(x_1)/f(x_2)$ for any two numbers x_1 and x_2. $(f(x_2) \neq 0)$.

(b) Compare $f(1/x)$ to $1/f(x)$.

(c) Compare $f(x^2)$ to $[f(x)]^2$.

(d) Find the difference quotient.

(e) Compare $f(x) + 1$ and $f(x+1)$.

(f) Compare $f(x_1 + x_2)$ and $f(x_1) + f(x_2)$.

(g) Compare $af(x)$ to $f(ax)$.

39. Suppose that y is inversely proportional to x, that is $y = f(x) = k/x$. Answer the questions in Exercise 38 for this function.

40. Let $f(x) = mx + b$.

(a) Compare $f(ax)$ and $af(x)$.   (b) Compare $f(x) + 1$ and $f(x+1)$.

41. What can you say about the following:

(a) $f(x_1 + x_2)$ and $f(x_1) + f(x_2)$ (b) $f(ax)$ and $af(x)$

(c) $f(x_1 x_2)$ and $f(x_1)f(x_2)$ (d) $f(\sqrt{x})$ and $\sqrt{f(x)}$

(e) $f\left(\dfrac{1}{x}\right)$ and $\dfrac{1}{f(x)}$

3.5
The Graph of a
Function

Most functions encountered in science, engineering, and business courses are "real" in the sense that both the domain and the range of the functions are real numbers. A function f defined by the set of ordered number pairs $\{(x, f(x))\}$ can then be plotted as points in the Cartesian plane. We call the resulting points the *graph of the function*. In keeping with tradition, let the ordinate values of the graph represent the functional values; that is, let $y = f(x)$.

Example 3.19   The graph of the function defined by $f = \{(1, 3), (-2, 2), (5, -1)\}$ is shown in Figure 3.14.

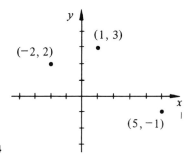

Figure 3.14

Example 3.20   The domain of a function, f, is $\{0, 1, 4, 9\}$ and the rule is $f(x) = -\sqrt{x}$. Figure 3.15 shows the graph of f.

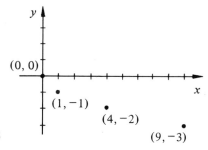

Figure 3.15

A graph implicitly defines a set of ordered pairs, corresponding to the points on the graph. The set of ordered pairs determined by a graph may or may not define a function; to define a function the pairing must obey the rule stressed in this chapter. *No ordered pair may have the same first element*. Graphically, this means that if a vertical line intersects the graph in more than one point, then the graph does not represent a functional relationship. The graphs in Figure 3.16(a) and (b) define functions and those in 3.16(c) and (d) do not.

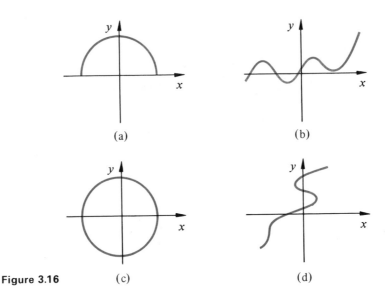

Figure 3.16

The domain of a function is frequently an interval of real numbers. The graphs of such functions can be constructed by plotting all points in the plane whose coordinates satisfy the function. However, this approach is impractical, since there is no limit to the number of such points that can be plotted. (Remember the makeup of the real line.) In practice, the graph of such a function is constructed by plotting a few selected points and then connecting these points with a smooth curve. As an illustration of this technique, consider the function defined by $y = x^2$, whose domain is the entire set of real numbers. By assigning values to x, we obtain the following set of ordered pairs.

x	-3	-2	-1	0	1	2	3
y	9	4	1	0	1	4	9

Now plot the set of ordered pairs in the Cartesian plane, as shown in Figure 3.17(a). The representation of the graph of $y = x^2$ can then be obtained by connecting the points with a smooth curve, as in Figure 3.17(b). This graph is, of course, only an approximation of the actual graph of the function. Its accuracy depends on the number of points plotted and the care taken in drawing the smooth curve connecting the points.

3 The Idea of a Function

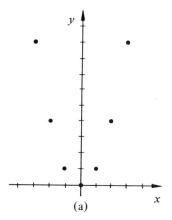 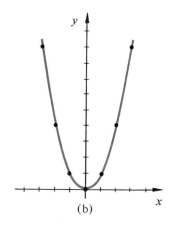

Figure 3.17   (a)   (b)

Usually only a segment of the graph in the vicinity of the origin is plotted, even though the graph may extend much farther. For instance, in Figure 3.17 only the portion of the curve from $x = -3$ to $x = 3$ is plotted, although the domain of the function is the set of all real numbers.

A graph provides a great deal of information about the properties of a function. The following example shows the graphical approach in analyzing the properties of a functional relationship between two physical variables.

Example 3.21   Consider a car moving at a constant speed of 50 mph along a highway. Suppose that in following a point on the tread of one of the tires through one complete revolution, we find that the horizontal speed of this point relative to the road varies with time according to $v = 1667t - 6940t^2$. Find the maximum horizontal speed of the point if Figure 3.18 is the graphical representation of the functional relationship between linear speed and time.

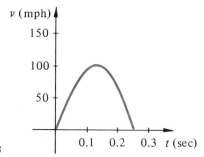

Figure 3.18

Solution   The maximum linear speed of a point on the tread of the tire is 100 mph since this is the upper extremity of the graph. The graph of a function usually demonstrates the properties of the function more clearly than any other form of description.

3.5 The Graph of a Function   71

Since the domain of a function comprises all values of x for which the function is defined, it also describes the physical extent of the graph of the function in the plane. In many cases the plotting process is facilitated by finding the domain of the function.

Example 3.22   Draw the graph of $y = \sqrt{4 - x}$.

Solution   The equation defines y as a real number for all values of $x \leq 4$. Hence, the graph of the given function lies entirely to the left of and including $x = 4$. Computing y for some convenient values of $x \leq 4$, we have the graph shown in Figure 3.19.

$y = \sqrt{4 - x}$

x	y
4	0
2	$\sqrt{2}$
0	2
-2	$\sqrt{6}$

Figure 3.19

Example 3.23   A numerically controlled milling machine produces a die whose cross-sectional height is described by the function $y = \sqrt{16 - 4x^2}$. Let y represent the height of the piece above the bed of the milling machine and let x represent the horizontal distance from the center line of the piece to the outer extreme. Draw the shape of the die.

Solution   The domain of this function is $\{x \mid -2 \leq x \leq 2\}$ since $16 - 4x^2 < 0$ for $x < -2$ and $x > 2$. The values in the table are computed from the given function and then plotted in Figure 3.20.

$y = \sqrt{16 - 4x^2}$

x	y
-2	0
-1	$\sqrt{12}$
0	4
1	$\sqrt{12}$
2	0

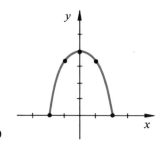

Figure 3.20

In many physical situations the nature of the problem restricts the domain of the function. For instance, the motion of a ball that is thrown upward with a velocity of 32 ft/sec is described by the function $h = 32t - 16t^2$, where t is the elapsed time and h is the vertical height. An analysis of this problem reveals that the ball will strike the ground 2 sec after it is thrown upward. The domain of the indicated function is, therefore, $\{t \mid 0 \leq t \leq 2\}$ since the equation has no meaning before the ball is thrown or after it hits the ground.

Example 3.24   Draw the graph of $h = 32t - 16t^2$ on $0 \leq t \leq 2$.

Solution   The table and graph in Figure 3.21 result from computing some convenient values of h in the interval $0 \leq t \leq 2$. A glance at the graph reveals that the maximum height to which the ball rises is 16 ft.

$h = 32t - 16t^2$

t	h
0	0
.5	12
1.0	16
1.5	12
2.0	0

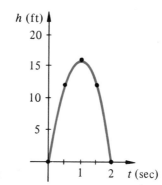

Figure 3.21

3.6
The Zeros of a
Function

The elements of the domain of a function f for which the range element is zero are called the **zeros** of the function. Thus, if $f(C) = 0$, where C is a number in the domain of f, then C is called a zero of f. The concept of a zero of a function has a simple graphical analog: *The zeros of a function correspond to points at which the graph of the function crosses the x-axis*. These points are called **x-intercepts**. In Figure 3.22a, the values x_1, x_2, and x_3 are zeros of the function. Figure 3.22b shows a function that has no zeros. Be sure to distinguish carefully between the zeros of a function and the value of the function when $x = 0$. The x-intercepts give the zeros, while the value of the y-intercept is $f(0)$. The zeros should always be indicated on the graph, at least approximately.

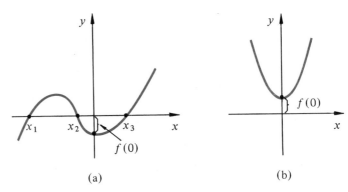

Figure 3.22   (a)   (b)

Example 3.25   Draw the graph of $f(x) = x^2 - 3x + 1$ and indicate the zeros.

       Solution   Computing $f(x)$ for some convenient values of x we get the graph shown in Figure 3.23.

$f(x) = x^2 - 3x + 1$

x	$f(x)$
-1	5
0	1
1	-1
2	-1
3	1
4	5

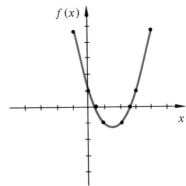

Figure 3.23

       Here the graph crosses the x-axis at approximately $x = 0.4$ and $x = 2.6$. Therefore, these points are the zeros of the function. Since we are using a graphical method, we can only estimate the zeros. Later, Chapter 6 explains how to determine them precisely.

74   3 The Idea of a Function

Exercises for
Sections 3.5 and 3.6

In Problems 1–6, indicate if the given graph determines a function.

1.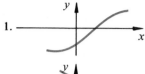

2.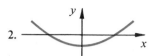

3.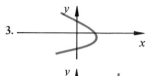

4.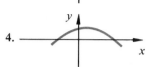

5.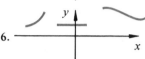

6.

Graph the functions in Exercises 7–28 and indicate the zeros where appropriate.

7. $\{(-2, 3), (0, 4), (2, 5)\}$

8. $\{(-1, 0), (0, 0), (1, 2), (3, -4)\}$

9. $f(x) = 3x + 5$ 10. $y = 2 - \frac{1}{2}x$

11. $y = x^3$ 12. $f(x) = -x^2$

13. $z = t^2 + 4$ 14. $i = r - r^2$

15. $y(x) = \sqrt{x}$ 16. $\phi = \dfrac{w^2}{2}$

17. $p = z^2 - z - 6$ 18. $v = 10 + 2t$

19. $y = \sqrt{16 - 4x^2}$ 20. $y = \sqrt{25 - x^2}$

21. $\alpha = \theta^{1/3}$ 22. $z = \sqrt[3]{t^2}$

23. $y(x) = \sqrt{x - 2}$ 24. $y = \sqrt[3]{2 - x}$

25. $v = s^3 - 4s^2$ 26. $a = \frac{1}{4}b^4$

27. $y = -x^3$ 28. $\beta = -\alpha^{1/2}$

29. The work w done in moving an object varies with the distance s according to $w = \sqrt[3]{2s}$. Show this relationship graphically.

30. The path of a certain projectile is described by the function $h = 100x - 2x^2$, where h is the vertical height in feet and x is the horizontal displacement in feet. Draw the path of the projectile.

31. An office machine is supposed to be serviced once a month. If it is not serviced, the cost of repairs is $20 plus 5 times the square of the number of months the machine goes unserviced. Express the cost of repairs as a function of the number of months the machine goes unserviced and draw the graph.

32. An archway is to be built in the form of a semiellipse. Draw the shape of the archway if it is described analytically by the function $y = \sqrt{64 - 4x^2}$, where y is the vertical height of the arch and x is the horizontal distance from the center line of the arch. Both x and y are measured in feet.

33. Torricelli's law states that the velocity of a stream of liquid issuing from a orifice is given by $v = \sqrt{2gy}$, where g is the acceleration of gravity and y is the depth, in feet, of the orifice below the surface of the liquid. Show the relationship between v and y if $g = 32$ ft/sec^2.

34. The following table describes the functional relationship between the safe speed at which a car can round a curve and the degree of the curve. Draw the graph of safe speed as a function of the degree of the curve.

Degrees of curve	5	10	15	20	25	30	35
Safe speed (mph)	70	68	66	63	58	50	34

35. A thermocouple generates a voltage when its two ends are kept at different temperatures. In laboratory experiments the cold end of the thermocouple is usually kept at 0°C while the temperature of the other end varies. The next table represents the results of an experiment in which the output voltage of the thermocouple was recorded for various thermocouple temperatures. Draw the graph of voltage versus temperature.

T (°C)	0	50	100	150	200	250
V (mv)	0	2.1	4.1	5.9	7.0	7.8

36. The following table shows men's height and corresponding normal weight in pounds. Draw the graph of weight vs. height.

Height	5'2"	5'4"	5'6"	5'8"	5'10"	6'0"	6'2"	6'4"
Weight	130	136	144	152	161	170	184	196

3.7
Multipart
Functions

Many practical situations are described by functions whose graphs contain discontinuities in the form of "jumps" or "gaps." For example, when you mail a letter, you pay 13¢ for the first ounce and 11¢ for each extra ounce. The table in Figure 3.24 gives the function describing this situation for weights up to 5 ounces. Plotting the graph of this function produces a series of line segments that are separated by discrete "jumps," as shown in Figure 3.24.

x	$f(x)$
Weight (oz)	Postage (cts)
$0 \leq x < 1$	13
$1 \leq x < 2$	24
$2 \leq x < 3$	35
$3 \leq x < 4$	46
$4 \leq x < 5$	57

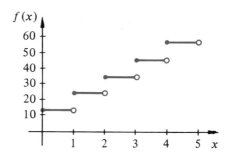

Figure 3.24

The cost of postage is a true function, since a vertical line at any x of the domain intersects the graph in only one place.

The following examples illustrate some additional functions that are defined by multipart rules. In each case the rule changes over different subsets of the domain.

Example 3.26   Draw the graph of f if the function is given by

$$f(x) = 4, \qquad x < 0$$
$$= -2x + 4, \qquad 0 \leq x \leq 3$$
$$= -2, \qquad x > 3$$

Solution   See Figure 3.25. Note that there are not three functions but *one* function whose rule for determining the correspondence is given in *three parts.*

3.7 Multipart Functions

x	$f(x)$
-2	4
-1	4
0	4
1	2
2	0
3	-2
4	-2

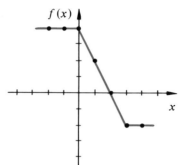

Figure 3.25

Example 3.27   In static testing an airplane wing for fatigue, a load is to be applied that simulates the actual loads encountered in a five-hour flight. If the load function L is given by

$$L(t) = 20{,}000 \text{ lb}, \qquad 0 \le t < 1$$
$$= 15{,}000 \text{ lb}, \qquad 1 \le t < 2$$
$$= 25{,}000 \text{ lb}, \qquad 2 \le t < 4$$
$$= 20{,}000 \text{ lb}, \qquad 4 \le t \le 5$$

plot the graph of the load being applied to the wing as a function of time.

Solution   See Figure 3.26. Notice that the physical situation restricts the domain of the load function to the set $\{t \mid 0 \le t \le 5\}$.

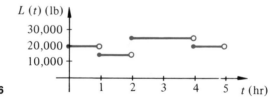

Figure 3.26

Example 3.28   The yearly maintenance cost for a water purification system is expected to vary with time according to

$$C(t) = 20t, \qquad\qquad 0 \le t < 10$$
$$= 30t - 100, \qquad 10 \le t \le 25$$

Plot the graph of this function if C is in dollars and t is in years.

Solution   Preparing the indicated table and then plotting these points produces the graph in Figure 3.27.

t	$C(t)$
0	0
5	100
10	200
15	350
20	500
25	650

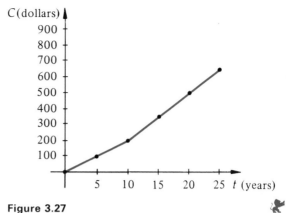

Figure 3.27

A very important multipart function is the **absolute value function**

$$f(x) = |x|$$

where $|x|$ is defined as follows.

Definition

The absolute value function of x is denoted and defined by

$$|x| = x, \qquad x \geq 0$$
$$= -x, \qquad x < 0$$

The domain of the absolute value function is the set of all real numbers and the range is the set of non-negative reals. The graph of $y = |x|$ is shown in Figure 3.28.

x	$y = |x|$
2	2
1	1
0	0
-1	1
-2	2

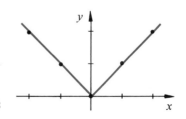

Figure 3.28

3.7 Multipart Functions

79

Slight variations on the absolute value function are important too. A simple example follows.

Example 3.29   Sketch the graph of $y = |x - 2|$.

Solution   This function is given by the two-part rule

$$y = (x - 2), \qquad x \geq 2$$
$$\ = -(x - 2), \qquad x < 2$$

The following table is used to obtain the graph, shown in Figure 3.29.

x	$x - 2$	$|x - 2|$
5	3	3
4	2	2
3	1	1
2	0	0
1	-1	1
0	-2	2
-1	-3	3

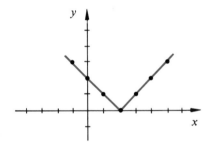

Figure 3.29

Exercises for
Section 3.7

Graph each of the functions in Exercises 1–20.

1. $f(x) = 2, \qquad x < 0$
$ = 3, \qquad x \geq 0$

2. $g(x) = -1, \qquad x < 0$
$ = 1, \qquad x \geq 0$

3 The Idea of a Function

3. $F(t) = 0, \qquad t \le 0$

$ = t, \qquad t > 0$

5. $h(x) = 0, \qquad x < 2$

$ = 2x - 4, \qquad x \ge 2$

7. $G(x) = 0, \qquad x < 0$

$ = 1, \qquad 0 < x < 2$

$ = 0, \qquad x \ge 2$

9. $y(x) = 0, \qquad x < -2$

$ = x^2 + 2, \qquad -2 < x < 0$

$ = 0, \qquad x > 0$

11. $f(x) = x, \qquad x < 1$

$ = -x, \qquad x \ge 1$

13. $f(x) = |x + 1|$

15. $g(t) = |t - 3|$

17. $H(x) = |2x|$

19. $y = |x| + 3$

4. $f(x) = x, \qquad x < 0$

$ = -2, \qquad x \ge 0$

6. $H(t) = -2, \qquad t < 0$

$ = t - 2, \qquad t \ge 0$

8. $f(t) = 0, \qquad t < 0$

$ = 2t, \qquad 0 \le t < 3$

$ = 6, \qquad t \ge 3$

10. $z(x) = x^2, \qquad x < 0$

$ = -x^2, \qquad x \ge 0$

12. $f(x) = 0, \qquad x$ an integer

$ = 1, \qquad x$ not an integer

14. $y = |x - 4|$

16. $F(x) = |x + \frac{1}{2}|$

18. $Z = |0.25t|$

20. $y = |x| - 5$

21. The load, in kilograms, applied to a tensile specimen varied with time according to

$$F(t) = 1000t, \qquad 0 \le t \le 5 \text{ minutes}$$

$$ = 5000, \qquad 5 < t \le 60 \text{ minutes}$$

Sketch the load-time curve.

22. The voltage applied to a given circuit varied with time according to

$$v(t) = 0 \text{ volts}, \qquad t < 2$$

$$ = 6 \text{ volts}, \qquad t \ge 2$$

Sketch the voltage-time curve.

23. The cost of concrete to a contractor varies with the number of yards delivered according to

$$c(n) = 60 \text{ dollars}, \qquad 0 \le n \le 3$$

$$ = 20n \text{ dollars}, \qquad 3 < n \le 10$$

Sketch the graph.

24. A chemical supply house charges \$1.50/gal for muriatic acid on orders up to 10 gal. For orders from 10 to 20 gal the price is \$1.25/gal and from 20 to 30 gal the price is \$1.10/gal. Orders in excess of 30 gal cost \$1.00/gal. Write the rule for the function that relates the cost per gallon to the size of the order. Sketch the graph.

25. If $f(x) = |x|$, give an example that shows that $f(x + y) \neq f(x) + f(y)$.

26. Compare $f(x) = |x|$ and $g(x) = |x - 2|$ by sketching their graphs on the same set of coordinates. How do the two graphs differ?

27. Compare $f(x) = |x|$ and $g(x) = |x| + 2$ by sketching their graphs on the same set of coordinates. How do the two graphs differ?

28. Compare $f(x) = |x|$, $g(x) = |2x|$, $h(x) = 2|x|$ by sketching their graphs on the same set of coordinates. How do the graphs differ?

3.8
Inverse Functions
and Composition*

The concept of a function was introduced in Section 3.4. In numerous instances you were given a function $y = f(x)$ and asked to determine the value of y corresponding to a given x. Sometimes, instead of computing values of the function for various values of the independent variable, we are interested in computing the value of the independent variable corresponding to a given functional value. For example, suppose that the velocity of a car (ft/sec) varies with time (sec) according to $v = 10 + 4t$ and we would like to know how much time elapses until the car reaches a velocity of 70 ft/sec. Inspection of the given function reveals that the answer is $t = 15$ sec. Underlying this example is an important mathematical concept that this section formalizes—the idea of obtaining a domain element from a given range element.

Under certain conditions a new function may be obtained from a given function f by merely interchanging the numbers in the functional pairings $(x, f(x))$. A function obtained in this manner is called the **inverse** of the given function and is denoted by f^{-1}. (The $^{-1}$ notation does not represent a negative exponent, but is simply a symbol for the inverse function.)

Suppose that we are given the function

$$f = \{(2, 1), (-3, 2), (0, 5)\}$$

Then the inverse function is given by

$$f^{-1} = \{(1, 2), (2, -3), (5, 0)\}$$

You should verify that f^{-1} is truly a function by noting that no two first elements are the same.

Figure 3.30, the graph of both f and f^{-1}, shows that

The graph of f^{-1} is the mirror reflection of f in the line $y = x$

---

* This section may be omitted now, although it should be reviewed before Section 8.3.

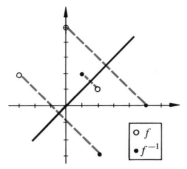

Figure 3.30

This is always the case when a function and its inverse are plotted on the same coordinate axes.

Not every function has an inverse function. For instance, suppose that f is given by the set

$$f = \{(2, 7), (4, 6), (5, 7), (6, 9)\}$$

The set g, obtained by interchanging the first and second elements in each of the ordered pairs of f is

$$g = \{(7, 2), (6, 4), (7, 5), (9, 6)\}$$

The set g does not define a function because 7 appears as the first element in the ordered pairs (7, 2) and (7, 5). As a further check, Figure 3.31 shows the graph

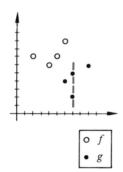

Figure 3.31

of g. A vertical line will intersect this graph in two points, implying that g is not a function.

Consider the equations $y = 2x + 4$ and $x = 2y + 4$. By solving the second equation for y in terms of x, we get $y = \frac{1}{2}x - 2$. By plotting these two equations on the same set of coordinates, their graphs prove to be mirror images in the line $y = x$ (Figure 3.32). Therefore, $x = 2y + 4$ is the inverse of $y = 2x + 4$. Notice that $y = 2x + 4$ and $x = 2y + 4$ are similar in form, except that x and y are interchanged. This is always the relationship between a function and its inverse. Therefore to find an inverse of a given function, we proceed as follows:

(1)   Interchange the x and y variables
(2)   Solve the new equation for the y variable.

3.8 Inverse Functions and Composition   83

$y = 2x + 4$		$y = \frac{1}{2}x - 2$	
x	y	x	y
−6	−8	−8	−6
−4	−4	−4	−4
−2	0	0	−2
0	4	4	0
2	8	8	2

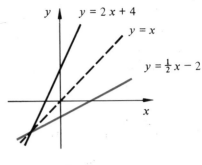

Figure 3.32

Example 3.30 Let $f(x) = (2x + 1)/(x + 3)$. Find the inverse of f.

Solution Let $y = (2x + 1)/(x + 3)$. Then by interchanging the x and y variables,

$$x = \frac{2y + 1}{y + 3}$$

Solving for y,

$$xy + 3x = 2y + 1$$

$$xy - 2y = 1 - 3x$$

$$y = \frac{1 - 3x}{x - 2}$$

Hence, the inverse of f is

$$f^{-1}(x) = \frac{1 - 3x}{x - 2}$$

Figure 3.33 shows the graph of $y = x^2 + 2$ and $y = \pm\sqrt{x - 2}$. These graphs are mirror images in the line $y = x$, but since $y = \pm\sqrt{x - 2}$ is *not* itself a function, it is not the inverse of $y = x^2 + 2$.

Functions that have inverses are called **one-to-one functions** because for each value of x there is exactly one value of y. Conversely, for each y there is at

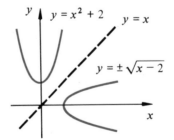

Figure 3.33

3 The Idea of a Function

most one value of x. More formally, *a function f is one-to-one if $f(a) = f(b)$ implies $a = b$.* Thus, the function

$$f = \{(2, 3), (4, 7), (6, 3)\}$$

is not one-to-one because $f(2) = 3 = f(6)$, but $2 \neq 6$.

Graphically, a one-to-one function is one for which *both* horizontal and vertical lines intersect the graph in, at most, one point. In Figure 3.34 the first function is one-to-one; the second is not.

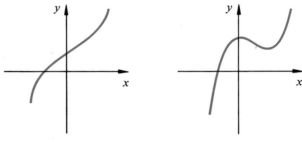

Figure 3.34   One-to-one   Not one-to-one

To obtain another characterization of an inverse function, consider the useful concept of composition of two functions.

Definition   *Composition of two functions:* The **composition** of a function f with a function g is defined to be the function defined by $y = f(g(x))$.

Note the tacit but important assumption that $g(x)$ is itself in the domain of f; otherwise $f(g(x))$ does not make sense.

Example 3.31   Find the composition $f(g(x))$ and $g(f(x))$, if $f(x) = 3x + 1$ and $g(x) = x - 4$.

Solution

$$g(f(x)) = g(3x + 1) = (3x + 1) - 4 = 3x - 3$$
$$f(g(x)) = f(x - 4) = 3(x - 4) + 1 = 3x - 11$$

Notice that $f(g(x)) \neq g(f(x))$ here. This is typical of the composition of functions, so we say composition does not have the commutative property.

Example 3.32   Let $f(x) = x + 1$ and $g(x) = \sqrt{x}$. What is the domain of the composite $g(f(x))$?

Solution   The composite function is $g(f(x)) = g(x + 1) = \sqrt{x + 1}$. Hence, the domain of the composite is $x \geq -1$, since these values yield real numbers for the range.

The formation of the composition of two functions is straightforward. However, one of the most important applications of compositions in calculus is

3.8 Inverse Functions and Composition   85

recognizing a relatively complicated functional expression as a composite of more elementary functions.

Example 3.33

(a) The function $(x + 1)^2$ may be considered as the composition $f(g(x))$, where $f(x) = x^2$ and $g(x) = x + 1$.

(b) The function $(x^5 + 1)^{1/3}$ may be considered as $f(g(x))$, where $f(x) = x^{1/3}$ and $g(x) = x^5 + 1$.

Although $f(g(x))$ and $g(f(x))$ are not usually equal, in one important instance equality does occur, as noted below.

If f is a $1 - 1$ function and f^{-1} is its inverse, then

$$f(f^{-1}(x)) = x = f^{-1}(f(x))$$

This fact can be used to show that two functions are respective inverses; however, it cannot be used to find the inverse of a given function.

Example 3.34   Show that $f(x) = 2x + 1$ and $g(x) = (x - 1)/2$ are inverse functions.

Solution

$$f(g(x)) = f\left(\frac{x - 1}{2}\right) = 2\left(\frac{x - 1}{2}\right) + 1 = x$$

$$g(f(x)) = g(2x + 1) = \frac{(2x + 1) - 1}{2} = x$$

Therefore, f and g are inverses.

Exercises for
Section 3.8

1. If $f(x) = 2x + 3$, for which x is $f(x) = 6$?

2. If $f(x) = 4/x$, for which x is $f(x) = 3$?

3. If $v = 10 + 4t$, when is $v = 20$?

4. If $f = \{(3, 0), (2, 6), (1, 5)\}$, for which x is $f(x) = 5$? For which x is $f(x) = 0$?

5. If $f = \{(0, 1), (2, 5), (3, 8), (5, 6)\}$, for which x is $f(x) = 8$? For which x is $f(x) = 3$?

Determine the inverse function in Exercises 6–13 *if it exists.*

6. $\{(2, 6), (3, 5), (0, 4)\}$ **7.** $\{(3, 7), (5, 9), (7, 3), (9, 5)\}$

8. $\{(-1, 2), (2, 3), (6, -2)\}$ **9.** $\{(1, 2), (2, 2)\}$

10. $\{(3, 2), (5, 4), (7, 2), (9, 8)\}$ **11.** $\{(-2, 3), (-1, 4), (0, 0)\}$

12. $\{(0, 1), (1, 0)\}$ **13.** $\{(0, 3), (1, 5), (2, 3), (6, 7)\}$

Determine graphically which of the pairs of functions in Exercises 14–21 are inverses of one another.

14. $y = 3x, \; y = \frac{1}{3}x$ **15.** $y = -2x, \; y = -\frac{1}{2}x$

16. $y = 6 - 3x, \; y = -\frac{1}{3}x + 2$ **17.** $y = x + 1, \; y = x - 2$

18. $y = \frac{1}{2}x + 1, \; y = 2x - 1$ **19.** $y = 5(x + 1), \; y = \frac{1}{5}x - 1$

20. $y = x^2, \; y = \sqrt{x}$ **21.** $y = x^3, \; y = \sqrt{x}$

22. Suppose that f and f^{-1} are defined by identical formulas. What can you say about the graph of f?

23. Which of the functions whose graphs are shown in the following figures have inverses? Sketch the graph of the inverse for those that do.

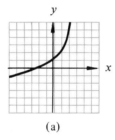

(a)

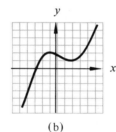

(b)

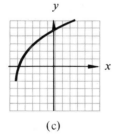

(c)

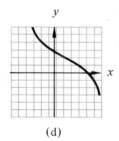

(d)

In the statements in Exercises 24–30, find $f(g(x))$ and $g(f(x))$.

24. $f(x) = 2x + 3, \; g(x) = 5x - 1$ **25.** $f(x) = 3x + 4, \; g(x) = 2x$

26. $f(x) = \dfrac{1}{x + 1}, \; g(x) = x + 1$ **27.** $f(x) = x, \; g(x) = x^2$

28. $f(x) = \sqrt{x}, \; g(x) = x^2$ **29.** $f(x) = x^3 - 1, \; g(x) = x^{1/3}$

30. $f(x) = 1/(x^2 + 1), \; g(x) = 1/x$

In each of the statements in Exercises 31–35, use composition to show that f and g are inverses.

31. $f(x) = -2x$, $g(x) = -x/2$.

32. $f(x) = 3x$, $g(x) = x/3$

33. $f(x) = 6 - 3x$, $g(x) = -\frac{1}{3}x + 2$

34. $f(x) = 1/(2x + 1)$, $g(x) = (1 - x)/2x$

35. $f(x) = 5(x + 1)$, $g(x) = \frac{1}{5}x - 1$

In each of the statements in Exercises 36–41, find the inverse function of f.

36. $f(x) = 3x + 2$

37. $f(x) = x - 3$

38. $f(x) = \frac{1}{2}x + 5$

39. $f(x) = 1/(x + 1)$

40. $f(x) = (2x - 1)/(3x + 5)$

41. $f(x) = \dfrac{x - 1}{x + 1}$

Test 1 for
Chapter 3

Answer true or false for Exercises 1–10.

1. If $f(x) = |x|$, then $f(x^2) = x^2$.

2. The distance from a to b is the same as that from b to a.

3. For any function f, $f(x + y) = f(x) + f(y)$.

4. $\{(2, 1)\}$ is a function.

5. $\{(x, y)\,|\,x^2 + y^2 = 1\}$ represents a function.

6. $\{(x, y)\,|\,x + y = 1\}$ represents a function.

7. In order for a formula to represent a function there must be a real value of $f(x)$ for every real x.

8. The graph of the absolute value function is never below the x-axis.

9. If y varies directly as x and x varies directly as t, then y varies directly as t.

10. The range of a real valued function is a subset of the real numbers.

11. The amount of money a man earns is directly proportional to the number of hours he works. If he makes $18.80 in an 8-hour day, write a formula for the amount of money he makes as a function of the hours he works.

12. Let $f(x) = x^2 + 5x + 2$. Find and simplify $[f(2 + h) - f(2)]/h$.

13. Make a careful sketch of the function

$$f(x) = x^2, \qquad x \le 0$$
$$= 2, \qquad 0 < x < 3$$
$$= -x, \qquad 3 \le x$$

14. Find the domain and range of each of the following real valued functions.

    (a) $f(x) = |x|$ (b) $f(x) = 1/x$ (c) $f(x) = \sqrt{x}$

15. Find the distance from $(2, \sqrt{2})$ to $(-2, 0)$.

16. Graph the set of points $\{(x, y) \mid x = 1\}$. Is this a function?

Test 2 for
Chapter 3

1. If s varies directly with t and if $s = 2$ when $t = 5$, find s when $t = 7$.

2. Find the distance between the points $(-2, -2)$ and $(-5, 3)$.

3. Graph $B \times A$ if $A = \{2, 3\}$ and $B = \{-1, 0\}$.

4. Which of the following define functions?

    (a) $\{(2, 1), (3, 5), (-2, 0)\}$ (b) $\{(-1, 3), (0, 3)\}$

    (c) $y < 3x + 2$ (d) $y = 3 - x^2$

5. Find the domain and range for the following functions

    (a) $\{(-1, 0), (0, 5), (5, 3)\}$

    (b) $y = 5x - 2$

    (c) $y = \sqrt{x - 3}$

6. Given $f(t) = 3t^2 - 4t + 6$, find $f(-2)$.

7. Draw the graph of $y = \sqrt{x - 5}$.

8. Draw the graph of $y = |2 - x|$.

9. Determine the inverse function for

    (a) $\{(-1, 2), (7, 6), (12, -3)\}$ (b) $y = 5x + 3$

10. Given $f(x) = 4/x^2$ and $g(x) = 3x$, find $f(g(x))$ and $g(f(x))$.

4
Linear Functions, Equations, and Inequalities

4.1
Linear Equations
in One Unknown

An equation is a statement that two expressions are equal. However, an equation is more than a simple statement of equality; it is a statement of fact that at the same time poses a question. For instance, the equation $x + 3 = 7$ states that "7 is 3 more than the number x." At the same time it raises the question, "What number x must be added to 3 to equal 7?" If 7 appears on the right side of the equation, then 7 must also appear on the left side. Since $4 + 3 = 7$, we conclude that $x = 4$ makes the equation a true statement. For any other real number, the statement is false. The number $x = 4$ is called the **solution** to the equation. More generally a set of numbers for which a given mathematical statement is true is called a **solution set**. To solve a mathematical expression always means to give the complete solution set. In the case of the equation $x + 3 = 7$ the solution set is the one-element set $\{4\}$. The solution set for the equation $x^2 = 4$ is the two-element set $\{-2, 2\}$.

Equations such as $x + 3 = 7$ and $x^2 = 4$, which are true for some but not all of the permissible values* of the variable, are called **conditional equations**. In some situations equations arise for which any of the permissible values of the variable will make the statement true. Equations of this kind are called **identities**. For instance, the equation $x + 3x = 4x$ is an identity because it is true regardless of which real numbers are assigned to x.

This section considers conditional **linear** *equations* in one variable; that is, equations that can be expressed in the form $ax + b = 0$, where a and b are constants and x is a variable. *Conditional linear equations have a a solution set of one element.* Later chapters consider more general equations.

The solution to a simple linear equation like $x + 3 = 7$ can usually be found by a trial and error process. In general, such an approach is impractical, so we will develop a more systematic method for solving equations.

Two equations are said to be **equivalent** if they have exactly the same solution set. Thus, the equations $x + 3 = 7$ and $x + 2 = 6$ are equivalent since each has the one and only solution $x = 4$. The equations $x = 2$ and $x^2 = 4$ are *not* equivalent since the solution set to the first one is $\{2\}$ and to the second, $\{2, -2\}$. The idea in solving an equation is to perform manipulations on the given equation to change it into an equivalent equation in which the solution is more or less obvious. Usually, the aim of the manipulations is to isolate the variable on one side of the equation. After a series of steps the solution set becomes obvious.

---

* The terms in an algebraic expression are assumed to have some common domain in which the equation makes sense as a real number. This set of values is called the set of *permissible* values of that statement. Thus, the permissible values of the expression $\sqrt{x - 1} = 1/(x - 4)$ are those values of $x \geq 1$ and $x \neq 4$, since $\sqrt{x - 1}$ is a real number only for $x \geq 1$ and $1/(x - 4)$ is undefined when $x = 4$.

We say that a manipulation is **allowable** if it transforms an equation into one that is equivalent. Two allowable manipulations are:

(1) Any quantity may be added or subtracted to both sides of a conditional equation.

(2) Both sides of a conditional equation may be multiplied or divided by any nonzero quantity.

The next two examples show the use of these manipulations to solve linear equations in one unknown. The actual sequence in which the manipulations are performed is not unique, but the solution set is unique.

Example 4.1   Solve the equation $3x + 12 = 48$.

Solution   Subtract 12 from each side to obtain

$$(3x + 12) - 12 = 48 - 12$$

which results in the equivalent equation

$$3x = 36$$

Dividing both sides of this equation by 3,

$$x = 12$$

and this gives the solution set explicitly.   🦋

Example 4.2   Solve $2(x + 3) = 3x$.

Solution   Expanding the left-hand side,

$$2x + 6 = 3x$$

Subtracting $3x + 6$ from both sides,

$$-x = -6$$

$$x = 6$$ 🦋

Example 4.3   A man has two types of solder: one is 55% tin and the other is 15% tin. How much of each must he mix to yield 75 lb of solder containing 40% tin?

Solution   Let n be the number of pounds of solder with 55% tin in the final mixture. Then $75 - n$ is the number of pounds of solder with 15% tin. The amount of tin in the two types of solder is then $0.55n$ and $0.15 (75 - n)$, respectively, and the total amount of tin in the 40% mixture is 0.40(75). Hence,

$$0.55n + 0.15(75 - n) = 0.40(75)$$

$$0.55n + 11.25 - 0.15n = 30.00$$

$$0.40n = 18.75$$

$$n = \frac{18.75}{0.40} = 46.9 \text{ lb of solder with } 55\% \text{ tin.}$$

And

$$75 - n = 75 - 46.9 = 28.1 \text{ lb of solder with } 15\% \text{ tin.}$$

If an equation has fractional terms, multiply each term of the equation by the lowest common denominator (LCD) of the fractions to yield an equation free of fractions. If the resulting equation is linear, it can be solved by methods shown previously. A word of caution before working some examples: The solution set may not include values of the variable for which the denominator is zero. This means that you must check each apparent solution for validity.

Example 4.4   Solve

$$\frac{1}{x} + \frac{3}{2x} = \frac{3}{x - 5}$$

Solution   Multiply each member of the equation by $2x(x - 5)$, the LCD of the fractional terms.

$$\frac{1}{x} \cdot 2x(x - 5) + \frac{3}{2x} \cdot 2x(x - 5) = \frac{3}{x - 5} \cdot 2x(x - 5)$$

Cancelling, we get

$$2(x - 5) + 3(x - 5) = 3(2x)$$
$$2x - 10 + 3x - 15 = 6x$$
$$2x + 3x - 6x = 10 + 15$$
$$-x = 25$$
$$x = -25$$

Check: Since none of the denominators is zero for $x = -25$, it is a valid solution.

Example 4.5   Solve

$$\frac{2}{x + 1} - \frac{4x}{x^2 - 1} = \frac{3}{x - 1}$$

Solution   In this case multiply each term by $(x + 1)(x - 1)$ to get

$$2(x - 1) - 4x = 3(x + 1)$$

Expanding,

$$2x - 2 - 4x = 3x + 3$$

Collecting like terms,

$$-5x = 5$$

$$x = -1$$

Check: Observe that $x = -1$ causes a zero in the denominator of the first and second terms and, therefore, is not a permissible solution. The value $x = -1$ is sometimes called an **extraneous solution** since it appears to be a solution, but is not. 🐾

Example 4.6 Solve

$$\frac{x-2}{x+2} - \frac{2}{x} = 1$$

Solution Here multiply by $x(x+2)$.

$$x(x-2) - 2(x+2) = x(x+2)$$

Expanding,

$$x^2 - 2x - 2x - 4 = x^2 + 2x$$

and $\qquad\qquad -6x = 4$

$$x = -\frac{2}{3}$$

Check: $x = -\frac{2}{3}$ is a solution since it does not cause a zero denominator in the original equation. 🐾

To solve equations that involve absolute values the methods of this section are often sufficient. The equation takes on differing forms caused by the absolute value expressions.

Example 4.7 Solve the equation $|x - 1| + |2x + 5| = 6$.

Solution Since

$$|x - 1| = x - 1 \qquad \text{for } x \geq 1,$$
$$= -(x - 1) \qquad \text{for } x < 1$$

and

$$|2x + 5| = 2x + 5 \qquad \text{for } x \geq -\frac{5}{2}$$
$$= -(2x + 5) \qquad \text{for } x \leq -\frac{5}{2}$$

there are three intervals on the real line to consider:

$$\left(-\infty, -\frac{5}{2}\right], \left[-\frac{5}{2}, 1\right], \text{ and } [1, \infty)$$

The given equation has the following three forms:

$$(x - 1) + (2x + 5) = 6 \text{ on } [1, \infty)$$

$$-(x - 1) + (2x + 5) = 6 \text{ on } \left[-\frac{5}{2}, 1\right]$$

$$-(x - 1) - (2x + 5) = 6 \text{ on } \left(-\infty, -\frac{5}{2}\right]$$

Each of these equations is linear. The solutions are, in order,

$$x = \frac{2}{3}, \, x = 0, \, x = -\frac{10}{3}$$

The "solution" $x = \frac{2}{3}$ is not in the allowable domain of values of that particular equation and hence must be rejected. Hence, the solution set for the given equation is

$$\left\{0, -\frac{10}{3}\right\}$$

Exercises for Section 4.1

In Exercises 1–20 find the solution set. Check for extraneous solutions when fractional expressions occur.

1. $2x + 5 = 2$

2. $6x - 1 = -x - 3$

3. $3(2x - 1) - x = 4 - (x + 3)$

4. $3(x - 2) + 7(2x + 4) = -x - 1$

5. $3x + 5 = 4(x - 2)$

6. $3y + 7(4 - y) = 3(5 - 2y)$

7. $\dfrac{4a}{3} - 5a + 2 = \dfrac{a}{2} - 1$

8. $\dfrac{3x}{5} + 4 = \dfrac{x}{2} + 5$

9. $\dfrac{2x + 1}{3} + 16 = 3x$

10. $\dfrac{x + 1}{3} + \dfrac{x + 2}{7} = 5$

11. $\dfrac{2}{c} + \dfrac{3}{c} = 10$

12. $\dfrac{4}{y} - 3 = \dfrac{5}{2y}$

13. $\dfrac{3x}{x + 5} - 4 = 0$

14. $\dfrac{4}{x + 2} + 4 = 0$

15. $\dfrac{3}{6y + 2} = \dfrac{4}{7y + 3}$

16. $\dfrac{2}{x + 3} = \dfrac{5}{2x - 1}$

17. $\dfrac{2}{x - 2} - \dfrac{3}{x + 5} = \dfrac{10}{(x - 2)(x + 5)}$

18. $\dfrac{1}{2x + 3} + \dfrac{1}{x - 1} = \dfrac{1}{(2x + 3)(x - 1)}$

19. $\dfrac{5}{5m - 11} = \dfrac{3}{m - 5} - \dfrac{4}{2m - 3}$

20. $\dfrac{2}{x + 3} + \dfrac{3}{x - 4} = \dfrac{5}{x + 6}$

21. Find three consecutive even integers whose sum is 312.

22. A man wishes to winterize his car and finds that his 10-quart radiator is 30% antifreeze. How much of the fluid should he drain and replace by pure antifreeze to double the strength of the mixture?

23. An airplane flew with the wind for 1 hour and returned the same distance against the wind in 2 hours. If the cruising (air) speed of the plane is 400 miles per hour, find the velocity of the wind.

24. In driving, suppose that you average 70 mph outside the city limits and 30 mph within the city limits. If you take 5 hours to make a 270-mile trip, how much of the time did you spend inside and outside the limits of cities?

25. The distance around the Indianapolis speedway track is $2\frac{1}{2}$ miles. If one driver averages 170 mph and another averages 165 mph, in how much time will the first driver "lap" the second?

26. If a man can build a house working alone in 30 days and if working with you he takes 20 days, in how much time could you build the house assuming you have the know-how?

27. In football a team scored 44 points by scoring equal numbers of touchdowns, extra points, and field goals and half as many safeties. How many of each scoring play did the team make?

28. Two gears together weigh 17 lb. If one gear weighs 3 lb more than the other, what is the weight of each?

29. Two resistors carry a total current of 20 amp. What is the current in each resistor if one resistor carries 2 amps more than the other?

Solve the equations in Exercises 30–39 with absolute value expressions by considering the different forms of the equation.

30. $|x| + x = 3$

31. $|x| + x = -2$

32. $|x - 1| + x = |x|$

33. $|x + 4| = |x - 5|$

34. $|3x + 1| = |x - 5|$

35. $|x + 3| + |x - 1| = 2$

36. $|x - 1| + 2|x + 4| = x$

37. $|x - 1| + 2|x + 4| = |x|$

38. $|x - 4| + |x + 1| = |2x + 5|$

39. $|3x + 4| + |2x - 1| = |x + 6| + |x|$

4.2
Linear
Functions

By a linear function we mean a function expressible in the form

$$f(x) = a_1 x + a_0$$

where a_1 and a_0 are constants. If we let $y = f(x)$, the class of linear functions

4 Linear Functions, Equations, and Inequalities

may be considered to be algebraic equations in the two variables x and y. In this case the expression

$$y = a_1 x + a_0$$

is often called simply a **linear equation**. As a special case, if either x or y is missing in the equation, the equation is still called linear.

The terminology "linear function" and "linear equation in two variables" may mean the same thing since both are described by exactly the same relation between x and y. Most often, in stressing the functional concept of pairing the x and the y, it will be called a linear function; otherwise it will be called a linear equation.

Example 4.8

(a) The equations $y = x$, $y = x + 1$, $y - 1 = x$, $y + x = 1$, and $2y + x = 7$ are all considered to be linear, since they can be put into the form $y = a_1 x + a_0$ with appropriate algebraic manipulations. The equations $y = 1/x$, $y = x^2$, $y^2 = x$ are all *nonlinear* equations.

(b) The equation $ax + by = c$ is linear since if $b \neq 0$, it can be put into the form $y = (a/b)x + c/b$. If $b = 0$, then the equation is $ax = c$, which does not represent a function but is still considered a linear equation.

Solution sets to linear equations consist of ordered pairs (x, y) such that the values of x and y satisfy the given equation. Whereas the solution sets to linear equations in one unknown are always one-element sets, solution sets for linear equations in two unknowns are infinite sets of ordered pairs.

Example 4.9   List some of the solutions to the linear equation $2x + y = 2$.

Solution   The usual way is to assign values to x and find the corresponding values of y. Thus, when $x = 0$, then $y = 2$; when $x = 1$, then $y = 0$, and so on. The following table is obtained.

x	0	1	-1	2	-2
y	2	0	4	-2	6

Chapter 3 explained that the graph of *any* set of ordered pairs is the graph of the corresponding points. In particular, the graph of the function f is the graph of the set

$$\{(x, y) \mid y = f(x)\}$$

Hence, the *graph of the linear function* $f(x) = a_1 x + a_0$ is the graph of the set

$$\{(x, y) \,|\, y = a_1 x + a_0\}$$

Similarly, the *graph of the linear equation* $ax + by = c$ is the set

$$\{(x, y) \,|\, ax + by = c\}$$

Example 4.10   Graph the linear equation of the previous example.

Solution   See Figure 4.1.

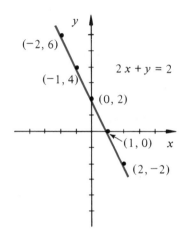

Figure 4.1

Example 4.10 shows the graph of $2x + y = 2$ to be a straight line. In fact, the graph of every linear equation is a straight line, although we will not prove it. Suffice it to say that the very terms *linear function* and *linear equation* arise from the fact that the graph of an equation of the form $y = a_1 x + a_0$ is always a straight line.

Since the graph of every linear equation is a straight line, the work of graphing a linear equation or linear function can be considerably shortened. Recall that a straight line is determined by two distinct points. Thus, any two ordered pairs,—say (x_1, y_1) and (x_2, y_2),—may be used as long as the coordinates satisfy the given linear equation. The two points easiest to use are the *intercepts*.

The *x*-intercept is the point obtained by letting $y = 0$ and the *y*-intercept is the point obtained by letting $x = 0$.

Example 4.11   Graph the equation $4x - 2y = 8$.

Solution Letting $x = 0$ gives $y = -4$ and then letting $y = 0$ gives $x = 2$. The two points $(0, -4)$ and $(2, 0)$ are sufficient to determine the graph of this equation since it is a straight line. (See Figure 4.2.)

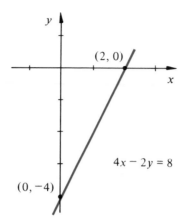

Figure 4.2

Another way of locating a line is with just one point and its inclination. What do we mean by the inclination of a line? Intuitively, the inclination of a straight line is the extent of the line's deviation from a vertical or horizontal position. Therefore, the inclination of a straight line is naturally described by the angle that the straight line makes with another fixed line. The *angle of inclination* of a straight line is defined to be the smallest positive angle between the line and the positive x-axis. Hence, the angle of inclination, denoted by α in Figure 4.3, is always less than $180°$. If a line is parallel to the x-axis, its angle of inclination is defined to be zero.

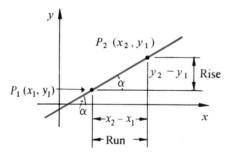

Figure 4.3

Another quantity used to describe the inclination of a straight line is its **slope**. The concept of slope is already familiar to you in an intuitive way. For instance, we talk about the slope of a hill or the slope of a roof top and understand that the slope describes the steepness of the inclined plane. The slope of an inclined plane is defined as the ratio of the vertical *rise* of the incline to the corresponding horizontal *run*; that is,

$$\text{Slope} = \frac{\text{Vertical rise}}{\text{Horizontal run}}$$

4.2 Linear Functions

Mathematics uses the identical definition of slope but expresses the concept in terms of the coordinates of two points on a line. Thus, if the coordinates of two points on a line are known, *the slope of the line is defined as the difference in the ordinates of the two points divided by the difference in the corresponding abscissas.* Applying this definition to the line segment $\overline{P_1 P_2}$ in Figure 4.3, the slope m of the line is expressed by the equation

(4.1) $$m = \frac{y_2 - y_1}{x_2 - x_1}$$

The following examples show how this definition is used.

Example 4.12   Find the slope of the straight line passing through the points $(-5, 1)$ and $(2, -3)$.

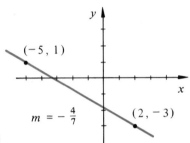

Figure 4.4

Solution   Letting $(x_1, y_1) = (-5, 1)$ and $(x_2, y_2) = (2, -3)$ and using Equation (4.1), the desired slope is

$$m = \frac{y_2 - y_1}{x_2 - x_1} = \frac{-3 - 1}{2 - (-5)} = \frac{-4}{7} = -\frac{4}{7}$$

If we interchange the labels of the given points and let $(x_1, y_1) = (2, -3)$ and $(x_2, y_2) = (-5, 1)$, the result is

$$m = \frac{y_2 - y_1}{x_2 - x_1} = \frac{1 - (-3)}{-5 - 2} = \frac{4}{-7} = -\frac{4}{7}$$

Hence, the order in labeling the given points is immaterial. We interpret a slope of $-4/7$ to mean that for every 7 units moved to the right in the direction of the x-axis, the straight line moves down 4 units.

Example 4.13   Draw the straight line passing through the point $(2, 1)$ with a slope $m = 2$.

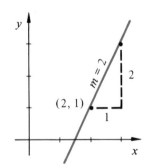

Figure 4.5

4 Linear Functions, Equations, and Inequalities

Solution   The slope $m = 2$ can be written as $m = 2/1$. To lay off the indicated slope, start at the point $(2, 1)$ and move 1 unit to the right and 2 units upward. This brings us to the point $(3, 3)$. The desired straight line is then the line that passes through the points $(2, 1)$ and $(3, 3)$.

Since the slope expresses the ratio of a change in y to the corresponding change in x, we also refer to this ratio as the *rate of change* of y with respect to x. The study of calculus extensively utilizes the concept of rate of change.

In working with straight lines, the following facts about slopes are useful. These properties can be verified by referring to the definition of slope.

- The slope of a straight line parallel to the x-axis is zero.
- The slope of a straight line parallel to the y-axis is undefined.
- Parallel straight lines have equal slopes.
- Perpendicular straight lines have slopes that are negative reciprocals; that is, $m_1 = -1/m_2$. This property is not easy to verify without the use of trigonometry, so we use it without proof.

Example 4.14   Find the slope of a line drawn perpendicular to a line passing through $(2, 1)$ and $(-4, 6)$.

Solution   The slope m of the given line is

$$m = \frac{y_2 - y_1}{x_2 - x_1} = \frac{6 - 1}{-4 - 2} = -\frac{5}{6}$$

The slope m' of a line perpendicular to the given line is then

$$m' = -\frac{1}{m} = -\frac{1}{-\frac{5}{6}} = \frac{6}{5}$$

Example 4.15   Draw the graph of the equation $y = 3$. What is its slope?

Solution   The graph is a straight line parallel to the x-axis and passing through $(0, 3)$. The slope is zero. (See Figure 4.6.)

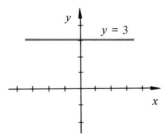

Figure 4.6

4.2 Linear Functions

The concept of slope is the ratio of the difference of two quantities. Such ratios occur in many areas of mathematics and have interpretations other than as the slope of a line. The following example is typical.

Example 4.16 The average velocity of an object is defined as the distance traveled divided by the corresponding elapsed time. If a car travels a distance of 100 miles in $2\frac{1}{2}$ hours, what is the average velocity of the car?

Solution In this example the distance traveled is 100 miles and the elapsed time is 2.5 hours. Therefore, the average velocity of the car is

$$v_{avg} = \frac{100}{2.5} = 40 \text{ mph}$$

Exercises for Section 4.2

Draw the graph of the linear equations in Exercises 1–12.

1.	$x + y = 1$	**2.**	$x - y = 1$	**3.**	$x = 5$
4.	$y = -2$	**5.**	$2x - y = 5$	**6.**	$3x + 2y = 5$
7.	$4x - y + 1 = 0$	**8.**	$x = 7 - y$	**9.**	$3y - 4x = 4$
10.	$y = \frac{1}{2}x - 3$	**11.**	$y = \dfrac{x-2}{3}$	**12.**	$15(x + y) = 10$

Sketch the straight line through the pairs of points in Exercises 13–20 and compute the slope.

13.	$(1, 2), (5, 4)$	**14.**	$(-5, 2), (3, -7)$	**15.**	$(-1, -1), (3, -6)$
16.	$(7, 3), (0, 5)$	**17.**	$(-2, -3), (-5, -7)$	**18.**	$(3, -2), (7, 6)$
19.	$(-2, 3), (5, 3)$	**20.**	$(\frac{1}{2}, \frac{1}{2}), (\frac{1}{2}, -\frac{2}{5})$		

21. Draw the straight line passing through $(2, 1)$ with a slope of $\frac{1}{3}$.

22. Draw the straight line passing through $(-3, 4)$ with a slope of 3.

23. Draw the straight line passing through $(2, -5)$ with a slope of $-\frac{2}{5}$.

24. Draw the straight line passing through $(-1, -2)$ with a slope of -2.

25. Find the slope of a 25-ft ladder that is leaning against a building if the foot of the ladder is 12 ft from the building.

26. Find the slope of the line drawn perpendicular to the line through $(1, 2)$ and $(-2, -5)$.

27. Find the slope of the line drawn perpendicular to the line through $(-3, 0)$ and $(5, -4)$.

28. The acceleration of a particle is defined as the change in velocity divided by the corresponding change in time. If the initial velocity is 25 ft/sec and the velocity is

40 ft/sec at the end of 10 sec, what is the acceleration? What units does acceleration have?

29. The equation $S = 25,000N + 200,000$ gives the sales of a company for its first five years of operation where N is the years since the company started and S is sales in dollars. Plot the sales curve of the company for the first five years.

30. A surveyor finds that the elevation h of a roadway varies with the distance x from a reference point according to $h = 0.3x + 1.5$. Draw the elevation of the roadway as a function of x.

4.3
Methods of
Describing a Line

The previous section presented some basic characteristics of straight lines in the Cartesian plane. The following example illustrates that every straight line can be represented by a linear equation. From Section 4.2 we know that the graph of every linear equation is a straight line.

Example 4.17 Show that the function describing the straight line passing through (2, 1) with a slope of $\frac{1}{3}$ is linear.

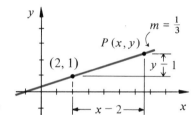

Figure 4.7

Solution Let $P(x, y)$ represent any point on the straight line other than (2, 1). Note that $P(x, y)$ is a general point and may be placed anywhere on the straight line. Then, by definition, the slope of the given line can be written as $(y - 1)/(x - 2)$. This quantity must be equal to the given slope, so that

$$\frac{y - 1}{x - 2} = \frac{1}{3}$$

Simplifying,

$$3y - 3 = x - 2$$

$$3y - x = 1$$

$$y = \frac{1}{3}x + \frac{1}{3}$$

which describes a linear equation. This equation is the expression of the relationship that exists between the abscissa and the ordinate of any point on the given straight line.

Whereas every straight line can be represented by a linear equation, sometimes certain *forms* of representation are important. There are two fundamental methods of describing a line with a linear equation: the point-slope form and the slope-intercept form. Each of the forms displays two properties of a line that can be determined by inspection.

The **point-slope form** is a generalization of the previous example. With this form, assume that we are given one point $P(x_1, y_1)$ on the line and that the line has a slope m as shown in Figure 4.8. Choose another point $P(x, y)$ on this

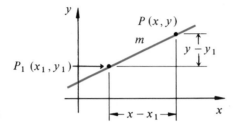

Figure 4.8

straight line. The location of $P(x, y)$ is arbitrary. Then, by the same reasoning as in Example 4.17,

$$\frac{y - y_1}{x - x_1} = m$$

so that

(4.2) $y - y_1 = m(x - x_1)$

This is the point-slope form. Note that since *any* point (x_1, y_1) may be used, the equation will *appear* different for various choices of the point, although each equation will be equivalent.

Example 4.18   The point-slope form of the equation representing the line that passes through $(2, 1)$ with slope $\frac{1}{3}$ is

$$y - 1 = \frac{1}{3}(x - 2)$$

However, the two points $(0, \frac{1}{3})$ and $(-1, 0)$ are also on the line so that two other point-slope forms of the same line are

$$y - \frac{1}{3} = \frac{1}{3}(x - 0) \quad \text{and} \quad y = \frac{1}{3}(x + 1)$$

Infinitely many other point-slope forms are possible.

If the point used in the point-slope form is the y-intercept $(0, b)$, a special case, called the **slope-intercept form**, arises. By substituting $x_1 = 0$ and $y_1 = b$ into the point-slope form,

$$\frac{y - b}{x} = m$$

from which

(4.3) $y = mx + b$

When an equation is in slope-intercept form, the constant on the right-hand side is the y-intercept and the coefficient of x is the slope. Given any linear equation, a few simple manipulations can represent the line in any desired form.

Example 4.19   Draw the graph of the linear equation $3x + 2y = -5$ and rearrange the representation into slope-intercept form.

Solution   To rearrange into slope intercept form, solve for y.

$$2y = -3x - 5$$

$$y = \underbrace{-\frac{3}{2}x}_{m} + \underbrace{\left(-\frac{5}{2}\right)}_{b}$$

from which we recognize the slope as $-\frac{3}{2}$ and the y-intercept as $(0, -\frac{5}{2})$. (See Figure 4.9.)

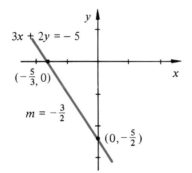

Figure 4.9

Physical situations arise that are described by linear equations and functions.

Example 4.20   The amount that a spring stretches is directly proportional to the applied force. Find the equation relating the length d of a spring to applied force f, if the length of the spring is 5 in. when a 6-lb weight is applied and 7 in. when a 14-lb weight is applied.

4.3 Methods of Describing a Line   105

Solution Since spring length is directly proportional to applied force, the desired equation is linear. Figure 4.10 shows this graphically. The slope of the straight line between these two points is then given by

$$m = \frac{d_2 - d_1}{f_2 - f_1} = \frac{7 - 5}{14 - 6} = \frac{1}{4}$$

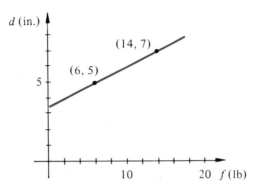

Figure 4.10

The point-slope form of this straight line can be written in the form

$$d - d_1 = m(f - f_1)$$

Now letting $(f_1, d_1) = (6, 5)$ and $m = \frac{1}{4}$,

$$d - 5 = \frac{1}{4}(f - 6)$$

or $4d - f = 14$

Since $d = \frac{7}{2}$ when $f = 0$, the free length of the spring is 3.5 in.

Equalities in two variables that involve absolute value expressions reduce to several different linear equations, each valid on some subset of the plane.

Example 4.21   Sketch the graph of the equation $|2x| + |y| = 1$.

Solution Since

$$|2x| = 2x \quad \text{for } x \geq 0 \qquad \text{and} \qquad |y| = y \quad \text{for } y \geq 0$$
$$= -2x \quad \text{for } x \leq 0 \qquad\qquad\qquad = -y \quad \text{for } y \leq 0$$

the given equation reduces to

$$2x + y = 1 \text{ in quadrant I}$$
$$-2x + y = 1 \text{ in quadrant II}$$
$$-2x - y = 1 \text{ in quadrant III}$$
$$2x - y = 1 \text{ in quadrant IV}$$

The graph is shown in Figure 4.11.

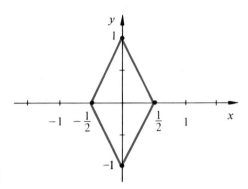

Figure 4.11

Exercises for
Section 4.3

In Exercises 1–4 draw the line passing through the given point with the given slope and then determine its equation.

1. $(2, 5)$, $m = \frac{1}{2}$ **2.** $(-1, -3)$, $m = 3$

3. $(5, -2)$, $m = -7$ **4.** $(3, 4)$, $m = -\frac{2}{5}$

In Exercises 5–10 draw the line through the given points and then find its equation.

5. $(1, 3)$, $(6, 2)$ **6.** $(2, 5)$, $(-3, -7)$

7. $(-1, -1)$, $(1, 2)$ **8.** $(0, 0)$, $(3, -2)$

9. $(0, 2)$, $(-5, 0)$ **10.** $(\frac{1}{2}, \frac{1}{3})$, $(-\frac{1}{2}, \frac{1}{3})$

Find the slope and the y-intercept of the equations in Exercises 11–22 and then draw the line.

11. $2x - 3y = 5$ **12.** $3x + 4y = 0$

13. $x + y = 2$ **14.** $5x + 2y = -3$

15. $4y - 2x + 8 = 0$ **16.** $-5x - y - 2 = 0$

17. $2y = x + 5$ **18.** $3x + 6 = 2y$

19. $y = 5$ **20.** $x + y = 1$

21. $x - 5y + 7 = 0$ **22.** $y = 1 - x$

In Exercises 23–26 find the equation of the line perpendicular to the given line at the indicated point.

23. $3x + 2y = 7$ at $(1, 2)$ **24.** $x + 3y = 11$ at $(2, 3)$

25. $x - y = 2$ at $(5, 3)$ **26.** $2x - 5y = 2$ at $(-4, -2)$

27. The current I in a resistor is a linear function of the applied voltage V. Find the equation relating the current to the voltage if the current is $\frac{1}{2}$ amp when the voltage is 6 volts and $\frac{2}{3}$ amp when the voltage is 8 volts.

28. In an experiment to determine the coefficient of friction, it is found that a 10-lb block has a frictional force of 3 lb and a 25-lb block has a frictional force of 7.5 lb. Find the equation relating frictional force to weight if the frictional force is a direct function of weight.

29. *Linear depreciation* is one of several methods approved by the Internal Revenue Service for depreciating business property. If the original cost of the property is C dollars and if it is depreciated linearly over N years, its value V remaining at the end of n years is given by

$$V = C - \frac{C}{N} n$$

Find the value after 5 years of a typewriter whose initial cost of \$300 is to be depreciated over 20 years.

30. If you borrow P dollars at the simple interest rate i, the annual interest is $P \cdot i$. Hence, the amount A owed at the end of n years is given by

$$A = P(1 + i \cdot n)$$

Find the amount you owe after 5 years if you borrow \$2000 at 8% simple interest.

31. Mr. Smith wants to borrow \$4000 to buy a new car. He wishes to pay off the loan with monthly payments stretching over 3 years. If he is charged 12% simple interest and if he computes the monthly payments by dividing the total amount due in 3 years by 36, how much will Mr. Smith have to pay each month?

32. A manufacturer of fountain pens can expect to sell 21,000 felt tip pens if he charges 80¢ per pen but only 10,000 if he raises the price to \$1.00. Assuming that the relationship is linear, find the equation of the line relating the number of pens to their price. How many felt tip pens can he sell if he charges 90¢?

33. The error E of a radar varies with slant range R according to the equation $5E - R = 3$. Graphically show the relationship between radar error and slant range.

34. The pressure at a point below the surface of a body of water is given by $P = 0.04D + 14.7$, where P is the pressure in psi and D is the depth in inches. Draw the graph of the relationship.

Sketch the graph of the equations in Exercises 35–44 by considering the different expressions caused by the absolute value function.

35. $\|x\| + \|y\| = 1$	36. $\|x\| - \|y\| = 1$
37. $\|x - 1\| = \|y + 2\|$	38. $\|2x + 5\| + \|y + 3\| = 5$
39. $\|y\| = 2\|x - 1\|$	40. $\|y\| = \|x\|$
41. $\|x + 1\| + y = \|y\|$	42. $\|y\| = -\|2x + 3\|$
43. $\|x\| + \|x - 1\| + \|y\| = 2$	44. $\|y\| = 2\|x\| - 1$

4.4
Linear Inequalities
in One Unknown

In addition to mathematical statements involving the equality of algebraic expressions, there is the corresponding problem of inequalities. The set of values for which the inequality is true is called the **solution set** and we say we have *solved* the inequality when we find the complete solution set. Two statements involving inequalities are equivalent if they have the same solution set.

The technique of solving inequalities closely resembles the technique for solving equations. The technique demands manipulations that give a chain of equivalent inequalities and at the same time isolate the variable on one side of the inequality. The description of *allowable* manipulations looks much like the corresponding description for allowable manipulations with equalities.

(1) Adding or subtracting the same quantity from both sides of an inequality results in an equivalent inequality; for example, if $x < y$, then $x + 3 < y + 3$.

(2) Multiplying or dividing both sides of an inequality by the same positive quantity results in an equivalent inequality; for example, if $x > y$, then $2x > 2y$.

(3) Multiplying or dividing both sides of an inequality by the same negative quantity results in an equivalent inequality if the sense of the inequality is reversed; for example, if $x < y$, then $-5x > -5y$.

The following examples illustrate the procedure for solving linear inequalities.

Example 4.22   Solve the inequality $x - 2 < 3$.

Solution   Adding 2 to each member of the inequality, we have

$$x - 2 + 2 < 3 + 2$$

or $x < 5$

Thus, the solution set consists of all real numbers less than 5.

Example 4.23   Solve the inequality $x + 1 < 3x - 2$.

Solution   To get the terms involving x on one side and the constants on the other, add $-3x$ and -1 to both members to get the equivalent inequality.

$$-2x < -3$$

Multiplying this result by $-\frac{1}{2}$ yields

$$x > 3/2$$

Notice that the sense of the inequality changed when we multiplied by $-\frac{1}{2}$. The solution set is obviously the set of all real numbers greater than $\frac{3}{2}$.

Example 4.24   Solve the inequality $|x - 2| < 3$.

Solution   The given inequality involves an absolute value, which means that

$$x - 2 < 3 \quad \text{and} \quad -(x - 2) < 3$$

The solution of the first inequality is

$$x < 5$$

To solve the second inequality, first multiply both members by -1 to get

$$x - 2 > -3$$

from which

$$x > -1$$

Thus, the solution set is the set of all real numbers greater than -1 and at the same time less than 5. Figure 4.12 represents the solution set graphically.

Figure 4.12 $-2 \quad -1 \quad 0 \quad 1 \quad 2 \quad 3 \quad 4 \quad 5 \quad 6$

The inequality of the previous example has the form $|x - p| < a$, which is equivalent to the two inequalities $x - p < a$ *and* $x - p > -a$. This is customarily written in so-called *double inequality* form $-a < x - p < a$. Similarly, an inequality of the form $|x - p| > a$ is equivalent to the two inequalities $x - p > a$ *or* $x - p < -a$, but in this case the two may not be written in double inequality form. Why not?

The most important use of the inequality with an absolute value lies in an alternate method of describing intervals on the real line. Recall from Section 3.2 that the horizontal distance between two points on the x-axis is given by the absolute value of the difference; that is, the distance from q to p is $|q - p|$. Thus, the notation $|x - p|$ stands for the distance from x to p. Now if we specify $|x - p| = a$, the values of x for which this equation is true are $x = p + a$ and $x = p - a$. Extending this thinking just a bit, the inequality $|x - p| < a$ represents all those values within a distance a units of p, and $|x - p| > a$ represents those values of x greater than a units from p. In summary,

---

$|x - p| < a$ represents the interval $(p - a, p + a)$.

$|x - p| > a$ represents the union of intervals $(-\infty, p - a)$ and $(p + a, \infty)$.

---

4 Linear Functions, Equations, and Inequalities

Example 4.25   Describe the interval on the real line using interval notation described by the inequality $|x - 2| < 5$. Also display graphically.

Solution   The point $x = 2$ is the midpoint of the interval that has a total length of 10. The given inequality may be written as

$$-5 < x - 2 < 5; \text{ that is, } -3 < x < 7$$

or, in terms of interval notation, $(-3, 7)$. Figure 4.13 displays the interval.

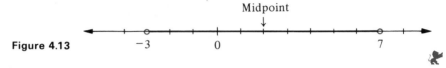

Figure 4.13

Sometimes we wish to describe an interval (a, b) using an absolute value with an inequality. To do this locate the midpoint of the interval, $(a + b)/2$, and determine half the length of the interval, $(a - b)/2$. Then, the inequality

$$|x - \text{midpoint}| < \text{half length of interval}$$

is another representation of (a, b).

A similar analysis describes the union of the two disjoint unbounded intervals $(-\infty, a)$ and (b, ∞) with an absolute value inequality.

Example 4.26   Describe the interval $(-4, 10)$ in terms of an absolute value and an inequality.

Solution   The midpoint of the interval is $x = 3$ and the half length is 7. Hence, the interval may be represented as

$$|x - 3| < 7$$

Example 4.27   Describe the union of the two intervals $(-\infty, -8)$ and $(0, \infty)$ in terms of one absolute value inequality, as shown in Figure 4.14.

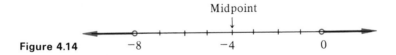

Figure 4.14

Solution   In this case the midpoint of -8 and 0 is -4 and the half-length of the interval that we wish to exclude is 4. Hence, the notation

$$|x - (-4)| > 4; \text{ that is, } |x + 4| > 4$$

describes the given interval.

Calculus demands a comprehension of inequalities of the absolute value type in two dimensions. For example, we may wish x to vary between a and b

4.4 Linear Inequalities in One Unknown   111 and y to vary between c and d. These two inequalities taken together describe a rectangle in the x-y plane, as shown in Figure 4.15.

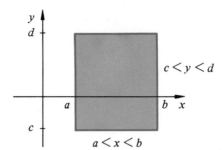

Figure 4.15

The last example in this section is an inequality involving multiple absolute value expressions. As with linear equalities, these are best handled by considering the different forms of the inequality caused by the absolute value.

Example 4.28   Solve the inequality $|2x + 5| < |3x - 7|$.

Solution   Since

$$|2x + 5| = (2x + 5) \qquad \text{for } x \geq -\frac{5}{2}$$

$$= -(2x + 5) \qquad \text{for } x < -\frac{5}{2}$$

and

$$|3x - 7| = (3x - 7) \qquad \text{for } x \geq \frac{7}{3}$$

$$= -(3x - 7) \qquad \text{for } x < \frac{7}{3}$$

the given inequality has the following three forms.

$$2x + 5 < 3x - 7 \qquad \text{for} \quad x \geq \frac{7}{3}$$

$$2x + 5 < -(3x - 7) \qquad \text{for} \ -\frac{5}{2} \leq x < \frac{7}{3}$$

$$-(2x + 5) < -(3x - 7) \qquad \text{for} \quad x < -\frac{5}{2}$$

The solutions of these three inequalities are, in order,

$$x > 12 \qquad \text{for} \quad x \geq \frac{7}{3}$$

$$x < \frac{2}{5} \qquad \text{for} \ -\frac{5}{2} \leq x < \frac{7}{3}$$

$$x < 12 \qquad \text{for} \quad x < -\frac{5}{2}$$

4 Linear Functions, Equations, and Inequalities

Thus, *considering the domain limitations for each of the solutions*, the solution set is the union of the intervals

$$\left(-\infty, \frac{2}{5}\right) \quad \text{and} \quad (12, \infty)$$

Exercises for
Section 4.4

Solve the inequalities in Exercises 1–14 and sketch the graph of each solution set on the number line.

1. $3x + 1 > x - 4$
2. $2 - 5x > -x$
3. $x + 1 \geq \sqrt{2} - x\sqrt{3}$
4. $x \leq x + 1$
5. $\frac{2}{3}x + 5 < \frac{7}{5}x + \frac{1}{3}$
6. $3(2x - 1) + 4(x - 2) > 0$
7. $(x - 3)(x + 4) > (x - 5)(x + 5)$
8. $x^2 - 9 \leq (x - 3)(x + 2)$
9. $(1/x) + 3 \geq (5/x) - 7$
10. $2x + x(x - 2) < (x - 3)(3 + x)$
11. $x(x - 1) > x(x - 3)$
12. $(2x - 1)^2 > (2x + 3)^2$
13. $x^2 - 5x + 4 < x(x - 2)$
14. $x(x^2 - 4) > x(x^2 - 9) + 5$

In Exercises 15–24 describe the given absolute value inequality by an interval or union of intervals.

15. $|x - 2| < 3$
16. $|3x + 6| > 9$
17. $|x + 2| < 5$
18. $|2x + 7| < 5$
19. $|x - 5| > 1$
20. $|x + 3| > 0$
21. $|\frac{1}{2}x - 3| \leq 5$
22. $|3x| \geq 6$
23. $|2x - 3| \leq 2$
24. $|x + 1| \leq 1$

In Exercises 25–34 describe the given interval or union of intervals by using one absolute value inequality.

25. $(2, 6)$
26. $(-\infty, -2) \cup (0, \infty)$
27. $(-10, 16)$
28. $(-\infty, 4) \cup (12, \infty)$
29. $(-\infty, -2) \cup (2, \infty)$
30. $(-\infty, 2] \cup [6, \infty)$
31. $[2, 7]$
32. $(-12, -3)$
33. Complement of the interval $(0, 5)$.
34. $[0, 5]$

In Exercises 35–40 write the given set using interval notation.

35. $\{x \mid 2x < 3\} \cap \{x \mid x + 5 > 2\}$
36. $\{x \mid x + 2 > 0\} \cap \{x \mid 3x - 1 > x + 2\}$

37. $\{x \mid |x + 1| > 1\} \cap \{x \mid |x - 1| < 2\}$

38. $\{x \mid |x + 5| < 5\} \cap \{x \mid |x - 5| < 5\}$

39. $\{x \mid |x - 1| < 2\} \cap \{x \mid |x + 1| < 3\}$

40. $\{x \mid |x - 2| < 3\} \cap \{x \mid x > 0\}$

The solution set to a double inequality $q < p < r$ is the intersection of the solution sets to the individual inequalities $q < p$ and $p < r$. Solve the double inequalities in Exercises 41–45.

41. $x + 2 < 2x + 5 \le 6x + 7$ **42.** $x - 1 \le 3x + 5 < 2x + 7$

43. $x < 2x + 3 < 3x - 5$

44. $x^2 - 2x < x^2 + 2x - 3 < (x - 3)(x - 2)$

45. $x^2 + 1 < (x - 3)(x - 4) \le (x + 3)(x + 5)$

In Exercises 46–50 describe graphically the given region in the x, y plane.

46. $|x - 2| < 1, \quad |y - 5| < \dfrac{1}{2}$ **47.** $|x| > 2, \quad |y - 1| < 1$

48. $|x| > 2, \quad |y| < 5$ **49.** $|x + 1| < \dfrac{1}{3}, \quad |y + 2| < \dfrac{1}{8}$

50. $|x + 1| < 1, \quad |y - 1| > 1$

Solve the inequalities in Exercises 51–58 by considering the different expressions for the absolute value.

51. $|x + 2x| > x - 2x$ **52.** $|x + 1| > x$

53. $|x - 1| \le |x + 4|$ **54.** $x \le |x|$

55. $|3x + 1| \le |x - 5|$ **56.** $|x + 3| < 4 - |x - 1|$

57. $|x - 1| + 2|x + 4| \le |x|$ **58.** $|x + 1| + |2x - 1| \ge |x + 5| + |x|$

4.5
Linear Inequalities
in Two Unknowns

This section extends the discussion of inequalities to those containing two variables. The operations established in the preceding section apply to inequalities in two variables and therefore need not be duplicated here. The solution set of an inequality in x and y is the set of all ordered pairs (x, y) that satisfy the inequality.

The concept of an inequality in two variables is closely related to the corresponding idea of an equality in two variables. This relationship is best explained in terms of a graphical illustration. Consider the linear equation

$$2x + 3y = -5$$

The graph of this equation is the straight line shown in Figure 4.16. Notice that the line L separates the plane into three disjoint subsets; namely,

(1) $L = \{(x, y) \mid 2x + 3y = -5\}$; the set of points making up the line L
(2) $A = \{(x, y) \mid 2x + 3y > -5\}$; the set of points *above* the line L
(3) $B = \{(x, y) \mid 2x + 3y < -5\}$; the set of points *below* the line L

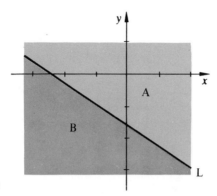

Figure 4.16

Thus, we see that the graph of a linear inequality in two variables corresponds to a *half plane* composing the region on one side of a straight line. Usually then, to graph a linear inequality, first draw the line of the corresponding linear equation and decide which half plane you need. The following examples illustrate how to do this.

Example 4.29 Graph the solution set for the inequality

$$2x + y < 1$$

Solution First draw the line $2x + y = 1$. Figure 4.17 pictures it as a dashed line to indicate its exclusion from the solution set. Now we must decide which side of this line represents the solution set. One way to do this is to select some point (x_1, y_1) not on the line and substitute it into the inequality. If (x_1, y_1) satisfies the inequality, this point lies

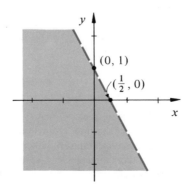

Figure 4.17

in the desired region and the half plane containing (x_1, y_1) is the graph. In this problem let us use the check point $(0, 0)$. Since $2(0) + 0 = 0 < 1$ satisfies the inequality, we conclude that the graph of $2x + y < 1$ is the half plane below the line. The shading in the figure indicates the set that is intended.

Example 4.30   Find and graph the solution set for the inequality

$$2x + y - 1 \le x + 3y + 4$$

Solution   By adding $-x - 3y + 1$ to both sides of the inequality, we obtain the equivalent inequality

$$x - 2y \le 5$$

We then graph $x - 2y = 5$, shown as a solid line in Figure 4.18 to indicate its inclusion in the solution set.

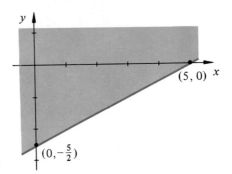

Figure 4.18

At the origin, we find that $x - 2y = 0$, which is < 5. Therefore, all points on the same side of the line as the origin satisfy $x - 2y \le 5$. Figure 4.18 graphs the solution set.

Example 4.31   A warehouse has 10,000 ft^2 of usable storage space in which to store refrigerators and air conditioners. If each refrigerator requires 6 ft^2 and each air conditioner requires 4 ft^2, write an inequality describing the number of each that can be stored in the warehouse. Draw the graph.

Solution   The total area needed to store x refrigerators is $6x$ ft^2 and that for y air conditioners is $4y$ ft^2. Therefore, the sum $6x + 4y$ must be less than or equal to 10,000 ft^2, that is,

$$6x + 4y \le 10,000$$

Figure 4.19 shows the graph of the line $6x + 4y = 10,000$. The desired half plane lies below this line, as indicated by the shading. Notice that there are some implied restrictions on this problem due to its physical nature. Since the number of both refrigerators and air conditioners must be greater than zero, the solution is restricted to the triangular region indicated by the dark shading.

116   4 Linear Functions, Equations, and Inequalities

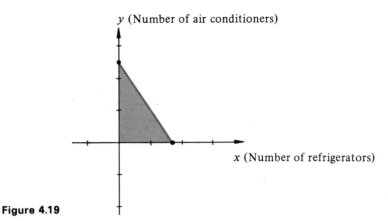

Figure 4.19

Exercises for Section 4.5

Graph the solution sets for the inequalities in Exercises 1–16.

1. $x < y$

2. $x \leq y$

3. $3x - y + 7 \leq 0$

4. $y < x + 4$

5. $x + y > x - y$

6. $y - x \geq y + x$

7. $2x - y - 8 > x - 2y + 8$

8. $6x - 2 < y + 1$

9. $3(x - 1) + 4x \geq 7x + y + 2(x - y)$

10. $3x + y + 2x - 3y \leq 2$

11. $|y| < 3$

12. $|x| < 1$

13. $|x| < y$

14. $x \leq |y|$

15. $|x| + |y| < 1$

16. $|x| + |y| > 1$

17. The formula relating Fahrenheit degrees to degrees Celsius is $F = (\frac{9}{5})C + 32$. For what values of C is $F < 0$?

18. The current in a certain electrical network is given by $i = 25 - 0.5t$ amps, where t is the elapsed time. For what time t is $i \geq 0$?

19. Suppose that you wish to purchase first class stamps (13¢ each) and air mail stamps (15¢ each) but your purchase is limited to $5.00. Make a sketch showing the possibilities.

20. In designing lighting for a given outdoor area, you are given two different kinds of light bulbs, one 100 watts and the other 200 watts. The lights will normally be on an average of 6 hours per night. Make a sketch showing the possible combinations of the two different kinds of light bulbs if you are limited to a cost of $1.00 per night and the cost per kilowatt hour is 5¢.

Answer true or false for Exercises 1–10.

1. $x + 1/x$ is a linear equation.

2. The slope of a straight line is a constant.

3. Values of x for which a denominator is 0 must be rejected as possible solutions.

4. If a line passes through the origin, one of its forms is $x + y = 1$.

5. The interval $|x - 2| < 1$ is 2 units long.

6. Values of (x, y) such that $x + 3y > 2$ are on the same side of the line $x + 3y = 2$ as the origin.

7. The graph of a linear inequality in two variables is a half plane.

8. The product of the slopes of perpendicular lines is -1.

9. The slope of a line parallel to the line $x = 4$ is 1.

10. $|x - 1| > 2$ represents the same set as $2 < x < -2$.

11. Solve for x: $3x + 5 = x - 10$.

12. Write the equation of the line that passes through $(1, 3)$ and $(-1, -2)$. Express in slope-intercept form. Make a sketch of the line.

13. Graph the inequality $x + 3 < y + 7$.

14. Represent the interval $(-10, 2)$ with an absolute value inequality.

15. Jane has a gallon mixture of orange concentrate and water that is 20% concentrate. How much concentrate must she add to make a 30% mixture? (Express the answer in gallons.)

16. Write the equation of the line that is perpendicular to $x - 3y = 7$ at the point $(1, -2)$.

1. Solve $3(x + 2) - 5x = 7$.

2. Solve $3/(x + 2) - 1/(x - 2) = 10/(x^2 - 4)$.

3. Draw the graph of $\frac{1}{2}x + 3y = -6$.

4. Find the equation of the line through $(-1, 3)$ and $(0, -5)$.

5. Find the equation of the line perpendicular to $5x - 2y = 4$ at $(2, 3)$.

6. Solve $3 + 2x < 5(x - 2)$.

7. Solve $|x + 4| \geq 8$. Graph the solution set.

8. Draw the graph of $5 - x \le 3x + 2y$.

9. Draw the graph of $y + |x| < 2$.

10. A girl paid $35 for a tennis racket and a pair of shoes. If the racket cost $7 more than the shoes, how much did each cost?

5
Systems of
Equations

5.1
Introduction

In the previous chapter we discussed the graphing of equations in two unknown variables x and y. The solution set was found to be the total set of ordered pairs (x, y) that satisfies the equation. Thus, the solution set to the equation $xy = 1$ is the set of ordered pairs $\{(x, y) | xy = 1\}$ that includes such ordered pairs as $(1, 1)$ $(2, \frac{1}{2})$ $(3, \frac{1}{3})$ $(\frac{1}{2}, 2)$ $(\frac{1}{3}, 3)$, and so on. In examining the extensions of this idea, we consider, in particular, two equations in two unknown variables. When considered together, the two equations are said to form *a system of equations*. (An example is the two equations $xy = 1$ and $x + y = 1$.) **The solution set of a system of equations is the set of solutions common to both equations.** Traditionally, those solutions that are members of the solution set are called **simultaneous** solutions of the system.

The topic of systems of equations includes equations for which the number of unknowns differs from the number of equations. However, our discussion is limited to those cases for which the number of unknowns equals the number of equations, concentrating for the most part on systems of *linear* equations. In order to simplify the discussion further, the examples are often limited to systems of two or three equations even though the methods themselves have a wider application.

5.2
Graphical Solutions
of Equations in Two Variables

Perhaps the most general method of solving a system of equations in two unknown variables is graphical. By representing each equation graphically, the simultaneous solution of the system of equations is found by approximating the values of the coordinates of the points of intersection of the two graphs. For example, suppose that you are to find the simultaneous solution of the system of linear equations

$$3x + 2y = 4$$

$$x - 5y = 7$$

From the preceding chapter the solution set of the linear equation $3x + 2y = 4$ is the infinite set of ordered pairs $\{(x, y) | 3x + 2y = 4\}$ and of $x - 5y = 7$ is the set $\{(x, y) | x - 5y = 7\}$. Recalling that the graph of a linear equation is a straight line, we graph each of these sets, as shown in Figure 5.1, and identify the coordinates of the point of intersection of the two lines as the solution set. Specifically, the point of intersection has coordinates $(2, -1)$, so the solution set is

$$\{(x, y) | 3x + 2y = 4\} \cap \{(x, y) | x - 5y = 7\} = \{(2, -1)\}$$

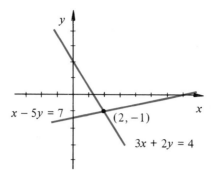

Figure 5.1

Thus, the ordered pair $(2, -1)$ is the **simultaneous solution** to the given system. Equivalently, the solution is often written $x = 2$, $y = -1$.

You can check this solution by substituting $x = 2$ and $y = -1$ into each of the given equations. Thus,

$$3(2) + 2(-1) = 4 \quad \text{(Check of } 3x + 2y = 4\text{)}$$
$$2 - 5(-1) = 7 \quad \text{(Check of } x - 5y = 7\text{)}$$

Example 5.1 Find the solution sets to each of the following three *linear* systems.

$$\text{I} \begin{cases} x + y = 2 \\ x + 2y = 3 \end{cases} \quad \text{II} \begin{cases} x - 2y = 6 \\ 2x - 4y = 12 \end{cases} \quad \text{III} \begin{cases} 2x + y = 4 \\ 6x + 3y = -6 \end{cases}$$

Solution Figure 5.2 shows a sketch of each of the three systems.

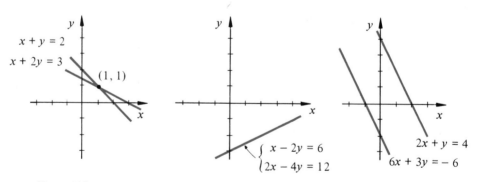

Figure 5.2

The two straight lines of system I cross at $(1, 1)$. Thus, the solution is $x = 1$, $y = 1$, which can easily be checked by direct substitution. Since the equations of system II have the same intercepts, the two lines coincide, and the solution set is the infinite set of ordered pairs given by the coordinates of the points on the line. In system III the lines do not intersect; that is, they are parallel. Hence the solution set is the *empty* set.

Example 5.1 shows the only three possibilities for linear systems of two equations in two unknowns. Since the graph of each of the equations is a straight line, one of the following statements must be true.

(1)   The lines intersect at one point. (The system is said to be *consistent.*)

(2)   The lines are parallel. (The system is said to be *inconsistent.*)

(3)   The lines coincide. (The system is said to be *dependent.*)

The graphical method can be lengthy, especially for systems of nonlinear equations for which we do not (as yet) have any general methods of graphing. The next two examples show how to use the graphical method for a system of nonlinear equations.

Example 5.2   Solve the system $x^2 + y^2 = 4$, $x^2 + 9y^2 = 9$ graphically.

Solution   In each equation we solve for y to obtain $y = \pm\sqrt{4 - x^2}$ and $y = \pm\sqrt{1 - (x^2/9)}$. Tables of values are computed as shown below.

x	$y = \pm\sqrt{4 - x^2}$
0	± 2
$\pm.5$	± 1.94
± 1	± 1.73
± 1.5	± 1.32
± 2	0

x	$y = \pm\sqrt{1 - (x^2/9)}$
0	± 1
± 1	$\pm.94$
± 1.5	$\pm.87$
± 2	$\pm.75$
± 2.5	$\pm.55$
± 3	0

The first of these curves is a circle of radius 2 and the second is an ellipse. Figure 5.3 shows the graphs of both. The points of intersection are approximately $(1.8, 0.8)$, $(1.8, -0.8)$, $(-1.8, 0.8)$, and $(-1.8, -0.8)$. These four ordered pairs constitute the solution to the given system.

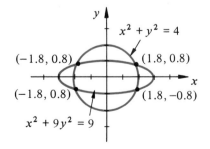

Figure 5.3

Example 5.3   Solve the systems

$$\text{I}\begin{cases} xy = 1 \\ x + y = 1 \end{cases} \qquad \text{II}\begin{cases} xy = 1 \\ x + y = 2 \end{cases} \qquad \text{III}\begin{cases} xy = 1 \\ x + y = 3 \end{cases}$$

Solution   In each of the three systems the first equation $xy = 1$ is not a linear equation and thus its graph is not a straight line. The following table of values gives the coordinates of sufficiently many points to draw an approximating curve.

x	± 1	± 2	± 3	± 4	$\pm\frac{1}{2}$	$\pm\frac{1}{3}$	$\pm\frac{1}{4}$
$y = 1/x$	± 1	$\pm\frac{1}{2}$	$\pm\frac{1}{3}$	$\pm\frac{1}{4}$	± 2	± 3	± 4

For each of the systems, the second equation is linear. The three systems are drawn in Figure 5.4. From this you can see that the first system has no solution, the second has the solution $x = 1$, $y = 1$, and the third has $x = 0.4$, $y = 2.6$, and $x = 2.6$, $y = 0.4$. In terms of set notation we could write the solution sets respectively as $\varnothing$, $\{(1, 1)\}$, and $\{(0.4, 2.6), (2.6, 0.4)\}$.

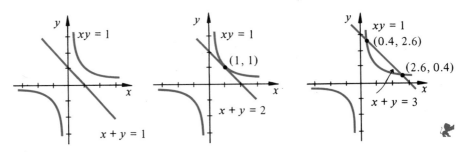

Figure 5.4

Exercises for
Sections 5.1 and 5.2

In Exercises 1–25 solve each system of equations graphically.

1. $x - 4y = 2$
     $-2x + y = 4$

2. $2x + 5y = 4$
     $4x + 3y = 6$

3. $3x + 4y = 23$
     $x - 3y = -1$

4. $x + y = 4$
     $x - y = 2$

5. $x - 4y = 8$
     $2x - 8y = 16$

6. $3x + 2y - 6 = 0$
     $x - 3y - 3 = 0$

7. $3x + 4y = 10$
     $6x + 8y = -2$

8. $3x + 5y = 2$
     $6x + 10y = 4$

9. $3x - y = 2$
     $2x + y = 6$

10. $2x + 3y = 7$
      $6x - y = 1$

11. $3x + y = 0$
      $2x - 2y = 2$

12. $x + 5y = 0$
      $3x + 15y = 3$

13. $x + 7y - 7 = 0$
      $8x - 7y - 3 = 0$

14. $3x + 5y = 4$
      $\frac{3}{2}x + \frac{5}{2}y = 2$

15. $4x + y = 4$
      $2x + 5y + 10 = 0$

16. $x^2 + y^2 = 4$
      $x^2 + 4y^2 = 16$

17. $x^2 + y^2 = 1$
      $x^2 - y^2 = 1$

18. $x^2 + y^2 = 4$
      $x^2 + y^2 = 1$

19. $x^2 + 4y^2 = 1$
$4x^2 + y^2 = 1$

20. $xy = 1$
$x^2 + y^2 = 1$

21. $x^2 - y^2 = 1$
$xy = 1$

22. $x^2 + y^2 = 16$
$y = 2$

23. $x + y = 7$
$x^2 + y = 4$

24. $x + y = 1$
$x^2 - y^2 = 1$

25. $x^2 - y^2 = 1$
$y^2 - x^2 = 1$

26. The velocity-time equation of car A is $v = 3t + 20$ ft/sec, where t is the time in seconds. If the velocity-time equation for car B is $v = 6t + 5$ ft/sec, at what time do both cars have the same velocity? What is this velocity?

27. A company buys a total of 25 grinders from two different companies. It buys 3 more Brand A grinders than Brand B. The total number of each brand of grinder can be found by solving the system of equations

$A + B = 25$

$A - B = 3$

Can you explain how these equations are derived? Solve for A and B.

28. The area of a field is to be 540 square yards with a perimeter of 128 yards. Find the dimensions of the field.

29. Solve the following problem graphically: Two integers have a sum of 30 and a product of 225. Find the two integers.

5.3
Algebraic
Solutions

The graphical method of finding the solution set of a system of equations is valuable since it gives a "picture" of the solution set. However, the method is often tedious and usually yields only an approximation to the solution. If more precision is desired, an algebraic approach is used. The basic idea is to alter the system of equations until a single equation in one unknown is obtained.

Two systems of equations are *equivalent* if both systems have precisely the same solution set. Thus, the systems

$$x - y = 10 \quad \text{and} \quad 4x + y = 16$$
$$3x + 2y = 6 \qquad\qquad 3x + 2y = 6$$

are equivalent systems because both have the simultaneous solution $x = \frac{26}{5}$, $y = -\frac{24}{5}$. (Check this!) In altering the form of a system of equations, the following operations will yield an equivalent system.

(1)   The position of any two equations can be changed. Thus,

$$3x + 5y = 6 \quad \text{and} \quad x - 3y = 4$$
$$x - 3y = 4 \qquad\qquad 3x + 5y = 6$$

are equivalent systems.

(2)   Any equation of a system may be replaced by a nonzero multiple of itself. For example, $x + 2y = 5$ can be replaced by $2x + 4y = 10$ or $-3x - 6y = -15$.

(3)   Any equation may be added to any other equation of the system.

Operations corresponding to (2) and (3) are frequently combined into a technique called **elimination of a variable**. The "trick" is to multiply each of the equations by just the right constants so that after adding the two equations, the coefficients of one of the variables vanishes. In this way the number of variables is essentially reduced by one. If there are only two variables initially, this process will yield one equation in one unknown which can be solved.

Example 5.4   Use the method of elimination of a variable to solve the system of equations

$$3x + 2y = 5$$

$$x - 2y = 3$$

Solution   First, decide which variable can most easily be eliminated by addition or subtraction of the two given equations. In this case the y variable can be eliminated by simply adding the two equations. Thus,

the system $\begin{cases} 3x + 2y = 5 \\ x - 2y = 3 \end{cases}$ is equivalent to the system $\begin{cases} 3x + 2y = 5 \\ \quad 4x = 8 \end{cases}$

Solving $4x = 8$ for x yields $x = 2$. Now find the value of y by substituting $x = 2$ into $3x + 2y = 5$. Thus,

$$3(2) + 2y = 5$$

and $\qquad y = -\dfrac{1}{2}$

Therefore, the solution of the given system of equations is $x = 2$, $y = -\frac{1}{2}$; or, in set notation, $\{(2, -\frac{1}{2})\}$.

The coefficients are not always as "nice" as those in the preceding example. In most cases one or both equations must be multiplied by an appropriate constant to eliminate one of the variables.

Example 5.5   Use the method of elimination of a variable to solve the system

$$3a + 2b = -4$$

$$4a + 9b = 1$$

Solution   Inspection of this system of equations reveals that neither of the variables will be eliminated by adding the corresponding members. However, in converting to an equivalent system in which either the a or b coefficients are equal, elimination of one of the variables will be possible. By multiplying the first equation by 4 and the second by 3, the numerical coefficient of the variable a will be 12 in each equation. Thus, writing these equivalent equations, we have

$$\begin{cases} 12a + 8b = -16 \\ 12a + 27b = 3 \end{cases}$$

Now subtraction of the second equation from the first yields the equivalent system

$$\begin{cases} 12a + 8b = -16 \\ -19b = -19 \end{cases}$$

Thus, $b = 1$. Substituting this value into one of the original equations yields

$$3a + 2(1) = -4$$

Solving for a,

$$a = -2$$

Example 5.6   Solve the following system algebraically.

$$2x + y = 4$$

$$6x + 3y = -6$$

Solution   The y variable can be eliminated if the first equation is multiplied by -3 and then added to the second equation. Thus, the given system is equivalent to

$$\begin{cases} -6x - 3y = -12 \\ 6x + 3y = -6 \end{cases}$$

which is equivalent to

$$\begin{cases} 0 = -18 \\ 6x + 3y = -6 \end{cases}$$

But $0 \neq -18$. This says that the system has no solution (that is, the given equations are inconsistent). Notice that this system is the same as one of the systems of Example 5.1 of the previous section.

Sometimes the process of elimination of a variable can be used for systems of nonlinear equations too. The approach is basically the same as for systems of linear equations.

5.3 Algebraic Solutions   127

Example 5.7   Solve the system

$$x^2 + y^2 = 4$$

$$x^2 + 4y^2 = 8$$

Solution   Multiplying the first of these equations by -1 and adding gives $3y^2 = 4$, from which

$$y = \pm \frac{2}{\sqrt{3}} = \pm \frac{2\sqrt{3}}{3}$$

Using this in the first equation,

$$x^2 = 4 - \frac{4}{3} = \frac{8}{3}$$

from which

$$x = \pm \sqrt{\frac{8}{3}} = \pm \frac{2\sqrt{6}}{3}$$

The solution set consists of the four ordered pairs

$$\left\{ \left(\frac{2\sqrt{6}}{3}, \frac{2\sqrt{3}}{3} \right), \left(\frac{2\sqrt{6}}{3}, \frac{-2\sqrt{3}}{3} \right), \left(\frac{-2\sqrt{6}}{3}, \frac{2\sqrt{3}}{3} \right), \left(\frac{-2\sqrt{6}}{3}, \frac{-2\sqrt{3}}{3} \right) \right\}$$

See Figure 5.5.

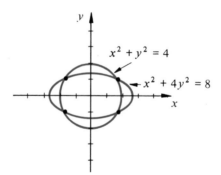

$$x^2 + y^2 = 4$$

$$x^2 + 4y^2 = 8$$

Figure 5.5

We can sometimes eliminate a variable by solving one of the given equations for one of the variables and then substituting into the remaining equations, in this way reducing the number of variables by one. This method of elimination is called the **method of substitution**.

Example 5.8   Solve the following system of equations by the method of substitution.

(5.1) $3x + 2y = 5$

(5.2) $x - 2y = 3$

128   5 Systems of Equations

Solution Begin with either equation, solving for either variable in terms of the other. We choose to solve the second equation for x since this choice obviates the need for fractions. Thus, Equation (5.2) becomes

(5.3) $x = 2y + 3$

Substituting this result into Equation (5.1),

$$3(2y + 3) + 2y = 5$$

Solving for y,

$$y = -\frac{1}{2}$$

Substituting this result into Equation (5.3),

$$x = 2\left(-\frac{1}{2}\right) + 3 = 2$$

Therefore, the desired solution is $x = 2$, $y = -\frac{1}{2}$.

The next two examples show how systems arise. No general technique or set of rules exists for converting a written problem into a set of equations.

Example 5.9   The graph of $ax^2 + by = 1$ passes through the points $(1, 4)$ and $(2, 7)$. Determine the values of a and b.

Solution Since both of the given points must satisfy the equation $ax^2 + by = 1$, we can write

(5.4) $a + 4b = 1$

and

(5.5) $4a + 7b = 1$

Thus, the coefficients a and b can be found by solving Equations (5.4) and (5.5) simultaneously. Using the method of substitution, write Equation (5.4) in the form

(5.6) $a = 1 - 4b$

Substituting Equation (5.6) into (5.5) yields

$$4(1 - 4b) + 7b = 1$$

so $4 - 16b + 7b = 1$

and $b = \dfrac{1}{3}$

Now using Equation (5.6),

$$a = 1 - 4\left(\frac{1}{3}\right) = -\frac{1}{3}$$

Therefore, the equation whose graph passes through points (1, 4) and (2, 7) is

$$-\frac{1}{3}x^2 + \frac{1}{3}y = 1$$

or $\qquad x^2 - y = -3$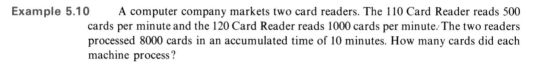

Example 5.10   A computer company markets two card readers. The 110 Card Reader reads 500 cards per minute and the 120 Card Reader reads 1000 cards per minute. The two readers processed 8000 cards in an accumulated time of 10 minutes. How many cards did each machine process?

Solution   In this problem let

A = number of cards processed by the 110 Card Reader

B = number of cards processed by the 120 Card Reader

Therefore,

(5.7) $\qquad A + B = 8000$

Also,

$$\frac{A}{500} = \text{time required to process } A \text{ cards on the 110 Card Reader}$$

and

$$\frac{B}{1000} = \text{time required to process } B \text{ cards on the 120 Card Reader}$$

Consequently,

$$\frac{A}{500} + \frac{B}{1000} = 10$$

or, equivalently,

(5.8) $\qquad 2A + B = 10000$

Solving Equation (5.7) for B and substituting the result in Equation (5.8),

$$2A + (8000 - A) = 10000$$

$$A = 2000 \text{ cards}$$

Therefore, $B = 6000$ cards.

Exercises for
Section 5.3

Solve the systems of equations in Exercises 1–14 by the method of adding or subtracting multiples of the two equations.

1. $x + y = 5$
    $5x - 3y = 17$

2. $x - y = 0$
    $4x - 2y = -6$

3. $2s + t = 5$
    $4s + 2t = 6$

4. $4x + 3y - 6 = 0$
    $2x + 5y + 4 = 0$

5. $3x + 5y = 5$
    $x + 4y = 11$

6. $4x - 7y = 29$
    $6x + 5y = -3$

7. $9z - 13w + 3 = 0$
    $6z - 7w = 3$

8. $5x + 4y = 0$
    $3x + 5y + 13 = 0$

9. $2x + 3y = -10$
    $3x - 2y = -2$

10. $x^2 + y^2 = 1$
    $x^2 - y^2 = 1$

11. $x^2 + y^2 = 4$
    $4x^2 + y^2 = 4$

12. $2x^2 + 3y^2 = 4$
    $x^2 + 2y^2 = 10$

13. $x^2 + 4y^2 = 2$
    $x^2 - y^2 = 3$

14. $x^2 + y^2 = 1$
    $x^2 + 2y^2 = 2$

Solve the systems of equations in Exercises 15–32 by the method of substitution.

15. $r - s = 3$
    $r - 2s = 5$

16. $2x - y - 2 = 0$
    $x + y + 5 = 0$

17. $x + 3y = 7$
    $2x + 6y = 9$

18. $2s - t = 5$
    $6s + 2t = -5$

19. $5y - x = 2$
    $2y + 3x = 11$

20. $x + y = 8$
    $-19x + 8y = 10$

21. $4x + 5y = -6$
    $3x - 2y = -16$

22. $4x = 10 - 5y$
    $7x = 41 + 3y$

23. $6x - 8y = 14$
    $3x - 4y = 7$

24. $x^2 + y^2 = 1$
    $2x^2 - y^2 = 2$

25. $2y^2 + x^2 = 9$
    $y^2 = x^2 + 3$

26. $y - x = 1$
    $x^2 - y^2 = 10$

27. $x^2 - 4y^2 = 25$
    $x - 2y = -1$

28. $y^2 + 2x^2 = 2$
    $x^2 + y^2 = 2$

29. $y - x^2 = 2$
    $x^2 + y = 10$

30. $2a^2 - 4b^2 = 7$
    $a^2 + 2b^2 = 3$

31. $xy = 4$
    $2x + y = 0$

32. $ab = 16$
    $a - b = 0$

33. The graph of $ax + by^2 = 2$ passes through the points $(4, -2)$ and $(-2, 2)$. Determine the coefficients a and b.

34. The sum of two numbers is 12 and the difference is 4. Find the two numbers.

35. The resistance of a wire is given by $R = aT + K$, where a and K are constants and T is the temperature in °C. Find a and K if $R = 25$ ohms when $T = 10°C$ and $R = 30$ ohms when $T = 100°C$.

36. A boat travels 60 miles upstream in 10 hours. If it returns in 8 hours, find the rate of the current and the boat. Assume that both rates are constant during the trip.

37. A truck enters a freeway traveling 50 mph. One hour later a car enters the freeway by the same ramp traveling 80 mph. How long does it take for the car to overtake the truck?

38. A technician needs 10 lb of an alloy that is 60% lead and 40% zinc by weight. If he has an alloy that is 80% lead and 20% zinc and another that is 50% lead and 50% zinc, how many pounds of each must he use to obtain the desired alloy?

39. Two water pipes running at the same time can fill a swimming pool in 6 hours. If both pipes run for 2 hours and the first is then shut off, the second pipe will take 5 more hours to fill the pool. How long does it take each pipe to fill the pool by itself?

40. A collection of nickels and dimes amounts to $2.50. If there are 35 coins in all, find the number of dimes.

5.4
Systems of Three
Linear Equations

This section extends the discussion of systems of equations to include those with more than two variables. In order to keep the discussion relatively simple, we restrict it to systems of linear equations in three unknowns.

An equation of the form $ax + by + cz = d$ is called a linear equation in three variables x, y, and z where a, b, c, and d are constants. A solution to this equation is an ordered triple of numbers corresponding to values of x, y, and z that make the equation true. A system of three linear equations in three unknowns will be of the form

$$a_1 x + b_1 y + c_1 z = d_1$$
$$a_2 x + b_2 y + c_2 z = d_2$$
$$a_3 x + b_3 y + c_3 z = d_3$$

A solution to such a system is any ordered triple that simultaneously satisfies each of the equations of the system.

The techniques for systems of two equations in two unknowns can be adapted to find the simultaneous solution of systems of three linear equations. Choose any pair of equations and eliminate one of the variables by one of the standard techniques, usually by adding multiples of two of the equations together. This yields an equivalent equation in two variables. Now eliminate the same variable in a different pair of equations. In this way the original three equations are essentially reduced to two linear equations in two variables—a system we know how to solve. The procedure is best described with a few typical examples.

Example 5.11　Solve the system

$$x - 6y + 3z = -2$$
$$2x - 3y + z = -2$$
$$3x + 3y - 2z = 2$$

Solution　Multiply the first equation by -2 and add it to the second equation to obtain the equivalent system

$$x - 6y + 3z = -2$$
$$9y - 5z = 2$$
$$3x + 3y - 2z = 2$$

Multiply the first of these equations by -3 and add it to the third.

$$x - 6y + 3z = -2$$
$$9y - 5z = 2$$
$$21y - 11z = 8$$

Now multiply the second equation of this system by 7 and the third by -3 and then add them to get

$$x - 6y + 3z = -2$$
$$9y - 5z = 2$$
$$-2z = -10$$

From the third of these equations $z = 5$. Substituting $z = 5$ into $9y - 5z = 2$, we get $y = 3$. Using $y = 3$ and $z = 5$ in $x - 6y + 3z = -2$ yields $x = 1$. Hence the solution is $x = 1$, $y = 3$, $z = 5$. In set notation this is written $\{(1, 3, 5)\}$.

Example 5.12　Solve the system

$$r \quad + \ t = 1$$
$$3s + 2t = 5$$
$$3r - s \quad = -8$$

Solution　One variable is missing from each of the three equations. Eliminate the r variable by multiplying the first equation by -3 and adding to the third.

$$r \quad + \ t = 1$$
$$3s + 2t = 5$$
$$-s - 3t = -11$$

Multiplying the last of these equations by 3 and adding to the second yields

$$r + \quad t = 1$$
$$3s + 2t = 5$$
$$-7t = -28$$

from which $t = 4$, $s = -1$, and $r = -3$.

5.4 Systems of Three Linear Equations　　　133

Sometimes, instead of writing the entire system each time, we write only those equations in which a variable has been eliminated. In this case number the equations for reference to promote awareness of the total system being considered. The following example illustrates the idea.

Example 5.13   A box contains 300 resistors, capacitors, and transistors. The number of capacitors and transistors together is 30 more than 2 times the number of resistors. The number of resistors and transistors together is 60 more than 3 times the number of capacitors. Find the number in each category.

Solution

$x = $ number of resistors

$y = $ number of capacitors

$z = $ number of transistors

Since the total number of items is 300, we have the equation $x + y + z = 300$. The next statement yields the equation $y + z - 30 = 2x$; and the final statement, the equation $x + z - 60 = 3y$. Rewriting and numbering these three equations, we have

(5.9) $x + y + z = 300$

(5.10) $-2x + y + z = 30$

(5.11) $x - 3y + z = 60$

Multiplying Equation (5.9) by -1 and adding it to Equation (5.10), we get

$$-x - y - z = -300$$
$$-2x + y + z = 30$$

(5.12)
$$-3x = -270$$
$$x = 90$$

Multiplying Equation (5.9) by -1 and adding it to Equation (5.11), we get

$$-x - y - z = -300$$
$$x - 3y + z = 60$$

(5.13)
$$-4y = -240$$
$$y = 60$$

Finally, substituting $x = 90$ and $y = 60$ into Equation (5.9) yields

$$90 + 60 + z = 300 \quad \text{or} \quad z = 150$$

Thus, the box holds 90 resistors, 60 capacitors, and 150 transistors.

Can you write the equivalent systems that were implicitly considered in this example?

Exercises for
   Section 5.4

Solve the given system of equations in Exercises 1–18

1. $x + y + z = 8$ 2. $x + 3y + 2z = 2$ 3. $x + 2y - z = 1$
   $x + y - z = 12$ $3x + 2y - z = -1$ $y + z = 3$
   $x - y + z = 2$ $x - 3y - 3z = 0$ $x - y = 2$

4. $2r - 3s + 4t = 5$ 5. $3x + 4y - 7z = 12$ 6. $x + y - z = -3$
   $5r - 7s + 4t = 4$ $6x + 3y + z = 0$ $2x - y + 3z = 12$
   $-2r + 3s - 5t = 2$ $6x + 8y - 14z = 3$ $x + 2y - 3z = -10$

7. $x + 2y - z = 0$ 8. $x + y + 2z = 4$ 9. $3a - 5b - 5c = 3$
   $x - y + z = 0$ $2x + 2y + 4z = 1$ $a + b - 2c = 7$
   $2x - 3y - 2z = 0$ $2y - z = 5$ $2a - 3b - 2c = 0$

10. $9a - 4b + 2c = 8$ 11. $6x - 8y + 3z = -5$ 12. $3r + 5s - 3t = 31$
   $3a + 2b + c = 1$ $15x + 12y + 7z = 12$ $2r - 3s + 2t = 13$
   $12a - 18b = 17$ $9x + 20y - 4z = 25$ $5r + 2s - 5t = 20$

13. $3x - 2y + z = 2$ 14. $x + y = 2$ 15. $x + z = 2$
   $x + y - z = -1$ $x + z = -1$ $x + y - 3z = 8$
   $2x + y + z = 0$ $y - z = 3$ $x - y + 2z = 3$

16. $x + 2y - 3z = 1$ 17. $x + 4y - 3z = 8$ 18. $x - y - z = 4$
   $y - z = 4$ $2x - 3y - z = 2$ $2x + y + z = -2$
   $-x + y + z = 5$ $x + y + z = 10$ $3x - 2y - z = 1$

In the remaining problems obtain the system of equations from the statement of the problem.

19. The total number of nickels, dimes, and quarters in a box is 900. There are 20 more nickels than there are dimes and the number of nickels and dimes together is 44 more than the number of quarters. How many coins of each denomination are in the box?

20. A triangle has a perimeter of 50 in. The longest side is 3 in. longer than the next longest and 10 in. longer than the shortest. Find the length of each side.

21. A company runs three production lines that together have an output of 45 parts per hour. Twice the production of the first line is equal to the sum of the other two lines, and the output of the second line is 4 parts per hour more than the third line. Find the production rate of each line.

22. A laboratory produces an alloy of copper, tin, and zinc having a weight of 37 grams. If the copper in the alloy weighs 3 grams more than the zinc and the zinc weighs 8 grams more than the tin, how much of each element is in the alloy?

5.5
Matrices

In mathematics, groupings of numbers such as

$$
\begin{array}{ccc}
\begin{array}{c} 7 \\ 8 \\ 3 \\ -1 \end{array}
&
\begin{array}{ccc} & 2 & -1 \\ 7 & 6 & \\ & & 0 \end{array}
&
\begin{array}{cccc} 2 & 3 & 5 & 2 \\ 6 & 7 & 8 & 9 \\ 3 & -2 & 0 & 6 \end{array}
\\
\text{(a)} & \text{(b)} & \text{(c)}
\end{array}
$$

are called **arrays**. A rectangular array is called a **matrix**. Thus, (a) and (c) are matrices. Do not think of a matrix as something having a numerical *value*, but as a scheme for conveniently listing or cataloging numbers. In fact, applications of matrices range from use as a filing system to the solution of difficult systems of equations.

The **dimension**, or size, of a matrix is indicated by giving the number of rows followed by the number of columns. Thus an $m \times n$ matrix is a rectangular array having m rows and n columns. A rectangular array of $m \times n$ and one of $n \times m$ are not considered to be the same size unless $m = n$.*

Of the preceding arrays the first is a 4×1 matrix, the second is nonrectangular and thus not a matrix, and the third is a 3×4 matrix. We denote matrices by capital letters and display them by enclosing them in brackets. Thus,

$$
A = \begin{bmatrix} 7 \\ 8 \\ 3 \\ -1 \end{bmatrix} \quad \text{and} \quad B = \begin{bmatrix} 2 & 3 & 5 & 2 \\ 6 & 7 & 8 & 9 \\ 3 & -2 & 0 & 6 \end{bmatrix}
$$

describe the two matrices mentioned earlier. While it need not be the case, all matrices discussed in this book have real number entries.

A **square matrix** has the same number of rows and columns. In this case the number of rows (or columns) is called the **order** of the matrix. Thus,

$$
\begin{bmatrix} 2 & 1 \\ 0 & -3 \end{bmatrix} \quad \text{and} \quad \begin{bmatrix} 0 & 5 & -2 \\ 2 & 3 & 0 \\ -1 & 7 & 9 \end{bmatrix}
$$

are matrices of orders 2 and 3, respectively.

Rectangular matrices can be of significant value in describing and solving linear systems of equations. Associated with each linear system is a rectangular array of numbers that represents the system completely, without the listing of

---

* The notation $m \times n$ is read "m by n."

the variables. The method of elimination proceeds more quickly if these variables do not have to be carried along from one equivalent system to another. The identification of a linear system and a three-by-four matrix appears below.

$$(5.14) \quad \begin{aligned} a_1 x + b_1 y + c_1 z &= d_1 \\ a_2 x + b_2 y + c_2 z &= d_2 \\ a_3 x + b_3 y + c_3 z &= d_3 \end{aligned} \quad \text{can be represented by} \quad \begin{bmatrix} a_1 & b_1 & c_1 & \vdots & d_1 \\ a_2 & b_2 & c_2 & \vdots & d_2 \\ a_3 & b_3 & c_3 & \vdots & d_3 \end{bmatrix}$$

The first three columns are the coefficients of the system. When standing alone, this three-by-three matrix is called the **matrix of coefficients**. With the last column of constants inserted, the matrix is called the **augmented matrix**.

A system of equations written in matrix form is solved using the same operations as in the method of elimination. The use of *equivalent matrices* corresponds to equivalent systems. Thus, two matrices are equivalent if

(1)   the position of any two rows is interchanged
(2)   a row of one matrix is a nonzero multiple of the other
(3)   a row of one matrix is the sum of two rows of the other.

The following examples show the use of the method of elimination along with matrix notation to solve a system of equations.

Example 5.14   Use matrix notation and the method of elimination to solve the system

$$3x + 2y = 5$$
$$x - 2y = 3$$

(See Example 5.4.)

Solution   This system is represented by the matrix

$$\begin{bmatrix} 3 & 2 & \vdots & 5 \\ 1 & -2 & \vdots & 3 \end{bmatrix}$$

Adding the first row to the second and replacing the second row by this sum gives the equivalent matrix

$$\begin{bmatrix} 3 & 2 & \vdots & 5 \\ 4 & 0 & \vdots & 8 \end{bmatrix}$$

In this form the last line represents the equation $4x = 8$, from which $x = 2$. The value $y = -\frac{1}{2}$ is found as in Example 5.4.   🦢

Example 5.15   Use the method of elimination with matrix notation to solve the system

$$x - 6y + 3z = -2$$
$$2x - 3y + z = -2$$
$$3x + 3y - 2z = 2$$

(See Example 5.11.)

5.5 Matrices

Solution This system is represented by the augmented matrix

$$\begin{bmatrix} 1 & -6 & 3 & \vdots & -2 \\ 2 & -3 & 1 & \vdots & -2 \\ 3 & 3 & -2 & \vdots & 2 \end{bmatrix}$$

Multiply the first row by -2 and add it to the second row. Then multiply the first row by -3 and add it to the third. The result is

$$\begin{bmatrix} 1 & -6 & 3 & \vdots & -2 \\ 0 & 9 & -5 & \vdots & 2 \\ 0 & 21 & -11 & \vdots & 8 \end{bmatrix}$$

Multiply the second row by 7 and add it to -3 times the third row.

$$\begin{bmatrix} 1 & -6 & 3 & \vdots & -2 \\ 0 & 9 & -5 & \vdots & 2 \\ 0 & 0 & -2 & \vdots & -10 \end{bmatrix}$$

In this form the system is readily solvable. Thus, $-2z = -10$, so $z = 5$. The other parts of the solution are $x = 1$ and $y = 3$. These are found by the same substitutions used in Example 5.11.

The operations for equivalent matrices are easily programmed for a computer. In this context the use of matrices to solve systems of equations by the elimination method is translated into a systematic algorithm.

5.6
Determinants

Addition and multiplication of matrices can be defined, but we shall not do so. Of primary interest in this section is an operation on square matrices that yields a real number called the **determinant** of the matrix. To display the determinant of a matrix, replace the brackets with vertical bars. We denote the determinant of a matrix A, by **det** A. Thus, if

$$A = \begin{bmatrix} 3 & 7 \\ -1 & 2 \end{bmatrix}$$

then det A is symbolized by

$$\det A = \begin{vmatrix} 3 & 7 \\ -1 & 2 \end{vmatrix}$$

Restricting ourselves for the moment to 2×2 matrices, we make the following definition for the value of det A.

Definition

Let

$$A = \begin{bmatrix} a_1 & b_1 \\ a_2 & b_2 \end{bmatrix}$$

Then the determinant of A is given by

$$\det A = \begin{vmatrix} a_1 & b_1 \\ a_2 & b_2 \end{vmatrix} = a_1 b_2 - a_2 b_1$$

Practically, det A is obtained by multiplying the element in the upper left by that in the lower right and then subtracting the product of the element in the lower left and that in the upper right. Remember, det A is a real number and not an array, whereas A itself is an array and not a number.

Example 5.16   If

$$A = \begin{bmatrix} 2 & 3 \\ -1 & 4 \end{bmatrix}$$

then

$$\det A = \begin{vmatrix} 2 & 3 \\ -1 & 4 \end{vmatrix} = 2(4) - (-1)(3) = 11$$

Example 5.17 $\begin{vmatrix} 3 & 2 \\ 5 & 3 \end{vmatrix} = 3(3) - (5)(2) = -1$

The definition of determinants of higher-order matrices depends upon the definition of 2×2 determinants and the definition of the minor, below. After defining a 3×3 matrix, the extension to 4×4, 5×5, and others is easy. A 3×3 matrix A can be written in the form

$$A = \begin{bmatrix} a_{11} & a_{12} & a_{13} \\ a_{21} & a_{22} & a_{23} \\ a_{31} & a_{32} & a_{33} \end{bmatrix}$$

The double subscript notation used here is typical. The first number of the subscript refers to the row of the matrix and the second to the column. In this way any element of the array can be determined. Thus, a_{ij} means the element in the ith row and the jth column.

Definition

The determinant obtained from A by deleting the ith row and jth column, called the **minor** of the element a_{ij}, is denoted by M_{ij}.

5.6 Determinants

Example 5.18   Given

$$A = \begin{bmatrix} 3 & 2 & 1 \\ 7 & 6 & -2 \\ 0 & 5 & 9 \end{bmatrix}$$

find the minors of a_{12} and a_{33}.

Solution   Find the minor of a_{12} by eliminating the first row and the second column of the given matrix. Thus,

$$M_{12} = \begin{bmatrix} 3 & 2 & 1 \\ 7 & 6 & -2 \\ 0 & 5 & 9 \end{bmatrix} = \begin{vmatrix} 7 & -2 \\ 0 & 9 \end{vmatrix} = 63$$

Similarly, the minor of a_{33} is

$$M_{33} = \begin{bmatrix} 3 & 2 & 1 \\ 7 & 6 & -2 \\ 0 & 5 & 9 \end{bmatrix} = \begin{vmatrix} 3 & 2 \\ 7 & 6 \end{vmatrix} = 4$$

With the use of the definition of a minor, we can give the following definition of the value of a **third-order determinant in terms of minors.**

Definition   A third-order determinant is the sum of the three products

$$(-1)^{i+j}a_{ij}M_{ij}$$

in any row or column. The value obtained is independent of the column or row used.

In other words, the definition says that a third-order determinant is the sum of the *three products* formed by multiplying each element of any row (or column) by its corresponding minor and assigning to each product a plus sign if the sum of the number of the column and the number of the row in which the element lies is even, and a minus sign if it is odd.

In using the ith column to expand the determinant, we say that we have "expanded the determinant about the ith column." An expansion about the jth row can also be described using similar terminology.

A third-order determinant can be expanded by minors in six different ways. Using elements of the first row,

$$\det A = (-1)^{1+1}a_{11}M_{11} + (-1)^{1+2}a_{12}M_{12} + (-1)^{1+3}a_{13}M_{13}$$
$$= a_{11}M_{11} - a_{12}M_{12} + a_{13}M_{13}$$

By elements of the second row:

$$-a_{21}M_{21} + a_{22}M_{22} - a_{23}M_{23}$$

By elements of the third row:

$$a_{31}M_{31} - a_{32}M_{32} + a_{33}M_{33}$$

By elements of the first column:

$$a_{11}M_{11} - a_{21}M_{21} + a_{31}M_{31}$$

By elements of the second column:

$$-a_{12}M_{12} + a_{22}M_{22} - a_{32}M_{32}$$

By elements of the third column:

$$a_{13}M_{13} - a_{23}M_{23} + a_{33}M_{33}$$

Each of these expansions yields exactly the same value. To complete the evaluation in each case is essentially a matter of computing three second-order determinants. The following expansion shows this in only the first case, that is, by elements of the first row.

(5.15) $$\det A = a_{11}\begin{vmatrix} a_{22} & a_{23} \\ a_{32} & a_{33} \end{vmatrix} - a_{12}\begin{vmatrix} a_{21} & a_{23} \\ a_{31} & a_{33} \end{vmatrix} + a_{13}\begin{vmatrix} a_{21} & a_{22} \\ a_{31} & a_{32} \end{vmatrix}$$

The fact that the value of the determinant is independent of the column or row used for the expansion is a theorem proved in more advanced mathematics courses. The next example demonstrates this fact.

Example 5.19   Find the value of the third-order determinant

$$\begin{vmatrix} 2 & -1 & 5 \\ 1 & 3 & -3 \\ 4 & 0 & 1 \end{vmatrix}$$

using expansion of minors (a) about the first column (b) about the third row.

Solution

(a) $$\begin{vmatrix} 2 & -1 & 5 \\ 1 & 3 & -3 \\ 4 & 0 & 1 \end{vmatrix} = (-1)^{1+1}(2)\begin{vmatrix} 3 & -3 \\ 0 & 1 \end{vmatrix} + (-1)^{2+1}(1)\begin{vmatrix} -1 & 5 \\ 0 & 1 \end{vmatrix}$$

$$+ (-1)^{3+1}(4)\begin{vmatrix} -1 & 5 \\ 3 & -3 \end{vmatrix}$$

$$= 2\begin{vmatrix} 3 & -3 \\ 0 & 1 \end{vmatrix} - \begin{vmatrix} -1 & 5 \\ 0 & 1 \end{vmatrix} + 4\begin{vmatrix} -1 & 5 \\ 3 & -3 \end{vmatrix}$$

$$= 2(3 - 0) - (-1 - 0) + 4(3 - 15)$$

$$= -41$$

5.6 Determinants

(b)
$$\begin{vmatrix} 2 & -1 & 5 \\ 1 & 3 & -3 \\ 4 & 0 & 1 \end{vmatrix} = (-1)^{3+1}(4) \begin{vmatrix} -1 & 5 \\ 3 & -3 \end{vmatrix} + (-1)^{3+2}(0) \begin{vmatrix} 2 & 5 \\ 1 & -3 \end{vmatrix}$$

$$+ (-1)^{3+3}(1) \begin{vmatrix} 2 & -1 \\ 1 & 3 \end{vmatrix}$$

$$= 4 \begin{vmatrix} -1 & 5 \\ 3 & -3 \end{vmatrix} - 0 + \begin{vmatrix} 2 & -1 \\ 1 & 3 \end{vmatrix}$$

$$= 4(3 - 15) + (6 - (-1))$$

$$= -41$$

Note the advantage of choosing to expand a determinant about rows or columns containing some zeros since they eliminate the need for some calculations.

Example 5.20   Evaluate the determinant of the matrix A.

$$A = \begin{vmatrix} 3 & -7 & 6 \\ 4 & 9 & 0 \\ 0 & -1 & 0 \end{vmatrix}$$

Solution   Both the third column and third row contain two zeros. Evaluating by the elements of the third row,

$$\det A = -(-1) \begin{vmatrix} 3 & 6 \\ 4 & 0 \end{vmatrix} = -24$$

Expanding using the third column,

$$\det A = 6 \begin{vmatrix} 4 & 9 \\ 0 & -1 \end{vmatrix} = 6(-4) = -24$$

In either case, the result is the same.

In working with determinants, you will find a knowledge of the following properties helpful. In stating these properties, we assume that A is a square matrix of any order.

(1)   If a row (or column) of A has all zeros, then $\det A = 0$.

(2)   If A is obtained from B by interchanging two rows (or columns), then $\det A = -\det B$.

(3)   If any two rows of A are equal, then $\det A = 0$.

(4)   If A and B are identical except that a row (or column) of B is k times the same row (or column) of A, then $\det A = k \det B$.

(5) The value of a determinant is unchanged if the rows and columns of the matrix are interchanged with each other.

(6) The value of a determinant is unchanged if a multiple of one row (or column) is added to another row (or column).

Property (6) is particularly useful when expanding by minors. The idea is to repeatedly apply this property until all the elements in a given row (or column) are zero except one. Then, when expanding by minors, only one (lower-order) determinant need be evaluated.

Example 5.21   Evaluate

$$\det A = \begin{vmatrix} 3 & -4 & 3 \\ 5 & 1 & 2 \\ 2 & 7 & -5 \end{vmatrix}$$

Solution   Since $a_{22} = 1$, multiply the second row by 4, add it to the first, and replace the first row with this sum. Then multiply the second row by -7, add it to the third, and replace the third row with this sum. Thus,

$$\det A = \begin{vmatrix} 23 & 0 & 11 \\ 5 & 1 & 2 \\ -33 & 0 & -19 \end{vmatrix}$$

Expanding by elements of the second column, we have

$$\det A = \begin{vmatrix} 23 & 11 \\ -33 & -19 \end{vmatrix} = 23(-19) - 11(-33) = -74$$

The complete expansion by minors of the third-order determinant

$$A = \begin{vmatrix} a_{11} & a_{12} & a_{13} \\ a_{21} & a_{22} & a_{23} \\ a_{31} & a_{32} & a_{33} \end{vmatrix}$$

yields

$$\det A = a_{11}a_{22}a_{33} + a_{12}a_{23}a_{31} + a_{13}a_{21}a_{32} \\ - a_{13}a_{22}a_{31} - a_{11}a_{23}a_{32} - a_{12}a_{21}a_{33}$$

This same result can be obtained by using the following device: *Rewrite the first two columns to the right of the determinant and form the indicated products, adding or subtracting as shown.*

(5.16)

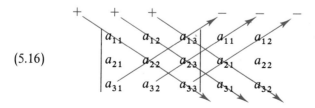

This device is not used to define a determinant because it cannot be generalized to higher-order determinants; that is, the device works only for 3×3 determinants.

Example 5.22   Evaluate the determinant in Example 5.21, using (5.16).

Solution

$$\begin{vmatrix} 3 & -4 & 3 \\ 5 & 1 & 2 \\ 2 & 7 & -5 \end{vmatrix} \begin{matrix} 3 & -4 \\ 5 & 1 \\ 2 & 7 \end{matrix} = (-15) + (-16) + (105) - (6) - (42) - (100) = -74$$

Exercises for
Sections 5.5 and 5.6

In Exercises 1–10 solve the given system using the method of elimination with matrix notation.

1. $x + 2y = 10$

   $x - 2y = -6$

2. $5x + 2y = 6$

   $3x + 4y = 12$

3. $3x - y = 5$

   $x + 4y = 6$

4. $x - 2y + z = 3$

   $2x + y - z = 7$

   $3x - y + 2z = 6$

5. $8x + 5y = 4$

   $5y - 3z = 1$

   $12x + 5z = 6$

6. $6x - 8y + 3z = -5$

   $15x + 12y + 7z = 12$

   $9x + 20y - 4z = 25$

7. $3x + 5y - 3z = 31$

   $2x - 3y + 2z = 13$

   $5x + 2y - 5z = 20$

8. $x + 2y - z = 1$

   $y + z = 3$

   $x - y = 2$

9. $2x - 5z = 2$

   $9y - 4z = 7$

   $3x - 12y = -2$

10. $x - 2y + z = 7$

   $2x + 3z = 4$

   $y + 2z = 1$

In Exercises 11–18 evaluate each of the determinants.

11. $\begin{vmatrix} 2 & 4 \\ 3 & 5 \end{vmatrix}$

12. $\begin{vmatrix} -1 & 7 \\ 2 & 1 \end{vmatrix}$

13. $\begin{vmatrix} 0 & 1 \\ 2 & 6 \end{vmatrix}$

14. $\begin{vmatrix} -3 & -4 \\ -2 & -7 \end{vmatrix}$

15. $\begin{vmatrix} 2 & -6 \\ 5 & -3 \end{vmatrix}$

16. $\begin{vmatrix} 4 & 4 \\ -3 & 2 \end{vmatrix}$

17. $\begin{vmatrix} 5 & 10 \\ 2 & 4 \end{vmatrix}$

18. $\begin{vmatrix} -3 & \frac{1}{2} \\ 6 & 4 \end{vmatrix}$

In Exercises 19–27 evaluate the given third-order determinant by two different methods. Compare the results.

19. $\begin{vmatrix} 2 & 0 & 0 \\ 3 & 2 & 4 \\ 1 & -3 & 5 \end{vmatrix}$

20. $\begin{vmatrix} -1 & 6 & 4 \\ -2 & 0 & 5 \\ 3 & 0 & -7 \end{vmatrix}$

21. $\begin{vmatrix} 2 & 3 & -4 \\ 2 & 0 & 3 \\ -1 & 6 & 5 \end{vmatrix}$

22. $\begin{vmatrix} 7 & 2 & 5 \\ 4 & -1 & 8 \\ 3 & 6 & 3 \end{vmatrix}$ **23.** $\begin{vmatrix} 3 & 1 & 9 \\ 6 & 1 & -2 \\ -4 & 1 & 5 \end{vmatrix}$ **24.** $\begin{vmatrix} \frac{1}{2} & 6 & 5 \\ 1 & 10 & 2 \\ -2 & 3 & -1 \end{vmatrix}$

25. $\begin{vmatrix} 6 & 7 & 6 \\ 2 & 5 & 2 \\ 3 & 1 & -3 \end{vmatrix}$ **26.** $\begin{vmatrix} 10 & -6 & 4 \\ 2 & -1 & 2 \\ 5 & 0 & 7 \end{vmatrix}$ **27.** $\begin{vmatrix} 9 & -6 & 0 \\ -1 & -3 & -1 \\ -5 & -4 & -7 \end{vmatrix}$

28. Solve the equation

$$\begin{vmatrix} 3 & 1 \\ -1 & x \end{vmatrix} = 0$$

29. Solve the equation

$$\begin{vmatrix} x & 1 \\ 1 & x \end{vmatrix} = 0$$

30. Solve the inequality

$$\begin{vmatrix} x & 2 \\ 3 & 5 \end{vmatrix} < \begin{vmatrix} 5 & 2x \\ 4 & 1 \end{vmatrix}$$

31. Compute the following determinant.

$$\begin{vmatrix} \begin{vmatrix} 3 & 1 \\ -1 & 2 \end{vmatrix} & \begin{vmatrix} 7 & 0 \\ 1 & 2 \end{vmatrix} \\ \begin{vmatrix} 5 & 0 \\ 0 & 1 \end{vmatrix} & \begin{vmatrix} 0 & 0 \\ 0 & 1 \end{vmatrix} \end{vmatrix}$$

32. Show that a third-order determinant with two identical rows is zero.

33. Solve the equation

$$\begin{vmatrix} x & 2 & 1 \\ -1 & 3 & 0 \\ 1 & x & 0 \end{vmatrix} = 0$$

34. For what values of k is the following determinant equal to zero?

$$\begin{vmatrix} k & 1 & 0 \\ 0 & 1 & 1 \\ 1 & 0 & 1 \end{vmatrix}$$

35. Evaluate

$$\begin{vmatrix} 1 & 4 & -2 & 0 \\ 0 & 1 & 1 & 2 \\ -3 & -2 & 1 & 0 \\ -1 & 1 & 2 & 3 \end{vmatrix}$$

36. Evaluate

$$\begin{vmatrix} 3 & -2 & 0 & 5 \\ -1 & 3 & 6 & 2 \\ 0 & 1 & -1 & 4 \\ 2 & -5 & 1 & 0 \end{vmatrix}$$

37. Prove the 6 properties of determinants for second-order determinants.

5.6 Determinants

145

5.7
Solution by
Determinants (Cramer's Rule)

Determinants have an immediate and important application to the solution of systems of n equations in n unknowns. To show the case of two equations in two unknowns, consider the following system of equations in x and y.

(5.17) $\qquad a_1 x + b_1 y = c_1$

(5.18) $\qquad a_2 x + b_2 y = c_2$

To solve this system algebraically for the x variable, multiply Equation (5.17) by b_2 and Equation (5.18) by $-b_1$ to get

$$a_1 b_2 x + b_1 b_2 y = c_1 b_2$$
$$-a_2 b_1 x - b_1 b_2 y = -c_2 b_1$$

Adding the two equations,

$$(a_1 b_2 - a_2 b_1)x = c_1 b_2 - c_2 b_1$$

Solving for x on the assumption that $a_1 b_2 - a_2 b_1 \neq 0$,

$$x = \frac{c_1 b_2 - c_2 b_1}{a_1 b_2 - a_2 b_1}$$

By a similar procedure,

$$y = \frac{a_1 c_2 - a_2 c_1}{a_1 b_2 - a_2 b_1}$$

Using the definition of a second-order determinant, the numerator and denominator of both expressions may be written in the form

(5.19) $\qquad x = \dfrac{\begin{vmatrix} c_1 & b_1 \\ c_2 & b_2 \end{vmatrix}}{\begin{vmatrix} a_1 & b_1 \\ a_2 & b_2 \end{vmatrix}} \qquad y = \dfrac{\begin{vmatrix} a_1 & c_1 \\ a_2 & c_2 \end{vmatrix}}{\begin{vmatrix} a_1 & b_1 \\ a_2 & b_2 \end{vmatrix}}$

Formula (5.19) is called **Cramer's rule** for the solution of two linear equations in two unknowns. In solving a system by use of this rule, good practice dictates the expression of all equations in the standard form $ax + by = c$.

The following observations make Cramer's rule easy to remember when the equations are written in standard form.

- The denominator in both cases is the determinant of the coefficient matrix of the system.

- The determinant in the numerator is obtained by replacing the column of coefficients of the variable being solved by the corresponding constant terms.

One of the advantages of Cramer's rule is that the solution of a system of equations may be found with a minimum of algebraic manipulation. If the determinant of the coefficient matrix is nonzero, the system has a unique solution given by Formula (5.19).

Example 5.23 Solve the following system of equations by Cramer's rule.

$$2x + 3y = 11$$

$$-x + 7y = -2$$

Solution

$$x = \frac{\begin{vmatrix} 11 & 3 \\ -2 & 7 \end{vmatrix}}{\begin{vmatrix} 2 & 3 \\ -1 & 7 \end{vmatrix}} = \frac{11(7) - (-2)(3)}{2(7) - (-1)(3)} = \frac{77 + 6}{14 + 3} = \frac{83}{17}$$

$$y = \frac{\begin{vmatrix} 2 & 11 \\ -1 & -2 \end{vmatrix}}{\begin{vmatrix} 2 & 3 \\ -1 & 7 \end{vmatrix}} = \frac{2(-2) - (-1)(11)}{17} = \frac{-4 + 11}{17} = \frac{7}{17}$$

Therefore, the solution is $x = \frac{83}{17}$, $y = \frac{7}{17}$.

Example 5.24 Solve the following system of equations by Cramer's rule.

$$-3x + 5y = 2$$

$$7x - 4y = 0$$

Solution

$$x = \frac{\begin{vmatrix} 2 & 5 \\ 0 & -4 \end{vmatrix}}{\begin{vmatrix} -3 & 5 \\ 7 & -4 \end{vmatrix}} = \frac{2(-4) - (0)(5)}{-3(-4) - (5)(7)} = \frac{8}{23}$$

$$y = \frac{\begin{vmatrix} -3 & 2 \\ 7 & 0 \end{vmatrix}}{\begin{vmatrix} -3 & 5 \\ 7 & -4 \end{vmatrix}} = \frac{-3(0) - (2)(7)}{-23} = \frac{14}{23}$$

Therefore, the solution is $x = \frac{8}{23}$, $y = \frac{14}{23}$.

5.7 Solution by Determinants (Cramer's Rule)

If the determinant of the coefficient matrix is zero and the determinants in the numerators of Formula (5.19) are nonzero, the system is *inconsistent*; that is, it has no solution. If both the determinant of the coefficient matrix and the determinants in the numerator are zero, the equations have the same solution set and the system is *dependent*.

Example 5.25   The system

$$3x + 5y = 2$$

$$6x + 10y = 1$$

is inconsistent, since the determinant of the coefficient matrix is

$$\begin{vmatrix} 3 & 5 \\ 6 & 10 \end{vmatrix} = 30 - 30 = 0$$

while the determinants in the numerator expressions are easily shown to be nonzero. The system

$$-2x + 2y = 0$$

$$x - y = 0$$

is dependent, since not only is the determinant of the coefficient matrix equal to zero but also the determinants in both numerators are zero. Indeed, the solution set in this latter case is the infinite set of ordered pairs:

$$\{(x, y) \mid x = y\}$$

Cramer's rule can easily be extended to systems of n equations in n unknowns but we will be content to show the result of this extension for the case of $n = 3$. The general system of three linear equations in three unknowns,

$$a_1 x + b_1 y + c_1 z = d_1$$

$$a_2 x + b_2 y + c_2 z = d_2$$

$$a_3 x + b_3 y + c_3 z = d_3$$

has a solution given by Cramer's rule.

$$(5.20) \quad x = \frac{\begin{vmatrix} d_1 & b_1 & c_1 \\ d_2 & b_2 & c_2 \\ d_3 & b_3 & c_3 \end{vmatrix}}{\begin{vmatrix} a_1 & b_1 & c_1 \\ a_2 & b_2 & c_2 \\ a_3 & b_3 & c_3 \end{vmatrix}}; \quad y = \frac{\begin{vmatrix} a_1 & d_1 & c_1 \\ a_2 & d_2 & c_2 \\ a_3 & d_3 & c_3 \end{vmatrix}}{\begin{vmatrix} a_1 & b_1 & c_1 \\ a_2 & b_2 & c_2 \\ a_3 & b_3 & c_3 \end{vmatrix}}; \quad z = \frac{\begin{vmatrix} a_1 & b_1 & d_1 \\ a_2 & b_2 & d_2 \\ a_3 & b_3 & d_3 \end{vmatrix}}{\begin{vmatrix} a_1 & b_1 & c_1 \\ a_2 & b_2 & c_2 \\ a_3 & b_3 & c_3 \end{vmatrix}}.$$

Notice that Formula (5.20) has the same form as the rule developed for two equations in two unknowns. As in that case, if the equations are written in standard form, $ax + by + cz = d$, the determinants in the denominator are formed from the coefficients of the variables. Similarly, the determinants in the numerator are formed by replacing the column of coefficients corresponding to the variable of interest by the constant terms on the right side of the equations.

Example 5.26   Solve the given system using Cramer's rule.

$$2x - y + 2z = 3$$
$$x + y - z = -3$$
$$x + z = 2$$

Solution

The equations are given in standard form, so Cramer's rule can be used. The determinant in the numerator of y is expanded about the first column, all others are expanded about the second column to take advantage of the zero element.

$$x = \frac{\begin{vmatrix} 3 & -1 & 2 \\ -3 & 1 & -1 \\ 2 & 0 & 1 \end{vmatrix}}{\begin{vmatrix} 2 & -1 & 2 \\ 1 & 1 & -1 \\ 1 & 0 & 1 \end{vmatrix}}$$

$$= \frac{(-1)(-1)^3 \begin{vmatrix} -3 & -1 \\ 2 & 1 \end{vmatrix} + (1)(-1)^4 \begin{vmatrix} 3 & 2 \\ 2 & 1 \end{vmatrix} + (0)(-1)^5 \begin{vmatrix} 3 & 2 \\ -3 & -1 \end{vmatrix}}{(-1)(-1)^3 \begin{vmatrix} 1 & -1 \\ 1 & 1 \end{vmatrix} + (1)(-1)^4 \begin{vmatrix} 2 & 2 \\ 1 & 1 \end{vmatrix} + (0)(-1)^5 \begin{vmatrix} 2 & 2 \\ 1 & -1 \end{vmatrix}}$$

$$= \frac{(-3 - (-2)) + (3 - 4) - (0)}{(1 - (-1)) + (2 - 2) - (0)} = \frac{-2}{2} = -1$$

$$y = \frac{\begin{vmatrix} 2 & 3 & 2 \\ 1 & -3 & -1 \\ 1 & 2 & 1 \end{vmatrix}}{\begin{vmatrix} 2 & -1 & 2 \\ 1 & 1 & -1 \\ 1 & 0 & 1 \end{vmatrix}} = \frac{2(-3 + 2) - (3 - 4) + (-3 + 6)}{2} = \frac{2}{2} = 1$$

$$z = \frac{\begin{vmatrix} 2 & -1 & 3 \\ 1 & 1 & -3 \\ 1 & 0 & 2 \end{vmatrix}}{\begin{vmatrix} 2 & -1 & 2 \\ 1 & 1 & -1 \\ 1 & 0 & 1 \end{vmatrix}} = \frac{(2 + 3) + (4 - 3)}{2} = \frac{6}{2} = 3$$

Thus, the solution is the ordered triple $(-1, 1, 3)$.

Example 5.27   A company buys three kinds of fasteners. Brand A fasteners are 30¢ each, Brand B fasteners 15¢ each, and Brand C fasteners 5¢ each. The total order of 150 fasteners cost $20.50. How many of each kind of fastener were purchased if there are twice as many of Brand C as there are of Brand A?

Solution   Let

$$N_A = \text{number of Brand } A \text{ fasteners}$$

$$N_B = \text{number of Brand } B \text{ fasteners}$$

$$N_C = \text{number of Brand } C \text{ fasteners}$$

Now form three linear equations in N_A, N_B, and N_C; that is,

$$N_A + N_B + N_C = 150 \qquad \text{(the total number of fasteners)}$$

$$30N_A + 15N_B + 5N_C = 2050 \qquad \begin{array}{l}\text{(the total value}\\ \text{of the fasteners in cents)}\end{array}$$

$$N_C = 2N_A \qquad \text{(relative number of Brands } A \text{ and } C)$$

Before using Cramer's rule, write the third equation in the standard form

$$-2N_A + N_C = 0$$

Then

$$N_A = \frac{\begin{vmatrix} 150 & 1 & 1 \\ 2050 & 15 & 5 \\ 0 & 0 & 1 \end{vmatrix}}{\begin{vmatrix} 1 & 1 & 1 \\ 30 & 15 & 5 \\ -2 & 0 & 1 \end{vmatrix}} = \frac{0 - 0 + (2250 - 2050)}{-2(5 - 15) - (0) + (15 - 30)} = \frac{200}{5} = 40$$

$$N_B = \frac{\begin{vmatrix} 1 & 150 & 1 \\ 30 & 2050 & 5 \\ -2 & 0 & 1 \end{vmatrix}}{5} = \frac{-2(750 - 2050) - (0) + (2050 - 4500)}{5} = \frac{150}{5} = 30$$

$$N_C = \frac{\begin{vmatrix} 1 & 1 & 150 \\ 30 & 15 & 2050 \\ -2 & 0 & 0 \end{vmatrix}}{5} = \frac{-2(2050 - 2250) - (0) + (0)}{5} = \frac{400}{5} = 80$$

Consequently, there are 40 Brand A, 30 Brand B, and 80 Brand C fasteners.

Exercises for
Section 5.7

Solve each of the systems of equations in Exercises 1–21 by determinants.

1. $x - 4y = 2$
       $-2x + y = -4$

2. $2x + 5y = -4$
       $4x + 3y = 6$

3. $3x + 4y = 23$
       $x - 3y = -1$

4. $x + y = 4$
$x - y = 2$

5. $x - 4y = 8$
$2x - 8y = 16$

6. $3x + 2y - 6 = 0$
$x - 3y - 3 = 0$

7. $3x + 4y = 10$
$6x + 8y = -2$

8. $3x + 5y = 2$
$6x + 10y = 4$

9. $3x - y - 2 = 0$
$2x + y - 6 = 0$

10. $r - s = 3$
$r - 2s = 5$

11. $2x - y - 2 = 0$
$x + y + 5 = 0$

12. $2s = t + s$
$6s + 2t = -5$

13. $x + y + z = 8$
$x + y - z = 12$
$x - y + z = 2$

14. $x + 2y - z = 1$
$y + z = 3$
$x - y = 2$

15. $r + 3s + 2t = 2$
$3r + 2s - t = -1$
$r - 3s - 3t = 0$

16. $3x + 4y - 7z = 12$
$6x + 3y + z = 0$
$6x + 8y - 14z = 3$

17. $2x - 3y + 4z = 5$
$5x - 7y + 4z = 4$
$-2x + 3y - 5z = 2$

18. $x + y - z + 3 = 0$
$2x - y + 3z - 12 = 0$
$x + 2y - 3z + 10 = 0$

19. $x + 2y - z = 0$
$x - y + z = 0$
$2x - 3y - 2z = 0$

20. $3m - 5n - 5p = 3$
$m + n - 2p = 7$
$2m - 3n - 2p = 0$

21. $9u - 4v + 2w = 8$
$3u + 2v + w = 1$
$12u - 18w = 17$

22. A company receives a shipment of 25 motors, both AC and DC. There are 3 more AC than DC motors. How many AC motors are there in the shipment?

23. The graph of the equation $ax^2 + by = 2$ passes through the points $(4, -2)$ and $(-2, 2)$. Find the coefficients a and b.

24. A chemist mixes 12 lb of one chemical with 10 lb of another and finds the cost to be $54. If a mixture of 8 lb of the first chemical and 15 lb of the second costs $61, what is the price per pound of each chemical used in the mixtures?

25. A rocket traveling at a constant rate of 50 fps passes a checkpoint. One second later a rocket traveling 60 fps passes the same checkpoint. How long does it take for the second rocket to overtake the first?

26. The total number of teeth on two gears is equal to 94. If twice the number of teeth on the small gear is 5 more than the larger, find the number of teeth on each gear.

27. A box contains $19 in nickels, dimes, and quarters. The total number of coins is 100 and there are three times as many nickels as dimes. How many dimes are in the box?

28. The power output of three amplifiers totals 45 watts. Twice the power of the first amplifier is equal to the sum of the other two amplifiers together and the output of the second amplifier is 4 watts more than the third. Find the power output of each amplifier.

29. Three antenna wires measure a total length of 50 meters. The longest wire is 5 meters longer than the next longest and 10 meters longer than the shortest. Find the length of each antenna wire.

30. An airplane made a 2000-mile trip with the wind in 3 hours and the return trip against the wind in 4 hours. If the speed of the wind was the same throughout the trip, find the speed of the wind and the average speed of the airplane in still air.

31. The two linear equations

$$R_1(x)u' + Q_1(x)v' = F(x)$$
$$R_2(x)u' + Q_2(x)v' = 0$$

arise in the solution of certain differential equations. Solve for u' and v' using Cramer's rule.

5.8
Systems of
Inequalities

In Section 4.5 you learned how to graph linear inequalities in two variables, the graph being a half plane consisting of the region on one side of the straight line. To solve a system of two or more inequalities, graph each inequality on the same plane. The solution set is then the region common to all of the given inequalities. Another way of stating this is to say that the solution set of the system is the intersection of the solution sets of the given inequalities.

Example 5.28 Solve the system

$$6x + 3y < 12$$
$$x + 2y \leq 2$$

Solution The shaded area in Figure 5.6 represents the solution set.

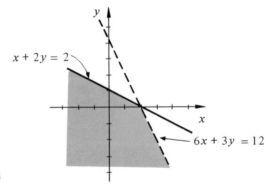

Figure 5.6

Example 5.29   Solve the system

$$6x + y \leq 24$$

$$2x + 3y \leq 24$$

$$x \geq 0$$

$$y \geq 0$$

Solution   If each of the four indicated half planes are drawn, their intersection is the shaded area shown in Figure 5.7.

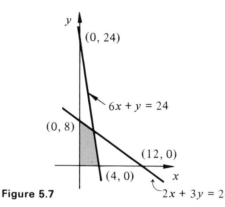

Figure 5.7

5.9
Linear
Programming

In the 1940's mathematicians developed several techniques to facilitate the decision-making process in fields such as business and economics when certain limitations, or constraints, are known to exist. One of these methods is called **linear programming**.

In the context of linear programming the term "programming" refers to the allocation of some usually limited resources to optimize some result such as minimizing cost, maximizing profit, minimizing distance. (Thus, the word programming in this sense is *not* synonymous with its meaning in computer programming.) These allocation problems are linear in the sense that the equations describing the constraints are linear. Thus, linear programming is a method for optimizing some linear function, called the **objective function**, subject to constraints given in linear form.

Example 5.30   The following is a typical linear programming problem.

Maximize $3x - 2y$, (objective function)

Subject to $x \geq 0$, $y \geq 0$, $x + y \leq 2$ (constraints)

Any pair of numbers x, y satisfying the linear constraints is called a **feasible solution**. If a feasible solution also maximizes the objective function, then it is the **optimal solution**. In Example 5.30 the values $x = 1$, $y = 1$ are obviously feasible since they satisfy the constraints. But is the objective function a maximum for $x = 1$, $y = 1$? The value of the objective function at that point is 1, but note that when $x = 2$, $y = 0$ (also feasible), the value of the objective function is 6. Hence, a procedure other than trial and error seems desirable to solve a problem such as Example 5.30.

Certain linear programming problems in two variables may be solved with a graphical method. First, graph the set of feasible solutions, which is merely a matter of graphically solving a system of inequalities. Figure 5.8 shows

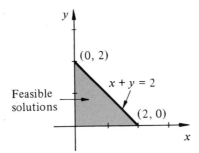

Figure 5.8

the set of feasible solutions for the constraints given in Example 5.30. From this set find the optimal solution. For the purposes of this book we use the following theorem.

**The optimal solution is found at a corner point
of the graph of the set of feasible solutions.**

Applying this principle to the set shown in Figure 5.8, we locate the corner points at $(0, 0)$, $(2, 0)$, and $(0, 2)$. The value of the objective function at each of these points is, in turn, 0, 6, and -4. Hence, the optimum feasible solution is $x = 2$, $y = 0$ and the maximum value is 6.

In summary, the graphical method of solving a linear programming problem in two variables is:

---

(1)   Find the solution set to the set of linear inequality constraints. This is the set of feasible solutions to the problem.

(2)   Determine the coordinates of all corner points.

(3)   Test all corner points to find the solution.

Example 5.31   Minimize $y - 5x$ subject to $x \geq 0$, $y \geq 0$, $2x + y \leq 4$, $x + 2y \geq 4$.

Solution   Figure 5.9 shows the set of feasible solutions. The corner points are $(0, 0)$, $(0, 2)$, $(2, 0)$, and $(\frac{4}{3}, \frac{4}{3})$. The value of $y - 5x$ at these four points is 0, 2, -10, and $-\frac{16}{3}$, respectively. Hence, the optimum feasible solution is $x = 2$, $y = 0$ and the minimum value is -10.

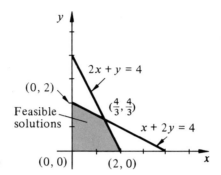

Figure 5.9

The practical applications of simple linear programming problems are numerous. Establishing the constraint inequalities is usually the most difficult task.

Example 5.32   A small company produces two styles of the same book, paperback and hardback. Producing the paperback yields a profit of \$400 per day while the hardback yields \$700 per day. The company can employ only one printing crew, which will work only a five-day week. Paper limitations demand that the paperback be produced no more than three days per week, whereas the hardback production is limited to four days or less per week. If you owned the company how would you assign the printing crew?

Solution   First, establish the constraints in mathematical terms. Let x equal the number of days the paperback is printed and let y equal the number of days the hardback is printed. Then we want to maximize the profit given by $P = 400x + 700y$. The constraints are

$x + y \leq 5$ (restriction to 5-day week)

$x \leq 3$ (restriction on paperback supplies)

$y \leq 4$ (restriction on hardback supplies)

$x \geq 0, y \geq 0$ (number of days must be positive or zero in either case)

Figure 5.10 displays the graph of the constraint inequalities. The corner points are $(0, 4)$, $(1, 4)$, $(3, 2)$, $(3, 0)$, and $(0, 0)$. The value of the profit at each of these points is

at $(0, 4)$, $P = 2800$

at $(1, 4)$, $P = 3200$

5.9 Linear Programming   **155**

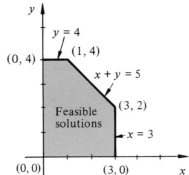

Figure 5.10

at $(3, 2)$, $P = 2600$

at $(3, 0)$, $P = 1200$

at $(0, 0)$, $P = 0$

Hence the crew should devote one day to paperbacks and four to hardbacks to realize a maximum profit of $3200.

Example 5.33   A small shop makes both drum brakes and disk brakes. Both types require a lathe and a grinder in production. Drum brakes require 2 hours on the lathe and 4 hours on the grinder, and disk brakes require 3 hours on the lathe and 2 hours on the grinder. The company makes $14 profit on drum brakes and $18 on disk brakes. Assuming that the company has one lathe and one grinder and that both machines are used 16 hours per day, how many of each should the company make in order to make the largest profit?

Solution   List the required times in a table.

	Lathe	Grinder
Drum brake	2 hr	4 hr
Disk brake	3 hr	2 hr

Let x equal the number of drum brakes produced and y equal the number of disk brakes. Then we want to maximize the profit, $P = 14x + 18y$. The constraints are

$2x + 3y \leq 16$ (restriction of lathe to 16-hour day)

$4x + 2y \leq 16$ (restriction of grinder to 16-hour day)

$x \geq 0, y \geq 0$ (the number of pieces made must be positive or zero)

Figure 5.11 pictures the graph of the constraint inequalities. We leave it for you to show that the corner point, $(2, 4)$, gives the maximum profit. Hence, the company makes the maximum profit by producing 2 drum brakes and 4 disk brakes. What is the maximum profit?

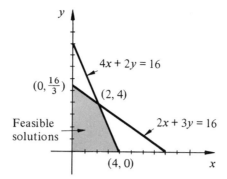

Figure 5.11

$4x + 2y = 16$

$(0, \frac{16}{3})$

$(2, 4)$

$2x + 3y = 16$

Feasible
solutions

$(4, 0)$

Exercises for
Sections 5.8 and 5.9

Use a graphical method to solve the systems of inequalities given in Exercises 1–15.

1. $x \le 2$
$y > 6$

2. $x > -1$
$x + y > 0$

3. $x \le 0$
$y \le x$

4. $x - 4y \le 2$
$-2x + y \ge -4$

5. $2x + 5y > -4$
$4x + 3y \le 6$

6. $x + y < 4$
$x - y > 2$

7. $x \ge 0$
$y \ge 0$
$2x + 3y \le 6$

8. $x \ge 0$
$y \ge 0$
$2x + y \ge 2$

9. $y \ge 0$
$x - 3y \ge -3$
$-2x + y \ge -4$

10. $x > 2$
$x < 5$
$y > -1$

11. $x + y < 4$
$2x + y < 8$
$x - y > 2$

12. $4x + 3y \le 6$
$2x + 5y \ge -4$
$-2x + y \le 2$

13. $x > 0, y > 0$
$x + y < 2$
$2x + y > 1$

14. $2x - y > 1$
$x - y < 1$
$x > 0, y > 0$

15. $x + 2y > 2$
$x - y < 1$
$x > 0, y > 0$

16. A businessman finds that his profit equation is $P = 5x + 2y$, where x is the number of desks and y is the number of book cabinets he sells. How many of each should he sell each day to maximize his profit if

$$x \ge 0, \quad y \ge 0, \quad x + \frac{1}{2}y \le 8, \quad \frac{1}{2}x + y \le 7$$

are the constraints on the profit equation.

17. A company makes $10 on steel castings and $8 on aluminum castings. If x is the number of steel castings and y the number of aluminum, the profit equation is

5.9 Linear Programming   157

$P = 10x + 8y$. Company engineers have found that they must satisfy the following constraints for each day's production:

$$x \geq 0, \qquad y \geq 0, \qquad 2x + 3y \leq 120, \qquad 4x + y \leq 90$$

How many of each kind of casting should the company make each day to maximize its profit?

18. A company produces deluxe and economy model radios. Each economy model yields a profit of $4, whereas each deluxe model yields $10 profit. Both models require approximately the same amount of material to build, and the supply allows for a total of 500 radios per day. The sales force reports that the demand for the economy model does not exceed 350 per day but the deluxe radio can be sold as fast as it is made. The deluxe model requires twice as much time to build as the economy, and if only the economy model were built there would be enough time to produce 700 radios per day. How many economy models and deluxe models should the company construct to maximize their profit?

19. A woman wishes to invest $20,000, part at 7 percent and part at 8.5 percent. The amount she invests at 8.5 percent cannot be more than twice the amount she invests at 7 percent. How much should she deposit at each rate to maximize total income?

20. A company produces two kinds of vacuum cleaners with profits of $5 and $8, respectively, on the economy and the deluxe models. No more than 1000 of the economy model can be made per day and the deluxe model takes three times as long to make. If only the economy model were made, time would allow for production of 1300 per day. Find the number of each that should be built to maximize the profit and find the maximum profit.

Test 1 for
Chapter 5

Answer true or false for Exercises 1–10.

1. The solution set to a system of two equations in two unknowns is empty if the graph of the two equations does not intersect.

2. Cramer's rule gives the solution to a system of linear equations in terms of determinants.

3. An equivalent system is obtained if both sides of any one equation are squared.

4. Another name for a matrix is a determinant.

5. Equivalent systems of equations have the same solution set.

6. The determinant of a matrix is always positive or zero.

7. A minor of a 2×2 matrix is any element of the matrix.

8. If every element in one row of a square matrix A is 0, then det $A = 0$.

9. If every element in one row of a square matrix A is 1, then det $A = 0$.

10. Solutions to a system of equations in two unknowns are displayed graphically as the points at which the graph of the equations cross the x-axis.

11. Solve the system

$$x + y + z = 1$$
$$x + y - z = 2$$
$$x - y + z = 3$$

12. Solve the following system by the method of elimination, using matrix notation.

$$x + y + z = 2$$
$$3x - y - 2z = 4$$
$$5x - 2y + 3z = -6$$

13. Solve the following system using Cramer's rule.

$$x - 5y = 7$$
$$3x + 2y = 4$$

14. Solve the system

$$x^2 + y^2 = 9$$
$$x^2 - y^2 = 1$$

15. Graphically solve the system

$$x + y > 1$$
$$2x - y \leq 5$$

16. Tickets for a special benefit dinner sold at $4.50 for adults and $1.75 for children. The 1573 tickets sold brought in $5340.50. How many of each kind were sold?

Test 2 for Chapter 5

1. Solve the following system graphically.

$$2x + 3y = 2$$
$$5x - 4y = -1$$

2. Solve the system in Problem 1 by the method of elimination.

3. Solve by elimination by substitution

$$3x^2 + y^2 = 2$$
$$x^2 + 2y^2 = 4$$

4. Evaluate the minor of a_{31} if

$$A = \begin{bmatrix} 1 & -2 & 1 \\ 0 & -1 & 4 \\ 3 & 5 & 2 \end{bmatrix}$$

5. Evaluate using expansion by minors.

$$\begin{vmatrix} 3 & 2 & -1 \\ 5 & 8 & 2 \\ -4 & 1 & 0 \end{vmatrix}$$

6. Solve the system

$$2r + s + 2t = 5$$
$$4r - s - 3t = 1$$
$$8r + s - t = 5$$

7. Use Cramer's rule to solve the system

$$3x - 4y = 5$$
$$-2x + y = -3$$

8. Use Cramer's rule to solve the system

$$x + z = 5$$
$$y - x = 0$$
$$z - y = -1$$

9. Graphically solve the system of inequalities

$$3x - 4y \leq 5$$
$$x + 2y > 2$$

10. Maximize the function $P = 3x + 4y$, subject to the constraints $x \geq 0$, $y \geq 0$, $x + 3y \leq 6$, $2x + y \leq 7$.

6
Quadratic
Functions

6.1
Graphing and
Factoring the Quadratic

Functions of the form

$$f(x) = ax^2 + bx + c$$

where a, b, and c are real constants and $a \neq 0$ are called **quadratic*** functions. This type function arises naturally in describing many physical variables such as the path of a projectile, the shape of a radar antenna, or the area of a circle. Our study of the quadratic function begins with a discussion of the unique nature of the quadratic graph.

Example 6.1   Let

$$f(x) = x^2 - 2x + 1$$
$$g(x) = 2x - x^2$$
$$h(x) = x^2 + 1$$

Construct a table of values for each of these functions and sketch the corresponding graphs.

Solution   To construct the table of values for each of these quadratic functions, assign some particular values to x and compute the corresponding functional value. Thus,

$$f(x) = x^2 - 2x + 1$$

x	$f(x)$
-2	9
-1	4
0	1
1	0
2	1
3	4

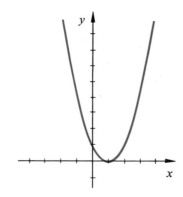

Figure 6.1

---

* The word "quadratic" originates with the Latin word for square.

$g(x) = 2x - x^2$

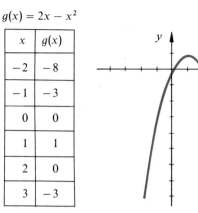

x	g(x)
−2	−8
−1	−3
0	0
1	1
2	0
3	−3

Figure 6.2

$h(x) = x^2 + 1$

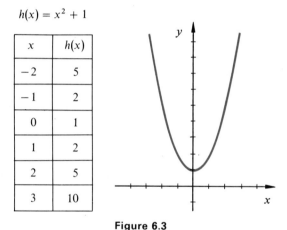

x	h(x)
−2	5
−1	2
0	1
1	2
2	5
3	10

Figure 6.3

Each graph has the same characteristic *parabolic* shape. The graphs themselves are called **parabolas**.

The parabolic shape is peculiar to quadratic functions just as the straight line is peculiar to linear functions. The high (or low) point of a parabola is its **vertex**. The parabola is **symmetric** about a vertical line through its vertex.

The constants a, b, and c affect both the shape and the location of the parabola. The discussion here does not explain precisely how the shape is changed when these constants are changed, but the three functions in Example 6.1 give a general idea. For example, the coefficients of the x^2 term for $f(x)$ and $g(x)$ are of opposite sign, and the graphs of the two functions open in opposite ways. The parabola corresponding to $f(x)(a > 0)$ is said to open upward, and that of $g(x)(a < 0)$ is said to open downward.

While the sign of the coefficient of x^2 determines if the graph opens up or down, the magnitude of a also affects the parabolic shape in another significant way. Figure 6.4 shows the graph of $y = x^2$, $y = 4x^2$, and $y = 9x^2$. As you can see, the larger the coefficient of x^2, the smaller the opening of the parabola. In

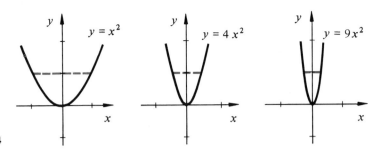

Figure 6.4

Figure 6.4 the opening of each parabola is measured with a horizontal line segment passing through (0, 1). (In fact, any other fixed point on the y-axis will do.) Using this point you can determine the length of the openings to be 2, 1, and $\frac{2}{3}$, respectively.

The constant b in the quadratic function has no fundamental effect on the shape of the parabola but causes the parabola to move to the right or left. Figure 6.5 shows the graphs of three functions: $y = x^2 - 3x + 2$,

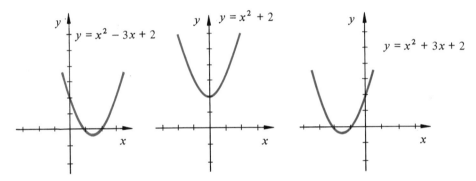

Figure 6.5

$y = x^2 + 0x + 2$, and $y = x^2 + 3x + 2$. As you can see, the basic parabola stays the same but is *translated to the left* as the coefficient of x increases. Note that the y-intercept is the same for each curve.

The constant c causes vertical translation. Figure 6.6 shows the cases $y = x^2 - x - 6$, $y = x^2 - x$, and $y = x^2 - x + 6$ and exhibits the fact that each

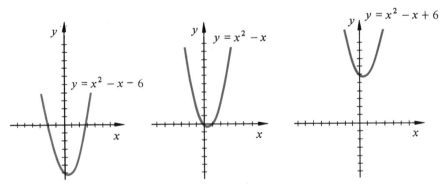

Figure 6.6

case produces the same kind of parabola but shifted vertically by the difference in the value of the constant term. Clearly, *the constant term is the y-intercept.*

From the nature of the parabola, you can see that it will have two, one, or no *x*-intercepts. Hence, the corresponding quadratic function will have two, one, or no real zeros, or **roots**. Obviously, the roots of a quadratic can be estimated by noting the *x*-intercepts of its graph. For instance, Figure 6.6 shows that the zeros of $y = x^2 - x - 6$ are $x = -2$ and 3, the zeros of $y = x^2 - x$ are $x = 0$ and 1, and there are no real zeros of $y = x^2 - x + 6$.

The roots of a quadratic function can also be found algebraically by taking advantage of a fundamental property of real numbers.

If $A(x)$ and $B(x)$ represent any two expressions and if $A(x) \cdot B(x) = 0$, then either $A(x) = 0$ or $B(x) = 0$.

Thus, if a quadratic function can be factored, its roots can be found by setting each of the factors equal to zero.

This section restricts the discussion to finding roots of those functions factorable by inspection. The general procedure is as follows.

(1) Arrange the given function in the form $ax^2 + bx + c$.

(2) Factor the expression into linear factors.

(3) Determine the value that will make each linear factor equal to zero. These are the roots of the given function.

Example 6.2   Find the roots of the quadratic function $f(x) = x^2 + 3x - 18$

Solution   We set

$$x^2 + 3x - 18 = 0$$

$$(x + 6)(x - 3) = 0$$

The factor $(x + 6)$ is zero for $x = -6$ and $(x - 3)$ is zero for $x = 3$. Hence, the roots are $x = -6$ and $x = 3$.

Example 6.3   Solve the equation $x^2 = 2x$.

Solution

$$x^2 = 2x$$

$$x^2 - 2x = 0$$

$$x(x - 2) = 0$$

Since the first factor is zero for $x = 0$ and the second is zero for $x = 2$, the roots are $x = 0$ and $x = 2$.

Example 6.4   Jack and Jim working together can complete a job in 6 days. Jack working alone can do it in 5 days less than the time required by Jim. In how much time does each do the job alone?

Solution   Let x be the time in days required by Jack. Then Jim takes $x + 5$ days. The fraction of the work done by Jack in 6 days is $6/x$; the fraction of the work done by Jim in 6 days is $6/(x + 5)$. Since the sum of these two fractions must be 1, we have

$$\frac{6}{x} + \frac{6}{x + 5} = 1$$

$$6x + 30 + 6x = x^2 + 5x$$

$$x^2 - 7x - 30 = 0$$

$$(x - 10)(x + 3) = 0$$

$$x = 10, \ -3$$

The root $x = -3$ obviously has no meaning in the context of this problem. Hence, Jack could do the job in 10 days and Jim in 15 days.

Example 6.5   Find the dimensions of a rectangular screen whose area is 36 cm² and whose length exceeds its width by 5 cm.

Solution   Let x equal the length of the rectangle, then $x - 5$ is its width. The area of a rectangle is the product of its length and its width, so

$$x(x - 5) = 36$$

or $$x^2 - 5x - 36 = 0$$

$$(x - 9)(x + 4) = 0$$

Therefore, the two roots are $x = 9$ and $x = -4$. Obviously, only $x = 9$ has meaning since a negative length is impossible. The width of the screen is $9 - 5$, or 4, and the desired dimensions are 9 by 4.

Sometimes we want to construct a quadratic function having certain roots. Since the roots a and b imply the linear factors $(x - a)$ and $(x - b)$, any quadratic function with these roots will have the form $f(x) = k(x - a)(x - b)$, where k is a constant. The value of k can be determined if an additional point on the parabola is known.

Example 6.6
(a)   Determine the form of a quadratic function with roots 5 and -3.

(b)   What is the quadratic function having these roots and a y-intercept of -15?

Solution

(a)   Any quadratic function having 5 and -3 as roots will have the form

$$y = k(x - 5)(x + 3)$$

(b) Since the y-intercept is -15, substitute $x = 0$ and $y = -15$ into the equation to get

$$-15 = k(-5)(3)$$

or $\qquad k = 1$

The desired equation is then

$$y = (x - 5)(x + 3) = x^2 - 2x - 15$$

Exercises for
Section 6.1

Sketch the graph of each of the quadratic functions in Exercises 1–10 and indicate the zeros of each function.

1. $f(x) = x^2 - 4$ 2. $y = 2x^2 - 6$

3. $y = x^2 + 1$ 4. $g(t) = t^2 + 5$

5. $f(x) = 9 - x^2$ 6. $y = x^2 + 2x$

7. $x(t) = t^2 - 3t$ 8. $s = 3t - 16t^2$

9. $y = x^2 - 5x + 6$ 10. $y = x^2 + 7x + 12$

In Exercises 11–14 determine the quadratic function whose graph is shown.

11.

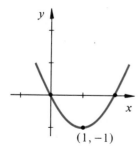

$(1, -1)$

12.

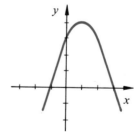

13.

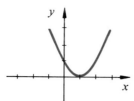

14.

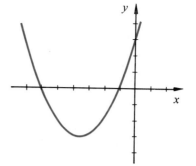

15. If $f(x) = x^2$, how are the graphs of $f(x)$ and $-f(x)$ related?

16. If $f(x) = x^2$, how are the graphs of $f(x)$ and $f(-x)$ related?

17. Sketch the graph of $y = |x^2 - 6x + 5|$.

18. When an object is thrown into the air, its height above the ground is a quadratic function of time. Sketch the graph of height versus time from $t = 0$ to $t = 3$ if the functional relationship is $h = 48t - 16t^2$.

19. Sketch the graph of electric current versus time if current varies according to $i = t^2 - 5t + 6$ amps. When is the current zero?

20. The load being applied to a cantilever beam varies with the distance from the fixed end according to $F = 32 - 2x^2$ pounds. Sketch the graph of this quadratic function from $x = 0$ to $x = 4$.

Solve the equations in Exercises 21–38 by factoring.

21. $x^2 - 2x = 0$ 22. $3x^2 + 5x = 0$

23. $x^2 - x - 2 = 0$ 24. $x^2 - x = 12$

25. $x^2 = x + 6$ 26. $x^2 + 7x + 12 = 0$

27. $z^2 + 3z - 10 = 0$ 28. $x^2 + 10x = 0$

29. $2x^2 + 5x - 12 = 0$ 30. $2x^2 = x + 6$

31. $3w^2 - 5w - 2 = 0$ 32. $4x^2 + 2 = 9x$

33. $10v^2 - 2v = 0$ 34. $6x^2 - x - 12 = 0$

35. $-t^2 + 3t + 10 = 0$ 36. $6y^2 + 7y = 3$

37. $35x^2 + 2x - 24 = 0$ 38. $60y^2 + y - 10 = 0$

In Exercises 39–47 write a quadratic function having the given roots.

39. $\{1, 2\}$ 40. $\{-2, 3\}$ 41. $\{0, 5\}$

42. $\{-1, -1\}$ 43. $\{4, -6\}$ 44. $\{0, \frac{3}{2}\}$

45. $\{-2, \frac{4}{3}\}$ 46. $\{\frac{1}{2}, -\frac{1}{2}\}$ 47. $\{\frac{5}{2}, 3\}$

Solve the systems of equations in Exercises 48–53 algebraically.

48. $y^2 = 4x$ 49. $x^2 + y^2 = 5$

      $x + y = 3$ $x - y = 1$

50. $x^2 = y^2 + 3$ 51. $a^2 - ab - 2b^2 = 4$

     $x = y + 3$ $a - b = 2$

52. $xy = -4$ 53. $cd = 4$

   $2x + y = -2$ $c^2 + d^2 = 8$

54. The area of a triangle is 14 square feet. Find the base and altitude of the triangle if the altitude exceeds the base by 3 feet.

55. The hypotenuse of a right triangle is 13 meters long. Find the lengths of the sides of the triangle if one side is 7 meters longer than the other.

56. Mary can audit a set of books in 7 hours less than Jane, and together they can do the work in 9 hours less than Mary alone. Find the time they take when they work together.

57. The amount of propellant remaining in a certain rocket decreases with time according to $w = 20 - t - t^2$ pounds, where t is measured in seconds. How long after ignition will the amount of propellant remaining equal 8 pounds?

58. A man finds that a trip of 70 miles driven at his normal speed can be decreased by 15 minutes if he travels 5 mph faster. What is his normal speed?

59. A boy mows a strip 7 ft wide around a rectangular yard that he determines to be 50 percent of the yard. Find the dimensions if the width of the yard is $\frac{3}{4}$ its length.

6.2
Solution by
Completing the Square

To find the zeros of a quadratic function not factorable by inspection, we use a process called **completing the square**. The basis for this method is the rule for squaring a binomial:

$$(x + k)^2 = x^2 + 2kx + k^2$$

In the expanded form of any perfect square the constant term is exactly the square of one-half of the coefficient of x. Thus, the expression $x^2 + 6x + c$ is a perfect square if c is equal to $(3)^2$. Likewise, $x^2 - 5x + k$ is a perfect square if k is equal to $(\frac{5}{2})^2$. To apply the preceding rule to quadratic expressions for which the coefficient of x^2 is not equal to 1, first factor out the coefficient of x^2.

The procedure for finding the zeros of the quadratic function $y = ax^2 + bx + c$ by the method of completing the square is summarized next.

1. Factor out the quantity a so that the coefficient of x^2 is 1.

2. Complete the square by adding the square of one-half the coefficient of x, being sure to subtract the same amount.

3. The quadratic function will now be in a form in which the zeros can be found by inspection.

Example 6.7   Solve the equation $x^2 + 10x + 9 = 0$ by completing the square.

Solution   First, isolate the x terms by writing $x^2 + 10x = -9$. Complete the square on $x^2 + 10x$ by adding $[\frac{1}{2}(10)]^2 = 5^2 = 25$. Of course, if we add 25 to the left side, we must also add 25 to the right side. Thus, we write the given equation as

$$x^2 + 10x + 25 = -9 + 25$$

or $(x + 5)^2 = 16$

Taking the square root of each side,

$$x + 5 = \pm 4$$

Or, equivalently,

$$x = -5 \pm 4$$

The roots are then -9 and -1.

Example 6.8 Solve the equation $2x^2 - 3x - 5 = 0$ by completing the square.

Solution Adding 5 to both sides,

$$2x^2 - 3x = 5$$

Dividing by 2 yields

$$x^2 - \frac{3}{2}x = \frac{5}{2}$$

Now adding $[\frac{1}{2}(\frac{3}{2})]^2 = \frac{9}{16}$ to both sides, we get

$$x^2 - \frac{3}{2}x + \frac{9}{16} = \frac{5}{2} + \frac{9}{16}$$

or

$$\left(x - \frac{3}{4}\right)^2 = \frac{49}{16}$$

Therefore,

$$x - \frac{3}{4} = \pm\frac{7}{4}$$

and

$$x = \frac{3}{4} \pm \frac{7}{4}$$

The solution set is then $\{-1, \frac{5}{2}\}$.

Example 6.9 Find the zeros of the quadratic function $y = 3x^2 + 7x + 1$.

Solution Factoring out the 3 yields $y = 3(x^2 + \frac{7}{3}x + \frac{1}{3})$. One-half the coefficient of x is $7/6$. Adding and subtracting $(7/6)^2$,

$$y = 3\left(x^2 + \frac{7}{3}x + \frac{49}{36} + \frac{1}{3} - \frac{49}{36}\right) = 3\left(x^2 + \frac{7}{3}x + \frac{49}{36}\right) + 3\left(\frac{1}{3} - \frac{49}{36}\right)$$

Simplifying,

$$y = 3\left(x + \frac{7}{6}\right)^2 - \frac{37}{12}$$

Hence, the zeros of this quadratic are those values of x for which

$$\left(x + \frac{7}{6}\right)^2 = \frac{37}{36}$$

Taking the square root of each side,

$$x + \frac{7}{6} = \pm \frac{\sqrt{37}}{6}$$

from which

$$x = \frac{-7 \pm \sqrt{37}}{6}$$

Example 6.10   A sounding rocket is thrust vertically upward with an initial velocity v_0. The height h of the rocket at time t is equal to the height it would attain in the absence of gravity $v_0 t$ minus the free-fall distance due to gravity $gt^2/2$. Thus,

$$h = v_0 t - \frac{1}{2} gt^2$$

We are neglecting air resistance and the variation of g with altitude. Show that the rocket attains a maximum height of $v_0^2/2g$ and that this height is attained at time v_0/g.

Solution   Complete the square.

$$h = -\frac{g}{2}\left[t^2 - 2\frac{v_0}{g} t + \left(\frac{v_0}{g}\right)^2 \right] + \frac{v_0^2}{2g}$$

$$= \frac{v_0^2}{2g} - \frac{g}{2}\left(t - \frac{v_0}{g} \right)^2$$

If $t \neq v_0/g$, then the second term is strictly negative and, consequently, $h < v_0^2/2g$. If, on the other hand, $t = v_0/g$, then $h = v_0^2/2g$.

Exercises for Section 6.2

Solve the equations in Exercises 1–15 by the method of completing the square.

1. $x^2 + 6x + 5 = 0$ 2. $x^2 - x - 2 = 0$ 3. $x^2 - x = 12$

4. $x^2 - 2x - 1 = 0$ 5. $x^2 - 3x - 2 = 0$ 6. $x^2 - 3x + 2 = 0$

7. $3x^2 + 2 = 5x$ 8. $3x^2 - 2 = 5x$ 9. $2x^2 + 5x - 12 = 0$

10. $5x^2 - 3 = 2x$ 11. $x^2 + x + 1 = 0$ 12. $2x^2 - x + 3 = 0$

13. $3x(x - 2) + 2 = 0$ 14. $4x^2 = x - 1$ 15. $3x^2 + x + 1 = 0$

16. In analyzing the motion of a certain spring-mass-damper system, the equation $D^2 + 6D + 7 = 0$ must be solved. What values of D satisfy the equation?

17. The equation $R^2 - 3R + 1 = 0$ arises when solving for the equivalent resistance of two electric circuits. What values of R satisfy this equation?

18. The bending moment of a certain simple beam is given by $M = 20x - x^2$, where x is the distance in feet from one end. For what values of x is $M = 60$?

19. A biologist finds that the number of water mites in a sample of river water depends upon the ambient temperature in °F. If $N = 100T - T^2$ describes this relationship, at what temperature is $N = 1100$?

20. The area of a triangular plate is 20 ft². Find its base and height if the base is 6 ft longer than the height.

21. A rectangular piece of metal is 10 cm long and 4 cm wide. Strips of equal width are to be added to one end and one side. Find the width of the strip necessary to double the area of the original rectangle.

22. Two fuel lines can fill a tank in 5 hours. If the larger pipe will fill the tank in 4 hours less than the smaller one, what time is required for the larger pipe to fill the tank?

23. A housewife bought some steaks for her freezer for a total of $120. If each steak had cost $1 more, she would have obtained 6 fewer steaks for her $120. How many steaks did she receive?

6.3
The Quadratic
Formula

The method of completing the square can be used with the general quadratic function $f(x) = ax^2 + bx + c$ to obtain a formula for the roots. Factoring out the coefficient of x, yields

$$f(x) = a\left(x^2 + \frac{b}{a}x + \frac{c}{a}\right)$$

Adding and subtracting $[(1/2)(b/a)]^2$,

$$f(x) = a\left(x^2 + \frac{b}{a}x + \frac{b^2}{4a^2} + \frac{c}{a} - \frac{b^2}{4a^2}\right)$$

Simplifying,

$$(6.1) \qquad f(x) = a\left[\left(x + \frac{b}{2a}\right)^2 - \left(\frac{b^2 - 4ac}{4a^2}\right)\right]$$

From equation (6.1) you can easily obtain the roots of the quadratic by setting $f(x) = 0$. Thus,

$$\left(x + \frac{b}{2a}\right)^2 - \frac{b^2 - 4ac}{4a^2} = 0$$

or $\quad \left(x + \frac{b}{2a}\right) = \pm \frac{1}{2a}\sqrt{b^2 - 4ac}$

from which

$$(6.2) \qquad x = \frac{-b \pm \sqrt{b^2 - 4ac}}{2a}$$

Formula (6.2) is called the **quadratic formula**. We use it by matching the coefficient of x^2 with a, the coefficient of x with b, and the constant term with c in the formula.

Example 6.11   Use the quadratic formula to solve $3x^2 = 2x + 5$.

Solution   To use the quadratic formula, write the given equation in the form $ax^2 + bx + c = 0$. Therefore, subtract $2x + 5$ from both sides of the given equation to get

$$3x^2 - 2x - 5 = 0$$

From this you can see that $a = 3$, $b = -2$, and $c = -5$.
Substituting these values in the quadratic formula we have

$$x = \frac{-(-2) \pm \sqrt{(-2)^2 - 4(3)(-5)}}{2(3)}$$

$$= \frac{2 \pm \sqrt{4 + 60}}{6}$$

$$= \frac{2 \pm 8}{6}$$

$$x = \frac{5}{3} \quad \text{and} \quad -1$$

From equation (6.1) we see that the term $[x + (b/2a)]$ vanishes when $x = -b/2a$. For this value of x the function is a minimum (or maximum, if $a < 0$) and thus the **vertex is located at the point where $x = -b/2a$**. This is often of great assistance in sketching a quadratic function especially when the roots of the quadratic are not real.

Example 6.12   Sketch the graph of the quadratic function $f(x) = 3x^2 - x + 10$.

Solution   In this case $a = 3$, $b = -1$, and $c = 10$. Hence, from the quadratic formula,

$$x = \frac{-(-1) \pm \sqrt{1 - 4(3)(10)}}{6}$$

$$= \frac{1 + \sqrt{-119}}{6}$$

Since the quantity inside the radical is negative, this equation has nonreal roots. That is,

$$x = \frac{1 \pm i\sqrt{119}}{6}$$

The roots are nonreal and consequently there are no intercepts on the x-axis.

Since $-b/2a = \frac{1}{6}$, the vertex is at the point where $x = \frac{1}{6}$. The y-value corresponding to $x = \frac{1}{6}$ is $y = 3(\frac{1}{6})^2 - \frac{1}{6} + 10 = \frac{119}{12}$. Hence, the vertex is at the point $(\frac{1}{6}, \frac{119}{12})$. The y-intercept is $y = 10$. The graph of this function is shown in Figure 6.7.

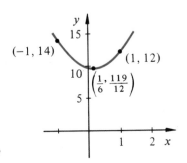

Figure 6.7

The quantity $D = b^2 - 4ac$ inside the radical, called the **discriminant of the quadratic**, determines the number and nature of the roots of a quadratic with integer or rational coefficients.

- If $D > 0$, there are two real roots $(-b \pm \sqrt{D})/2$. Further, if D is a perfect square, the roots are rational; otherwise they are irrational.
- If $D = 0$, there is one root—a rational root, $-b/2$.
- If $D < 0$, there are two nonreal roots, $(-b \pm i\sqrt{|D|})/2$. The quantities $-b \pm i\sqrt{|D|}$ are said to be *complex conjugate pairs*.

Example 6.13   Solve the quadratic equation $2x^2 - 3x - 7 = 0$.

Solution   Since the discriminant is $9 + 56 = 65$, which is > 0, this equation has two real (irrational) roots, namely,

$$x = \frac{3 \pm \sqrt{65}}{4}$$

Example 6.14   Determine k so that $kx^2 + 3kx + 2k + 1 = 0$ has equal roots.

Solution   In this case $a = k$, $b = 3k$, and $c = 2k + 1$. Since for equal roots the discriminant must be 0,

$$b^2 - 4ac = (3k)^2 - 4k(2k + 1) = 0$$

174   6 Quadratic Functions

Simplifying,

$$9k^2 - 8k^2 - 4k = 0$$

or

$$k(k - 4) = 0$$

Hence,

$$k = 4$$

Why is $k = 0$ not a valid solution?

The two roots to a quadratic equation may be written separately as

$$x_1 = \frac{-b + \sqrt{b^2 - 4ac}}{2a} \qquad x_2 = \frac{-b - \sqrt{b^2 - 4ac}}{2a}$$

From this it is easy to show that $x_1 + x_2 = -b/a$ and that $x_1 x_2 = c/a$; that is, the sum and the product of the roots of a quadratic equation can be expressed in terms of the coefficients a, b, and c.

Example 6.15 Determine the values of b and c so that $2x^2 + bx + c = 0$ has roots of 5 and -4.

Solution Here we have $x_1 = 5$, $x_2 = -4$, and $a = 2$. Therefore,

$$5 - 4 = \frac{-b}{2} \quad \text{or} \quad b = -2$$

Likewise,

$$5(-4) = \frac{c}{2} \quad \text{or} \quad c = -40$$

Example 6.16 The height, in feet, of a projectile t sec after it is fired from a gun is given by

$$h(t) = kt - \frac{1}{2}gt^2$$

where g is the constant acceleration of gravity and k is a constant that depends upon the angle of elevation of the gun and the initial velocity of the projectile. Assuming that $k = 100$ and $g = 32$, how long does it take the projectile to reach a height of 50 ft?

Solution Substituting the indicated values into the given equation,

$$50 = 100t - \frac{1}{2}(32)t^2$$

or $$-16t^2 + 100t - 50 = 0$$

Since this is a quadratic equation in the variable t, use the quadratic formula to write

$$t = \frac{-100 \pm \sqrt{100^2 - 4(-16)(-50)}}{2(-16)}$$

$$= \frac{-100 \pm \sqrt{6800}}{-32}$$

$$= \frac{-100 \pm 82.5}{-32}$$

$$= \frac{-17.5}{-32} \quad \text{and} \quad \frac{-182.5}{-32}$$

$$t = 0.55 \quad \text{and} \quad 5.7 \text{ sec}$$

The graph of the quadratic function $h(t) = 100t - 16t^2$ is shown in Figure 6.8. The points at which the projectile is at 50 ft and the fact that a maximum height of 156.2 ft is reached when $t = 3.125$ sec are clearly shown.

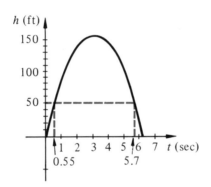

Figure 6.8

Exercises for
    Section 6.3

Solve Exercises 1–15 by using the quadratic formula.

1.	$3x^2 + 4x - 4 = 0$	**2.**	$2x^2 + 4x - 5 = 0$
3.	$5x^2 + 2x - 3 = 0$	**4.**	$8x^2 + 3x - 5 = 0$
5.	$2x^2 - x - 2 = 0$	**6.**	$3x^2 + x + 9 = 0$
7.	$x(2x - 1) = 4$	**8.**	$x(x + 1) = 3$
9.	$x^2 - 5x + 5 = 0$	**10.**	$12x^2 + x - 1 = 0$
11.	$5x^2 + 12x + 6 = 0$	**12.**	$2x^2 - x + 5 = 0$
13.	$3x^2 - 2x + 2 = 0$	**14.**	$6x(x - 1) + 1 = 0$
15.	$2x^2 - 2x + 5 = 0$		

Determine the value of k for which the roots of the equations in Exercises 16–25 satisfy the indicated condition.

16. $x^2 + 2x + k = 0$; the product of the roots is -1.

17. $kx^2 - 3x + 1 = 0$; the sum of the roots is π.

18. $2x^2 - kx + 7 = 0$; the sum of the roots is 10.

19. $kx^2 + x + 8 = 0$; both roots are real.

20. $x^2 + 4x + k = 0$; both roots are complex.

21. $x^2 - kx - 5 = 0$; give two values of k for which the roots are rational.

22. $x^2 + x - (k + 3) = 0$; one of the roots is zero.

23. $x^2 - kx + k - 1 = 0$; the two roots are equal.

24. $2x^2 + x = -k$; one root is the reciprocal of the other.

25. $kx^2 - 2kx + 5 = 0$; one root exceeds the other by 3.

Graph the quadratic functions in Exercises 26–33 after first locating the x-intercepts, if any, the y-intercept, and the vertex.

26. $f(x) = x^2 + 7x + 12$ **27.** $f(x) = 2x^2 - 3x - 5$

28. $f(x) = 3 + x + x^2$ **29.** $f(x) = 3 + x - x^2$

30. $f(x) = 5 - x + 2x^2$ **31.** $f(x) = 1 + x + x^2$

32. $f(x) = \frac{1}{2}x^2 - x - 2$ **33.** $f(x) = x^2 + 2x + 4$

34. How long does it take the projectile in Example 6.16 to reach a height of 120 ft?

35. A man can row 20 miles downstream and back in $7\frac{1}{2}$ hours. If his rate of rowing in still water is 6 mph, find the rate of the stream.

36. The percent markup on the cost price of a pair of shoes is the same as the cost price in dollars. If the shoes sold for $24, what was the cost price of the shoes?

37. The ionization constant of an acid is $K = x^2/[5(1 - x)]$. For what value of x is $K = 3$?

38. The specific heat of a substance varies with temperature in accordance to $c = 5.1T^2 + 0.3T$. For what values of T is $c = 6.0$?

39. A new labor contract provides for an increase of $1 per hour and a reduction of 5 hours in the work week. A worker who receives $240 per week would recieve $5 more per week under the new contract. How long was the work week before the new contract?

40. Jack and Jim working together can mow and manicure a lawn in three hours less than Jack alone. Jim alone takes 1 hour more than Jack. Find the approximate time they take when they work together.

41. Find three consecutive integers the sum of whose squares equals 434.

42. A 2-inch square is cut from each corner of a rectangular piece of cardboard whose length exceeds the width by 4 inches. The sides are then turned up and a box is formed. Find the three dimensions of the box if the volume is 64 cubic inches.

43. The sum of the areas of the two inner circles in the following figure is 0.8 of the area of the outer circle. What is the radius of the smallest circle?

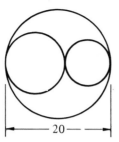

44. Show that the sum of the two roots to a quadratic is $-b/a$.

45. Show that the product of two roots to a quadratic is c/a.

6.4
Equations in
Quadratic Form

Some equations that are not strictly quadratic can be solved using the methods of the previous sections by first making an appropriate substitution. In this section we consider equations of the form

$$a[f(x)]^2 + b[f(x)] + c = 0$$

which can be transformed into the quadratic equation

$$az^2 + bz + c = 0$$

by letting $z = f(x)$. The process is illustrated in the following examples.

Example 6.17 Solve the equation $x^4 + x^2 - 12 = 0$.

Solution The solution of this equation is obtained by letting $z = x^2$ and writing

$$z^2 + z - 12 = 0$$

which can be factored into

$$(z + 4)(z - 3) = 0$$

From this we get $z = -4$ and $z = 3$. In order to find the roots of the equation $x^4 + x^2 - 12 = 0$, we note that $z = x^2$ and, therefore,

$$x^2 = -4 \quad \text{and} \quad x^2 = 3$$

$x^2 = -4$ has the roots $\pm 2i$ and the solution to $x^2 = 3$ is $\pm \sqrt{3}$. Hence the solution set of the given equation is

$$\{\sqrt{3}, -\sqrt{3}, 2i, -2i\}$$

🐎

Example 6.18   Solve $(6/x)^2 + (1/x) = 1$.

Solution We can convert $(6/x^2) + (1/x) = 1$ into a quadratic equation by making the transformation $z = 1/x$. Making this substitution, we get

$$6z^2 + z = 1$$

or $6z^2 + z - 1 = 0$

Factoring yields

$$(3z - 1)(2z + 1) = 0$$

from which $z = \frac{1}{3}$ and $z = -\frac{1}{2}$. Thus, $1/x = \frac{1}{3}$ and $1/x = -\frac{1}{2}$. Solving for x in both cases gives the solution set

$$\{-2, 3\}$$

🐎

Equations that contain a square root term can frequently be solved by squaring both sides to eliminate the radical. However, since "squaring" is not one of the admissible operations, the validity of each root must be tested by substituting it into the given equation. Any root that does not satisfy the original equation is extraneous and must be rejected. The following examples are typical.

Example 6.19   Solve the equation $\sqrt{5x - 1} = x - 3$.

Solution   Squaring both sides, we get

$$5x - 1 = x^2 - 6x + 9$$

Collecting like terms,

$$x^2 - 11x + 10 = 0$$
$$(x - 1)(x - 10) = 0$$
$$x = 1 \quad \text{and} \quad x = 10$$

Only the root $x = 10$ satisfies the original equation since $\sqrt{50 - 1} = 10 - 3$ but $\sqrt{5 - 1} \neq 1 - 3$. Consequently, the solution is $x = 10$. 🐎

Example 6.20   Solve the equation $\sqrt{3x + 1} - \sqrt{x - 1} = 2$.

6.4 Equations in Quadratic Form   179

Equations involving two radical terms are usually most easily solved by putting one radical on each side of the equation. Thus, we write the given equation as

$$\sqrt{3x + 1} = \sqrt{x - 1} + 2$$

Now, squaring both sides, we get

$$3x + 1 = (x - 1) + 4\sqrt{x - 1} + 4$$

Collecting all terms without a radical on one side of the equation, yields

$$2x - 2 = 4\sqrt{x - 1}$$

Squaring both sides again

$$4x^2 - 8x + 4 = 16x - 16$$
$$4(x^2 - 6x + 5) = 0$$
$$x = 1 \quad \text{and} \quad x = 5$$

Both values are roots since $\sqrt{3 + 1} - \sqrt{1 - 1} = 2$ and $\sqrt{15 + 1} - \sqrt{5 - 1} = 2$. ✦

Exercises for
Section 6.4

Solve the equations in Exercises 1–18.

1. $x^4 - x^2 - 12 = 0$
2. $4x^2 - x^4 = 0$
3. $x^4 - 6x^2 - 16 = 0$
4. $3x^4 = 2x^2 + 1$
5. $x^4 + 9x^2 + 8 = 0$
6. $x^{-2} + x^{-1} - 6 = 0$
7. $2x^{-2} - 5x^{-1} - 3 = 0$
8. $x^{-4} - 9x^{-2} + 14 = 0$
9. $3x^{-2} = 4(x^{-1} + 1)$
10. $(x - 3)^2 + 5(x - 3) + 6 = 0$
11. $(x + 2)^2 - 2(x + 2) - 8 = 0$
12. $(x^2 + x)^2 - 18(x^2 + x) + 72 = 0$
13. $(x^2 + 2)^2 + 12(x^2 + 2) + 11 = 0$
14. $(x + 3)^4 = 4 - 3(x + 3)^2$
15. $(x - 2)^{-2} + 35 = (x - 2)^{-1}$
16. $(x^2 - 1)^2 - 3(x^2 - 1) + 2 = 0$
17. $4(x^2 + 1)^2 - 7(x^2 + 1) - 2 = 0$
18. $(x^2 + 3)^2 - 7(x^2 + 3) - 8 = 0$

Solve the radical equations in Exercises 19–36.

19. $\sqrt{x - 6} = 3$
20. $\sqrt{x + 2} = 4$
21. $\sqrt{2y + 3} = 5$
22. $\sqrt{3z - 5} = 1$
23. $\sqrt{x^2 - 16} = 3$
24. $\sqrt{y^2 - 11} = 5$
25. $\sqrt{3x + 1} = \sqrt{x - 5}$
26. $\sqrt{x + 2} = \sqrt{2x + 4}$
27. $y + 1 = \sqrt{3y + 7}$
28. $z - 2 = \sqrt{z - 2}$
29. $2x - 1 = \sqrt{2x + 5}$
30. $\sqrt{1 + 9p} = p + 1$

6 Quadratic Functions

31. $\sqrt{x + 5} = \sqrt{x} - 1$ **32.** $2\sqrt{x} = x - 3$

33. $\sqrt{3y - 5} - \sqrt{y + 7} = 2$ **34.** $\sqrt{2x + 3} - \sqrt{x + 1} = 1$

35. $\sqrt{5z + 4} - \sqrt{z} = 2$ **36.** $\sqrt{5x + 6} - \sqrt{3x + 7} = 1$

37. One side of a right triangle is 12 in. long. If the other side is lengthened by 4 in., the hypotenuse is lengthened by 2 in. Find the perimeter of the triangle.

38. Find the dimensions of a rectangle whose area is 192 in.^{2} and whose diagonal is 20 in.

39. The surface area of a right circular cone is given by the formula

$$S = \pi r \sqrt{r^2 + h^2}$$

Solve this equation for h.

40. If the electric current in a circuit is given by the equation $i = 2t - \sqrt{2t + 5}$, where t is time, at what time will $i = 1$?

41. If the pressure in a waste disposal tank varies with time according to the equation $P = 3 + \sqrt{t + 2}$ pounds, at what time will $P = 5$?

6.5
Quadratic
Inequalities

An inequality involving a quadratic expression is called a *quadratic inequality*. There are two fundamental methods to solve this kind of inequality—one a graphical technique and another based upon finding the zeros of the quadratic.

As a basic rule for solving quadratic inequalities (and indeed for solving any inequality), begin by gathering all terms to one side of the inequality. Thus, without loss of generality, consider the inequalities to be of the form $f(x) > 0$ or $f(x) < 0$.

The graphical method, although at times lengthy, is very simple to understand. First, make a rough sketch of the graph of $f(x)$, being especially careful to obtain the values for the x-intercepts. Then, examine the graph for the intervals for which the curve is above and below the x-axis.

Example 6.21   Solve the inequality $x^2 + 5x < 3x^2 - 2x - 8$.

Solution   First, gather all the terms to the left side of the equation to obtain

$$-2x^2 + 7x + 8 < 0$$

which becomes, after changing signs,

$$2x^2 - 7x - 8 > 0$$

The zeros of this quadratic function, $2x^2 - 7x - 8$, are

$$x = \frac{7 \pm \sqrt{49 + 64}}{4} = \frac{7 \pm \sqrt{113}}{4}$$

These are approximately 4.4 and -0.9. The graph is shown in Figure 6.9.

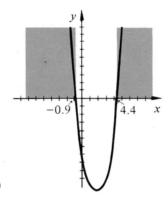

Figure 6.9

The graph shows that the curve is above the x-axis for

$$x < \frac{7 - \sqrt{113}}{4}$$

and for

$$x > \frac{7 + \sqrt{113}}{4}$$

These intervals are the solutions to the given inequality.

As you can tell from the graphical method, the only information actually used to solve the inequality involves the zeros of the quadratic function and the position of the graph above (or below) the x-axis between the two zeros.

The second method, based on the graphical method, employs a sign diagram to help solve the inequality. This diagram gives the signs of the individual factors, from which the sign of the complete expression is determined. The technique is shown in the following examples.

Example 6.22   Solve the inequality $4x^2 + 2x + 4 < 2x^2 + 13x + 25$.

Solution   Gathering all the terms to the left side of the inequality and simplifying,

$$2x^2 - 11x - 21 < 0$$

Factoring the quadratic expression,

$$(2x + 3)(x - 7) < 0$$

The linear factor $2x + 3$ is positive for $x > -\frac{3}{2}$ and negative otherwise. The factor $x - 7$ is positive for $x > 7$. To display these facts, construct a sign diagram for the linear factors as shown in Figure 6.10.

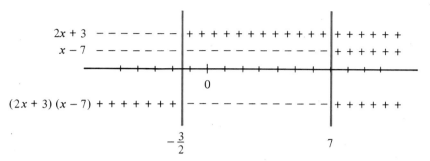

Figure 6.10

Using the fact that an algebraic product of like signs gives a positive number, the sign of the product of the two linear factors is shown in the figure. Since we wish those values of x for which the product is negative, the diagram tells us immediately that the solution is $-\frac{3}{2} < x < 7$.

Sign diagrams are useful whenever we can factor the resulting inequality into linear factors, or at least into factors whose sign we can determine. Remember to bring all the terms to one side of the inequality before proceeding.

Example 6.23   Solve the inequality $\dfrac{2x + 1}{x - 2} \geq 1$.

Solution   First, observe that the given inequality is equivalent to $2x + 1 \geq x - 2$ *only if* $x > 2$, for on that interval the factor $x - 2$ is positive. Even though we could proceed by separately considering $2x + 1 \geq x - 2$ for $x > 2$ and $2x + 1 < x - 2$ for $x < 2$, the method with the most generality follows.

$$\frac{2x + 1}{x - 2} - 1 \geq 0$$

Simplifying,

$$\frac{2x + 1 - x + 2}{x - 2} \geq 0$$

$$\frac{x + 3}{x - 2} \geq 0$$

The sign diagram in Figure 6.11 associated with this quotient shows the signs of the individual factors $x + 3$ and $x - 2$ for any real number and the last line shows the sign of the quotient. From that line read off the solution set, $(-\infty, -3] \cup (2, \infty)$.

6.5 Quadratic Inequalities

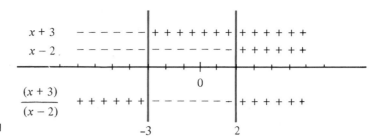

Figure 6.11

The nice thing about using a sign diagram to solve inequalities is that sign diagrams can be used for any number of factors.

Example 6.24   Solve the inequality

$$\frac{x^2(3 - x)(x + 1)}{(x + 10)(x - 1)} \geq 0$$

Solution   Figure 6.12 shows the associated sign diagram. The factor x^2 is always non-negative, so it affects the solution set only when it is equal to zero. From the sign

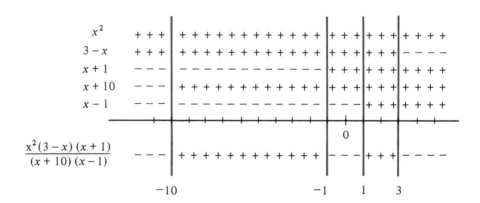

Figure 6.12

diagram we are able to determine the sign of the entire expression for all values of x. The solution set is $(-10, -1] \cup \{0\} \cup (1, 3]$.

The values of x for which the numerator is zero are included here because the inequality specifically asks for equality also. The values of x for which the denominator is zero are never included since the given expression is meaningless for those values.

Solve each of the quadratic inequalities in Exercises 1–10 by the graphical method.

1. $x^2 + 2x - 3 < 0$

2. $x^2 < 2x^2 + 5$

3. $x^2 - 3x < 4x + 10$

4. $(x + 1)(x + 2) > 0$

5. $x < x^2$

6. $3x^2 - x + 4 > 0$

7. $(x + 1)^2 < 0$

8. $x^2 < 1 + 4x$

9. $(x - 3)(x - 5) < (2x + 1)$

10. $(x - 4)(x + 2) < (2x - 5)(x + 3)$

Use sign diagrams to solve the quadratic inequalities in Exercises 11–20.

11. $x^2 + 2x \geq 3$

12. $x^2 < x + 2$

13. $5x < 3x^2 - 2$

14. $(x + 1)(x - 3) > 4x^2 - 10x + 2$

15. $x(6 - x) \geq 3x^2 + 2x - 15$

16. $x^2 + 3x + 2 < 11x^2 + 6x - 16$

17. $x - 1 < x^2 + 1$

18. $3x^2 - 4 < (x - 4)^2$

19. $(x + 4) < x^2 - 4$

20. $(x - 3)^2 > (2x + 1)^2$

Solve the inequalities in Exercises 21–32 by the method of sign diagrams. Be sure to bring everything to one side of the inequality before proceeding.

21. $\dfrac{(x + 4)(x + 5)}{x + 1} < 0$

22. $\dfrac{x + 1}{x + 2} < 1$

23. $\dfrac{x + 1}{2x + 3} \leq 1$

24. $\dfrac{(x + 5)(x + 2)(x - 1)}{x^2 - 4} \leq 0$

25. $\dfrac{(x^2 - 1)(x^2 + 1)}{x^2 - 4} \leq 0$

26. $\dfrac{(x + 5)(x - 3)(2 - x)}{x^2 - 4} \geq 0$

27. $\dfrac{x^2 + 1}{x^2 + 4} \leq 1$

28. $\dfrac{x^2 + x + 1}{x + 1} \geq 0$

29. $\dfrac{(x - 2)}{x^2 + x - 1} \geq 0$

30. $\dfrac{x^2}{(x^2 + 4)(x - 3)} \geq 0$

31. $\dfrac{x + 2}{x^2 - 3} \leq 1$

32. $\dfrac{(x + 1)(x^2 - 1)}{(x^2 - 9)(x + 5)} \leq 0$

33. Determine the values of k such that both the roots of the equation $4x^2 - kx + 3 = 0$ are real.

34. Determine the values of k such that the function $f(x) = 2kx^2 + 7x + 2k$ is always positive.

35. Determine the value(s) of k such that the graph of the function $f(x) = kx^2 + x + k$ touches but does not cross the x-axis.

36. Determine the values of k such that the function $f(x) = 2x^2 + kx + 3$ will have real roots.

6.5 Quadratic Inequalities

37. Suppose that the profit in a business varies in an 8-hour day according to the formula $P = 15t - 3t^2$. For what values of t is $P > 0$? (Assume that $t \geq 0$.)

38. The height of a certain projectile above ground level is given by $h(t) = 32t - 16t^2$, where t is the time in seconds. For what values of t $(t > 0)$ is $h > 4$ ft?

39. The tensile strength of a new plastic varies with temperature according to $S = 500 + 600T - 20T^2$ psi. For what temperature range is $S > 4500$?

Test 1 for Chapter 6

Answer true or false in Exercises 1–10.

1. The graph of a quadratic function is a parabola.

2. The graph of a quadratic always intersects the y-axis.

3. If the coefficients of a quadratic function are real, then both the roots are real.

4. If a quadratic function has real roots, the value of the x-coordinate of the vertex is the average of these roots.

5. Quadratic inequalities have solution sets that are intervals, one number, or the empty set.

6. The domain of a quadratic function is the set of non-negative real numbers.

7. The function $f(x) = (x - 1)(1 + x)$ is a quadratic.

8. The function $f(x) = 1 - \dfrac{1}{x^2}$ is a quadratic.

9. The quadratic formula can be used to solve the equation $bx^2 + cx + a = 0$.

10. A quadratic function with real roots can be written as a product of real linear factors.

11. Solve the equation $x^2 + 5x + 2 = 0$.

12. Factor the function into linear factors: $f(x) = 2x^2 - x - 2$.

13. For what value(s) of k will the quadratic function $f(x) = 2x^2 + kx + 2$ have complex roots?

14. Two water lines can fill a swimming pool in 6 hours. The larger of the lines will fill the pool in 2 hours less than the smaller. What time is required for the larger water line to fill the pool?

15. Solve the inequality $x(x - 1) < 2(x + 2)(x + 1)$.

16. Solve the inequality $\dfrac{2x - 1}{x + 1} \leq 1$.

Test 2 for Chapter 6

1. Sketch the graph of $y = x^2 - x - 12$. Indicate the zeros.

2. Solve $2x(x + 5) = 12$ by factoring.

3. Solve $x^2 - 6x + 2 = 0$ by completing the square.

4. Solve $3x^2 = x - 2$ using the quadratic formula.

5. Find two real numbers such that $x^{2/3} - 3x^{1/3} - 4 = 0$.

6. Solve $\sqrt{x + 12} - \sqrt{x} = 3$.

7. Use the method of sign diagrams to solve $3x^2 - 2x + 5 < 5x + 3$.

8. The formula for the area of a right circular cylinder is $A = 2\pi r^2 + 2\pi rh$, where r is the radius of the cylinder and h is its height. If the height of a cylindrical can is 6 in., what must the radius be to give an area of 14π in.^{2}?

7
Polynomial and
Rational Functions

7.1
Polynomial
Functions

The linear function

$$f(x) = ax + b$$

and the quadratic function

$$f(x) = ax^2 + bx + c$$

are special cases of a class of functions called **polynomials**. In general, a function defined by the rule

$$f(x) = a_n x^n + a_{n-1} x^{n-1} + \cdots + a_1 x + a_0 , \qquad a_n \neq 0$$

is called a *real* polynomial function of degree n, if n is a positive integer and a_n, $a_{n-1}, \ldots, a_0$ are arbitrary but constant real numbers. Using this definition, you can see that a quadratic function is a polynomial function of degree two and a linear function is a polynomial function of degree one.

The sum of two or more terms is not necessarily a polynomial. For instance, functions such as

$$f(x) = x + \frac{1}{x} \quad \text{or} \quad g(x) = \sqrt{x} + 1$$

are not polynomials. Mathematical discussions are often limited to polynomial functions, so it is important to have a clear understanding of what constitutes a polynomial.

7.2
Some Special
Polynomials

The graph of a function is useful because it shows how the function " behaves." In this section we discuss two kinds of polynomials that are easy to graph; namely, the single-term polynomial and the factored polynomial.

Since every polynomial is a linear combination of functions of the form x^n, where n is a positive integer, a knowledge of the graphs of single-term polynomials can be useful in sketching more general polynomials. Figure 7.1(a) shows the graphs of $y = x^n$, $n = 1, 2, 3, 4$ on the interval $0 \leq x \leq 5$. Notice that for $x > 1$ the higher-degree function always appears above the lower-degree function and that the difference in the values of any two powers increases as x becomes large. We say that the higher-degree function **dominates** the lower-degree functions as x becomes large.

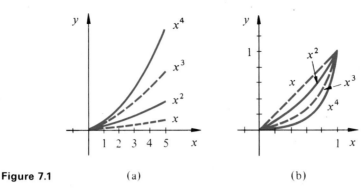

Figure 7.1   (a)   (b)

In Figure 7.1(a) the relative position of each of the graphs is barely distinguishable on $0 \le x \le 1$. To see what happens to the graphs on this interval the four functions are redrawn in Figure 7.1(b) using a more appropriate scale. Clearly the relative position of the graphs are reversed from their positions for $x > 1$; i.e., x dominates x^2, which dominates x^3, and so forth.

Understanding that one function dominates another can be useful in making a quick sketch of a simple polynomial. For example, if $f(x) = x^4 + x$, we would consider the x term to be the most important for, say, $x < 0.8$, and the term x^4 dominant for, say, $x > 2$. In between, of course, the values of both terms would contribute significantly to the sum. Figure 7.2 shows the graph of $f(x) = x^4 + x$ from $x = 0$ to $x = 3$.

Once you know how the graph of the basic power function looks, the extension to some simple linear combinations is straightforward.

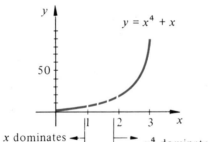

Figure 7.2

Example 7.1   Sketch the graph of $f(x) = -x^3 + 1$.

Solution   Figure 7.3(a) presents the graph of $-x^3$. Adding 1 to each ordinate value gives the graph of $y = -x^3 + 1$, as shown in Figure 7.3(b).

Polynomials in factored form are easy to sketch because the zeros of each factor give the value of the intercepts on the x-axis. To determine where the graph is above or below the axis, we use a sign diagram as in solving an inequality.

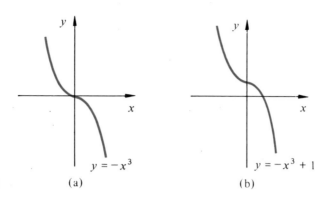

$y = -x^3$

(a)

$y = -x^3 + 1$

(b)

Figure 7.3

Example 7.2   Sketch the graph of $y = (x - 1)(2x + 1)(x - 3)$.

Solution   Since $x = 1$, $-\frac{1}{2}$, and 3 are roots of this polynomial, they are the x-intercepts. By letting $x = 0$ we obtain $y = 3$ as the y-intercept. The value of y is positive for $x > -\frac{1}{2}$ and then alternates in sign as the curve passes through each of its intercepts. Figure 7.4 shows not only the curve but some additional values of y for x between the intercepts. The graph has the distinctive cubic character.

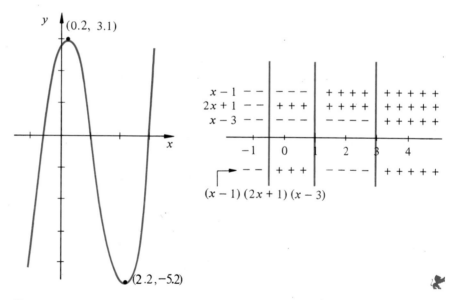

Figure 7.4

Example 7.3   Sketch the graph of $y = x^2(x + 1)(x + 2)$.

Solution   Figure 7.5 shows the graph of this quartic. The points on the x-axis for $x = 0$, -1, and -2 are easily obtained. The graph does not cross the x-axis at $x = 0$ because x^2 is always non-negative in the vicinity of $x = 0$.

7.2 Some Special Polynomials

191

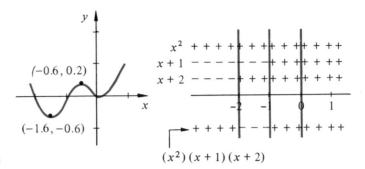

Figure 7.5

$(x^2)(x + 1)(x + 2)$

Exercises for
Sections 7.1 and 7.2

Sketch the graph of the polynomials in Exercises 1–20.

1. $y = x^3 + 1$ 2. $y = x^4 + x$

3. $y = 1 - x^4$ 4. $y = x^4 + x^2$

5. $y = x^4 - x^2$ 6. $y = x^3 + x$

7. $y = x^3 - x$ 8. $y = x^3 - x^2$

9. $y = x^5 + 1$ 10. $y = x^6 - 1$

11. $y = (x)(x - 1)(x + 3)$ 12. $y = (x - 1)(x + 4)(x - 10)$

13. $y = (x + 1)^2(x)(x - 1)$ 14. $y = (x^2 - 3x + 2)(x^2 - 9)$

15. $y = (x^2 - 9)(x^2 + 4)$ 16. $y = (x^2 - 1)(x + 1)^2$

17. $y = (x + 2)(x - 3)(x + 5)$ 18. $y = (x + 5)(x + 2)(x - 1)x$

19. $y = (x^2 - 6x + 5)(x^2 + 4x + 4)$ 20. $y = x^2(x^2 - 1)(x + 2)$

7.3
The Remainder
Theorem and the Factor Theorem

Polynomial functions may be combined with other polynomials by addition, subtraction, multiplication, or division. The sum, the difference, or the product of any two polynomials is a polynomial, but the quotient is not necessarily a polynomial. For instance, if the polynomial $f(x) = 2x^3 + x^2 - 5x - 17$ is divided by $x^2 - 2x + 3$, the result is

$$
\begin{array}{r}
2x + 5 \\
x^2 - 2x + 3 \overline{)2x^3 + x^2 - 5x - 17} \\
\underline{2x^3 - 4x^2 + 6x} \\
5x^2 - 11x - 17 \\
\underline{5x^2 - 10x + 15} \\
-x - 32 \text{ Remainder}
\end{array}
$$

7 Polynomial and Rational Functions

Thus,

$$\frac{2x^3 + x^2 - 5x - 17}{x^2 - 2x + 3} = 2x + 5 - \frac{x + 32}{x^2 - 2x + 3},$$

which is not a polynomial.

This chapter stresses the division of polynomials by linear factors of the form $(x - r)$, where r is a rational number. Much of what we study is concerned with the form of the remainder term in the quotient. When $f(x) = 2x^3 - 3x^2 - 4x - 17$ is divided by $x - 3$, the remainder is -2.

$$
\begin{array}{r}
2x^2 + 3x + 5 \\
x - 3 \overline{)2x^3 - 3x^2 - 4x - 17} \\
\underline{2x^3 - 6x^2} \\
3x^2 - 4x \\
\underline{3x^2 - 9x} \\
5x - 17 \\
\underline{5x - 15} \\
-2 \quad \text{Remainder}
\end{array}
$$

Here is an interesting observation. Not only is the remainder a constant but, in evaluating $f(x) = 2x^3 - 3x^2 - 4x - 17$ at $x = 3$, we get

$$f(3) = 2(3)^3 - 3(3)^2 - 4(3) - 17$$

$$= 54 - 27 - 12 - 17$$

$$= -2$$

This is the same remainder as when $f(x)$ is divided by $x - 3$, and motivates a theorem known as the **remainder theorem**:

Theorem 7.1

If $f(x)$ is divided by the linear factor $(x - r)$ until a constant remainder R is obtained, then $f(r) = R$; that is, the remainder is always a constant equal to the value of the function at $x = r$.

Proof

By assumption

$$\frac{f(x)}{x - r} = q(x) + \frac{R}{x - r}$$

Therefore,

(7.1) $f(x) = (x - r)q(x) + R$

Letting $x = r$,

$$f(r) = (r - r)q(r) + R = R$$

Example 7.4   What is the remainder when $x^5 + x^4 + 6$ is divided by $x + 2$?

Solution   In this case $f(x) = x^5 + x^4 + 6$ and $r = -2$. Thus,

$$R = f(-2) = (-2)^5 + (-2)^4 + 6 = -32 + 16 + 6 = -10$$

Example 7.5   Find the remainder when $f(x) = x^3 - 1$ is divided by $x - 1$.

Solution   Here $r = 1$, so $R = f(1) = 1^3 - 1 = 0$.

The remainder theorem leads directly to another important theorem known as the **factor theorem**. If, in particular, r is a zero of $f(x)$, then $f(r) = R = 0$. Thus, from equation (7.1),

$$f(x) = (x - r)q(x)$$

which means that $(x - r)$ is a factor of $f(x)$.

Theorem 7.2   The polynomial $f(x)$ has a root $x = r$ if and only if $(x - r)$ is a factor of the polynomial.

More generally, a root of a polynomial is of *multiplicity k* if and only if $(x - r)^k$ is a factor of the polynomial.

Example 7.6   Show that $x - 2$ is a factor of $f(x) = x^3 + 2x^2 - 5x - 6$.

Solution   Here $r = 2$ and $f(2) = 2^3 + 2(2)^2 - 5(2) - 6 = 0$. Hence, by the factor theorem, $(x - 2)$ is a factor.

Example 7.7   Use the factor theorem to determine whether or not $(2x - 1)$ is a factor of $f(x) = 4x^3 - 5x + 2$.

Solution   First, note that $2x - 1$ is not of the form $x - r$ and, therefore, we may not use the value of $f(1)$ to determine if $2x - 1$ is a factor. However, $2x - 1 = 2(x - \frac{1}{2})$, which means that if $x - \frac{1}{2}$ is a factor; so is $2x - 1$. Thus, we evaluate $f(\frac{1}{2})$ to find that

$$f\left(\frac{1}{2}\right) = 4\left(\frac{1}{2}\right)^3 - 5\left(\frac{1}{2}\right) + 2 = 0$$

which shows that $2x - 1$ is a factor of $4x^3 - 5x + 2$.

If the zeros (and their multiplicities) are known, the polynomial itself is completely determined.

Example 7.8   Find the fourth-degree polynomial with zeros at -2, 1, and 3 and y-intercept 2 if the zero at -2 is of multiplicity 2.

Solution   Since each of the zeros gives a factor,

$$f(x) = a(x + 2)^2(x - 1)(x - 3)$$

To evaluate the constant, note that the graph must pass through $(0, 2)$. Substituting these values for x and $f(x)$,

$$12a = 2 \quad \text{or} \quad a = \frac{1}{6}$$

Hence, $f(x) = (\frac{1}{6})(x + 2)^2(x - 1)(x - 3)$ is the desired polynomial.

Not all polynomials can be written as a product of real linear factors; (for example, $f(x) = x^2 + 1$). However, a very important theorem of advanced mathematics says that every real polynomial can be written as a product of real linear and irreducible quadratic factors.* Hence, all the real roots of a polynomial are displayed by their linear factors; the nonreal roots arise from the irreducible quadratics.

Exercises for
Section 7.3

Perform the divisions in Exercises 1–10. Check the remainder using the remainder theorem.

1. $(x^2 - 6x + 2) \div (x - 1)$ **2.** $(3x^2 + 5x - 7) \div (x + 2)$

3. $(x^3 + 2x^2 - 3x + 4) \div (x + 1)$ **4.** $(x^3 - 2x^2 + 3x - 1) \div (x - 2)$

5. $(2x^3 - 4x^2 + x - 1) \div (x + 2)$ **6.** $(x^3 - 3x + 9) \div (x + 3)$

7. $(3x^4 - 3x^3 + 2x^2 - 8x + 1) \div (x + 1)$ **8.** $(2x^3 - 4x^2 + 6x - 2) \div (x + 3)$

9. $(x^4 - 2x^2 + 3x - 2) \div (x + 2)$ **10.** $(x^5 - 32) \div (x - 2)$

Use the factor theorem to determine whether or not the second expression is a factor of the first in Exercises 11–22.

11. $x^2 - 5x + 4, \quad x - 4$

12. $x^2 + 7x + 12, \quad x - 3$

13. $x^3 - 1, \quad x + 1$

14. $x^4 - x^3 + 2x^2 - 72, \quad x - 3$

15. $4x^3 + x^2 - 16x - 4, \quad x - 2$

16. $2x^4 - 7x^3 - x^2 + 8, \quad x - 5$

17. $3x^5 + 7x - 8, \quad x - 2$

* An irreducible quadratic is one that cannot be written as a product of *real* linear factors.

18. $x^3 + 27, \quad x + 3$

19. $x^4 + 2x^3 - 15x^2 - 32x - 16, \quad x - 4$

20. $x^4 - 8x^3 + 6x^2 + 40x - 56, \quad x - 2$

21. $3x^3 + 2x^2 - 4x + 1, \quad 3x - 1$

22. $3x^3 - 20x^2 + 23x + 10, \quad 3x + 1$

Write expressions for the polynomials in Exercises 23–28 with the indicated properties.

23. Third-degree polynomial with zeros at 1, -1, and 2. Has y-intercept of -2.

24. Fifth-degree polynomial with zeros of $-3, 0, 0, 2$, and 1. Passes through $(3, -1)$.

25. Fourth-degree polynomial with zeros of $1, 1, 2$, and 2. Has y-intercept of 3.

26. Sixth-degree polynomial with zeros of $-2, -1, 0, 1, i$, and $-i$. Passes through $(2, 1)$.

27. Third-degree polynomial with zeros of $(2 - i)$, $(2 + i)$, and $\sqrt{2}$. Has y-intercept of 2.

28. Fourth-degree polynomial with zeros of $(1 \pm \sqrt{2})$, $\sqrt{3}$, and π. Has y-intercept of $1/\pi$.

7.4
Synthetic Division
(optional)

As the degree of a polynomial function $f(x)$ increases, the problem of evaluating $f(r)$ becomes tedious because we must find and combine high powers of r. A shorthand technique of dividing a polynomial by a linear factor, called **synthetic division**, when combined with the remainder theorem, facilitates finding $f(r)$. The method, which is related to long division, is developed in this context in the next example.

Example 7.9

(a) Divide $3x^3 - 7x^2 - x - 2$ by $x - 3$.

(b) Use this problem to develop the method of synthetic division.

Solution

(a) Using long division, we have

$$
\begin{array}{r}
3x^2 + 2x + 5 \\
x - 3 \overline{\smash{)}\ 3x^3 - 7x^2 - x - 2} \\
\underline{3x^3 - 9x^2} \\
2x^2 - x \\
\underline{2x^2 - 6x} \\
5x - 2 \\
\underline{5x - 15} \\
13
\end{array}
$$

(b)   The method of synthetic division is the method of long division with all redundancy removed, that is, all unnecessary operations stripped away. First, observe that in long division the coefficients are the only important quantities. Since the powers of x are not needed, we omit them and write the indicated division as

$$
\begin{array}{r}
3 \quad\ 2 \quad\ 5 \\
-3\,)\overline{③\ -\ 7\ -\ 1\ -\ 2} \\
3\ -\ 9 \\
\overline{} \\
②\ -\ 1 \\
2\ -\ 6 \\
\overline{} \\
⑤\ -\ 2 \\
5\ -\ 15 \\
\overline{} \\
13
\end{array}
$$

Next, notice that the three circled coefficients are identical to those of the quotient, so we eliminate the quotient and other identical terms.

$$
\begin{array}{r}
-3\,)\overline{③\ -\ 7\ -\ 1\ -\ 2} \\
-\ 9 \\
\overline{} \\
② \\
-\ 6 \\
\overline{} \\
⑤ \\
-\ 15 \\
\overline{} \\
13
\end{array}
$$

Now the numbers below the dividend may be written on two lines as

$$
\begin{array}{r}
-3\,)\overline{③\ -\ 7\ -\ 1\ -\ 2} \\
-\ 9\ -\ 6\ -\ 15 \\
\overline{② \quad ⑤ \quad 13}
\end{array}
$$

All coefficients of the quotient appear below the line except the first. We, therefore, write this one below the line. It is always the same as the first coefficient of the dividend.

$$
\begin{array}{r}
-3\,)\overline{3\ -\ 7\ -\ 1\ -\ 2} \\
-\ 9\ -\ 6\ -\ 15 \\
\overline{\nearrow \ \nearrow \ \nearrow} \\
3 \quad 2 \quad 5 \quad\ 13
\end{array}
$$

After bringing down the first coefficient, notice that $3(-3) = -9$; subtracting -9 from -7 yields 2. Next, $2(-3) = -6$; subtracting -6 from -1 yields 5. Finally, $5(-3) = -15$; subtracting -15 from -2 the remainder is 13. In each of these operations we subtracted the second line from the first. By changing the sign of the divisor, we can add the terms instead of subtracting them; hence, the entire outline takes on a false, or *synthetic*, appearance. The original division problem can now be performed and written as

$$
\begin{array}{r}
3\,)\overline{3\ -\ 7\ -\ 1\ -\ 2} \\
9 \quad 6 \quad\ 15 \\
\overline{\nearrow \ \nearrow \ \nearrow} \\
3 \quad 2 \quad 5 \quad 13
\end{array}
$$

7.4 Synthetic Division (optional)   197

The meaning of the various coefficients relative to the original problem is indicated next.

$$x - 3 \quad 3x^3 - 7x^2 - x - 2$$

$$
\begin{array}{r|rrrr}
\underline{3)}3 & -7 & -1 & - & 2 \\
 & 9 & 6 & & 15 \\
\hline
3 & 2 & 5 & & 13 = \text{Remainder}
\end{array}
$$

Quotient $= 3x^2 + 2x + 5$

The preceding example illustrates the method of synthetic division. To divide a polynomial $f(x)$ by $x - r$ using this method, proceed as follows:

(1) Arrange the coefficients of $f(x)$ in order of descending powers of x, remembering that missing terms have a coefficient of zero.

(2) Replace $x - r$ by r.

(3) Bring down the coefficient of the highest power of x, multiply it by r, and add the result to the coefficient of the next highest power of x. Multiply this sum by r and add to the next coefficient. Continue this process until there is a product added to the constant term.

(4) The last number in the bottom row is the remainder. The numbers to the left of the remainder are the respective coefficients of the quotient. Notice that the degree of the quotient is one less than that of $f(x)$.

Example 7.10   Divide $5x^4 - 18x^2 - 6x + 3$ by $x + 2$ using synthetic division.

Solution   Since the divisor is $x + 2$, $r = -2$. Thus,

$$
\begin{array}{r|rrrrr}
-2)5 & 0 & -18 & - & 6 & 3 \\
 & -10 & 20 & - & 4 & 20 \\
\hline
5 & -10 & 2 & & -10 & 23
\end{array}
$$

The quotient is $5x^3 - 10x^2 + 2x - 10$ with a remainder of 23.

Example 7.11   Given $f(x) = 8x^5 - x^3 + 2$, find $f\left(\frac{1}{2}\right)$ using synthetic division and the remainder theorem.

Solution

$$
\begin{array}{r|rrrrrr}
\frac{1}{2})8 & 0 & -1 & 0 & 0 & 2 \\
 & 4 & 2 & \frac{1}{2} & \frac{1}{4} & \frac{1}{8} \\
\hline
8 & 4 & 1 & \frac{1}{2} & \frac{1}{4} & \frac{17}{8}
\end{array}
$$

The remainder is $\frac{17}{8}$. Therefore, by the remainder theorem, $f\left(\frac{1}{2}\right) = \frac{17}{8}$.

7.5
The Nested
Multiplication Algorithm (optional)

Closely related to the use of synthetic division and the remainder theorem to evaluate a polynomial, $P(x)$, at x_0 is an algorithmic approach especially suitable for hand calculators (or better still, larger computers). This technique is called the method of **nested multiplications**, for the polynomial is put into a form whereby its evaluation consists of simple multiplications and additions. The technique is based on the recognition of the following pattern.

(1) First-degree polynomials: $P(x) = a_1 x + a_0$. $P(x_0)$ can be found in two steps:

(a) Compute $a_1 x_0$.   (b) Compute the sum of step (a) $+ a_0$.

(2) Second-degree polynomials:

$$P(x) = a_2 x^2 + a_1 x + a_0 = (a_2 x + a_1)x + a_0 .$$

$P(x_0)$ can be found in four steps:

(a) Compute $a_2 x_0$.   (b) Add step (a) to a_1.   (c) Multiply step (b) by x_0.   (d) Add step (c) to a_0.

(3) Third-degree polynomials:

$$P(x) = a_3 x^3 + a_2 x^2 + a_1 x + a_0 = [(a_3 x + a_2)x + a_1]x + a_0 .$$

$P(x_0)$ can be found in six steps:

(a) Compute $a_3 x_0$.   (b) Add step (a) to a_2.   (c) Multiply step (b) by x_0.   (d) Add step (c) to a_1.   (e) Multiply step (d) by x_0.   (f) Add step (e) to a_0.

Now convince yourself that the general nth-degree polynomial can be evaluated in $2n$ steps by alternately multiplying the previous quantity by x_0 and then adding the next coefficient. The algorithm permits the computation of any polynomial without specifically using the exponent, an advantage not only when a calculator with an "exp" button is unavailable but also when accuracy is very important, since the exp function in a computer often introduces an undesirable amount of round-off error.

Example 7.12   Use the nested multiplication algorithm to evaluate

$$P(x) = 2x^5 + 3x^4 - 5x^2 + x - 6 \text{ at } x_0 = 3$$

Solution   Let $a_5 = 2$, $a_4 = 3$, $a_3 = 0$, $a_2 = -5$, $a_1 = 1$, and $a_0 = -6$. Using the method of nested multiplications, proceed as follows to evaluate $P(3)$.

1. $a_5 x_0 = 2 \cdot 3 = 6$
2.   Step (1) $+ a_4 = 6 + 3 = 9$
3.   Step (2) $\cdot x_0 = 9 \cdot 3 = 27$

4. Step (3) $+ a_3 = 27 + 0 = 27$
5. Step (4) $\cdot x_0 = 27 \cdot 3 = 81$
6. Step (5) $+ a_2 = 81 - 5 = 76$
7. Step (6) $\cdot x_0 = 76 \cdot 3 = 228$
8. Step (7) $+ a_1 = 228 + 1 = 229$
9. Step (8) $\cdot x_0 = 229 \cdot 3 = 687$
10. Step (9) $+ a_0 = 687 - 6 = 681$

Hence, $P(3) = 681$.

The following flow diagram (Figure 7.6) illustrates the simplicity of the method of nested multiplications for computer applications. You may want to write this program and use the computer to solve Exercises 19 through 24.

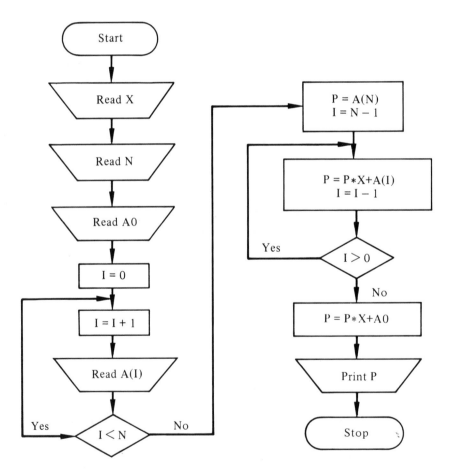

Figure 7.6

7 Polynomial and Rational Functions

Exercises for

Section 7.4 and 7.5

Perform the divisions in Exercises 1–12 using synthetic division.

1. $(x^2 - 5x + 4) \div (x - 4)$
2. $(x^2 + 7x + 12) \div (x - 3)$
3. $(x^3 - 2x^2 + 3x - 1) \div (x - 2)$
4. $(x^3 + 2x^2 - 3x + 4) \div (x + 1)$
5. $(x^3 - 3x + 9) \div (x + \frac{1}{2})$
6. $(x^3 - 1) \div (x + 1)$
7. $(x^4 - x^3 + 2x^2 - 72) \div (x - 3)$
8. $(2x^3 - 4x^2 + x - 1) \div (x + 2)$
9. $(8 + 7x - 3x^5) \div (x - 2)$
10. $(4x^3 + x^2 - 16x - 4) \div (x + \frac{1}{2})$
11. $(3x^3 - 20x^2 + 23x + 10) \div (x + \frac{1}{3})$
12. $(3x^3 + 2x^2 - 4x + 1) \div (x - \frac{1}{3})$

Use the remainder theorem and synthetic division to find the functional values in Exercises 13–18.

13. $f(3)$ for $f(x) = x^3 + 2x - 5$
14. $f(-4)$ for $f(x) = x^4 + 3x^3 - x^2 - 2x + 6$
15. $f(\frac{1}{2})$ for $f(x) = 3x^3 + 2x^2 - 4x + 1$
16. $f(-\frac{1}{2})$ for $f(x) = 3x^3 + 2x^2 - 4x + 1$
17. $f(0.1)$ for $f(x) = -6x^4 + 5x^2 - 2$
18. $f(0.2)$ for $f(x) = 3 + x - 4x^2 - 7x^3$

Use the nested multiplication algorithm to evaluate the functional values in Exercises 19–24.

19. $P(2)$ for $P(x) = x^3 + 8x + 12$
20. $P(5)$ for $P(x) = x^6 + 9x^3 + x^2 + 5$
21. $P(-3)$ for $P(x) = 3x^7 - 2x^4 + 7x^2 - 5$
22. $P(10)$ for $P(x) = 5x^4 - x^3 + 6x^2 + x + 6$
23. $P(2.4)$ for $P(x) = 2x^4 - 3x^3 + 5x + 25$
24. $P(1.6)$ for $P(x) = 1.2x^3 + 5.7x^2 + 0.4x + 17.9$

7.6
The Roots of a
Polynomial Function

This section presents two important theorems concerning the roots of a polynomial. The first is called the fundamental theorem of algebra and states that

---

Theorem 7.3 Every polynomial function has at least one root.

Thus, if $f(x)$ is a polynomial of degree n, it must have at least one root, say

$x = r_1$. By the factor theorem we can write

$$f(x) = f_1(x)(x - r_1)$$

where $f_1(x)$ is the polynomial quotient found by dividing $f(x)$ by $x - r_1$. The degree of f_1 is one less than the degree of f. Since f_1 is a polynomial, it must have at least one root, say $r = r_2$. Therefore, $x - r_2$ is a factor of f_1 and we can write

$$f(x) = (x - r_1)(x - r_2)f_2(x)$$

Similarly, f_2 must have at least one root. Continuing this reasoning, we would obtain after n steps

$$f(x) = c(x - r_1)(x - r_2)(x - r_3) \cdots (x - r_n)$$

where c is a constant. In words, we have shown the following:

Theorem 7.4   **A polynomial function of degree n has exactly n roots.**

The roots are not necessarily distinct, but the total number, including multiple roots, equals the degree of the polynomial.

Example 7.13   Given that $x = -4.7$ is a root of $f(x) = x^3 + 0.4x^2 - 16.49x + 17.484$, determine the other roots.

Solution   Since $x = -4.7$ is a root, $(x + 4.7)$ is a factor. By dividing $f(x)$ by $(x + 4.7)$, we obtain $f_1(x) = x^2 - 4.3x + 3.72$. The roots to this quadratic are obtained using the quadratic formula.

$$x = \frac{4.3 \pm \sqrt{(4.3)^2 - 4(3.72)}}{2} = \frac{4.3 \pm 1.9}{2}$$

$$x = 3.1, \; 1.2$$

Thus, the three roots of the given cubic are -4.7, 3.1, and 1.2.

Some of the roots may, of course, be nonreal, but if the polynomial itself is real (that is, if it has real coefficients), then any nonreal roots must occur in complex *conjugate pairs*, $a + bi$ and $a - bi$. The product of the two linear factors that result from these pairs $(x - a - bi)(x - a + bi)$ leads to a quadratic factor that is irreducible in the sense that it cannot be expressed as a product of real linear factors.

7.7
Rational Roots

In the previous section you learned that an nth degree polynomial has n roots but no hint was given as to how these roots were to be found. Of course, for degree two, the quadratic formula may be used. Similar procedures using radicals exist for finding the roots for third- and fourth-degree polynomials but the formulas are hard to memorize and, consequently, are seldom used. For equations of degree greater than four, no general method to find roots exists, although there are a number of good numerical approximation methods. Numerical methods usually require the use of a computer to be of any real practical value. Aside from these more advanced numerical methods, we frequently resort to methods of trial and error. These trial and error methods, however, should not be pure guesswork. For example, do not try a positive root for a polynomial of the type $y = x^3 + 2x^2 + x + 2$. Why not?

In some instances we are able to identify any rational roots of a polynomial. The following *rational root theorem* shows that the number of possible rational roots is, relatively, very small.

Theorem 7.5   If the coefficients of $f(x) = a_n x^n + a_{n-1} x^{n-1} + \cdots + a_1 x + a_0$ are integers, then any rational roots must be of the form of a factor of a_0 divided by a factor of a_n.

Note that this theorem, with only a slight restatement, may also be applied if the coefficients are rational.

This theorem limits the number of trials we must make in finding any rational roots. For example, do not bother to try $x = 2$ as a root of $x^4 - 7x^3 + 3x^2 + 2x + 15$, because 2 is not a factor of 15.

Example 7.14   Find the roots of the polynomial $f(x) = 3x^4 + 11x^3 + 3x^2 - 20x - 12$.

Solution   Any rational root must be a factor of 12 divided by a factor of 3; that is, $\pm n/d$, where n is 12, 6, 4, 3, 2, or 1 and d is 3 or 1. We find that $x = -2$ is a root. Hence,

$$f(x) = (x + 2)(3x^3 + 5x^2 - 7x - 6)$$

Any rational root of the cubic factor is a factor of 6 divided by a factor of 3; that is, ± 6, ± 3, ± 2, ± 1, $\pm \frac{2}{3}$, or $\pm \frac{1}{3}$. We find that $x = -\frac{2}{3}$ is a root. Therefore,

$$f(x) = 3(x + 2)\left(x + \frac{2}{3}\right)(x^2 + x - 3)$$

Since this expression has a quadratic factor, we immediately use the quadratic formula to obtain

$$x = \frac{-1 \pm \sqrt{1 + 12}}{2}$$

Therefore, the desired roots are -2, $-\frac{2}{3}$, $(-1 + \sqrt{13})/2$, and $(-1 - \sqrt{13})/2$.

Exercises for
Sections 7.6 and 7.7

Find all the roots of the equations in Exercises 1–17.

1. $x^3 + 2x^2 - x - 2 = 0$ 2. $x^3 - 4x^2 + x + 6 = 0$

3. $y^3 + 2y^2 + y + 2 = 0$ **4.** $m^3 - 3m^2 - 4m + 12 = 0$

5. $2x^3 + x^2 - 18x - 20 = 0$ **6.** $x^3 - 9x^2 + 23x - 15 = 0$

7. $z^4 - 2z^3 - 7z^2 + 8z + 12 = 0$ **8.** $2r^4 - 9r^3 + 15r^2 - 11r + 3 = 0$

9. $3p^3 - 10p^2 + 12p - 3 = 0$ **10.** $y^4 + 2y^3 - 4y^2 - 5y + 6 = 0$

11. $x^4 - 6x^2 - 8x - 3 = 0$ **12.** $x^3 + 8 = 0$

13. $9w^3 - w + 2 = 0$ **14.** $16x^4 - 150x^3 + 381x^2 - 262x - 39 = 0$

15. $2x^3 - 3x^2 + 5x = 2$ **16.** $12x^3 + 4x^2 - 3x = 1$

17. $x^5 - x^3 - 8x^2 + 8 = 0$

18. A psychologist finds that the response to a certain stimulus varies with age group according to $R = x^3 - 4x^2 - 19x - 10$, where R is response in milliseconds and x is age group in years. For what age group is the response equal to 4 milliseconds? (Ignore negative solutions.)

19. In analyzing trends in a public opinion poll, a researcher found that the percentage P of people favoring a particular issue varied with age according to $P = x^3 - 21x^2 - 45x - 8$, where x is age in years. In what age group did 15% of the people indicate a favorable opinion? (Ignore negative solutions.)

20. A box without a top is to be constructed from a 10 in. by 16 in. metal sheet. The box is formed by cutting equal squares from each corner of the sheet and then bending up the sides. What size square should be cut to give a box with a volume of 144 cubic inches?

7.8
The Real Roots of
a Polynomial by Graphing

In the previous section you learned how to locate the rational roots of a polynomial, but that technique was restricted to polynomials that have integral (or rational) coefficients. Thus, the zeros of polynomials such as $f(x) = \sqrt{2}x^3 - x^2 + x - \pi$ or even the nonrational roots of a polynomial with integer coefficients cannot be found from the rational root theorem.

In theory, if not in practice, a relatively simple method of approximating the real roots of a polynomial is a graphical one. Obviously, the real roots of the polynomial correspond to the x-intercepts of the graph. The accuracy of the estimates depends upon the scale chosen and the care taken in drawing the graph.

Example 7.15   Find the real roots of the equation $x^3 - 4x + 1 = 0$.

Solution   To determine any real roots of this equation, we plot the graph of $f(x) = x^3 - 4x + 1$ (Figure 7.7). The table of values follows.

x	$f(x)$
3	16
2	1
1	-2
0	1
-1	4
-2	1
-3	-14

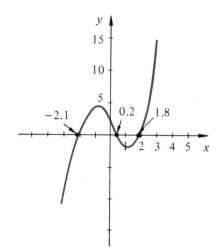

Figure 7.7

From the graph we estimate the roots to be $x_1 = -2.1$, $x_2 = 0.2$, $x_3 = 1.8$.

Example 7.16   Find the real roots of the equation $3x^4 - 4x^3 + 1 = 0$.

Solution   The graph shown in Figure 7.8 was obtained with $f(x) = 3x^4 - 4x^3 + 1$. The table of values is included below.

x	$f(x)$
2	17
$\frac{3}{2}$	$\frac{43}{16}$
1	0
$\frac{1}{2}$	$\frac{11}{16}$
0	1
$-\frac{1}{2}$	$\frac{27}{16}$
-1	8

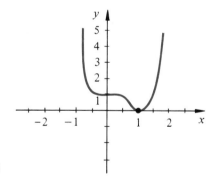

Figure 7.8

The graph and the table verify that $x = 1$ is a root. To show that it is a double root (and that there is no other real root in the vicinity of $x = 1$), divide $3x^4 - 4x^3 + 1$ by $x - 1$ to obtain $3x^3 - x^2 - x - 1$. This cubic also has the root $x = 1$ and when divided by $x - 1$ gives $3x^2 + 2x + 1$. This latter quadratic is irreducible, and hence, the only real root of the given polynomial is at $x = 1$.

7.8 The Real Roots of a Polynomial by Graphing

Find the real roots of the polynomial equations in Exercises 1–24 by graphing the corresponding polynomial function.

1. $2x^3 + x^2 + 5x - 3 = 0$

2. $x^3 + 2x^2 - x - 2 = 0$

3. $x^3 - 3x + 1 = 0$

4. $x^3 + 2x + 20 = 0$

5. $2x^3 - 3x^2 - 12x + 6 = 0$

6. $x^3 - 6x^2 + 16 = 0$

7. $x^4 - x^3 - 5x^2 + 3x + 2 = 0$

8. $2x^4 - 5x^3 + 6x^2 - 2x = 0$

9. $8x^4 + 2x^3 + 15x^2 + 4x - 2 = 0$

10. $2x^4 - x^3 - 5x^2 - 3x - 3 = 0$

11. $2x^3 + 5x^2 - 8x - 6 = 0$

12. $x^3 + \frac{2}{3}x^2 + 9x + 6 = 0$

13. $x^4 - x^3 - 2x^2 - x - 3 = 0$

14. $2x^4 - 3x^3 - 6x^2 + 2x - 15 = 0$

15. $x^4 + x^3 - 3x^2 + x - 5 = 0$

16. $x^5 + x = 0$

17. $x^5 + x^3 - x + 1 = 0$

18. $x^5 + x^4 - 3x^2 + 2 = 0$

19. $2.1x^3 + 3.4x^2 - 1.8x + 5.3 = 0$

20. $4.3x^3 - 1.4x + 5.6 = 0$

21. $3.1x^4 - 5.6x^3 + 7.2x^2 - 3.1x + 4.2 = 0$

22. $6.3x^4 - 2.5x^2 - 6.3 = 0$

23. $\sqrt{2}x^3 + \sqrt{3}x - \pi = 0$

24. $\sqrt{5}x^3 - \sqrt{3}x^2 + \sqrt{3}x - 7.23 = 0$

7.9
Rational Functions

Functions formed by taking the ratio of two polynomials are called **rational functions**. Specifically, if $N(x)$ and $D(x)$ are polynomials without common factors, then

$$f(x) = \frac{N(x)}{D(x)}$$

is called a rational function of x. Notice the similarity between rational functions and rational numbers. Rational numbers are quotients of integers, whereas rational functions are ratios of polynomials. Some examples of rational functions are

$$\frac{3x^5 + 5}{20x^3 + x - 16}, \quad \frac{4}{x^2 - 4}, \quad \frac{3x^2 + 5x - 6}{(x - 5)(x + 3)}$$

If the degree of N is less than that of D, then N/D is called a *proper fraction*; otherwise, N/D is an *improper fraction*. Using the division process, any improper fraction may be expressed as a polynomial quotient and a remainder that is a proper fraction.

This section concerns the graphs of rational functions. To this end, consider an arbitrary rational function

$$f(x) = \frac{N(x)}{D(x)}$$

The method of finding the zeros of a rational function is identical to that for polynomials because the zeros of a rational function are the same as the numerator polynomial, $N(x)$. Graphically, of course, the zeros of the function are the x-intercepts.

The (real) zeros of the denominator are important, too. They are the values of x for which $f(x)$ does not exist because division by zero is undefined. Let us see how the function behaves in the neighborhood of a value x_0 such that $D(x_0) = 0$.

Since N/D is well defined for all values except x_0, we may consider the value of the function at real numbers as close to x_0 as we please. This consideration is usually described by saying that x "approaches" arbitrarily close to x_0. As x approaches x_0, $D(x)$ approaches zero; since $N(x)$ and $D(x)$ have no common factors, the value of $f(x)$ becomes larger and larger as x approaches x_0. Graphically, think of the curve moving farther and farther away from the x-axis as x approaches x_0. In this case, the vertical line through $(x_0, 0)$ is called a **vertical asymptote** of the graph of the rational function.

To illustrate the meaning of a vertical asymptote, consider the rational function

$$f(x) = \frac{1}{x}$$

The function does not exist at $x = 0$; however, it is defined for all other values of x. Here the y-axis is a vertical asymptote. To determine the behavior of the graph, note that as x approaches 0 from the right, $f(x)$ is positive and increases indefinitely. We say that $f(x)$ increases without bound. Similarly, as x approaches 0 from the left, $f(x)$ is negative and decreases indefinitely. Using this knowledge and computing some points on either side of $x = 0$ yields the graph shown in Figure 7.9.

Notice that as x increases, the graph comes closer to the x-axis and, similarly, as x decreases the graph comes closer to the x-axis, although negative. In fact, as x increases without bound, the value of $1/x$ approaches zero. (But no matter how large x becomes, $1/x$ will not equal zero.) The same observation holds as x decreases without bound. The line $y = 0$ is called a **horizontal asymptote** of the graph.

From the foregoing discussion you can see that the asymptotes of a rational function are very helpful in sketching its graph. Use the following rule to determine the vertical asymptotes of a rational function:

If $D(x)$ represents the denominator function and if $D(k) = 0$, then $x = k$ is a vertical asymptote.

7.9 Rational Functions

x	y
-3	$-\frac{1}{3}$
-2	$-\frac{1}{2}$
-1	-1
$-\frac{1}{2}$	-2
$-\frac{1}{4}$	-4
$\frac{1}{4}$	4
$\frac{1}{2}$	2
1	1
2	$\frac{1}{2}$
3	$\frac{1}{3}$

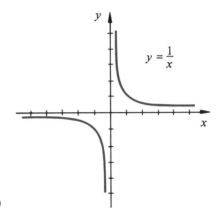

Figure 7.9

Notice that a rational function may have more than one vertical asymptote, determined by the zeros of the denominator function. Thus, the rational function $(2x^2 + 5)/(x^2 - 9)$ has two vertical asymptotes, the lines $x = 3$ and $x = -3$.

The graph of a rational function may have more than one vertical asymptote, but it may not have more than one horizontal asymptote. A convenient method for finding the horizontal asymptote of $N(x)/D(x)$ is to divide $N(x)$ and $D(x)$ by the highest power of x that occurs in either. If the resulting expression approaches a constant c as x becomes large, then the line $y = c$ is a horizontal asymptote of the function. If the expression becomes large as x becomes large, there is no horizontal asymptote.

To illustrate the technique, consider the function $y = (2x^2 + 5)/(x^2 - 9)$. Dividing the numerator and the denominator of this function by x^2,

$$y = \frac{2 + 5/x^2}{1 - 9/x^2}$$

Now as x becomes large, both $5/x^2$ and $9/x^2$ approach zero. Hence, the value of the function approaches 2 as x becomes large, and we conclude that $y = 2$ is a horizontal asymptote. As an example of a rational function that does not have a horizontal asymptote, consider

$$y = \frac{x^3 - 6}{5x + 1}$$

Dividing the numerator and the denominator by x^3,

$$y = \frac{1 - 6/x^3}{5/x^2 + 1/x^3}$$

7 Polynomial and Rational Functions

As x becomes large, both terms in the denominator approach zero and, therefore, y cannot approach a finite number.

Notice that the horizontal asymptote of a proper rational function is the x-axis. This condition follows from the fact that in a proper rational function the degree of the numerator is less than that of the denominator.

Example 7.17   Sketch the graph of $y = 3x/(x - 2)$.

Solution   *Intercepts*: $x = 0$, $y = 0$.

Vertical Asymptotes: The denominator of the function is zero for $x = 2$. Since the numerator and the denominator have no common factors, the line $x = 2$ is a vertical asymptote.

Horizontal Asymptote: To find the horizontal asymptote, divide the numerator and the denominator by x to get

$$y = \frac{3}{1 - 2/x}$$

As x becomes large, the fraction $2/x$ approaches zero and, therefore, the value of y approaches 3. The line $y = 3$ is the horizontal asymptote.

Finally, determine some additional points in the vicinity of the vertical asymptote as shown in the table. The graph is now readily determined. (See Figure 7.10.)

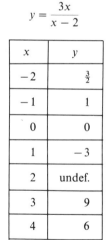

$$y = \frac{3x}{x - 2}$$

x	y
-2	$\frac{3}{2}$
-1	1
0	0
1	-3
2	undef.
3	9
4	6

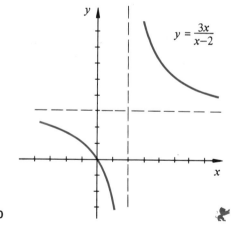

Figure 7.10

Example 7.18   Sketch the graph of $y = (2x - 3)^2/(x^2 - 4)$.

Solution   The graph of this function has two vertical asymptotes, the lines $x = 2$ and $x = -2$, since the denominator is zero for both these values of x. By dividing the numerator and the denominator by x^2, we find that y approaches 4 when x is large. Hence, $y = 4$ is a horizontal asymptote.

7.9 Rational Functions

209

The x-intercept is obtained by equating the numerator to 0. Hence, $x = \frac{3}{2}$ is the x-intercept. The y-intercept is obtained by letting $x = 0$. Thus, $y = -\frac{9}{4}$ is the y-intercept.

Sketch the complete graph after computing a few additional points. The graph in Figure 7.11 shows that a curve may cross its own asymptote for some smaller value of x. We find this point by letting $y = 4$ and solving the equation $4 = (2x - 3)^2/(x^2 - 4)$. The solution to this equation is $x = \frac{25}{12}$, with the corresponding point shown on the graph.

$$y = \frac{(2x - 3)^2}{x^2 - 4}$$

x	y
-10	5.5
-5	8.0
-4	10.1
-3	16.2
-1	-8.3
0	-2.25
1	-0.3
3	1.8
4	2.1
5	2.33
10	3.00

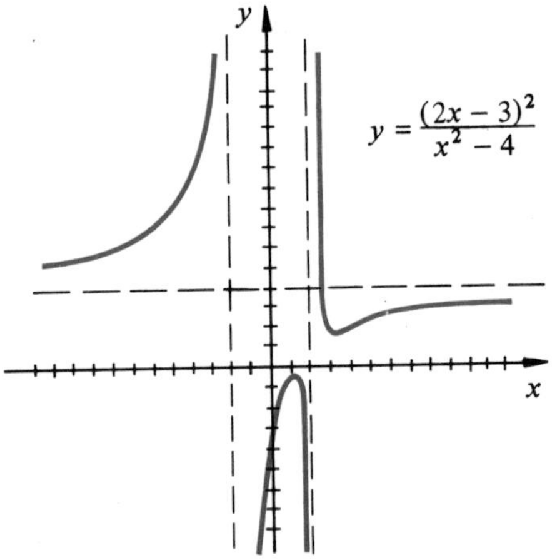

$$y = \frac{(2x - 3)^2}{x^2 - 4}$$

Figure 7.11

Example 7.19   The heat generated by a certain chemical process varies with time according to

$$H = \frac{t}{t^2 + 4}$$

where H is the heat in calories and t is the time in seconds. Draw the graph of this function and find the maximum heat output.

Solution   This rational function has no vertical asymptotes since there is no real value of t for which $t^2 + 4 = 0$. However, the t-axis is a horizontal asymptote. Since a negative time has no physical significance, we consider only positive values of t. Plotting a few additional points and drawing the curve so that it approaches zero as t increases, we obtain the graph in Figure 7.12. The graph illustrates that the heat output increases rapidly at first, reaching a peak of 0.25 cal at about 2.0 sec. From this point the heat output decreases gradually toward zero.

$$H = \frac{t}{t^2 + 4}$$

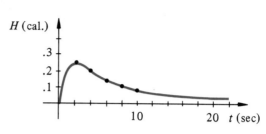

t	H
0	0
2	.25
4	.20
6	.15
8	.12
10	.09

Figure 7.12

Exercises for
Section 7.9

Compute intercepts and locate asymptotes (if any). Then graph the rational functions in Exercises 1–18.

1. $y = -\dfrac{1}{x}$

2. $y = \dfrac{5x + 2}{2 - x}$

3. $y = \dfrac{3x - 2}{x - 4}$

4. $z = \dfrac{2}{t - 1}$

5. $p = \dfrac{1}{w + 1}$

6. $v = \dfrac{t^2 - 1}{t^2 + 1}$

7. $s = \dfrac{5w^2}{4 - w^2}$

8. $m = \dfrac{u + 1}{u^2 - 1}$

9. $y = \dfrac{x^2}{x^2 - 9}$

10. $y = \dfrac{-2x}{x^2 - 4}$

11. $s = \dfrac{(t + 2)^2}{t^2 + 2t}$

12. $w = \dfrac{3x^2}{x^2 - 3x}$

13. $y = \dfrac{3}{w^2 - 9w}$

14. $r = \dfrac{5z + 10}{3z - z^2}$

15. $y = \dfrac{1}{p^2 - 3p - 4}$

16. $n = \dfrac{1 + s^2}{s^2 - s - 2}$

17. $y = \dfrac{5x + 3}{x^2 + x}$

18. $y = \dfrac{x^2 + 3x + 2}{x^2 + x}$

19. The force between two unit masses varies with the distance between them according to the formula $F = 1/d^2$. The force is in dynes when the distance is measured in centimeters. Show this relationship graphically.

20. Due to leakage, the pressure in a hydraulic system varies with time according to $P = 10/(t^2 + 1)$ psi, where t is the time in seconds. Show this pressure variation graphically.

21. The coefficient of friction, μ, of a plastic block sliding on an aluminum table varies according to $\mu = (v^2 + 3)/(4v^2 + 5)$, where v is the velocity of the block in cm/sec. Draw the graph of this function.

7.9 Rational Functions

211

Answer true or false for Exercises 1–10.

1. Quadratic functions are polynomials.

2. A polynomial is any algebraic expression with two or more terms.

3. The rational root theorem says that the only possible rational roots of $x^2 + x - 10 = 0$ are ± 10, ± 5, ± 2, and ± 1.

4. The real roots of a polynomial are graphically represented as the x-intercepts of the graph of the polynomial.

5. A polynomial with real coefficients has real roots.

6. Rational functions are zero only where the numerator is zero.

7. When a polynomial is divided by $x + a$, the remainder is $f(a)$.

8. For any x, $x^4 \geq x$.

9. If $x = a$ is a root of a polynomial, then $x - a$ is a factor of that polynomial.

10. A cubic has at least one real root.

11. Sketch the graph of $y = x^4 + 2$.

12. Use the remainder theorem to find the remainder when dividing $x^5 - x^3 + x^2 + 5$ by $x - 1$.

13. Write an expression for a third-degree polynomial with roots 3, -2, and 1.

14. The graph of a fifth-degree polynomial is shown in Figure 7.12. Write the expression for the polynomial.

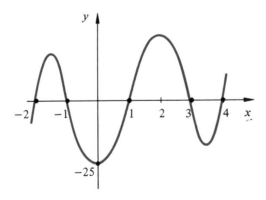

15. Sketch the graph of the rational function

$$f(x) = [(x - 1)(x + 2)]/[(2x + 9)(x - 3)]$$

Be sure to indicate all intercepts and asymptotes.

16. Approximate the roots to $f(x) = x^4 - x - 3$ by sketching the graph of $f(x)$.

1. Answer the following statements true or false.

   (a) $f(x) = x^2 + x^{-2}$ is a polynomial.

   (b) For $x > 1$, x^3 dominates x^2.

   (c) A fifth-degree polynomial has five distinct roots.

   (d) The vertical asymptotes of a rational function correspond to the roots of the function.

   (e) $x = -\frac{3}{2}$ is a potential rational root of $2x^3 + 4x^2 - x + 6 = 0$.

2. Show that $x - 2$ is a factor of $3x^4 - 4x^2 - x - 30$.

3. Use synthetic division to find the quotient and remainder of

   $$\frac{2x^4 + 2x^3 - 5x^2 - x + 3}{2x - 4}$$

4. Find all of the roots of the equation $x^4 + x^3 - x^2 + x - 2 = 0$.

5. Locate the vertical and horizontal asymptotes of $y = \dfrac{3x^2 - 2}{x^3 - 4x}$.

6. Draw the graph of $y = \dfrac{5}{x^2 + 2x}$.

7. Write the third-degree polynomial with zeros at 0, 2, 3, and passing through (4, 5).

8. Use a graphical method to estimate the real roots of $y = x^4 - x - 5$.

8
Exponential and
Logarithmic Functions

8.1
Exponential
Functions

In Chapter 2 we reviewed the basic concept of an exponent. The initial use of an exponent is as an indicator of the *power* of a given number. Thus, the notation a^n means

$$\underbrace{a \cdot a \cdot a \cdot a \cdots a}_{n \text{ factors}}$$

From this definition come several important properties, or rules, called the *rules for exponents.*

Rule 1 $a^m a^n = a^{m+n}$

Rule 2 $(a^m)^n = a^{mn}$

Rule 3 $a^m \div a^n = a^{m-n}$

The extension of the idea of an exponent to the entire set of integers is made by the two definitions $a^{-n} = 1/a^n$ and $a^0 = 1$, $a \neq 0$. These two definitions are consistent in that the choice of a^0 to be 1 is at least a necessity if we wish the same rules for exponents to hold for integers as for natural numbers. Thus,

$$a^0 = a^{n-n}$$

$$= (a^n)(a^{-n}) \quad \text{by rule 1}$$

$$= (a^n) \div (a^n) \quad \text{by definition of a negative exponent}$$

$$= 1 \quad \text{by the law of cancellation}$$

The extension to rational numbers is made by defining $y = a^{1/q}$ to mean $y^q = a$. Then, as before, assuming that the rules for exponents continue to hold,

$$a^{p/q} = (a^{1/q})^p$$

which thereby allows any fractional exponent.

For $a < 0$ and q a positive even integer, $a^{1/q}$ is nonreal. Hence, the discussion of exponents is limited to the case in which $a > 0$. In extending the meaning of the idea of an exponent from the natural numbers to the integers to the rational numbers, the three basic laws of exponents continue to hold. There is nothing mysterious about this—it is deliberately planned that way!

We now wish to extend the definition of an exponent to include all real numbers. A detailed discussion of irrational exponents belongs more properly to a course in calculus but we can get some idea of the meaning attached to the quantity, say 2^π, by the following argument. Since π has a decimal expansion 3.14159 ..., consider the numbers 2^3, $2^{3.1}$, $2^{3.14}$, $2^{3.141}$, and so forth to be obtained by using successively closer rational approximations to the irrational number π. The corresponding rational powers of 2 then become closer to what we consider the value of 2^π. Each rational power of 2 obtained using the approximations of π is in some sense an approximation to 2^π, with the accuracy increasing as more of the digits of π are used. In this way we see that irrational exponents have a definite interpretation to which the three basic exponential laws apply. Hence, accepting the fact that a^x is defined for all real x, if $a > 0$, we make the following definition.

Definition

If a is any fixed constant > 0, $a \neq 1$, then the **exponential function with base a** is defined by

$$f(x) = a^x$$

The domain of the exponential function is all real numbers and the range is the positive real numbers.

The next example shows the characteristic shape of the graph of an exponential function.

Example 8.1 Sketch the graph of 2^x and of $(\tfrac{1}{2})^x$.

Solution Figure 8.1 shows a table of values for each of the functions along with the graph.

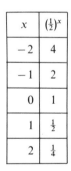

x	$(\tfrac{1}{2})^x$
-2	4
-1	2
0	1
1	$\tfrac{1}{2}$
2	$\tfrac{1}{4}$

x	2^x
-2	$\tfrac{1}{4}$
-1	$\tfrac{1}{2}$
0	1
1	2
2	4

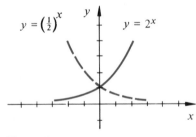

Figure 8.1

In general, we can make the following observations about the function $f(x) = a^x$, if $a > 1$.

(1) $a^x > 0$ for all values of x.
(2) When $x = 0$, $y = a^0 = 1$.
(3) When $x = 1$, $y = a^1 = a$.
(4) As x increases without bound, y increases without bound.
(5) As x decreases without bound, y approaches 0.
(6) If $x_1 < x_2$, then $a^{x_1} < a^{x_2}$.

216   8 Exponential and Logarithmic Functions

Figure 8.1 is typical of the shape of *exponential curves*, while properties (1) to (6) are the corresponding *analytic* or *functional properties* of exponential functions. If $0 < a < 1$, then properties (4)–(6) become

(4′) As x increases without bound, y approaches 0.

(5′) As x decreases without bound, y increases without bound.

(6′) If $x_1 < x_2$, then $a^{x_1} > a^{x_2}$.

Property (6) is described by saying that if $a > 1$, then a^x is an *increasing function*, while property (6′) describes the fact that if $0 < a < 1$, then a^x is a *decreasing function*. An increasing function has a graph that rises from left to right, while a decreasing function has a graph that falls from left to right.

A different exponential function is obtained for each value of a, although the shape of the graph remains basically the same and the same kind of functional properties as (1)–(6) continues to hold.

Figure 8.2 shows the graph of a^x for $a = \frac{1}{4}, \frac{1}{2}, 1, 2$, and 4. The value of $a = 1$ is excluded from the class of exponential functions since not only is the

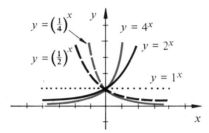

Figure 8.2

graph of 1^x trivial, but it is not of exponential shape. Further, $f(x) = 1^x$ does not obey the functional properties (1) through (6), which are ordinarily associated with the exponential functions. Henceforth, the only acceptable bases will be $a > 0$, $a \neq 1$.

The next example shows that when f is the exponential function, $f(x)$ and $f(y)$ are related to $f(x + y)$ in a very unique way.

Example 8.2 Given that $f(t) = a^t$, show that $f(x + y) = f(x) \cdot f(y)$.

Solution If $f(t) = a^t$, then

$$f(x + y) = a^{x+y} = a^x a^y = f(x) \cdot f(y)$$

The formula $f(x + y) = f(x) \cdot f(y)$ is called the *addition formula* for the exponential function. This formula is a distinctive functional property of the exponential function in that no other function has an addition formula quite like this one.

Be aware of the fact that -3^x and $(-3)^x$ have different meanings. The latter is an "unacceptable" exponential function since $-3 < 0$, while -3^x is merely the negative of 3^x. (See Figure 8.3.)

8.1 Exponential Functions   217

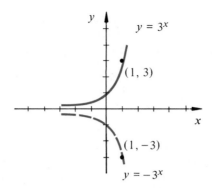

Figure 8.3

In some applications we work with functions defined by

$$f(x) = a^{g(x)}$$

where $g(x)$ might be, for example, an algebraic expression such as x^2 or $\sqrt[3]{x}$. To sketch such functions we use the basic functional properties of an exponential function supplemented by a few selected points.

Example 8.3   Sketch $y = 2^{-x^2}$.

Solution   When $x = 0$, $y = 1$. When $x = \pm 1$, $y = \frac{1}{2}$. And as x increases positively without bound, y approaches 0. Also, for $x < 0$, $y > 0$ and approaches zero as x decreases. The graph is shown in Figure 8.4.

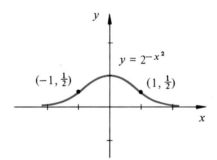

Figure 8.4

8.2
Applications
of Exponential Functions

The exponential function is one of the most useful functions for describing physical and social phenomena, of which the following are just a few.

● Electric current
● Atmospheric pressure

- Decomposition of uranium
- Population growth
- Learning process
- Compound interest

If a physical quantity obeys a law that is described by an exponential function and is increasing, it is said to *increase exponentially*. If it is exponential in character but is decreasing, it is said to *decay exponentially*.

Example 8.4   A company finds that the net sales of its product double every year. Write this fact as an exponential function.

Solution   Let $s(t)$ represent sales at any time t and let s_0 be the initial sales, then we can write

$$s(0) = s_0$$
$$s(1) = 2s_0$$
$$s(2) = 2s(1) = 2^2 s_0$$
$$s(3) = 2s(2) = 2^3 s_0$$

We could continue this process but we would not gain any new information. It is obvious from what we have done that

$$s(t) = s_0 2^t$$

is the desired equation.

Example 8.5   A psychologist finds that the output rate of a group of production workers is given by $R = 5(1 - 3^{-t})$. Draw the graph of this output curve.

Solution   The graph in Figure 8.5 shows that R increases rapidly at first and then levels off as t becomes large.

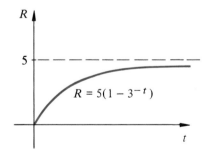

Figure 8.5

Example 8.6   An approximate rule for atmospheric pressure at altitudes less than 50 miles is the following: *Standard atmospheric pressure, 14.7 pounds per square inch, is halved for each 3.25 miles of vertical ascent.*

8.2 Applications of Exponential Functions   219

(a) Write an exponential function to express this rule.

(b) Compute the atmospheric pressure at an altitude of 19.5 miles.

Solution

(a) Letting P denote the atmospheric pressure at altitudes less than 50 miles and h the altitude in miles,

$$P = 14.7\left(\frac{1}{2}\right)^{h/3.25}$$

(b) Using the expression for P and letting $h = 19.5$,

$$P = 14.7\left(\frac{1}{2}\right)^{19.5/3.25}$$

$$= 14.7\left(\frac{1}{2}\right)^{6}$$

$$= \frac{14.7}{64}$$

$$= 0.23 \text{ lb/in.}^2$$

In applications the most important base for an exponential function is the irrational number e, which is equal to approximately 2.718. Table A in the appendix gives values of e^x and e^{-x} for $0 \le x \le 10$.

Example 8.7 An unmanned satellite has a radioisotope power supply whose power output in watts is given by the equation

$$P = 50e^{-t/260}$$

where t is the time in days that the battery has been in operation. How much power will be available at the end of one year?

Solution Applying the given formula with $t = 365$,

$$P = 50e^{-365/260}$$

$$= 50e^{-1.4}$$

From Table A,

$$e^{-1.4} = 0.2466$$

Hence,

$$P = (50)(0.2466)$$

$$= 12.33 \text{ watts}$$

Example 8.8 Population growth P varies with time approximately according to the equation

$$P = P_0 e^{kt}$$

where P_0 is the initial population size, t is the elapsed time, and k is a constant. Plot the graph of the yearly population growth on the asteroid Malthus from 1975 to 1985 if the population in 1975 was 500 and $k = 0.05$.

Solution The growth equation for this population is

$$P = 500e^{0.05t}$$

Using Table A we construct a table of values for $t = 0$ to $t = 10$. The yearly growth curve is then drawn in Figure 8.6.

Year	t	P
1975	0	500
1977	2	553
1979	4	611
1981	6	675
1983	8	746
1985	10	824

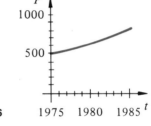

Figure 8.6

A system of equations that includes exponential equations is usually best solved graphically.

Example 8.9 Solve the equations $3x + 2y = 6$ and $y = 2^{x-1}$ for x and y.

Solution Solving these equations simultaneously by algebraic means is impractical. However, the solution may be approximated graphically by plotting the graphs of both curves and estimating their point of intersection. From Figure 8.7 we estimate that the

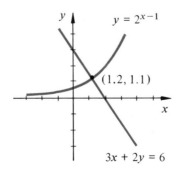

Figure 8.7

8.2 Applications of Exponential Functions

221

two curves intersect at $x = 1.2$ and $y = 1.1$. By substitution into the two equations we see that this is a reasonably accurate approximation.

Exercises for
Sections 8.1 and 8.2

Sketch the graph of the exponential functions in Exercises 1–12.

1. $y = 5^x$ **2.** $y = 3^{-x}$ **3.** $y = e^x$

4. $y = 2e^x$ **5.** $y = e^{-x}$ **6.** $y = 2 + 2^x$

7. $y = 2 - 2^x$ **8.** $y = (\sqrt{2})^x$ **9.** $y = e^{1-x}$

10. $y = 1 + e^x$ **11.** $y = e^{x/2}$ **12.** $y = 10 + e^{3x/2}$

Solve the systems in Exercises 13–16 by graphical means.

13. $y = e^x$ **14.** $y = 10^x$ **15.** $y = 3 - 2^x$ **16.** $y = e^{2-x}$

     $y + x = 2$ $y = 3 - x^2$ $3y = x - 2$ $y = x^3$

17. Make a careful sketch of the graph of $y = 2^x$. Using this graph, approximate the values of $2^{\sqrt{2}}$, 2^π, $2^{3/2}$, $2^{-3/2}$, and $2^{1/3}$.

18. Why is the base of exponential functions restricted to positive numbers?

19. Discuss the exponential function with base 1.

In Exercises 20–25 say how the graph of the given exponential compares with the graph of $y = 2^x$. In each case make a sketch to show the comparison.

20. 2^{-x} **21.** -2^x **22.** $2^{|x|}$

23. $|2^x|$ **24.** $3 + 2^x$ **25.** 2^{x+3}

26. The population of water spiders on a pond is estimated to be 1000. Using the population growth equation, estimate the population when $t = 25$, if $k = 0.02$.

27. The mass m of a certain radioactive substance decays with time according to

$$m = 100e^{-0.1t} \text{ kilograms}$$

where t is the time in days. Use Table A to draw an accurate sketch of mass versus time for $t > 0$. Using this graph, estimate the half-life of the substance. *Hint:* The half-life is the time in which a substance decays to one-half of its original value.

28. A company has found that a person new to the assembly line produces items according to the function

$$N = 50 - 50e^{-.5t}$$

where t is the number of days he has worked on the line. How many items will the new worker produce on the fifth day? Graph this function for $t > 0$, assuming it to be a function of real numbers, not just the positive integers. This graph is called the *learning curve*.

29. If P dollars is deposited in a bank paying i interest compounded annually for t years, the amount of money A in the account is given by the formula

$$A = P(1 + i)^t$$

Find the amount of money in an account after 5 years if the initial investment was $1000 and the interest rate is 5 percent.

30. In the absence of promotional activity, the sales of a product decreases at a rate described by the exponential function

$$A(t) = A_0 e^{-kt}$$

where A_0 is the amount of the sales when $t = 0$, and k is the *sales decay constant*. Find the sales after 1 year if $A_0 = 10,000$ for a sales decay constant of 0.5.

8.3
The Logarithm
Function*

The graph of the exponential function $y = a^x$ shows that any horizontal line will intersect the graph only once. Hence, the function is one-to-one; that is, for each value of x there is at most one value of y and for each value of y there is a unique x. Using this property we can define another important function.

Definition

Let $a > 0$ and $a \neq 1$. Then by

$y = \log_a x$ **is meant** $x = a^y$.

The function $y = f(x)$ is called the **logarithm function** of x to the base a.

Thus, the value of $y = \log_a x$ is nothing more than the exponent to which a must be raised to give the value x. Another way of saying the same thing is that *every logarithm is an exponent of the base*. The next example shows how the logarithm of a number is found directly from the definition.

Example 8.10

(a) $\log_2 16 = 4$ because $2^4 = 16$.

(b) $\log_2 (\frac{1}{8}) = -3$ because $2^{-3} = \frac{1}{8}$.

(c) $\log_{10} (1/1000) = -3$ because $10^{-3} = 1/1000$.

In each of the cases note that the logarithm is an exponent. 🐦

Example 8.11 Find $\log_2 32$.

Solution Let $y = \log_2 32$. Then $32 = 2^y$, or $y = 5$. 🐦

---

* Section 3.8 should be reviewed before reading this section.

Example 8.12   Solve for x: $3 = \log_4 (x^2 + 2)$.

Solution   Using the definition of the logarithm,

$$3 = \log_4 (x^2 + 2)$$
$$4^3 = x^2 + 2$$

which means that

$$x^2 = 62$$

Hence,

$$x = \pm \sqrt{62}$$

Because of the definition, the domain and the range of the logarithm function are the same as the range and the domain of the exponential function, respectively. Thus, the domain of $y = \log_a x$ is all positive reals (sometimes we say that the logarithm of a nonpositive number is undefined) and the range is all real numbers.

In practice, many problems that involve logarithms call for little more than shifting from the exponential relation to the logarithm relation or vice-versa.

Since the logarithm and exponential functions are really the same relation between sets of numbers expressed in two different ways,* there might seem to be little reason to study both in detail. However, on some occasions it is more natural to express a quantity in terms of a logarithm; hence, both exponential and logarithmic properties must be clearly understood.

Example 8.13   The intensity (energy) level β of a soundwave with intensity I is defined to be

$$\beta = 10 \log_{10} (I/I_0) \text{ decibels}$$

where I_0 is the minimum intensity detectable by the human ear. When two sounds differ in intensity by a factor of 10, they differ in loudness by 1 bel; a difference of 100 means a loudness difference of 2 bels. In practice, the unit used is the decibel, one-tenth of a bel.

Example 8.14   The velocity of a space vehicle at launch when its propellant is burned to depletion is expressed by the equation

$$v = c \log_e R$$

where v is the velocity gained during the burn, c is the exhaust velocity, and R is the mass ratio, defined by take-off weight/burn-out weight.

---

* Recall from Section 3.8 that a pair of functions, such as the exponential and the logarithm, are called *inverses* of one another.

Example 8.15   The intensity of a beam of radiation after passing through a material is given by the equation

$$I = I_0 10^{-kt}$$

where I_0 is the original intensity, t the thickness in centimeters, and k an absorption coefficient. If a beam of gamma radiation is reduced from 1 million electron volts to 500,000 electron volts while passing through a sheet of material with $k = 0.08$, find the thickness of the material.

Solution   Using the given values in the equation,

$$5 \times 10^5 = (10^6)10^{-0.08t}$$

from which

$$0.5 = 10^{-0.08t}$$

This exponential relation may be expressed in terms of logarithms to base 10 as

$$\log_{10} 0.5 = -0.08t$$

Hence,

$$t = \frac{-\log_{10} 0.5}{0.08} \text{ cm}$$

This is the desired answer. To find a decimal equivalent, we need only know the value of $\log_{10} 0.5$. (This comes in Section 8.6.)

Although the base of a logarithm may theoretically be any positive number except 1, in practice we seldom use bases other than 10 and e. Logarithms with base 10 are called **common logarithms** and are discussed in detail in Section 8.6. In an oft-used convention $\log_{10} x$ is written **log x**, with the subscript 10 understood. This convention is far from universal, however, so use it with care. Logarithms with base e, called **natural logarithms**, are most often denoted with the alternate notation **ln x**. That is, $\log_e x$ and $\ln x$ mean the same thing. Natural logarithms are used throughout the study of calculus.

Exercises for
Section 8.3

Write a logarithmic equation equivalent to the exponential equations in Exercises 1–5.

1. $x = 2^3$ 2. $y = 3^8$ 3. $M = 5^{-3}$

4. $N = 10^{-2}$ 5. $L = 7^2$

Find the base of the logarithm function (Exercises 6–10) such that

6. $f(8) = 1$ 7. $f(4) = 2$

8. $f(0.25) = -2$ 9. $f(100) = 2$

10. $f(b) = 1$

Solve the equations in Exercises 11–34 for the unknown.

11. $\log_{10} x = 4$ 　　　　　　　　 12. $\log_5 N = 2$

13. $\log_x 10 = 1$ 　　　　　　　　 14. $\log_x 25 = 2$

15. $\log_x 64 = 3$ 　　　　　　　　 16. $\log_{16} x = 2$

17. $\log_{27} x = \frac{2}{3}$ 　　　　　　　 18. $\log_2 \frac{1}{8} = x$

19. $\log_3 9 = x$ 　　　　　　　　 20. $\log_{10} 10^7 = x$

21. $\log_b b^a = x$ 　　　　　　　　 22. $\log_b x = b$

23. $\log_x 2 = \frac{1}{3}$ 　　　　　　　 24. $\log_x 0.0001 = -2$

25. $\log_x 6 = \frac{1}{2}$ 　　　　　　　 26. $\log_b x = 0$

27. $6^{\log_6 x} = 6$ 　　　　　　　　 28. $x^{\log_x x} = 3$

29. $\log_2 (x + 3) = -1$ 　　　　　 30. $\log_2 (x - 1) = 3$

31. $\log_3 (x + 1) < 2$ 　　　　　　 32. $\log_2 (2 - x) > -1$

33. $2 \le \log_2 x \le 3$ 　　　　　　 34. $0 < \log x < 1$

35. Let $f(x) = \log_3 x$. Find $f(9)$, $f(\frac{1}{27})$, and $f(81)$.

36. Let $f(x) = \log_2 x$. By example show that
    (a) $f(x + y) \ne f(x) + f(y)$ 　　　　(b) $f(ax) \ne af(x)$

37. A power supply has a power output in watts approximated by the equation

$$P = 64(2)^{-3t}$$

where t is in days. Solve this expression for t.

38. A certain radioactive material decays exponentially by the equation

$$A(t) = A_0 2^{-t/5}$$

Find the half-life of the material.

8.4
Graphs of
Logarithmic Functions

Since $y = \log_a x$ means that $x = a^y$, we may sketch the graph of the logarithm function by first constructing a table of values. The tables for $y = \log_2 x$ and $y = \log x$ are included below and the corresponding graphs are presented in Figure 8.8.

x	$\frac{1}{16}$	$\frac{1}{8}$	$\frac{1}{4}$	$\frac{1}{2}$	1	2	4	8	16
$\log_2 x$	-4	-3	-2	-1	0	1	2	3	4

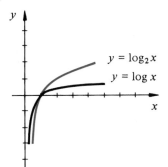

Figure 8.8

x	$\frac{1}{1000}$	$\frac{1}{100}$	$\frac{1}{10}$	1	10	100
$\log x$	-3	-2	-1	0	1	2

Each of the curves of Figure 8.8 is characteristic of what is called logarithmic shape. This figure clearly demonstrates the following functional characteristics of the logarithm function. Any function that obeys these properties is said to *behave logarithmically*.

(1) $\log_a x$ is not defined for $x \leq 0$.

(2) $\log_a 1 = 0$.

(3) $\log_a a = 1$.

(4) $\log_a x$ is negative for $0 < x < 1$ and positive for $x > 1$.

(5) As x approaches 0, y decreases without bound.

(6) As x increases without bound, y increases without bound.

More generally, in the applications we must work with functions of the type $y = \log [g(x)]$, where $g(x)$ is some function of x.

Example 8.16   Sketch the graph of the function $y = \log_2 (-x)$.

Solution   At first glance you might conclude that this function is undefined since the logarithm of a negative number is undefined. However, $-x$ is positive when $x < 0$, so $\log_2 (-x)$ has a domain of $x < 0$. Its graph is shown in Figure 8.9.

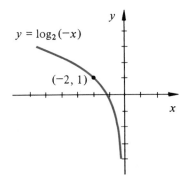

Figure 8.9

8.4 Graphs of Logarithmic Functions

227

Example 8.17   Sketch the graph of the $y = \log_5 (2x - 1)$.

Solution   Here we note that the function is *not* defined for values of $x \le \frac{1}{2}$. Furthermore, when $x = 1$, $y = \log_5 1 = 0$, and when $x = 3$, $y = \log_5 5 = 1$. These facts are summarized in the table and the graph drawn in Figure 8.10.

$y = \log_5 (2x - 1)$

x	y
$\frac{1}{2}$	undef.
1	0
3	1
inc. w/o bound	inc. w/o bound

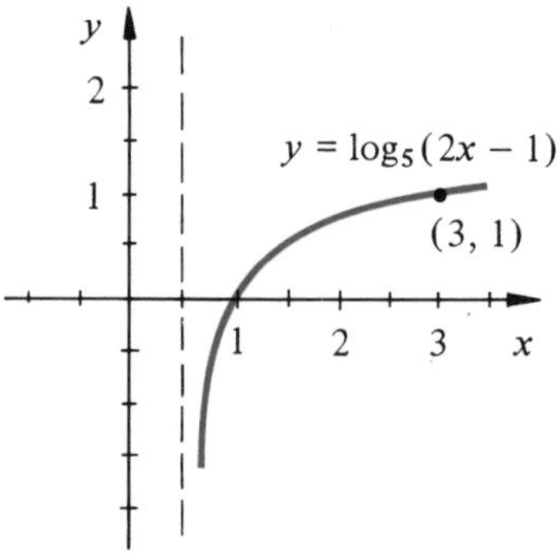

Figure 8.10

Exercises for Section 8.4

Sketch a graph of the functions in Exercises 1–9. (Remember that $\log x$ means $\log_{10} x$.)

1. $f(x) = \ln x$ 2. $f(x) = -\log x$ 3. $f(x) = \log |x|$

4. $f(x) = \log (x - 1)$ 5. $f(x) = \log 2x - \log 4x$ 6. $g(x) = \log_3 (-x)$

7. $f(x) = \log_2 (1 - x)$ 8. $f(x) = \log_2 (1 + x)$ 9. $f(x) = \log_2 |1 + x|$

In Exercises 10–15 say how the graph of the given logarithmic function is related to the graph of $y = \log x$. In each case make a sketch to show the comparison.

10. $\log (-x)$ 11. $-\log x$ 12. $\log |x|$

13. $|\log x|$ 14. $3 + \log x$ 15. $\log (x + 3)$

16. On the same set of axes, sketch $\log_2 x$ and $\log_3 x$ and
    (a) solve the equation $\log_2 x = \log_3 x$.
    (b) solve the equation $\log_2 x = \log_3 1$.
    (c) solve the inequality $\log_2 x > \log_3 x$.

17. How are the graphs of $y = \log_2 x$ and $y = 2^x$ related?

Find the base of the logarithm function $y = \log_a x$ whose graphs contain the following points:

18. $(100, 2)$ 19. $(4, 2)$ 20. $(64, 4)$ 21. $(0.1, -1)$ 22. $(0.5, -1)$

23. Let $f_b(x) = \log_b x$. For any acceptable base the graph of $f_b(x)$ passes through a point independent of b. What is that point?

8.5
Basic Properties
of the Logarithm

There are three rules for simplifying logarithmic expressions that you must know. These three rules or properties of logarithms correspond precisely to the three fundamental rules for exponents and are necessary consequences of them.

Rule 1 $\quad$ $\mathbf{Log_a\ MN = log_a\ M + log_a\ N}$

Proof $\quad$ Let $u = \log_a M$ and $v = \log_a N$. Then,

$$a^u = M \quad \text{and} \quad a^v = N$$

from which

$$MN = a^u a^v = a^{u+v}$$

Reexpressing in terms of logarithms,

$$\log_a MN = u + v = \log_a M + \log_a N$$

Rule 2 $\quad$ $\log_a M^c = c \log_a M$, where c is any real number.

Proof $\quad$ Let $u = \log_a M$. Then,

$$a^u = M \quad \text{and} \quad (a^u)^c = a^{uc} = M^c$$

In terms of logarithms, this may be expressed as

$$\log_a M^c = uc = c \log_a M$$

Rule 3 $\quad$ $\log_a (M/N) = \log_a M - \log_a N$

Proof $\quad$ $M/N = M(N)^{-1}$. Now apply the previous two rules.

In words, Rule 1 states that the logarithm of a product is equal to the sum of the logarithms of the individual terms; Rule 2 states that the logarithm of a number to a power is the power times the logarithm of the number; and Rule 3 states that the logarithm of a quotient is the difference of the logarithms of the individual terms. Examine these rules carefully and notice where they apply as well as where they do *not* apply. For example, there is *no* rule for simplifying expressions of the form $\log_a (x + y)$ or $\log_a (x - y)$.

Example 8.18

(a) $\log_2 (8)(64) = \log_2 8 + \log_2 64 = 3 + 6 = 9$

(b) $\log_3 \sqrt{243} = \log_3 243^{1/2} = \frac{1}{2} \log_3 243 = \frac{1}{2}(5) = 2.5$

(c) $\log_2 (\frac{3}{5}) = \log_2 3 - \log_2 5$

(d) $\log 4 \cdot 29/5 = \log 4 + \log 29 - \log 5$

Example 8.19 Write the expression $\log x - 2 \log x + 3 \log (x + 1) - \log (x^2 - 1)$ as a single term.

Solution Proceed as follows:

$$\log x - 2 \log x + 3 \log (x + 1) - \log (x^2 - 1)$$
$$= \log x - \log x^2 + \log (x + 1)^3 - \log (x^2 - 1)$$
$$= \log \frac{x(x + 1)^3}{x^2(x^2 - 1)} = \log \frac{(x + 1)^2}{x(x - 1)}$$

Exercises for Section 8.5

Evaluate the logarithms in Exercises 1–8.

1. $\log_2 32 \cdot 16$ **2.** $\log_2 16^5$ **3.** $\log_5 25^{1/4}$

4. $\log_3 27$ **5.** $\log_3 27 \cdot 9 \cdot 3$ **6.** $\log_2 64 \cdot 32 \cdot 8$

7. $\log_2 (8 \cdot 32)^3$ **8.** $\log_3 (9 \cdot 81)^8$

Given that $\log 2 = 0.3010$, $\log 3 = 0.4771$, and $\log 7 = 0.8451$, find the logarithms in Exercises 9–20.

9. $\log \frac{3}{2}$ **10.** $\log 4$ **11.** $\log 12$

12. $\log 30$ **13.** $\log 90$ **14.** $\log \sqrt{2}$

15. $\log \sqrt{5}$ **16.** $\log 21^{1/3}$ **17.** $\log 2400$

18. $\log 0.00018$ **19.** $\log 0.0014$ **20.** $\log 42000$

Simplify Exercises 21–28 by combining the logarithmic expressions.

21. $\log_2 x^2 - \log_2 x$

22. $\log_2 (x^2 - 1) - \log_2 (x - 1)$

23. $\log x + \log \dfrac{1}{x}$

24. $\log 3x + 3 \log (x + 2) - \log (x^2 - 4)$

25. $\log 5t + 2 \log (t^2 - 4) - \frac{1}{2} \log (t + 3)$

26. $\log z - 3 \log 3z - \log (2z - 9)$

27. $3 \log u - 2 \log (u + 1) - 5 \log (u - 1)$

28. $\log t + 7 \log (2t - 8) + 3$

29. Let $\ln I = (-R/L)t + \ln I_0$. Show that $I = I_0 e^{-Rt/L}$.

30. If y is directly proportional to x^p, what relation exists between $\log y$ and $\log x$?

31. Compare the functions $f(x) = \log x^2$ and $g(x) = 2 \log x$. In what way are they the same? In what way different?

32. Let $f(x) = \log_a x$ and $g(x) = \log_{1/a} x$. Show that $g(x) = f(1/x)$.

33. If $\log_a x = 2$, find $\log_{1/a} x$ and $\log_a (1/x)$.

34. Compare the graphs of the functions $f(x) = \log_2 2x$, $g(x) = \log_2 x$, $h(x) = \log_2 \sqrt{x}$, and $m(x) = \log_2 x^2$.

35. Given the graph of $y = \log x$, is there a convenient way to obtain the following graphs?

(a) $\log x^p$ (b) $\log px$ (c) $\log (x + p)$ (d) $\log (x/p)$

36. If $f(x) = \log_b x$, is $f(x + y) = f(x) + f(y)$?

8.6
Common
Logarithms

As noted earlier, logarithms to the base 10 are called common logarithms. Historically, common logarithms assumed the most practical importance, especially in simplifying certain numerical computations. However, with the advent of the digital computer the importance of logarithms as a computational tool has diminished. Nonetheless, any engineer or scientist must have some knowledge of the computational usefulness of logarithms.

Table B in the appendix is a listing of common logarithms of numbers between 1 and 10 in steps of 0.01. This is a "four-place" table, which means that it gives an approximation accurate to four decimal places. To find the logarithm of a number between 1 and 10, locate the first two digits of the number in the left column. The third digit of the number heads the column. Thus, to find the logarithm of 5.31, look down the left-hand column to 5.3. Then move over to the column headed by 1 to find that $\log 5.31 = 0.7251$.

To find the number whose logarithm is given use Table B in reverse, a procedure often called finding **antilogarithms**. Thus, since $\log 2 = 0.3010$, antilog $0.3010 = 2$.

Table B lists logarithms for numbers m such that $1 \leq m \leq 10$. The corresponding range values are $0 \leq \log m \leq 1$; that is, all the values in the table are fractions between 0 and 1.

To find the logarithm of any number, recall that any positive number M may be written as the product of a number m (where m is between 1 and 10) and 10^c (where c is an integer). That is,

$$M = m \cdot 10^c, \quad 1 \leq m < 10$$

A number so written is in *scientific form*. Several examples follow.

Example 8.20

$$53.1 = 5.31 \times 10^1$$

$$0.00531 = 5.31 \times 10^{-3}$$

$$5310000 = 5.31 \times 10^6$$

Thus, for any number M,

$$\log M = \log (m \cdot 10^c)$$

Using **Rule 1** for logarithms,

$$\log M = \log 10^c + \log m$$

Using **Rule 2**,

$$\log M = c \log 10 + \log m$$

$$= c + \log m$$

This is the **standard**, or uniform, way to express logarithms—as the sum of an integer and a positive number between 0 and 1. The quantity $\log m$, called the **mantissa** of $\log M$, is always a number between 0 and 1. The integer c, called the **characteristic** of $\log M$, is always an integer.

Example 8.21   Use the fact that $\log 5.31 = 0.7251$ to find (a) $\log 53.1$; (b) $\log 5{,}310{,}000$; (c) $\log 0.00531$.

Solution

(a)   Since $53.1 = 5.31 \times 10^1$,

$$\log 53.1 = 1 + \log 5.31 = 1 + 0.7251 = 1.7251$$

(b)   Since $5{,}310{,}000 = 5.31 \times 10^6$,

$$\log 5{,}310{,}000 = 6 + \log 5.31 = 6 + 0.7251 = 6.7251$$

(c)   Since $0.00531 = 5.31 \times 10^{-3}$,

$$\log 0.00531 = -3 + \log 5.31 = -3 + 0.7251$$

Notice in (c) that the negative characteristic is not combined with the mantissa, since its combination would obscure it and cause difficulty in recovering it when finding the antilog. Usually, we express a negative characteristic as a positive number minus ten. Thus, since $-3 = 7 - 10$, we prefer to write

$$\log 0.00531 = 7.7521 - 10$$

Example 8.22   Use the fact that antilog $(0.4099) = 2.57$ to find (a) antilog (2.4099); (b) antilog $(7.4099 - 10)$; (c) antilog (-6.5901).

Solution

(a)   antilog $(2.4099) = 2.57 \times 10^2 = 257$

(b)   antilog $(7.4099 - 10) = 2.57 \times 10^{-3} = 0.00257$

(c)   antilog $(-6.5901) = $ antilog $(3.4099 - 10) = 2.57 \times 10^{-7}$

In part (c) write the number -6.5901 as the sum of a number between 0 and 1 and an integer before consulting a table of logarithms. Note, for example that -6.5901 is *not* equal to $-6 + 0.5901$, but rather $-7 + 0.4099 = 3.4099 - 10$. ✄

Example 8.23   Find the value of $10^{-4.0969}$.

Solution   Let $N = 10^{-4.0969}$. Then

$$\log N = -4.0969 = -5 + 0.9031 = 5.9031 - 10$$

From Table B, in the appendix, antilog $0.9031 = 8$. Therefore

$$N = 8 \times 10^{-5} = 0.00008$$ ✄

The logarithm of a number to any base can be found from a table of common logarithms. For example, to find the *natural* logarithm of M, denoted ln M, let $y = $ ln M. Then, by definition,

$$M = e^y$$

Taking the common logarithm of both sides,

$$\log M = y \log e$$

from which

(8.1) $\mathbf{ln}\ M = \dfrac{\log M}{\log e}$ (Note that $y = $ ln M.)

Tables of natural logarithms are often available, but if they are not the above formula will be sufficient along with the fact that

$$\log e = 0.4343$$

Example 8.24   Solve for x: $e^x = 2640$.

Solution   In terms of natural logarithms this equation becomes

$$x = \ln 2640$$

8.6 Common Logarithms   233

Using formula (8.1)

$$x = \frac{\log 2640}{\log e}$$

$$\log 2640 = \log (2.64 \times 10^3) = 3 + \log 2.64 = 3.4216$$

Hence,

$$x = \frac{3.4216}{0.4343} = 7.88$$

This same result can be obtained by taking the common logarithm of each side of the given equation and solving for x.

Example 8.25   Solve for x: $2^x = .0075$.

Solution   By the definition of a logarithm,

$$x = \log_2 0.0075$$

Converting this to common logarithm form,

$$x = \frac{\log .0075}{\log 2}$$

$$\log 0.0075 = -3 + 0.8751 = -2.1249$$

Hence,

$$x = \frac{-2.1249}{0.3010}$$

$$= -7.059$$

In each example for this section Table B in the appendix was sufficient to find the mantissas directly. In the next section we discuss a method of extending the use of this table to numbers having four significant digits.

Exercises for Section 8.6

Evaluate Exercises 1–15.

1. (a) log 5.41   (b) log 5410   (c) log 0.00541

2. (a) log 1.25   (b) log 125   (c) log 0.125

3. (a) log 9.03   (b) log 0.000903   (c) log 903,000

4. (a) log 8.89   (b) log 88.9   (c) log 0.0889

5. (a) log (5.25)(3.65)   (b) log (5.25/3.65)

6. (a) log (8.03)(7.54) (b) log (8.03/7.54)

7. (a) log (0.255)(85.6) (b) log (0.255/85.6)

8. (a) log (0.295)(3.11) (b) log (0.295/3.11)

9. (a) log (258)(3670) (b) log (258/3670)

10. (a) log (1110)(56300) (b) log (1110/56300)

11. (a) antilog 3.2601 (b) antilog 0.2601

    (c) antilog 8.2601 − 10

12. (a) antilog 0.9258 (b) antilog 5.9258

    (c) antilog 9.9258 − 10

13. (a) antilog 1.1818 (b) antilog 3.1818 − 10

    (c) antilog 6.1818

14. (a) antilog 2.8692 (b) antilog 7.8692

    (c) antilog 3.8692 − 10

15. (a) antilog 0.6053 (b) antilog −2.3947

    (c) antilog −0.3947

Solve for x in Exercises 16–27.

16. $10^x = 20$ 17. $10^x = 25$ 18. $10^x = (1.54)(674)$

19. $10^x = \sqrt{20}$ 20. $10^{x+2} = 17^4$ 21. $10^{x-1} = 5^{10}$

22. $3^x = 15$ 23. $e^{3x} = 195$ 24. $5^{-x} = 0.045$

25. $2^{2x} = 0.009$ 26. $3^x = (15.3)^5$ 27. $e^{x+2} = 10^{-3}$

8.7
Interpolation

Table B does not include the logarithm of every number between 1 and 10, only those in steps of 0.01. To approximate the logarithms of numbers written with one more digit accuracy, you may proceed in one of a variety of ways. Perhaps the simplest way is to round off the given number. For example, the number 2573 may be rounded off to 2570 and then the logarithm of 2570 used as an approximation to log 2573. Under a round-off scheme log 2570 would serve as the approximation to log 2565 through log 2574. Admittedly, the approach may lead to intolerable errors but this technique of approximation is easy and is used frequently.

An interpolation technique, also fairly easy to use and slightly more accurate, assumes that small changes in a number result in proportional changes in the value of the logarithm. Thus, if the number M is in the interval

$M_1 < M < M_2$, then

$$\frac{\log M - \log M_1}{M - M_1} = \frac{\log M_2 - \log M_1}{M_2 - M_1}$$

Solving for $\log M$,

$$\log M = \log M_1 + \frac{M - M_1}{M_2 - M_1}(\log M_2 - \log M_1)$$

This formula is called interpolation by proportional parts, or more commonly, **linear interpolation**.

From a graphical standpoint the method of linear interpolation assumes that the graph of $y = \log x$ is essentially linear for small changes in the value of x. Figure 8.11 shows an exploded view of a small portion of the logarithm

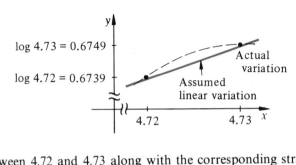

Figure 8.11

graph between 4.72 and 4.73 along with the corresponding straight line connecting the points (4.72, log 4.72) and (4.73, log 4.73). The curvature of the logarithm curve is purposely exaggerated to show the difference between it and the interpolated line.

Linear interpolation is used frequently in mathematics. It seems to be a very natural way to approximate, but do not use it indiscriminantly. Inaccurate results may occur if the interval of interest is not restricted to be relatively small.

The basic idea of linear interpolation in finding, say log 2.573, is to note that 2.573 is $\frac{3}{10}$ of the way from 2.57 to 2.58 and hence log 2.573 is $\frac{3}{10}$ of the way from log 2.57 to log 2.58.

Example 8.26   Use linear interpolation to approximate log 2573.

Solution   Since $2573 = 2.573 \times 10^3$, the characteristic is 3. The mantissa lies between the mantissa for 2.570 and 2.580. From Table B, the entries for 2.570 and 2.580 are found to be 0.4099 and 0.4116, respectively.

Number	Mantissa
$10\begin{bmatrix} 3\begin{bmatrix} 2.570 \\ 2.573 \end{bmatrix} \\ 2.580 \end{bmatrix}$	$\begin{bmatrix} .4099 \\ .... \end{bmatrix}c \\ .4116 \end{bmatrix}17$

We can establish the following proportion

$$\frac{c}{17} = \frac{3}{10}$$

or $c = \dfrac{3}{10}(17) = 5.1 \approx 5$

The required mantissa of log 2.573 is then $0.4099 + 0.0005 = 0.4104$. Therefore, log 2573 = 3.4104.

Note that in the preceding example we rounded off the number c to four digits after the decimal point. Otherwise, it would seem that interpolation was increasing the accuracy of the table which, of course, is impossible.

Example 8.27   Find the antilog of 2.4059.

Solution   Since the mantissa is 0.4059 and the characteristic is 2, we must find the number corresponding to the mantissa 0.4059 and then multiply by 10^2. Using Table B, we arrange the work as follows:

Number	Mantissa
$10\left[n\begin{bmatrix}2.540 \\ \cdots \\ 2.550\end{bmatrix}\right.$	$\left.\begin{bmatrix}.4048 \\ .4059 \\ .4065\end{bmatrix}\begin{matrix}11\end{matrix}\right]17$

$$\frac{n}{10} = \frac{11}{17}$$

$$n = \frac{11}{17}(10) = 6.4 \approx 6$$

Therefore, the desired number is $2.546 \times 10^2 = 254.6$.

Example 8.28   Find $\log \sqrt[3]{0.7568}$.

Solution   From the properties of logarithms,

$$\log \sqrt[3]{0.7568} = \frac{1}{3}\log 0.7568$$

Using Table B we arrange the work as

Number	Mantissa
$10\left[8\begin{bmatrix}0.7560 \\ 0.7568 \\ 0.7570\end{bmatrix}\right.$	$\left.\begin{bmatrix}0.8785 \\ \cdots \\ 0.8791\end{bmatrix}c\right]6$

8.7 Interpolation

237

We have the following proportion:

$$\frac{c}{6} = \frac{8}{10}$$

from which

$$c = 4.8 \approx 5$$

Therefore, log $0.7568 = 9.8790 - 10$. To obtain the desired logarithm, divide $9.8790 - 10$ by 3. Since 3 does not divide evenly into 10 and to keep the answer consistent with the standard form for negative characteristics, write log $0.7568 = 29.8790 - 30$. Now, dividing by 3 gives

$$\log \sqrt[3]{0.7568} = 9.9597 - 10$$

Exercises for
Section 8.7

Use the method of linear interpolation to approximate the common logarithm of the numbers in Exercises 1–15. (Calculators are off limits for this exercise.)

1.	2.361	**2.**	5842	**3.**	.009573
4.	3.142	**5.**	2.718	**6.**	49,990
7.	642,300	**8.**	5.011	**9.**	1,005
10.	62.45	**11.**	$\sqrt[3]{19.79}$	**12.**	$(158,800)^4$
13.	$\sqrt{0.003965}$	**14.**	$\sqrt[5]{0.1113}$	**15.**	$(0.1975)^3$

In Exercises 16–25 find the number x to 4 significant digits by using linear interpolation.

16.	$\log x = 2.1110$	**17.**	$\log x = 8.1284 - 10$
18.	$\log x = 7.814$	**19.**	$\log x = 3.4141$
20.	$\log x = 7.7228 - 10$	**21.**	$\log x = \frac{1}{2}$
22.	$\log x = 0.25$	**23.**	$\log x = \frac{1}{3}$
24.	$\log x = \pi$	**25.**	$\log x = -\pi$

Find the number x in Exercises 26–30.

26.	$10^x = e$	**27.**	$10^x = \pi$	**28.**	$e^2 = 10^x$
29.	$10^x = 0.1441$	**30.**	$10^x = \sqrt{2.169}$		

Write the expressions in Exercises 31–35 as a decimal (accurate to 4 significant digits).

31.	$\sqrt[4]{20}$	**32.**	10^π	**33.**	π^e
34.	$\sqrt{10}$	**35.**	$10^{0.4368}$		

36. Using log $3 = 0.4771$ and log $4 = 0.6021$, approximate log 3.5 by linear interpolation and compare to the value in Table B.

37. Use the fact that $\sqrt{4} = 2$ and $\sqrt{9} = 3$ and linear interpolation to approximate $\sqrt{7}$. Is the approximation high or low?

38. Let $f(x) = 2x - 3$. Use the values of $f(2)$ and $f(3)$ along with linear interpolation to approximate $f(2.5)$. How accurate is your result?

8.8
Computations
with Logarithms

With the advent of high-speed mechanical and electronic computing devices, the use of common logarithms for computational purposes has assumed a minor role. Even so, a basic understanding of logarithmic computation remains important. Further, the arithmetic of logarithmic computation increases your appreciation for some of the background theory. We choose not to explore all of the short cuts and conventions related to logarithmic computation, but to show the fundamental techniques.

Some of the following examples could as easily have been worked by conventional arithmetic. The aim here is to illustrate the use of logarithms, so do not be too concerned if the preferred technique might not be logarithms.

Example 8.29   Use logarithms to evaluate

$$M = \frac{2158 \times 0.512}{0.00042}$$

Solution   Find log M and use the rules of logarithms to write

$$\log M = \log 2158 + \log 0.512 - \log 0.00042$$

Log 2158 is found by interpolation to be 3.3341.
Log 0.512 is found directly to be $-10 + 9.7093$.
Log 0.00042 is found directly to be $-10 + 6.6232$.
Hence,

$$\log M = 3.3341 + (-10 + 9.7093) - (-10 + 6.6232)$$

$$= 3 + 0.3341 - 1 + 0.7093 + 4 - 0.6232$$

Adding the characteristics yields

$$\log M = 6 + (0.3341 + 0.7093 - 0.6232)$$

$$= 6 + 0.4202$$

$$= 6.4202$$

By interpolation, antilog $0.4202 = 2.631$, and hence

$$M = 2.631 \times 10^6$$

Example 8.30   Use logarithms to approximate $(25.4)^{1/4}$.

Solution   Let $M = (25.4)^{1/4}$. Then $\log M = \log (25.4)^{1/4} = \frac{1}{4} \log 25.4$. From Table B, $\log 25.4 = 1.4048$ and hence,

$$\log M = 0.3512$$

By interpolation,

$$M = 2.245$$

Example 8.31   Approximate $M = (85.1 + \sqrt[4]{25.4})/\log 3$

Solution   There is no formula for the logarithm of a sum, so the two terms of the numerator must be added before $\log M$ can be found. From the previous example, $\sqrt[4]{25.4} = 2.245$, so that

$$M = \frac{85.1 + 2.245}{0.4771} = \frac{87.345}{0.4771}$$

$$\log M = \log 87.34 - \log 0.4771$$

$$= 1.9412 - (9.6786 - 10)$$

$$\log M = 2.2626$$

$$M = 183.1$$

Exercises for
Section 8.8

Use logarithms to approximate the computations in Exercises 1–15 to four significant digits. (No calculators, please.)

1. $(65.7)(0.00411)$

2. $\dfrac{365 \times 1.423}{120 \times 0.00133}$

3. $(2563^{1/3})(0.5792^{1/2})$

4. $\dfrac{\log 23.7}{\log 0.00505}$

5. $\sqrt[3]{0.9711} \cdot \sqrt[5]{8}$

6. $(5.6)^4 \cdot (0.16)^3$

7. $3.1^{3.1}[2.112]$

8. $\dfrac{21.2 + 46.33}{\sqrt{57.12}}$

9. $[e^2 + 2^e][176 + (51.3)(0.756)]$

10. $\dfrac{76.1 + \log (8 \times 10^{40})}{\log 5.3}$

11. $\dfrac{-52.3 \times 64}{\log 3.83}$

12. $\dfrac{0.6003(0.0237)}{0.0114(0.00934)}$

13. $\dfrac{1.123(0.6975)}{0.0075(1278)}$

14. $3^{1.212}$

15. $\dfrac{(\sqrt{2})(\sqrt{3})}{\sqrt{5}}$

Solve for x in Exercises 16–28.

16. $3^x = \pi$ **17.** $2^x = \pi$ **18.** $7.1^x = 4.667$

19. $2^x = \dfrac{2015}{3143}$ **20.** $(0.5)^x = 5.555$ **21.** $2.6^x = 5.26$

22. $21^x = 213$ **23.** $1.4^x = 3.665$ **24.** $9.2^x = 100$

25. $4.1^{x+1} = 15.9$ **26.** $2.3^{x-1} = 12$ **27.** $25.3^{x+2} = 17$

28. $6.54^{x-2} = 8.35$

8.9
Exponential and
Logarithmic Equations

Equations in which the variable occurs as an exponent are called **exponential equations**. To solve these equations we use the fact that the logarithm is a one-to-one function. Thus, if $\log x = \log y$, then $x = y$. Hence, taking the logarithm of both sides is an admissible operation, if both sides may be assumed positive.

Example 8.32 Solve the exponential equation

$$3^x = 2^{2x+1}$$

Solution Taking the common logarithm of both sides,

$$\log 3^x = \log 2^{2x+1}$$

and using rule 2 for logarithms,

$$x \log 3 = (2x + 1) \log 2$$

Solving for x,

$$x(\log 3 - 2 \log 2) = \log 2$$

$$x = \frac{\log 2}{\log 3 - 2 \log 2}$$

$$x = \frac{0.3010}{-0.1249} = -2.41$$

Example 8.33 The expression $(e^x - e^{-x})/2$ is called the hyperbolic sine of x and is denoted by $\sinh x$. Solve the equation

$$\sinh x = 3$$

Solution   We must solve the exponential equation

$$\frac{e^x - e^{-x}}{2} = 3$$

Thus,

$$e^x - e^{-x} = 6$$

Multiplying both sides by e^x and bringing all terms to one side,

$$e^{2x} - 6e^x - 1 = 0$$

Let $u = e^x$. Then this equation becomes

$$u^2 - 6u - 1 = 0$$

which is quadratic in u. Using the quadratic formula,

$$u = \frac{6 \pm \sqrt{40}}{2} = 3 \pm \sqrt{10}$$

Since $u = e^x$ is always positive, discard the root $3 - \sqrt{10}$, which is negative. Thus,

$$e^x = 3 + \sqrt{10}$$

Then

$$x = \ln\,(3 + \sqrt{10})$$

is the desired solution.

Equations involving logarithms are called **logarithmic equations**. The use of one of the rules of logarithms frequently gives the needed simplification to allow you to solve such an equation.

Example 8.34   Solve the logarithmic equation

$$\log\,(x^2 - 1) - \log\,(x - 1) = 3$$

Solution   Simplifying the left-hand side by combining the two logarithm terms,

$$\log\,\frac{x^2 - 1}{x - 1} = 3$$

$$\log\,(x + 1) = 3$$

Thus, $x + 1 = 10^3$. (Can you tell why this is true?) Or

$$x = -1 + 10^3$$

Example 8.35   Solve the equation

$$x^{\log x} = \frac{x^3}{100}$$

Solution   Taking the common logarithm of both sides, we have

$$(\log x)(\log x) = \log x^3 - \log 100$$

or $(\log x)^2 - \log x^3 + \log 100 = 0$

Note that $(\log x)^2$ is not equal to $2 \log x$ but that $\log x^3 = 3 \log x$. Hence, the equation becomes

$$(\log x)^2 - 3 \log x + 2 = 0$$

Factoring gives

$$(\log x - 2)(\log x - 1) = 0$$

from which

$$\log x = 2 \text{ or } \log x = 1$$

Thus, $x = 100$ or 10.

Example 8.36   A certain power supply has a power output in watts governed by the equation

$$P = 50e^{-t/250}$$

where t is the time in days. If the equipment aboard a satellite requires 10 watts of power to operate properly, what is the operational life of the satellite?

Solution   Solving the equation $10 = 50e^{-t/250}$ for t gives

$$\frac{-t}{250} = \ln \frac{10}{50}$$

$$= \ln 0.2 = \frac{\log 0.2}{\log e} = \frac{-1 + 0.3010}{0.4343} = \frac{-0.6990}{0.4343}$$

$$= -1.609$$

or $t = 250 \times 1.609$

$$= 402 \text{ days}$$

Hence, the operational life of the satellite is 402 days.

Exercises for
Section 8.9

Solve for x in Exercises 1–16.

1. $7^{x+1} = 2^x$

2. $3^x 2^{2x+1} = 10$

3. $10^{x^2} = 2^x$

4. $8^x = 10^x$

5. $2^{1+x} = 3$

6. $\left(\dfrac{1}{2}\right)^x > 3$

7. $2^{\log x} = 2$

8. $\log \log \log x = 1$

9. $(\log x)^{1/2} = \log \sqrt{x}$

10. $(\log x)^2 = \log x^2$

11. $(\log x)^3 = \log x^3$

12. $x^{\log x} = 10$

13. $x^7 = 3$

14. $x^3 = 18$

15. $\log (x - 2) - \log (2x + 1) = \log \dfrac{1}{x}$

16. $\log (x^2 + 1) - \log (x - 1) - \log (x + 1) = 1$

17. The expression $(e^x + e^{-x})/2$ is called the hyperbolic cosine of x and is denoted by $\cosh x$. Solve the equation $\cosh x = 2$. (Hint: Let $u = e^x$.)

18. Solve the two equations $y = 50e^{-2x}$ and $y = 2^x$ simultaneously by making a sketch of each of the two equations on the same coordinate system.

19. Explain why if $\log u(x) = v(x)$, then $u(x) = 10^{v(x)}$.

20. Show that if $y = e^{\ln f(x)}$, then $y = f(x)$.

21. The radioactive chemical element strontium 90 has a half-life of approximately 28 years. The element obeys the radioactive decay formula, $A(t) = A_0 e^{-kt}$, where A_0 is the original amount and t is in years. Find the value of k.

22. Repeat Exercise 21 for the element iodine, whose decay formula is the same type. Express t in days. The half-life is 8 days.

23. What is the half-life of the power supply of Example 8.36?

24. The difference in intensity level of two sounds with intensities I and I_0 is defined by $10 \log (I/I_0)$ decibels. Find the intensity level in decibels of the sound produced by an electric motor which is 175.6 times greater than I_0.

25. As previously pointed out, the population growth curve is given by $P = P_0 e^{kt}$, where P_0 is the initial size, t is time in hrs., and k is a constant. If $k = 0.0132$ for a bacteria culture, how long does it take for the culture to double in size?

Test 1 for Chapter 8

Answer true or false in Exercises 1–10.

1. If $f(x) = 2^x$, then $f(x + y) = f(x) \cdot f(y)$.

2. If $f(x) = 2^x$, then if $x_1 < x_2, f(x_1) > f(x_2)$.

3. If $a > b, a^x > b^x$.

4. $\log 0 = 1$.

5. $\log (x + y) = \log x + \log y$.

6. Interpolation is a method of estimating the values of a function between tabulated values.

7. $2^{\log_2 7} = 7$.

8. The domain of $\log(-x)$ is the empty set.

9. The domain of $\log(-x^2)$ is the empty set.

10. The logarithm is the reciprocal of the exponential.

11. Make a careful sketch of $y = 2^x$, $y = 2^{x+3}$, and $y = 2^x + 3$ on the same coordinate axes.

12. Make a careful sketch of $y = \log x$, $y = -\log x$, and $y = \log(-x)$ on the same coordinate axes.

13. If $\log v = 5.4371$, find the value of v.

14. Find x if $10^{x^2 - 4} = 7$.

15. (a) Solve for x: $2^{x+1} > 0$.   (b) Solve for x: $\log(x+1) > 0$.

16. Find x if $x^{4.3} = 2.1$.

Test 2 for Chapter 8

1. Sketch the graph of (a) $y = 2^{x-3}$; (b) $y = \log_2(x - 5)$.

2. Solve for x if (a) $\log_x 8 = -3$; (b) $\log_3 x = 4$.

3. Express as a single logarithmic term: $3 \log x - \log(x^2 - 2) + 2 \log(x + 1)$.

4. Evaluate (a) $\log_5 (125 \cdot 625)$; (b) $\log_2 (128 \cdot 64)$.

5. Use Table B to evaluate (a) $\log 3956$; (b) $\log 0.00075$; (c) antilog $6.7838 - 10$.

6. Using the results in Problem 5, evaluate $N = 3956/0.00075$.

7. Solve for x if $3^x = 2^{x+1}$.

8. Solve for x if $\log x + \log(x - 3) = 1$.

9. Given $m = ce^{-kt}$, find k if $m = 50$, $c = 20$, and $t = 2$.

10. Use logarithms to find $\sqrt[5]{0.0596}$.

9
Right Triangle
Trigonometry

9.1
Angles and Their
Measurement

In this and the next few chapters we turn to a study of trigonometry. Histor-ically, this subject has its roots in problems solvable by the use of similar triangles. Indeed, the development in this text is, initially at least, heavily oriented to the use of right triangles in making the fundamental definitions. Only later do we introduce the analytic generalizations that are so important to mathematics and physics. This introductory section provides the necessary background knowledge for angles and triangles.

When two line segments meet, they form an **angle**. We ordinarily think of an angle as formed by two half-lines OA and OB that extend from some common point O, called the **vertex**. The half-lines are called the **sides** of the angle. (See Figure 9.1)

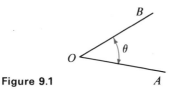

Figure 9.1

We refer to an angle by mentioning a point on each of its sides and the vertex. Thus, the angle in Figure 9.1 is called "the angle AOB," and is written $\angle AOB$. If there is only one angle under discussion whose vertex is at O, we sometimes simply say, "the angle at O," or more simply, "angle O." Greek letters customarily designate angles. For example, $\angle AOB$ might also be called the angle θ (read "theta").

Often in trigonometry we must conceive of an angle as being formed by rotating one of the sides about its vertex while keeping the other side fixed, as shown in Figure 9.2. If we think of OA as being fixed and OB as rotating about the vertex, OA is called the **initial** side and OB, the **terminal** position of the generated angle. Other terminal sides such as OB' and OB'' result in different

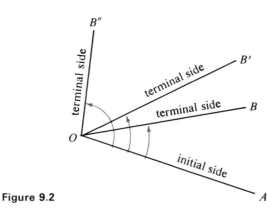

Figure 9.2

angles. The *size* of the angle depends on the amount of rotation of the terminal side. Thus, $\angle AOB$ is considered smaller than $\angle AOB'$ which, in turn, is smaller than $\angle AOB''$. Two angles are equal in size if they are formed by the same amount of rotation of the terminal side.

The most commonly used unit of angular measurement is the **degree**. We will take as a definition that the measure of an angle formed by one complete revolution of the terminal side about its vertex is 360 degrees, also written 360°. One-half of this angle, 180°, is called a **straight angle** (see Figure 9.3(a)), and one-fourth of it, 90°, is called a **right angle** (see Figure 9.3(b)).

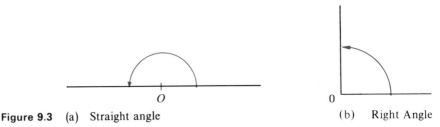

Figure 9.3 (a) Straight angle   (b) Right Angle

An angle is **acute** if its size is less than a right angle. It is **obtuse** if it is larger than a right angle but smaller than a straight angle (see Figure 9.4).

Figure 9.4   Acute Angle   Obtuse Angle

Angles with the same initial and terminal sides are **coterminal**. The two angles in Figure 9.5 are coterminal, but they are obviously not equal. Coterminal angles are sometimes considered equal, but there are many important considerations, both practical and theoretical, when we must know how the angle was formed.

Figure 9.5   **Coterminal Angles**

To distinguish between an angle and its measurement, we write $m(A)$ to denote the measurement of the angle A. Popular usage, however, allows us to say "the 30° angle" rather than the more precise "the angle whose measure is 30°." The context should always be sufficient for you to tell in what sense the word "angle" is being used.

Sometimes it is necessary to consider the angle to be "directed," that is, to make a distinction between the direction of rotation of the terminal side in forming the angle. The almost universal convention is to consider those angles obtained by a counterclockwise rotation of the terminal side as *positive* and those obtained by a clockwise rotation as *negative* angles, as shown in Figure 9.6.

The measure of an angle has no numerical limit, since a terminal side may be rotated either clockwise or counterclockwise as much as desired.

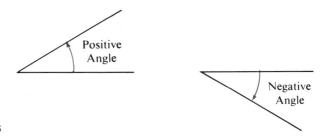

Figure 9.6

Example 9.1   Draw the following angles: (a) θ (theta) of measurement 42°, (b) ϕ (phi) of $-450°$, (c) β (beta) of 1470°, and (d) α (alpha) of $-675°$.

Solution   See Figure 9.7.

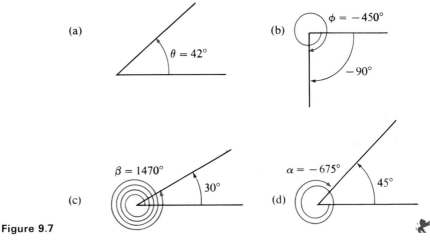

Figure 9.7

Example 9.2   Determine angles whose measurements are between $-180°$ and 180° and that are coterminal with angles whose measure is the same as those of the previous example.

Solution   Using Figure 9.7, we can see that (a) 42° is the desired angle, (b) $-90°$ is coterminal with $-450°$, (c) 30° is coterminal with 1470° and (d) 45° is coterminal with $-675°$.

The basic angular unit of the degree is subdivided into 60 parts, each of which is called a **minute** and denoted by the symbol ('). The minute is further

9.1 Angles and Their Measurement   249 subdivided into 60 parts, each of which is called a **second** and is denoted by the symbol ("). As the next example shows, arithmetic calculations are sometimes more cumbersome with these subdivisions than with the decimal system.

Example 9.3 Find the sum and the difference of the two angles whose measurements are 45°41′09″ and 32°52′12″.

Solution Find the sum of the two angles by adding the corresponding units; that is, degrees to degrees, minutes to minutes, and seconds to seconds. Thus,

$$45°41′09″ + 32°52′12″ = (45 + 32)°(41 + 52)′(09 + 12)″$$

$$= 77°93′21″$$

Here 93′ = 1°33′, so the answer is 78°33′21″.
To find the difference in the two angles, write 45°41′09″ in the following form:

$$45°41′09″ = 45°40′69″ = 44°100′69″$$

Thus,

$$45°41′09″ - 32°52′12″ = (44 - 32)°(100 - 52)′(69 - 12)″$$

$$= 12°48′57″$$

In passing, note that if the sum of the measures of two angles is 90°, the two angles are **complementary**. If the sum of the measures is 180°, they are **supplementary** (see Figure 9.8).

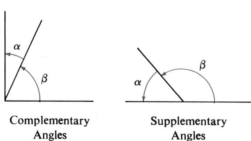

| | Complementary | Supplementary |
| **Figure 9.8** | Angles | Angles |

Another commonly used measure of an angle is the **radian**. Although less familiar to the beginner, in a sense the radian is a more natural choice for a unit of angular measure than the degree. Radian measure is used almost exclusively in more advanced applications of trigonometry.

Definition One *radian* is the measure of an angle whose vertex is at the center of a circle and whose sides intersect an arc on the circle equal in length to the radius of the circle (see Figure 9.9).

Hence, the radian is a measure of the ratio of arc length to radius. Since the circumference C of a circle of radius r is known to be $2\pi r$, it follows that

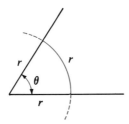

Figure 9.9   One radian

$C/r = 2\pi$. Thus, an angle of $360°$ consists of 2π radians. In equation form,

$$2\pi \text{ radians} = 360°$$

from which

1 degree = $\pi/180$ radians ≈ 0.0175 radians

and

1 radian = $180/\pi$ degrees ≈ 57.3 degrees

The next two examples illustrate how to use these formulas to convert from degrees to radians and vice versa.

Example 9.4   Express in radian measure (a) $60°$, (b) $225°$.

Solution

(a)   60 degrees = $60(\pi/180)$ radians = $\pi/3$ radians
(b)   225 degrees = $225(\pi/180)$ radians = $5\pi/4$ radians

When the radian measure is a convenient multiple of π, you will usually find that conversion to a decimal fraction is *not* beneficial. When such a conversion is necessary, 3.14 is a good decimal approximation to π.

Example 9.5   Express $\pi/6$ radians, $3\pi/4$ radians, and 2.6 radians in degrees.

Solution

$$\pi/6 \text{ radians} = (\pi/6)(180/\pi) \text{ degrees} = 30 \text{ degrees}$$
$$3\pi/4 \text{ radians} = (3\pi/4)(180/\pi) \text{ degrees} = 135 \text{ degrees}$$
$$2.6 \text{ radians} = 2.6(57.3) = 148.98 \text{ degrees}$$

Table 9.1 is a conversion table showing frequently occurring angles with both their degree and radian measure. Eventually, you should know the entries in this table without making the conversion calculation.

9.1 Angles and Their Measurement   251

Angle in Degrees	Angle in Radians
0	0
30	$\pi/6$
45	$\pi/4$
60	$\pi/3$
90	$\pi/2$
120	$2\pi/3$
135	$3\pi/4$
150	$5\pi/6$
180	π
270	$3\pi/2$
360	2π

The word " radian " is often understood without being written. However, you must always include the units of degree measurement.

Example 9.6   Compare the angle of 60 degrees with that of 60 radians.

Solution   Note from Figure 9.10 that the angle of 60 radians is obtained by 9 repeated revolutions of the terminal side (each revolution being approximately 6.28 radians) plus an additional 3.48 radians. Thus, the angle of 60 radians is coterminal with one whose measure is 3.48 radians. Figure 9.10 shows the angle of 60 radians along with the angle of 60°.

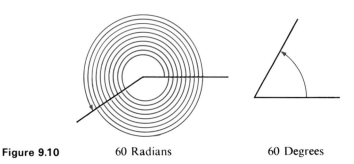

Figure 9.10   60 Radians   60 Degrees

Whether to measure an angle in degrees or radians is sometimes a matter of personal preference, but more often than not the particular problem under discussion dictates the unit. For instance, the length s of the arc intercepted by the central angle θ in Figure 9.11 can be found by the formula

(9.1) $s = r\theta$

if the angle θ is measured in radians. Formula (9.1) follows immediately from the definition of a radian as the ratio of arc length to radius, that is, $\theta = s/r$. *Formula 9.1 is not valid if θ is measured in degrees.*

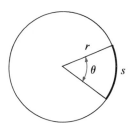

Figure 9.11

Example 9.7   Find the length of arc on a circle of radius 5 inches which subtends a central angle of 38°.

Solution   To use Formula (9.1), first convert the degree measure to radian measure. Thus,

$$38 \text{ degrees} \times \pi/180 \text{ radians} = 19\pi/90 \text{ radians}$$

Therefore, $s = 5 \times 19\pi/90$ inches ≈ 3.32 inches.

Exercises for
Section 9.1

1.   What is the difference in radian measure of two coterminal angles?

2.   What is the difference in degree measure of two coterminal angles?

In Exercises 3–12 find the sum $A + B$ and the difference $A - B$ of the two given angles.

3. $A = 45°10', B = 30°5'$

4. $A = 72°12', B = 30°38'$

5. $A = 58°35'40'', B = 50°34'20''$

6. $A = 42°40'10'', B = 65°50'50''$

7. $A = 60°10'15'', B = 70°45'$

8. $A = 138°40'20'', B = 23°52'30''$

9. $A = 240°45'40'', B = 333°25'14''$

10. $A = 320°50'20'', B = -30°55'10''$

11. $A = -40°42'57'', B = -80°18'13''$

12. $A = -90°0'49'', B = 269°57'1''$

In Exercises 13–28 draw the angles and name the initial and terminal sides. Indicate another angle between $-180°$ and $+180°$ coterminal with the given one. Express each of the given angles in radians.

13.   30°   14. $-30°$ 15.   45°   16.   500°

17. $-225°$ 18. $-270°$ 19.   290°   20.   120°

21.   720°   22.   780°   23.   840°   24.   765°

25.   1485°   26.   2000°   27. $-25°$ 28. $-205°$

9.1 Angles and Their Measurement

In Exercises 29–38 draw the angles and name the initial and terminal sides. Indicate another angle between $-\pi$ and $+\pi$ coterminal with the one given. Express each of the given angles in degrees.

29. 1   **30.** 2π **31.** π **32.** $\pi/6$

33. -3π **34.** -100 **35.** 100   **36.** 30

37. 100π **38.** -100π

39. A pendulum 10 feet long swings through an arc of 30°. How long is the arc described by its midpoint?

40. A racing car travels a circular course about the judges' stand. If the angle subtended by the line of sight is 120° while the car travels 1 mile, how large is the entire track?

9.2
Definitions of the
Trigonometric Functions

Trigonometry was invented as a means of indirectly measuring the parts of a right triangle; in fact, the word "trigonometry" means "three-angle measure." Today, trigonometry has many applications that have nothing to do with triangles, but the basic concepts are still best understood relative to the right triangle. For this reason, we begin the discussion of trigonometry with the right triangle. In Figure 9.12 the capital letters A, B, and C designate the vertices and

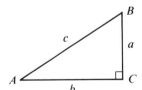

Figure 9.12

the corresponding angles at these vertices, whereas the lowercase letters a, b, and c designate the lengths of the sides opposite these angles. This convention is somewhat standard and will be used throughout this book.

Consider a right triangle ABC as shown in Figure 9.12. For reasons that you will understand shortly, we are interested in the ratios of the lengths of the sides of the triangle. By inspection you can see that the three sides a, b, and c can be used to form six ratios, namely,

$$\frac{a}{c}, \frac{b}{c}, \frac{a}{b}, \frac{b}{a}, \frac{c}{b}, \frac{c}{a}$$

For similar right triangles these six ratios are independent of the lengths a, b, and c. The following argument shows the truth of this statement. Two similar right triangles ABC and $A_1B_1C_1$ are shown in Figure 9.13, one obviously larger than the other.

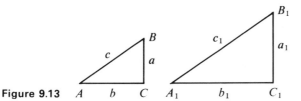

Figure 9.13

From our knowledge of the geometry of similar triangles, we know that the corresponding sides of the two triangles are proportional. Thus, since triangles ABC and $A_1B_1C_1$ are similar,

$$\frac{a}{a_1} = \frac{c}{c_1} \quad \text{and} \quad \frac{b}{b_1} = \frac{c}{c_1} \quad \text{and} \quad \frac{a}{a_1} = \frac{b}{b_1}$$

or, rearranging terms,

$$\frac{a}{c} = \frac{a_1}{c_1} \quad \text{and} \quad \frac{b}{c} = \frac{b_1}{c_1} \quad \text{and} \quad \frac{a}{b} = \frac{a_1}{b_1}$$

Each proportion says that the ratio of two given sides in the smaller triangle is equal to the ratio of the corresponding sides in the larger triangle. Recognizing that these are the first three ratios of the six ratios mentioned earlier and that the other three could be handled in a like manner, we conclude that the six ratios are independent of the lengths of the sides of the triangle.

While the six ratios are independent of the length of the sides, they are dependent upon the angles. For instance, if in Figure 9.12 angle A increases, the ratio a/c increases and the ratio b/c decreases. Thus, the six ratios are functions of the angle A and have come to be called the **trigonometric functions**. To facilitate discussion of the trigonometric functions, each is given a name as indicated in the following definition.

Definition

With reference to Figure 9.12, the six trigonometric functions of angle A are as follows.

$$\text{sine } A = \frac{a}{c} \quad \text{(abbreviated sin } A\text{)}$$

$$\text{cosine } A = \frac{b}{c} \quad \text{(abbreviated cos } A\text{)}$$

$$\text{tangent } A = \frac{a}{b} \quad \text{(abbreviated tan } A\text{)}$$

$$\text{cotangent } A = \frac{b}{a} \quad \text{(abbreviated cot } A\text{)}$$

$$\text{secant } A = \frac{c}{b} \quad \text{(abbreviated sec } A\text{)}$$

$$\text{cosecant } A = \frac{c}{a} \quad \text{(abbreviated csc } A\text{)}$$

The sides of a right triangle are often referenced to one of the two acute angles. For example, the side of length a is called the **side opposite** angle A, the side of length b is called the **side adjacent** to angle A, and the side of length c is called the **hypotenuse**. Using this terminology, the six trigonometric functions in the definition become

$$\mathbf{sin}\ A = \frac{a}{c} = \frac{\text{opposite side}}{\text{hypotenuse}} \qquad \mathbf{cos}\ A = \frac{b}{c} = \frac{\text{adjacent side}}{\text{hypotenuse}}$$

(9.2) $\qquad \mathbf{tan}\ A = \frac{a}{b} = \frac{\text{opposite side}}{\text{adjacent side}} \qquad \mathbf{cot}\ A = \frac{b}{a} = \frac{\text{adjacent side}}{\text{opposite side}}$

$$\mathbf{sec}\ A = \frac{c}{b} = \frac{\text{hypotenuse}}{\text{adjacent side}} \qquad \mathbf{csc}\ A = \frac{c}{a} = \frac{\text{hypotenuse}}{\text{opposite side}}$$

The abbreviated names of the trigonometric functions are most often used. Remember that they denote certain ratios of lengths. Thus, when someone mentions sin A, you should automatically think "the ratio of a to c" or "side opposite angle A to hypotenuse."

Example 9.8   Consider a right triangle whose sides have the values as shown in Figure 9.14. Find the six trigonometric functions for the angle θ.

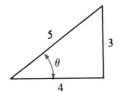

Figure 9.14

Solution

$$\sin \theta = \frac{\text{side opposite}}{\text{hypotenuse}} = \frac{3}{5} \qquad \cos \theta = \frac{\text{side adjacent}}{\text{hypotenuse}} = \frac{4}{5}$$

$$\tan \theta = \frac{\text{side opposite}}{\text{side adjacent}} = \frac{3}{4} \qquad \cot \theta = \frac{\text{side adjacent}}{\text{side opposite}} = \frac{4}{3}$$

$$\sec \theta = \frac{\text{hypotenuse}}{\text{side adjacent}} = \frac{5}{4} \qquad \csc \theta = \frac{\text{hypotenuse}}{\text{side opposite}} = \frac{5}{3}$$

Example 9.9   A man on the ground 50 feet from the foot of a building views an antenna whose top is 150 feet above the ground. Find the sine of the angle of elevation from the observer to the top of the antenna. (The angle of elevation is the angle between the horizontal and the line of sight when looking up to the object.) Ignore the distance from the ground to the man's eye.

Solution   Figure 9.15 shows the situation. From the Pythagorean theorem compute the slant distance to the top of the antenna.

$$s^2 = 150^2 + 50^2$$

$$= 22,500 + 2,500$$

$$= 25,000.$$

Hence, $s \approx 158$. From this, $\sin \theta = 150/158 \approx 0.95$.

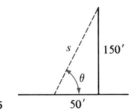

Figure 9.15   50′

Exercises for

Section 9.2

Draw right triangles whose sides have the values given in Exercises 1–16 and find the six trigonometric functions of the angle A.

1. $a = 4, b = 3, c = 5$
2. $a = 3, b = 2, c = \sqrt{13}$
3. $a = 12, b = 5, c = 13$
4. $a = 1, b = \frac{1}{2}$
5. $a = 2, b = 1$
6. $a = 2, c = 7$
7. $a = 1, b = 2$
8. $a = 1, c = 2$
9. $a = 1, b = 1$
10. $a = \sqrt{2}, c = \sqrt{10}$
11. $a = 5.2, c = 8.3$
12. $a = 44.1, c = 103.2$
13. $a = 16.3, b = 25.4$
14. $b = 41.5, c = 74.6$
15. $a = 3.5, b = 4.9$
16. $a = 25.6, c = 102.5$

17. A 6-foot man casts a shadow of 4 feet. Find the tangent of the angle that the rays of the sun make with the horizontal.

18. A wire 30 feet long braces a flagpole. If the wire is attached to the pole 25 feet above the level ground, what is the cosine of the angle made by the wire with the ground?

19. The line of sight distance to the top of a 100-foot-high building is 300 feet. What is the tangent of the angle of elevation?

9.2 Definitions of the Trigonometric Functions   257

20. Suppose that a boy is flying a kite at the end of a 100-foot string that makes an angle of 45° with the ground. Find the cosine of the angle the string makes with the ground.

21. A man on a 100-foot cliff looks down on a rowboat known to be 30 feet from the base of the cliff. What is the sine of the angle of depression? (The angle of depression is the angle between the horizontal and the line of sight when looking down on an object.)

9.3
Functions of
Complementary Angles

The definitions of the trigonometric functions were made in terms of angle A in the right triangle ABC (see Figure 9.12). Of course, these definitions apply to either one of the two acute angles in a right triangle. As the next example shows, the sides of the triangle must simply be named relative to the chosen angle.

Example 9.10   Find sin B, cos B, and tan B if $a = 3$ and $b = 2$ (see Figure 9.16).

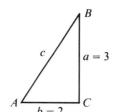

Figure 9.16

Solution $c = \sqrt{3^2 + 2^2} = \sqrt{13}$
Then

$$\sin B = \frac{\text{side opposite } B}{\text{hypotenuse}} = \frac{b}{c} = \frac{2}{\sqrt{13}}$$

$$\cos B = \frac{\text{side adjacent to } B}{\text{hypotenuse}} = \frac{a}{c} = \frac{3}{\sqrt{13}}$$

$$\tan B = \frac{\text{side opposite } B}{\text{side adjacent to } B} = \frac{b}{a} = \frac{2}{3}$$

From plane geometry we know that the sum of the interior angles of a triangle must equal 180°. Therefore, the two acute angles of a right triangle are complementary angles. Using this fact we can establish an interesting and useful relationship for trigonometric ratios of complementary angles. Referring to the general right triangle in Figure 9.12, it follows that

$$\sin B = \frac{\text{side opposite } B}{\text{hypotenuse}} = \frac{b}{c} = \frac{\text{side adjacent to } A}{\text{hypotenuse}} = \cos A$$

$$\cos B = \frac{\text{side adjacent to } B}{\text{hypotenuse}} = \frac{a}{c} = \frac{\text{side opposite } A}{\text{hypotenuse}} = \sin A$$

$$\tan B = \frac{\text{side opposite } B}{\text{side adjacent to } B} = \frac{b}{a} = \frac{\text{side adjacent to } A}{\text{side opposite } A} = \cot A$$

Similarly,

$$\cot B = \tan A, \ \sec B = \csc A, \ \csc B = \sec A$$

These relations involving the trigonometric functions of complementary angles is one of the main reasons that the sine and cosine are called **complementary functions**, or **cofunctions**. Similarly, the tangent and cotangent are complementary and the secant and cosecant are complementary. Making use of the fact that $B = 90° - A$,

$$\sin A = \cos (90° - A) \qquad \cos A = \sin (90° - A)$$
$$\tan A = \cot (90° - A) \qquad \cot A = \tan (90° - A)$$
$$\sec A = \csc (90° - A) \qquad \csc A = \sec (90° - A)$$

or, in general,

(9.3)
$$\left\{ \begin{array}{c} \textbf{Trigonometric function of} \\ \textbf{an acute angle } A \end{array} \right\} = \left\{ \begin{array}{c} \textbf{Complementary function of} \\ \textbf{(90° } - A\textbf{)} \end{array} \right\}$$

Example 9.11

(a) $\sin 30° = \cos (90° - 30°) = \cos 60°$. As you will learn in Section 9.5, $\sin 30° = \frac{1}{2}$. Hence, $\cos 60° = \frac{1}{2}$.

(b) $\tan 50° = \cot (90° - 50°) = \cot 40°$. The value of $\tan 50°$ is 1.1918. Hence, $\cot 40° = 1.1918$. 🕊

9.4
Fundamental
Relations

The values of the six trigonometric functions are related by some very simple formulas. From the definitions,

9.4 Fundamental Relations

$$\sin\theta = \frac{\text{opposite}}{\text{hypotenuse}} = \frac{1}{\text{hypotenuse/opposite}} = \frac{1}{\csc\theta}$$

(9.4)
$$\cos\theta = \frac{\text{adjacent}}{\text{hypotenuse}} = \frac{1}{\text{hypotenuse/adjacent}} = \frac{1}{\sec\theta}$$

$$\tan\theta = \frac{\text{opposite}}{\text{adjacent}} = \frac{1}{\text{adjacent/opposite}} = \frac{1}{\cot\theta}$$

These three relations are called the *reciprocal relationships* for the trigonometric functions. Further,

(9.5)
$$\tan\theta = \frac{\text{opposite}}{\text{adjacent}} = \frac{\text{opposite/hypotenuse}}{\text{adjacent/hypotenuse}} = \frac{\sin\theta}{\cos\theta}$$

As the following two examples demonstrate, a knowledge of one trigonometric ratio for an acute angle of a right triangle is sufficient to determine the other five ratios.

Example 9.12   Given that $\sin\beta = \frac{1}{2}$, find the values of the other trigonometric functions. We assume that β is an acute angle.

Solution   It is convenient to draw a typical right triangle with $\sin\beta = \frac{1}{2}$. Figure 9.17 is one possibility, with the opposite side equal to 1 and the hypotenuse equal to 2. From

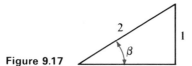

Figure 9.17

the Pythagorean theorem, the adjacent side is equal to $\sqrt{3}$. Knowing the three sides of the right triangle, we can write immediately

$$\cos\beta = \frac{\sqrt{3}}{2}, \tan\beta = \frac{1}{\sqrt{3}}, \cot\beta = \sqrt{3}, \sec\beta = \frac{2}{\sqrt{3}}, \csc\beta = 2$$

As in the previous example, the values of the trigonometric functions are often left in a form involving a radical. If the ratios are actually used for computational purposes, you will need to convert to approximate decimal values. For instance, in Example 9.12,

$$\cos\beta \approx \frac{1.732}{2} \approx 0.866$$

Example 9.13   Given $\sin A = \frac{1}{\sqrt{5}}$ and $\cos A = \frac{2}{\sqrt{5}}$, use (9.4) and (9.5) to find $\sec A$ and $\tan A$.

Solution $\sec A = \dfrac{1}{\cos A} = \dfrac{1}{2/\sqrt{5}} = \dfrac{\sqrt{5}}{2}$ $\tan A = \dfrac{\sin A}{\cos A} = \dfrac{1/\sqrt{5}}{2/\sqrt{5}} = \dfrac{1}{2}$

The validity of these values can be checked using Figure 9.18.

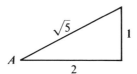

Figure 9.18

With the use of the Pythagorean theorem, we can derive a very famous relation between the sine and cosine functions. Consider any right triangle. From the Pythagorean theorem

$$(\text{opposite})^2 + (\text{adjacent})^2 = (\text{hypotenuse})^2$$

Dividing both sides of this equation by the square of the hypotenuse,

$$\left(\frac{\text{opposite}}{\text{hypotenuse}}\right)^2 + \left(\frac{\text{adjacent}}{\text{hypotenuse}}\right)^2 = 1$$

or, in terms of the trigonometric functions,

$$(\sin \theta)^2 + (\cos \theta)^2 = 1$$

It is customary to write $(\sin \theta)^2$ as $\sin^2 \theta$ and $(\cos \theta)^2$ as $\cos^2 \theta$. (A similar convention holds for expressing powers of the other trigonometric functions.) Thus, the equation reads

(9.6) $\sin^2 \theta + \cos^2 \theta = 1$

a formula that is often called the *Pythagorean relation* of trigonometry.

Example 9.14   Given that $\sin \theta = \frac{1}{4}$, use the Pythagorean relation to find $\cos \theta$.

Solution   Solving the Pythagorean relation for $\cos \theta$, we have

$$\cos \theta = \sqrt{1 - \sin^2 \theta}$$

Therefore,

$$\cos \theta = \sqrt{1 - \left(\frac{1}{4}\right)^2} = \sqrt{1 - \frac{1}{16}} = \frac{\sqrt{15}}{4}$$

Exercises for
Sections 9.3 and 9.4

Find the other five functions of the acute angle θ in Exercises 1–10.

1. $\cos \theta = 3/5$ 2. $\tan \theta = 2$ 3. $\sin \theta = 1/3$

9.4 Fundamental Relations   261

4. $\sin \theta = 1/2$ **5.** $\cos \theta = 1/2$ **6.** $\sec \theta = \sqrt{2}$

7. $\sin \theta = u/v$ **8.** $\tan \theta = u/v$ **9.** $\cos \theta = u$

10. $\sin \theta = 1/v$

Find the trigonometric functions of the angle complementary to θ, if (Exercises 11–20)

11. $\cos \theta = 1/2$ **12.** $\sin \theta = \sqrt{3}/2$ **13.** $\tan \theta = 1$

14. $\sec \theta = 3$ **15.** $\cot \theta = 5$ **16.** $\sin \theta = 1/\sqrt{3}$

17. $\tan \theta = t$ **18.** $\cos \theta = u/v$ **19.** $\sin \theta = 1/t$

20. $\csc \theta = 1/t$

21. Given that $\cos \theta = 1/\sqrt{3}$, use the Pythagorean relation to find $\sin \theta$.

22. Repeat Problem 21 if $\cos \theta = \sqrt{3}/2$.

9.5
Values of the Trigonometric Functions

The values of the trigonometric functions for some angles can be obtained from some applications of elementary geometry.

Example 9.15   Find the values of the trigonometric functions for 45°.

Solution   A 45° acute angle for a right triangle means that the triangle is isosceles, a typical one being shown in Figure 9.19. Using the Pythagorean theorem, the length of the hypotenuse is given by

$$\sqrt{a^2 + a^2} = a\sqrt{2}$$

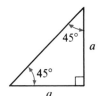

Figure 9.19

Hence,

$$\sin 45° = \frac{a}{a\sqrt{2}} = \frac{1}{\sqrt{2}} = \frac{\sqrt{2}}{2} \approx 0.707$$

$$\cos 45° = \frac{a}{a\sqrt{2}} = \frac{1}{\sqrt{2}} = \frac{\sqrt{2}}{2} \approx 0.707$$

$$\tan 45° = \frac{a\sqrt{2}}{a\sqrt{2}} = 1$$

$$\cot 45° = 1$$

$$\sec 45° = \sqrt{2} \approx 1.414$$

$$\csc 45° = \sqrt{2} \approx 1.414$$

Example 9.16   Find the trigonometric functions of 60°.

Solution   Consider an equilateral triangle and draw the bisector of one of the angles. This bisector divides the equilateral triangle into two congruent right triangles, as shown in Figure 9.20. The altitude of each of these right triangles is given by

$$h = \sqrt{a^2 - \left(\frac{1}{2}a\right)^2} = \frac{a\sqrt{3}}{2}$$

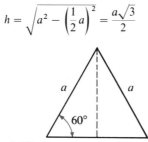

Figure 9.20

Hence,

$$\sin 60° = \frac{a\sqrt{3}/2}{a} = \frac{\sqrt{3}}{2} \approx 0.866 \qquad \cot 60° = \frac{1}{\sqrt{3}} \approx 0.577$$

$$\cos 60° = \frac{a/2}{a} = \frac{1}{2} = 0.5 \qquad \sec 60° = \frac{2}{1} = 2$$

$$\tan 60° = \frac{a\sqrt{3}/2}{a/2} = \sqrt{3} \approx 1.732 \qquad \csc 60° = 2/\sqrt{3} \approx 1.155$$

The values for an angle of 30° are obtained from the previous example and from the cofunction relation for complementary acute angles.

Table 9.2 summarizes the foregoing discussion. Study it carefully. You should know how to derive it.

Table 9.2 is obviously incomplete since it tabulates the functional values only at the special angles of 30°, 45°, and 60°. Specific values of the trigonomet-

Table 9.2   Values for Some Important Angles

θ(degrees)	θ(radians)	$\sin \theta$	$\cos \theta$	$\tan \theta$	$\cot \theta$	$\sec \theta$	$\csc \theta$
30	$\pi/6$	$1/2$	$\sqrt{3}/2$	$1/\sqrt{3}$	$\sqrt{3}$	$2/\sqrt{3}$	2
45	$\pi/4$	$\sqrt{2}/2$	$\sqrt{2}/2$	1	1	$\sqrt{2}$	$\sqrt{2}$
60	$\pi/3$	$\sqrt{3}/2$	$1/2$	$\sqrt{3}$	$1/\sqrt{3}$	2	$2/\sqrt{3}$

9.5 Values of the Trigonometric Functions

ric ratios for the other angles are computed by methods beyond the scope of this book and put into tables for convenience. Two representative tables of trigonometric functions are included in the appendix. Table D is tabulated in 10′ increments from 0° to 90°. Table E is given in increments of .01 radians from 0 to 1.57 (the radian measure of an acute angle being within these limits). The functional values of both tables are accurate to four decimal places.

Table D is representative of most trigonometry tables that are tabulated in degrees and minutes in that it apparently includes only those angles between 0° and 45°. This is so because the values of the functions for angles between 45° and 90° are the same as the values of the cofunction between 0° and 45°. Thus, sin 57° = cos (90° − 57°) = cos 33°. Most tables take advantage of this relation between the cofunctions of complementary angles by placing the complementary angle to the right of the table. The names of the function to be read for angles between 45° and 90° are then located at the bottom; thus, the table does double duty.

Summarizing the use of Table D:

- To find the values of the trigonometric ratios for angles between 0° and 45°, locate the angle at the left-hand side of the table and the name of the function at the top of the column. Read the value of the trigonometric ratio opposite the angle in the appropriate column.

- To find the values of the trigonometric ratios for angles between 45° and 90°, locate the angle at the right-hand side of the table and the name of the function at the bottom. Read the value of the trigonometric ratio opposite the angle in the appropriate column.

Example 9.17   Use Tables D and E to verify the following.

(a)   sin 34°10′ = 0.5616   (d)   sin 0.72 = 0.6594

(b)   cos 54°30′ = 0.5807   (e)   cot 1.11 = 0.4964

(c)   tan 65°40′ = 2.2113   (f)   sec 0.23 = 1.027

Trigonometry tables are used in two ways. The first is to find the value of a trigonometric function if an angle is given. The other is to find the value of the angle when the value of the trigonometric function is known. For example, if you are given that $\cos \theta = \frac{1}{2}$, you know that $\theta = 60°$.

Example 9.18   Use Table D in the appendix to find the angle θ if sin $\theta = 0.5925$.

Solution   Examine Table D, running down the column headed "sin x" until you come to 0.5925. Then read across to find that this corresponds to an angle of 36°20′. This is written

$$\sin \theta = 0.5925; \theta = 36°20′$$

Example 9.19   Use Table D to find ϕ if tan $\phi = 1.5900$.

Solution   Running down the column headed "tan," we fail to reach 1.5900 before coming to 45°; therefore, continue to look in the column headed "tan" at the bottom until coming to 1.5900. Reading "angle" from the right-hand column, we find that $\phi = 57°50'$; that is

$$\tan \phi = 1.5900; \phi = 57°50'$$

Exercises for

Section 9.5

Use Table D or Table E to find the values of the indicated trigonometric functions in Exercises 1–24.

1. sin 13°	**2.** sin 46°10'	**3.** tan 17°30'
4. cos 61°40'	**5.** sec 5°10'	**6.** tan 44°
7. cot 17°50'	**8.** csc 38°20'	**9.** sin 75.5°
10. cot 56.5°	**11.** cos 80°	**12.** sec 49°10'
13. sin 14°20'	**14.** cos 47°40'	**15.** sec 64°50'
16. tan 25°30'	**17.** cot 57°20'	**18.** csc 70°40'
19. tan 1.23	**20.** sin 0.54	**21.** cot 1.00
22. sec 0.02	**23.** cot 0.78	**24.** csc 0.50

Using Table D, find the degree measure of the angle ϕ if (Exercises 25–30)

25. sin $\phi = 0.4617$	**26.** cot $\phi = 0.5354$	**27.** tan $\phi = 3.7321$
28. sec $\phi = 2.0957$	**29.** cos $\phi = 0.5568$	**30.** csc $\phi = 1.2335$

Using Table E, find the radian measure of the angle ϕ if (Exercises 31–36)

31. sin $\phi = 0.8415$	**32.** cos $\phi = 0.8253$	**33.** tan $\phi = 4.072$
34. cot $\phi = 1.462$	**35.** sec $\phi = 1.180$	**36.** csc $\phi = 5.295$

9.6
Interpolation

Interpolation is a method of estimating a value between two given values. Since all trigonometric tables are tabulated in discrete steps, you will find it necessary to use interpolated values of trigonometric functions for angles between two tabulated values. For example, to estimate the value of sin 41°15' from Table D, use the values given for sin 41°10' and sin 41°20' and proceed with linear interpolation. This type of interpolation was explained in Section 8.7 in connection with tables of logarithms. The following examples demonstrate the technique relative to the trigonometric functions.

Example 9.20   Use Table D and the method of linear interpolation to approximate sin 31°14′.

Solution   From Table D, sin 31°10′ = .5175 and sin 31°20′ = .5200. For an increase of 10′ of the angle, the sine increases by .5200 − .5175 = .0025. Since 14′ is .4 of the difference of 20′ and 10′, the sine is assumed to increase by (0.4)(0.0025) = 0.0010. Because sin 31°20′ is greater than sin 31°10′, the difference is *added* to sin 31°10′ to give 0.5185. The next table summarizes this discussion.

		Angle	Sine		
		31°10′	0.5175		
10	4	31°14′	...	c	0.0025
		31°20′	0.5200		

$$\frac{c}{.0025} = \frac{4}{10}$$
$$c = 0.0010$$

Example 9.21   Use Table D to find cos 52°15′.

Solution   From Table D, cos 52°10′ = 0.6134 and cos 52°20′ = 0.6111.

		Angle	Cosine		
		52°10′	0.6134		
10	5	52°15′	...	c	0.0023
		52°20′	0.6111		

$$\frac{c}{0.0023} = \frac{5}{10}$$
$$c = \frac{5}{10}(0.0023)$$
$$= 0.0012$$

Since cos 52°15′ < cos 52°10′, subtract the correction from 0.6134. Thus,

cos 52°15′ = 0.6134 − 0.0012 = 0.6122.

Interpolation is also used to approximate the measure of an unknown angle whose trigonometric ratio is given but does not correspond exactly to any of the tabulated values.

Example 9.22   Use Table D to find angle θ if tan θ = 0.3.

Solution   From Table D, tan 16°40′ = 0.2994 and tan 16°50′ = 0.3026.

		Angle	Tangent	
10	c	⌈16°40'⌉ ⌊ ... ⌋	⌈0.2994⌉ ⌊0.3000⌋ 0.0006	0.0030
		16°50'	0.3026	

$$\frac{c}{10} = \frac{0.0006}{0.0030}$$

$$c = \frac{0.0006}{0.0030}(10) = 2'$$

Adding this $2'$ correction to 16°40' yields $\theta = 16°42'$.

Example 9.23   Use Table E to estimate the value of angle θ if $\cos \theta = 0.8145$.

Solution   From Table E, $\cos 0.61 = 0.8196$ and $\cos 0.62 = 0.8139$.

		Angle	Cosine	
0.010	c	⌈0.610⌉ ⌊ ... ⌋	⌈0.8196⌉ ⌊0.8145⌋ 0.0051	0.0057
		0.620	0.8139	

$$\frac{c}{0.010} = \frac{0.0051}{0.0057}$$

$$c = 0.009$$

The correction c is rounded off to the nearest thousandth to be consistent with the accuracy of the table. Therefore, $\theta = 0.619$ radian.

Exercises for
Section 9.6

By interpolation find the value of the trigonometric functions in Exercises 1–9. Use Table D in the appendix.

1. $\sin 38°38'$ **2.** $\tan 15°32'$ **3.** $\cos 26°55'$

4. $\sec 42°15'$ **5.** $\cot 38°45'$ **6.** $\csc 70°5'$

7. $\sin 65°26'$ **8.** $\cos 15°9'$ **9.** $\tan 50°43'$

By interpolation find the value of the trigonometric functions in Exercises 10–18. Use Table E in the appendix.

10. $\tan 1.425$ **11.** $\sin \pi/8$ **12.** $\sin 1/8$

13. $\cos (\sqrt{3}/2)$ **14.** $\sec 1.083$ **15.** $\tan (\sqrt{2}/2)$

16. $\sin 0.531$ **17.** $\cos 0.012$ **18.** $\cot (\sqrt{3}/2)$

Use Table D in the Appendix to find the value of θ in degrees and minutes to the nearest minute by interpolation in Exercises 19–30.

19. $\sin \theta = 0.776$ **20.** $\cos \theta = 0.3000$ **21.** $\tan \theta = 1.4$

22. $\cot \theta = 2$ **23.** $\cos \theta = 0.5108$ **24.** $\sin \theta = 0.4804$

25. $\tan \theta = 0.5$ **26.** $\cot \theta = 0.5$ **27.** $\sec \theta = 1.8$

28. $\tan \theta = 0.3692$ **29.** $\csc \theta = 4$ **30.** $\sin \theta = 0.1234$

Use Table E to find the radian measure of θ to the nearest thousandth, where θ is a positive acute angle, in Exercises 31–42. Use interpolation when necessary.

31. $\sin \theta = 0.1365$ **32.** $\cos \theta = 0.7976$ **33.** $\tan \theta = 0.4040$

34. $\sin \theta = \pi/6$ **35.** $\cos \theta = \pi/8$ **36.** $\tan \theta = \pi/3$

37. $\sin \theta = 0.6541$ **38.** $\tan \theta = 2$ **39.** $\sin \theta = 0.105$

40. $\cot \theta = 0.9602$ **41.** $\cos \theta = 0.7$ **42.** $\sec \theta = 2$

9.7
Solution of
Right Triangles

One of the principal uses of the trigonometric functions is in computing dimensions of right triangles. This may seem to be largely of academic interest, but, as you will see in this section, the applications can be quite modern.

A right triangle is composed basically of six parts, the three sides and the three angles. To *solve a triangle* means to find the values of each of these six parts. Of course, they are not all independent. For example, if two of the angles are known, so is the other. If two of the sides of a right triangle are known, the remaining side is not of arbitrary length; it must be such that all three sides together satisfy the Pythagorean theorem.

When a right triangle is given, you may determine all six parts if you know two parts, at least one of which is a side.

- If an angle and one of the sides is given, then the third angle is simply the complement of the one given. The other two sides are obtained from the values of the known trigonometric functions.

- If two sides are given, the value of the third side is obtained from the Pythagorean theorem. The angles may then be determined by taking ratios of the sides that will uniquely determine the value of some trigonometric function.

Thus, in solving right triangles, we make use of the trigonometric functions, the Pythagorean theorem, and the fact that the two acute angles are complementary.

Usually it is advantageous to make a rough sketch of the triangle. This will help you to determine what is given and which trigonometric functions must be used to find the unknown parts.

Example 9.24   If in Figure 9.21 angle $\alpha = 27°$, and if the side adjacent is 6 units, solve the complete triangle.

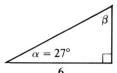

Figure 9.21   6

Solution   Since α and β are complementary, $\beta = 90° - 27° = 63°$. Also,

$$\tan \alpha = \frac{\text{side opposite } \alpha}{6}$$

and thus

$$\text{side opposite } \alpha = 6(\tan 27°)$$
$$= 6(.5095) = 3.057$$

Hence, the hypotenuse is given by

$$\sqrt{6^2 + (3.057)^2} = \sqrt{36 + 9.35} = \sqrt{45.35} \approx 6.7$$

Example 9.25   A ladder of 20 feet reaches a gable of a house 15 feet above the ground. What angle does the ladder make with the level ground?

Solution   The angle θ is the desired angle. From Figure 9.22 we see that

$$\sin \theta = \frac{\text{side opposite}}{\text{hypotenuse}} = \frac{15}{20} = \frac{3}{4} = 0.75$$

Figure 9.22

From Table D, sin 48°30′ = 0.7490 and sin 48°40′ = 0.7509. Hence, by interpolation,

		Angle	Sine		
		48°30′	0.7490		$\dfrac{c}{10} = \dfrac{0.001}{0.0019}$
10	c	...	0.7500	0.001	0.0019
		48°40′	0.7509		$c = 5′$

We have $\theta = 48°35′$.

Example   9.26   An engineer wishes to know the width of a river at a certain spot. He proceeds as follows: From a point directly across from a tree on the opposite bank he walks 100 yards downstream. Then with his transit he measures the angle that he now makes with the tree and finds it to be 55°. Find the width of the river.

9.7 Solution of Right Triangles   269

Solution From Figure 9.23 you can see that this problem is typical in right triangle trigonometry, in which the "side opposite" the 55° angle represents the unknown distance across the river. Thus,

$$\frac{d}{100} = \tan 55°$$

from which

$$d = 100(1.4281)$$
$$= 142.81 \text{ yd}$$

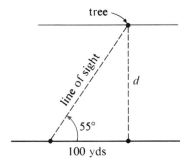

Figure 9.23

100 yds

Example 9.27 In Figure 9.24 a radar station tracking a missile indicates the angle of elevation to be 20° and the line of sight distance (called the "slant range") to be 40 miles. Determine the altitude and horizontal range of the missile.

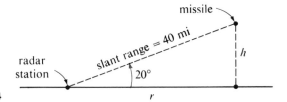

Figure 9.24

r

Solution The altitude is

$$h = (40)(\sin 20°)$$
$$= 13.7 \text{ mi}$$

and the horizontal range is

$$r = (40)(\cos 20°)$$
$$= 37.6 \text{ mi}$$

Example 9.28 Show how to obtain the height of a mountain (or a building) by measuring the angle of elevation at two different locations if you measure the distance between the two locations.

Another variation on essentially the same problem reads: Two tracking stations d

miles apart measure the angle of elevation of a weather balloon to be α and β, respectively. Derive a formula for the altitude h of the balloon in terms of the distance d and the angles α and β.

Solution   Figure 9.25 is a picture of the situation. We have two equations:

$$\tan \beta = \frac{h}{x}$$

$$\tan \alpha = \frac{h}{x + d}$$

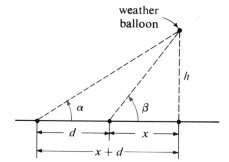

Figure 9.25

The only unknowns in these two equations are x and h. Solving the first for x yields $x = h \cot \beta$. Using this expression for x in the second equation,

$$\tan \alpha = \frac{h}{h \cot \beta + d}$$

Solving this equation for h,

$$h \cot \beta \tan \alpha + d \tan \alpha = h$$

$$h = \frac{d \tan \alpha}{1 - \cot \beta \tan \alpha}$$

$$= \frac{d}{\cot \alpha - \cot \beta}$$

Exercises for
    Section 9.7

Solve the right triangles in Exercises 1–5.

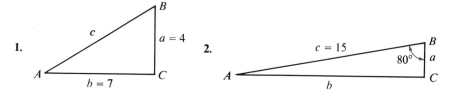

1.

2.

9.7 Solution of Right Triangles

271

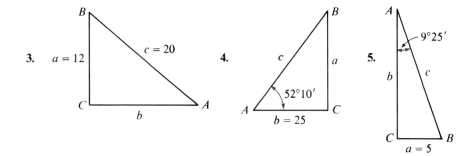

3. $a = 12$ **4.**   **5.**

6. One side of a rectangle is half as long as the diagonal. If the diagonal is 5 feet long, how long are the sides of the rectangle?

7. A man is walking on the prairie and stops to measure the angle of inclination to a high mountain. It measures 30°. Then he walks a mile toward the mountain and measures again. This time the angle of inclination is 45°. How high is the mountain?

8. In Japan it is common to brace trees by poles. Suppose that a pole 14 feet long braces a tree standing on level ground and suppose that the end of the pole touching the ground is 10 feet away from the base of the tree. What is the size of the angle that the pole makes with the ground?

9. One morning a man 6 feet tall wanted to know the time, but no one in the vicinity had a timepiece of any kind. The man knew that on that day the sun rose at 6:00 A.M. and would be directly overhead at noon. A friend measured the man's shadow to be 10 feet long. Approximately what time was it?

10. A television antenna stands on top of a house that is 20 feet tall. The angle subtended by the antenna from a point 500 feet from the base of the building is 15°. Find the height of the antenna.

11. In designing a steel truss for a bridge as shown in the following figure, BC should be 10 feet and AC should be 7 feet. What angle does AB make with AC? With BC?

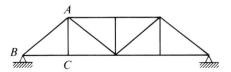

12. At noon in the tropics, when the sun is directly overhead, a fisherman holds his 15-foot pole inclined 30° to the horizontal. How long is the shadow of the pole? How high is the tip of the pole above the level of the other end?

13. A boy walking southward along a straight road turns to the left at a point P and continues along a path that runs straight for a distance of 500 feet to a spring S. He then takes another path running at right angles to the road and returns to the road at point Q, which is 190 feet from P. Find the angle at P that the left-hand path makes with the road and the angle at S between the two paths.

14. A flagpole broken over by the wind forms a right triangle with the ground. The angle that the broken part makes with the ground is 60°, and the distance from the tip of the pole to the foot is 40 feet. How tall was the pole?

15. The length of each blade of a pair of shears from the pivot to the point is 6 inches. When the points of the open shears are 4 inches apart, what angle do the blades make with each other?

In alternating current theory, the impedance Z, resistance R, and reactance X, obey a right triangle relationship, as demonstrated in following figure.

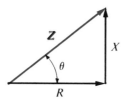

In Problems 16–21 solve for the missing components.

16. $R = 30, \theta = 60°$ **17.** $R = 30, Z = 60$

18. $Z = 100, \theta = 20°$ **19.** $R = 200, X = 100$

20. $Z = 1000, X = 800$ **21.** $X = 25, \theta = 30°$

9.8
Components
of a Vector

The trigonometric ratios have many applications in physics, some of which you will learn in this chapter. This section concerns applications to **vectors**. Vectors are entities, such as velocity and force, that require both a magnitude and a direction for their description. Graphically, we may think of a vector as an arrow whose length represents the magnitude of the vector and whose angle with a reference line represents its direction. For example, an automobile traveling 60 mph at an angle of 30° north of east can be represented by the vector diagram in Figure 9.26.

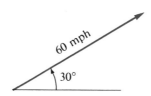

Figure 9.26   Velocity vector

By convention, we usually place vectors with their initial point at the origin of a rectangular coordinate system and use the positive x-axis as the reference line for the direction angle. We designate vectors in bold type. The magnitude of a vector $\mathbf{F}$ is denoted by $|\mathbf{F}|$.

The projections of the vector onto the x- and y-axes are called the **components** of the vector. We say that a vector is resolved into its x- and y-components, called the horizontal and vertical components of **F**, respectively. Resolving a vector into its x- and y-components is a simple problem of trigonometry. From Figure 9.27,

$$F_x = x \text{ component of } \mathbf{F} = |\mathbf{F}| \cos \theta$$

$$F_y = y \text{ component of } \mathbf{F} = |\mathbf{F}| \sin \theta$$

Obviously,

$$F_x^2 + F_y^2 = |\mathbf{F}|^2$$

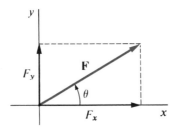

Figure 9.27   Components of a vector

Example 9.29   Find the horizontal and vertical components of a force vector of magnitude 15 lb acting at an angle of 30° to the horizontal.

Solution

$$F_x = |\mathbf{F}| \cos \theta = (15)(0.866) = 13$$

$$F_y = |\mathbf{F}| \sin \theta = (15)(0.5) = 7.5$$

Example 9.30   Find the magnitude and the direction of the vector whose components are shown in Figure 9.28.

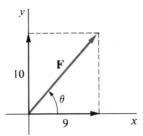

Figure 9.28

Solution   The magnitude is

$$|\mathbf{F}| = \sqrt{10^2 + 9^2} = \sqrt{181} \approx 13.45$$

The angle that the vector makes with the horizontal is determined from

$$\tan \theta = \frac{10}{9} = 1.111$$

$$\theta \approx 48°$$

Example 9.31 Two wires act on a weight as shown in Figure 9.29. If the tension in the wires is measured at 100 lb and 60 lb, what is the cumulative horizontal and vertical effect?

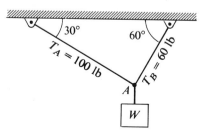 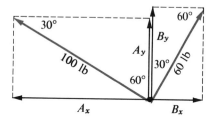

Figure 9.29

Solution The components of the 100-lb force are:

Horizontal: $A_x = 100 \cos 30° = 86.6$ lb to the left

Vertical: $A_y = 100 \sin 30° = 50.0$ lb upward

The components of the 60-lb force are:

Horizontal: $B_x = 60 \cos 60° = 30.0$ lb to the right

Vertical: $B_y = 60 \sin 60° = 52.0$ lb upward

Hence, the net force in each direction is:

Horizontal: $A_x - B_x = 86.6 - 30.0 = 56.6$ lb to the left

Vertical: $A_y + B_y = 50.0 + 52.0 = 102.0$ lb upward

The weight of an astronaut on the moon is one-sixth his weight on the earth. This fact has a marked effect on such simple acts as walking, running, jumping, and the like. To study these effects and to train astronauts for working under lunar gravity conditions, scientists at NASA Langley Research Center have designed an inclined plane apparatus to simulate reduced gravity.

The apparatus consists of an inclined plane and a sling that holds the astronaut in a position perpendicular to the inclined plane as shown in Figure 9.30. The sling is attached to one end of a long cable that runs parallel to the inclined plane. The other end of the cable is attached to a trolley that runs along a track high overhead. This device allows the astronaut to move freely in a plane perpendicular to the inclined plane.

9.8 Components of a Vector

275

Example 9.32   Let W be the weight of the astronaut and θ the angle between the inclined plane and the ground. Make a vector diagram to show the tension in the cable and the force exerted by the inclined plane against the feet of the astronaut.

Solution   The weight of the astronaut is resolved into two components, one parallel to the inclined plane, the other perpendicular to it. These components are $W \sin \theta$ and $W \cos \theta$, respectively. To be in equilibrium, the component $W \sin \theta$ must be balanced by the tension in the cable, and the component $W \cos \theta$ must be balanced by the force exerted by the inclined plane (see Figure 9.30).

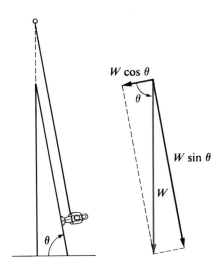

Figure 9.30

Example 9.33   From the point of view of the astronaut in the sling, the inclined plane is the ground and his weight; that is, the downward force against the inclined plane, is $W \cos \theta$. What is the value of θ required to simulate lunar gravity? What is the tension in the cable?

Solution   To simulate lunar gravity, we must have $W \cos \theta = W/6$. Thus,

$$\cos \theta = \tfrac{1}{6} = 0.1667$$

$$\theta = 80°24' \text{ to the nearest minute}$$

The tension in the cable is

$$W \sin 80°24' = 0.986 \ W$$

Exercises for
Section 9.8

Find the horizontal and the vertical components of the given force in Exercises 1–6.

1. $F = 25$ lb, $\theta = 45°10'$ 2. $F = 100$ lb, $\theta = 65°20'$

3. $F = 0.02$ lb, $\theta = 9°15'$ 4. $F = 9050$ lb, $\theta = 40°17'$

5. $F = 16.7$ lb, $\theta = 29.6°$ 6. $F = 397.6$ lb, $\theta = 2.7°$

Find the resultant force for the given components in Exercises 7–12.

7. $F_x = 20$ lb, $F_y = 15$ lb   8. $F_x = 56$ lb, $F_y = 13$ lb

9. $F_x = 17.5$ lb, $F_y = 69.3$ lb   10. $F_x = 0.012$ lb, $F_y = 0.200$ lb

11. $F_x = 0.13$ lb, $F_y = 0.08$ lb   12. $F_x = 1930$ lb, $F_y = 565$ lb

13. The north and west components of the velocity of an aircraft are 300 mph and 900 mph, respectively. What is the magnitude of the velocity?

14. A balloon rises at the rate of 20 feet per second and is being carried horizontally by a wind that has a velocity of 25 mph. Find its actual velocity and the angle that its path makes with the vertical (60 mph = 88 fps).

15. A boat travels at the rate of 5 mph in still water and points directly across a stream having a current of 3 mph. What is the actual speed of the boat and in which direction will the boat go?

16. What is the angle of the inclined plane used to simulate gravity for a 200-lb astronaut where the gravity is to be one-eighth that of the earth's?

17. If the plane used to simulate gravity is inclined at 60°, what percentage of the astronaut's weight would bear against the plane?

18. A girl weighing 100 lb sits in a swing. The swing is pulled by a horizontal force until the swing rope makes an angle of 15° with the vertical. What is the tension in each of the supporting ropes?

19. From the top of a building that is 220 feet high an observer looks down on a parking lot. If the lines of sight of the observer to two different cars in the lot is 28°15′ and 36°20′ below the horizontal, respectively, what is the distance between the two cars?

20. An airplane having a speed of 190 knots starts to climb at an angle of 13° above the horizontal. How fast is the airplane rising vertically?

21. The weight of an object is represented by a vector acting vertically downward. If a 15.3-lb block rests on plane inclined at 28.4° above the horizontal, what is the force acting perpendicular to the plane?

Test 1 for Chapter 9

Answer true or false in 1–9.

1. For any acute angle θ, $\cos \theta = 1/\csc \theta$.

2. If θ is acute and $\tan \theta = \cot \theta$, then $\theta = 45°$.

3. If θ and α are complementary angles, then $\sin^2 \theta + \sin^2 \alpha = 1$.

4. If θ is acute and $\sin \theta = \frac{1}{2}$, then $\theta = 30°$.

5. For acute angles, if $\theta_1 < \theta_2$, then $\cos \theta_1 < \cos \theta_2$.

6. If $\theta = 45°$, then $\sin \theta = \cos \theta$.

7. $\sin^2 60° + \cos^2 30° = 1$.

8. $\tan^2 42° + 1 = \sec^2 42°$.

9. Vectors are quantities requiring both a magnitude and a direction for their description.

10. Use Table E to find α if tan $\alpha = 0.7310$.

11. Find the other five trigonometric functions of θ if sec $\theta = u/v$.

12. Solve for θ where $0 < \theta < 90°$.
    (a) sin $\theta = 2$ (b) cos $\theta = \frac{1}{2}$

13. By interpolation, using Table D, approximate the value of x.
    (a) $x = \sin 33°13'$ (b) cos $x = 0.2461$

14. Solve the right triangle ABC if $A = 32°$ and $a = 3$. (The angle C is the 90° angle.)

15. The angle of elevation to a balloon from two tracking stations is 30° and 45°. If the balloon is at an altitude of 50,000 feet, how far apart are the two tracking stations?

Test 2 for Chapter 9

1. Find the angle between 0° and 360° that is coterminal with 825°.

2. Express (a) 125° in radian measure, (b) -3.2 radians in degrees.

3. Find the sin θ and cos θ if tan $\theta = \frac{5}{12}$.

4. Find the value of (a) sin 15°23', and (b) tan 76°54'.

5. Given tan $\phi = 0.5679$, find the acute angle ϕ using Table D.

6. Solve the right triangle with $A = 32°20'$ and $b = 22$.

7. Solve the right triangle with $a = 5$ and $c = 8$.

8. A tunnel through a mountain ascends at an angle of 5°25' with the horizontal. If the tunnel is 5000 ft long, what is the vertical rise of the tunnel?

9. Eight holes are equally spaced on the circumference of a circle. If the center-to-center distance between the holes is 3.8 cm, what is the radius of the circle?

10. A horizontal force of 15# is applied to a block resting on a plane inclined at 23° with the horizontal. Resolve the force into components—one parallel to the plane and one perpendicular to the plane.

10
Trigonometric Functions
for Any Angle

10.1

Extending the

Basic Definitions

The definitions of the six basic ratios given in the preceding chapter are adequate as long as the study of trigonometry is limited to the solution of right triangles. In order to include some of the more important applications of trigonometry, it is necessary to generalize the basic definitions. We begin by redefining the six trigonometric functions in terms of an angle in **standard position*** in the coordinate plane.

Consider an angle θ in standard position in the coordinate plane as shown in Figure 10.1. The terminal side of θ could obviously lie in any one of

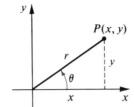

Figure 10.1

the four quadrants. Let P be a point on the terminal side of the angle θ, having coordinates (x, y) and let the distance from the origin to the point P be r. This line segment, called the **radius vector**, is always considered to have a positive length. By the Pythagorean theorem,

$$r = \sqrt{x^2 + y^2}$$

To be consistent with the definitions of Chapter 9, the trigonometric functions of the angle θ in Figure 10.1 must then be given by

$$(10.1) \quad
\begin{aligned}
\sin \theta &= \frac{\text{ordinate of } P}{\text{radius vector}} = \frac{y}{r} & \csc \theta &= \frac{\text{radius vector}}{\text{ordinate of } P} = \frac{r}{y} \\[2mm]
\cos \theta &= \frac{\text{abscissa of } P}{\text{radius vector}} = \frac{x}{r} & \sec \theta &= \frac{\text{radius vector}}{\text{abscissa of } P} = \frac{r}{x} \\[2mm]
\tan \theta &= \frac{\text{ordinate of } P}{\text{abscissa of } P} = \frac{y}{x} & \cot \theta &= \frac{\text{abscissa of } P}{\text{ordinate of } P} = \frac{x}{y}
\end{aligned}$$

Note that each of the functions is expressed in the terminology of the rectangular Cartesian coordinate plane. Using this terminology to state the definitions of the six trigonometric functions of an angle in standard position, the formulas of equation (10.1) are the extensions of formulas in 9.2 to angles greater than 90°. To write the values for the trigonometric functions of any

---

* An angle is in standard position if its initial side is along the positive x-axis.

angle, we need to know the abscissa, the ordinate, and the radius vector of a point on the terminal side of the angle.

Example 10.1   An angle θ in standard position has the point (6, 3) on its terminal side. Find the values of the six trigonometric functions of the angle θ. (See Figure 10.2.)

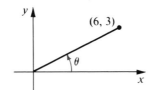

Figure 10.2

Solution   Using equation (10.1) with $x = 6$, $y = 3$, and $r = \sqrt{6^2 + 3^2} = \sqrt{45} = 3\sqrt{5}$,

$$\sin \theta = \frac{y}{r} = \frac{3}{3\sqrt{5}} = \frac{1}{\sqrt{5}} = \frac{\sqrt{5}}{5} \qquad \csc \theta = \frac{r}{y} = \frac{3\sqrt{5}}{3} = \sqrt{5}$$

$$\cos \theta = \frac{x}{r} = \frac{6}{3\sqrt{5}} = \frac{2}{\sqrt{5}} = \frac{2\sqrt{5}}{5} \qquad \sec \theta = \frac{r}{x} = \frac{3\sqrt{5}}{6} = \frac{\sqrt{5}}{2}$$

$$\tan \theta = \frac{y}{x} = \frac{3}{6} = \frac{1}{2} \qquad \cot \theta = \frac{x}{y} = \frac{6}{3} = 2$$

Example 10.2   The terminal side of an angle θ in standard position passes through the point $(3, -4)$. Find the six trigonometric functions of the angle. (See Figure 10.3.)

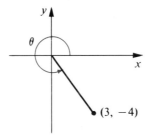

Figure 10.3

Solution   Using equation (10.1) with $x = 3$, $y = -4$, and $r = \sqrt{3^2 + (-4)^2} = 5$,

$$\sin \theta = \frac{y}{r} = \frac{-4}{5} = -\frac{4}{5} \qquad \csc \theta = \frac{r}{y} = \frac{5}{-4} = -\frac{5}{4}$$

$$\cos \theta = \frac{x}{r} = \frac{3}{5} \qquad \sec \theta = \frac{r}{x} = \frac{5}{3}$$

$$\tan \theta = \frac{y}{x} = \frac{-4}{3} = -\frac{4}{3} \qquad \cot \theta = \frac{x}{y} = \frac{3}{-4} = -\frac{3}{4}$$

10.1 Extending the Basic Definitions

281

Example 10.2 is interesting in that four of the six values are negative. Remembering that r is always positive, it should be clear that the signs of the trigonometric functions depend upon the signs of x and y.

The sine function is the ratio of y to r, which means that it is positive for angles in the first and second quadrant and negative for those in the third and fourth. This is because y is positive above the x-axis and negative below.

The cosine function, which is the ratio of x to r, is positive for angles in the first and fourth quadrants and negative in the second and third. This is because x is positive to the right of the y-axis and negative to the left.

The tangent function, which is the ratio of y to x, is positive in the first and third quadrants because y and x have the same signs in these quadrants. The tangent is negative in the second and fourth quadrants. The signs of the remaining three functions can be analyzed in the same way. Table 10.1 summarizes the results for all six functions.

Table 10.1

Quadrant	Positive Functions	Negative Functions
I	All	None
II	sine cosecant	cosine, secant tangent, cotangent
III	tangent cotangent	sine, cosine secant, cosecant
IV	cosine secant	sine, cosecant tangent, cotangent

The definitions of the trigonometric functions of any angle show that the functional values are completely determined by the location of the terminal side when the angle is in standard position. Thus, *coterminal angles have equal functional values.* For instance, since $30°$ and $390°$ are coterminal, sin $30° =$ sin $390°$, cos $30° =$ cos $390°$, and tan $30° =$ tan $390°$. Thus, in finding values of trigonometric functions, we need consider only angles between $0°$ and $360°$.

An angle whose terminal side lies on a coordinate axis is called a **quadrantal angle**. Angles of $0°$, $\pm90°$, and $\pm180°$ are examples. For these angles one of the coordinates of a point on the terminal side must be zero. Since division by zero is undefinable, two of the six trigonometric functions will be undefined at each quadrantal angle.

Example 10.3   Find the trigonometric functions of an angle θ whose terminal side passes through the point $(-1, 0)$, as shown in Figure 10.4.

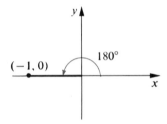

Figure 10.4

Solution In this case $x = -1$, $y = 0$, and $r = 1$. Since $\theta = 180°$,

$$\sin 180° = \frac{y}{r} = \frac{0}{1} = 0 \qquad \csc 180° = \frac{r}{y} = \frac{1}{0} \text{ (undefined)}$$

$$\cos 180° = \frac{x}{r} = \frac{-1}{1} = -1 \qquad \sec 180° = \frac{r}{x} = \frac{1}{-1} = -1$$

$$\tan 180° = \frac{y}{x} = \frac{0}{-1} = 0 \qquad \cot 180° = \frac{x}{y} = \frac{-1}{0} \text{ (undefined)}$$

Example 10.3 exhibits the values for a quadrantal angle of 180° or one coterminal with it. The values of the other quadrantal angles, found by a similar procedure, are listed in Table 10.2.

Table 10.2

Deg.	Rad.	$\sin \theta$	$\cos \theta$	$\tan \theta$	$\cot \theta$	$\sec \theta$	$\csc \theta$
0	0	0	1	0	undefined	1	undefined
90	$\pi/2$	1	0	undefined	0	undefined	1
180	π	0	−1	0	undefined	−1	undefined
270	$3\pi/2$	−1	0	undefined	0	undefined	−1

10.2
Elementary
Relations

From the definitions given in the previous section you can see that the same reciprocal relationships hold for the general trigonometric functions as in Chapter 9. Thus,

$$\sin \theta = \frac{1}{\csc \theta}, \quad \cos \theta = \frac{1}{\sec \theta}, \quad \tan \theta = \frac{1}{\cot \theta}$$

Also, the fact that $\tan \theta = y/x$ enables us to write

$$\tan \theta = \frac{y}{x} = \frac{y/r}{x/r} = \frac{\sin \theta}{\cos \theta}$$

Because of this and the reciprocal relations, the values of all six trigonometric functions can be determined by knowing the value of one of them and the quadrant of the terminal side of the angle. If the quadrant is not given, two sets of values are possible.

Example 10.4   Given that $\tan \theta = -4/3$ and that θ in standard position has its terminal side in quadrant II, find the values of the other five trigonometric functions.

Solution   Choose a convenient point on the terminal side, in this case $(-3, 4)$ as shown in Figure 10.5. (If we had been told to locate the point in quadrant IV, it would be the point $(3, -4)$.) The desired trigonometric functions for the given angle are

$$\sin \theta = \frac{4}{5} \quad \cos \theta = \frac{-3}{5} \quad \cot \theta = \frac{-3}{4} \quad \sec \theta = \frac{5}{-3} \quad \csc \theta = \frac{5}{4}$$

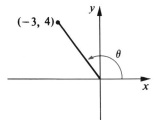

Figure 10.5

Example 10.5   Given that $\cos \theta = -5/13$, find the values of the other trigonometric functions. (See Figure 10.6.)

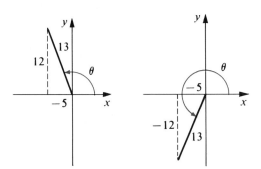

Figure 10.6

Solution   Since the quadrant is not specified, two angles between 0 and 2π will satisfy the given condition. One is in the second quadrant and the other in the third quadrant. For the second quadrant angle,

$$\sin \theta = \frac{12}{13} \quad \tan \theta = -\frac{12}{5} \quad \cot \theta = -\frac{5}{12} \quad \sec \theta = -\frac{13}{5} \quad \csc \theta = \frac{13}{12}$$

For the third quadrant angle,

$$\sin \theta = -\frac{12}{13} \quad \tan \theta = \frac{-12}{-5} = \frac{12}{5} \quad \cot \theta = \frac{-5}{-12} = \frac{5}{12}$$

$$\sec \theta = -\frac{13}{5} \quad \csc \theta = -\frac{13}{12}$$

Exercises for
Sections 10.1 and 10.2

Find the values of the trigonometric functions at an angle in standard position whose terminal side passes through the point given in each of Exercises 1–9.

1. $(2, 4)$

2. $(-1, 5)$

3. $(-9, 16)$

4. $(3, 1)$

5. $(2, -7)$

6. $(-1, -1)$

7. $(3, -1)$

8. $(1, -1)$

9. $(-\sqrt{3}, -1)$

10. Show that the values of the trigonometric functions are independent of the choice of the point P on its terminal side.

11. In which quadrants must he terminal side of θ lie for $\sin \theta$ to be positive? $\cos \theta$? $\tan \theta$?

12. Find the six trigonometric functions of $90°$ by noticing that $(0, 1)$ lies on the terminal side of the angle of $90°$ when it is placed in standard position.

13. Show that $\sin 60° = \sin 420°$.

14. Find the six trigonometric functions of $0°$. Use $(1, 0)$ as a point on the terminal side.

15. Find the six trigonometric functions of $270°$. Use $(0, -1)$ as a point on the terminal side.

16. For which values of θ is $\sin \theta = 1$? For which values is $\cos \theta = 1$?

Find the trigonometric functions at an angle θ that satisfies the conditions given in Exercises 17–31.

17. $\tan \theta = \frac{3}{4}$ in quadrant I

18. $\sec \theta = -3$

19. $\tan \theta = \frac{3}{4}$ in quadrant III

20. $\tan \theta = \frac{1}{2}$ in quadrant III

21. $\cos \theta = -1$

22. $\cot \theta = \pi$ in quadrant IV

23. $\sin \theta = 0$

24. $\sin \theta = \sqrt{3}/2$

25. $\sin \theta = -\frac{1}{2}$

26. $\sin \theta = \frac{1}{5}$

27. $\tan \theta = 10$ in quadrant I

28. $\csc \theta = 2$

29. $\cos \theta = \frac{12}{13}$

30. $\cos \theta = -\dfrac{\sqrt{3}}{2}$ in quadrant II

31. $\tan \theta = -\pi$

10.3
The Use of Tables
for Angles That Are Not Acute

As you learned in the previous section, the values of the trigonometric functions are defined, with a few exceptions, for any angle. Now you will learn how to use trigonometric tables to find values for angles greater than $90°$. The process is not difficult, but it does require some explanation since trigonometric tables are traditionally tabulated from 0° to 90°.

For an idea of the general procedure, consider finding tan 150°. Figure 10.7 shows a generated angle of 150°. The acute angle formed by the terminal

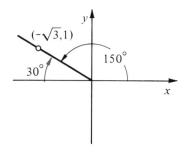

Figure 10.7

side and the *x*-axis is obviously 30°. This angle is called the *reference angle of 150°*. Now from our knowledge of the 30–60° right triangle, we know that the terminal side must pass through the point $(-\sqrt{3}, 1)$. Therefore,

$$\tan 150° = -1/\sqrt{3} \quad \text{and} \quad \tan 30° = 1/\sqrt{3}$$

Of interest here is the fact that tan 150° has the same numerical value as the tangent of its reference angle. The example implies that tan 150° can be found by finding tan 30° in a table and then prefixing the appropriate numerical sign. The general procedure for finding trigonometric functions for any generated angle is outlined in the remainder of this section.

Consider angles α, β, γ, and δ, in standard position, each of whose terminal sides lie in a different quadrant, as shown in Figure 10.8(a). To find the values of the trigonometric functions for each of these angles, first find the measure of the acute angle made by the terminal side of the given angle and

(a)

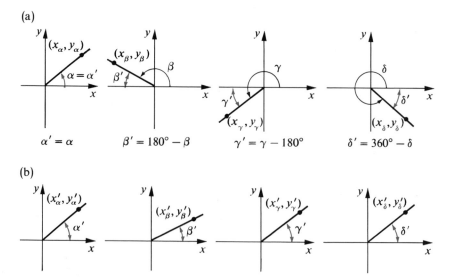

(b)

Figure 10.8

the x-axis. This angle is called the **reference angle** for the given angle. In Figure 10.8(a) each reference angle is denoted with a prime and can be found by using the following rules.

(1) First quadrant angle: $\alpha' = \alpha$
(2) Second quadrant angle: $\beta' = 180° - \beta$
(3) Third quadrant angle: $\gamma' = \gamma - 180°$
(4) Fourth quadrant angle: $\delta' = 360° - \delta$

The reference angles in Figure 10.8(a) are shown in standard position in Figure 10.8(b). The coordinates of the intersection of the terminal side of each angle in Figure 10.8(a) with a circle of radius r are numerically equal (except for sign) to those obtained for the reference angles placed in standard position. It follows then that, except possibly for numerical sign, any trigonometric function of an angle has the identical value as the same function of the reference angle. For example,

$$\tan \alpha = \frac{y_\alpha}{x_\alpha} = \frac{y'_\alpha}{x'_\alpha} = \tan \alpha'$$

$$\tan \beta = \frac{y_\beta}{x_\beta} = \frac{y'_\beta}{-x'_\beta} = -\tan \beta'$$

$$\tan \gamma = \frac{y_\gamma}{x_\gamma} = \frac{-y'_\gamma}{-x'_\gamma} = \tan \gamma'$$

$$\tan \delta = \frac{y_\delta}{x_\delta} = \frac{-y'_\delta}{x'_\delta} = -\tan \delta'$$

Notice that these results agree with those given in Table 10.1 with respect to the numerical sign of the tangent in each quadrant.

Thus, the functional values of the reference acute angle determine completely the values of the trigonometric functions of an angle in standard position. The algebraic sign is determined by the quadrantal location of the terminal side. In summary, to determine values of the trigonometric functions for any angle, proceed as follows:

---

(1) Determine the positive coterminal angle with measure between 0° and 360° corresponding to the given angle.
(2) Sketch the angle in standard position.
(3) Determine the reference acute angle.
(4) Find the value of the trigonometric function of the reference acute angle, usually from the tables in the appendix.
(5) The value of the trigonometric function of the reference acute angle is the same as the value of the trigonometric function of the given angle except perhaps for the sign. Determine the sign from the location of the terminal side of the given angle.

10.3 The Use of Tables for Angles That Are Not Acute

287

Example 10.6   Find cos 145°20′. (See Figure 10.9.)

Solution   We see that 145°20′ is a second quadrant angle, and therefore, the reference angle is

$$\theta' = 180° - 145°20' = 34°40'$$

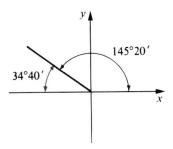

Figure 10.9

The reference angle is indicated in the figure. Remembering that the cosine function is negative in the second quadrant,

$$\cos 145°20' = -\cos 34°40'$$
$$= -0.8225 \qquad \text{(Table D, appendix)}$$

Example 10.7   Find tan 4. (See Figure 10.10.)

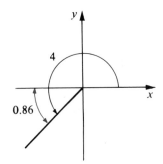

Figure 10.10

Solution   An angle of 4 radians lies in the third quadrant, as in Figure 10.10. The reference angle is then

$$\theta' = 4 - \pi = 4 - 3.14 = 0.86$$

Since the tangent function is positive in the third quadrant,

$$\tan 4 = \tan 0.86$$
$$= 1.16 \qquad \text{(Table E, appendix)}$$

Example 10.8   Find sin 1000 and sin 1000°.

288   10 Trigonometric Functions for Any Angle

Solution Dividing 1000 by 6.28, we find that the angle of 1000 radians is coterminal with the angle of 1.48 radians. Since this is a first quadrant angle,

$$\sin 1000 = \sin 1.48$$

$$= 0.9959 \qquad \text{(Table E)}$$

Since $1000°/360° = 2$ with a remainder of $280°$, the angle of $1000°$ is coterminal with a fourth quadrant angle. The reference acute angle is $80°$. Hence,

$$\sin 1000° = \sin 280°$$

$$= -\sin 80°$$

$$= -0.9848 \qquad \text{(Table D)}$$

From the previous discussion it is clear that there are always two angles on the interval $0° \leq \theta < 360°$ that have the same trigonometric ratio. Consequently, finding an angle corresponding to a given trigonometric ratio is more involved than it was for acute angle trigonometry. For example, if $\sin \theta = \frac{1}{2}$, it follows that both $\theta = 30°$ and $\theta = 150°$ are correct answers for $0° \leq \theta < 360°$. This redundancy can be avoided by stipulating certain conditions on angle θ. Thus, if we stipulate $\sin \theta = \frac{1}{2}$ and $\cos \theta < 0$, then $\theta = 150°$ is the only answer, since $\sin \theta > 0$ and $\cos \theta < 0$ implies that θ is in the second quadrant.

Example 10.9   Given $\tan \beta = 0.3185$ and $\sin \beta < 0$, find β on the interval $0° \leq \beta < 360°$.

Solution   Since $\tan \beta$ is positive and $\sin \beta$ is negative, β must be a third quadrant angle. From Table D, $\tan 17°40' = 0.3185$. Therefore,

$$\beta = 180° + 17°40' = 197°40'$$

By considering cases in which the angle θ has, in turn, its terminal side in each of the four quadrants, the following general relations may be shown.

$$\sin \theta = -\sin (-\theta) \qquad \cos \theta = \cos (-\theta)$$

$$\sin (\pi - \theta) = \sin \theta \qquad \cos (\pi - \theta) = -\cos \theta$$

$$\sin (\pi + \theta) = -\sin \theta \qquad \cos (\pi + \theta) = -\cos \theta$$

$$\sin (2\pi - \theta) = -\sin \theta \qquad \cos (2\pi - \theta) = \cos \theta$$

Do not memorize this type of relation but rather be able to work out any of the results listed by the methods of this section.

10.3 The Use of Tables for Angles That Are Not Acute

Express the trigonometric functions in Exercises 1–10 in terms of the same function of a positive acute angle.

1. cos 125°   2. tan 94°   3. sin 225°

4. csc 252°28′   5. tan 1243°   6. tan 100

7. sec 10   8. sin 90   9. cos 45

10. cos 5

Evaluate Exercises 11–20.   (Use Table D)

11. sin 154°   12. sin 333°   13. tan 96°

14. cos 205°   15. sec 163°20′   16. tan 200°35′

17. cos 285°50′   18. csc 261°   19. sin 247°36′

20. cos 108°29′

Evaluate Exercises 21–30.   (Use Table E)

21. sin 100   22. tan −100   23. sin 4.22

24. cos 5.16   25. csc 20   26. sec (−4)

27. cot 1.335   28. tan −2.745   29. cos 3.01

30. cos −7.485

Evaluate Exercises 31–40.

31. sin 13π/3   32. csc 41π/4   33. tan 69π/6

34. cos 19π/6   35. tan 22π/3   36. cot 27π/4

37. cos 61π/2   38. sin (−35π/6)   39. sec 43π/6

40. sin 1000π

Find θ where $0 \leq \theta < 2\pi$ (Exercises 41–45).

41. sin θ = −0.6157,   cos θ > 0   42. cos θ = 0.4226,   tan θ < 0

43. cot θ = 0.9004,   sin θ < 0   44. cos θ = 0.8241,   sin θ > 0

45. tan θ = −1.804,   sec θ > 0

Find θ where $0 \leq \theta < 360°$ (Exercises 46–51).

46. sin θ = 0.4331,   cos θ < 0   47. sin θ = −0.4253,   tan θ < 0

48. cos θ = −0.8635,   cot θ > 0   49. cot θ = 3.0326,   csc θ < 0

50. cos θ = 0.9012,   sec θ > 0   51. tan θ = −6.8269,   csc θ > 0

52. Construct a table showing the exact values of the trigonometric functions for angles with radian measure of 0, π/6, π/4, π/3 and angles symmetric to these around the unit circle.

10.4
Oblique Triangles*

Any triangle that is not a right triangle is called **oblique**. Hence, in an oblique triangle none of the angles is equal to 90°. Section 9.2 explained that a right triangle is uniquely determined by two of its five unknown parts, if at least one of the two is the length of a side. In this chapter we study conditions under which an oblique triangle is solvable and arrive at roughly the same conclusion: a knowledge of at least three of the six parts is necessary to solve the general triangle.

The three parts needed to solve a triangle are not completely arbitrary. For example, if the three angles of a triangle are given, no unique solution is possible, because many triangles have these angles but different side lengths. All such triangles would be *similar* but not *congruent*.† As the chapter develops, other more subtle cases arise in which three parts assigned arbitrarily yield impossible or ambiguous situations. The question to answer is, "What information is necessary and sufficient to obtain a unique solution of an oblique triangle?" The answer is contained in the following theorems from plane geometry dealing with congruent triangles.

Theorem 10.1: Two triangles are congruent if and only if two sides and the included angle of one are equal respectively to two sides and the included angle of the other.

Theorem 10.2: Two triangles are congruent if and only if three sides of one are equal respectively to three sides of the other.

Theorem 10.3: Two triangles are congruent if and only if two angles and the included side of one are equal respectively to two angles and the included side of the other.

From the perspective of solving oblique triangles, the preceding theorems say that a triangle is uniquely determined if:

Case 1 Two sides and the included angle are given.

Case 2 Three sides are given.

Case 3 Two angles and the included side are given.

A fourth case that arises in solving oblique triangles is important even though the information given does not necessarily yield a unique solution.

* The remainder of the material in this chapter may be omitted without loss of continuity.

† The word "congruent" means of the same shape and size. Thus, two triangles that are congruent coincide exactly in all their parts if placed properly one upon the other.

Case 4   Two sides and an angle opposite one of the sides are given.

This case is sometimes referred to as the *ambiguous* case since two triangles, one triangle, or no triangles may result from data given in this form.

10.5
The Law of
Cosines

The theorems, or laws, that allow us to solve oblique triangles are derived by subdividing a general oblique triangle into two right triangles. In this section we derive a formula, known as the law of cosines, that can be used to solve case 1 and case 2 triangles. The **law of cosines** is a formula that permits the solution of an oblique triangle when two sides and the included angle or when three sides are given.

Consider any oblique triangle ABC; for example, either of the triangles in Figure 10.11. Drop a perpendicular from the vertex B to side AC or its extension. Call the length of this perpendicular h. In either case $h = c \sin A$, and hence,

$$h^2 = c^2 \sin^2 A$$

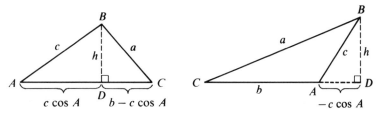

Figure 10.11   Law of cosines

Or using

$$\sin^2 A + \cos^2 A = 1$$

yields

$$h^2 = c^2(1 - \cos^2 A)$$

Referring to Figure 10.11, we also have from right triangle BCD that

$$h^2 = a^2 - (b - c \cos A)^2$$

Equating the right-hand sides of the two preceding equations,

$$c^2(1 - \cos^2 A) = a^2 - (b - c \cos A)^2$$
$$c^2 - c^2 \cos^2 A = a^2 - b^2 + 2bc \cos A - c^2 \cos^2 A$$

By simplifying this expression,

(10.2) $a^2 = b^2 + c^2 - 2bc \cos A$

In a similar manner, it can be shown that

$$b^2 = a^2 + c^2 - 2ac \cos B$$

and

$$c^2 = a^2 + b^2 - 2ab \cos C$$

Each of these formulas is a statement of the law of cosines. In words, it says that the square of any side of a triangle is equal to the sum of the squares of the other two sides minus twice their product and the cosine of the angle between them. If the angle is 90°, the law of cosines reduces to the theorem of Pythagoras so that it is quite properly considered to be an extension of that famous theorem.

The law of cosines gives the relationship between three sides and one of the angles of any triangle. Thus, given any of these three parts, we can compute the remaining parts or show that such a triangle is impossible. For example, if three sides of a triangle are given, angle A can be found from equation (10.2) by solving for $\cos A$ to obtain an alternate form of the law of cosines:

(10.3) $\cos A = \dfrac{b^2 + c^2 - a^2}{2bc}$

Similar formulas may be obtained for $\cos B$ and $\cos C$. Note that in this form the law says that the cosine of an angle may be found by computing a fraction whose numerator is the sum of squares of the adjacent sides minus the square of the opposite side and whose denominator is twice the product of the adjacent sides.

Example 10.10   Solve the triangle with side $a = 5$, side $b = 6$, and angle $C = 60°$ as shown in Figure 10.12.

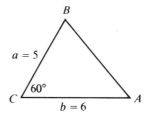

Figure 10.12

Solution

$$c^2 = a^2 + b^2 - 2ab \cos C$$
$$= 25 + 36 - 60 \cos 60°$$
$$= 31$$

10.5 The Law of Cosines   293

Therefore,

$$c = \sqrt{31} \approx 5.6$$

To solve for angle A, use equation (10.3) of the law of cosines.

$$\cos A = \frac{b^2 + c^2 - a^2}{2bc}$$

$$= \frac{36 + 31 - 25}{67.2}$$

$$= \frac{42}{67.2} = 0.6250$$

Therefore,

$$A = 51°19'$$

The remaining angle could also be found from the law of cosines, but since the sum of the angles is 180°,

$$B = 180° - 60° - 51°19'$$

$$= 68°41'$$

Example 10.11   Two airplanes leave an airport at the same time, one going northeast at 400 mph and the other going directly west at 300 mph. How far apart are they two hours after leaving?

Solution   From Figure 10.13 and from the law of cosines,

$$D^2 = 600^2 + 800^2 - 2(600)(800) \cos 135°$$

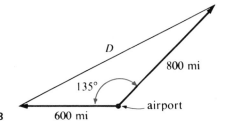

Figure 10.13

Notice that

$$\cos 135° = -\cos 45° = -0.707$$

$$D^2 = 360,000 + 640,000 - (960,000)(-0.707)$$

$$= 1,678,720$$

$$D \approx 1295 \text{ miles}$$

Example 10.12   In a steel bridge one part of a truss is in the form of an isosceles triangle, as in Figure 10.14. At what angles do the sides of the truss meet?

294   10 Trigonometric Functions for Any Angle

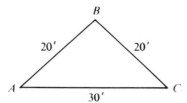

Figure 10.14

Solution

$$\cos A = \frac{20^2 + 30^2 - 20^2}{(2)(20)(30)} = \frac{900}{1200} = 0.75$$

Hence,

$$A = 41°25'$$

This is also the value of angle C since the triangle is isosceles. Then,

$$B = 180° - 82°50'$$

$$= 97°10'$$

Suppose that we had decided to use the law of cosines to find angle B. Then,

$$\cos B = \frac{20^2 + 20^2 - 30^2}{(2)(20)(20)} = \frac{800 - 900}{800} = -\frac{1}{8} = -0.125$$

The fact that $\cos B$ is negative tells us that angle B is greater than 90° and less than 180° The angle whose cosine is 0.125 is 82°50', and therefore,

$$B = 180° - 82°50' = 97°10'$$

This answer agrees with the previous result. Notice how the fact that $\cos B$ is negative affected the determination of angle B. 🦊

The form of the law of cosines as in equation (10.3) further allows you to see that information given on the sides of triangles is not arbitrary. For example, if $a = 1$, $b = 3$, and $c = 1$, then using equation (10.3),

$$\cos A = \frac{(3)^2 + (1)^2 - (1)^2}{2(3)(1)} = \frac{9}{6} = \frac{3}{2}$$

However, this condition is impossible since $|\cos A| \le 1$. Hence, no such triangle exists.

Exercises for
Sections 10.4 and 10.5

In each of Exercises 1–6 use the law of cosines to find the unknown side.

1. $a = 45, b = 67, C = 35°$ **2.** $a = 20, b = 40, C = 28°$

10.5 The Law of Cosines

3. $a = 10, b = 40, C = 120°$ **4.** $b = 10, c = 10, B = 30°$

5. $b = 38, c = 42, A = 135°$ **6.** $a = 3.49, b = 3.54, C = 5°24'$

In each of Exercises 7–12 use the law of cosines to find the largest angle.

7. $a = 7, b = 6, c = 8$ **8.** $a = 16, b = 17, c = 18$

9. $a = 18, b = 14, c = 10$ **10.** $a = 3, b = 5, c = 6$

11. $a = 17, b = 25, c = 12$ **12.** $a = 56, b = 67, c = 82$

In each of Exercises 13–18 use the law of cosines to solve the triangles.

13. $a = 4, b = 1, C = 30°$ **14.** $a = 5, b = 5, C = 60°$

15. $a = 120, b = 145, C = 94°25'$ **16.** $a = 9, b = 7, c = 5$

17. $a = 2, b = 3, c = 4$ **18.** $a = 5, c = 5, B = 28°$

19. In a triangular lot ABC the stake that marked the corner C has been lost. By consulting the deed to the property, the owner finds that $\overline{AB} = 80$ feet, $\overline{BC} = 50$ feet, and $\overline{CA} = 40$ feet. At what angle with AB should he run a line so that by laying off 40 feet along this line he can locate corner C?

20. An airplane flying directly north toward a city C alters its course toward the northeast at a point 100 miles from C and heads for city B, approximately 50 miles away. If B and C are 60 miles apart, what course should the airplane fly to get to B?

21. In planning a tunnel under a hill, an engineer lays out the triangle ABC as shown in the following figure in order to determine the course of the tunnel. If $\overline{AB} = 3500$ feet, $\overline{BC} = 4000$ feet, and angle $B = 60°$, what are the sizes of the angles A and C and what is the length of AC?

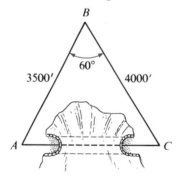

22. If two forces, one of 500 pounds and the other of 400 pounds, act from a point at an angle of 60° with each other, what is the size of the resultant? (See the following figure.)

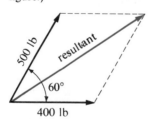

23. In order to measure the distance between two points A and B on opposite sides of a building, a third point C is chosen such that the following measurements can be made: $\overline{CA} = 200$ feet, $\overline{CB} = 400$ feet, and the angle ACB measures $60°$. What is the distance between A and B?

24. Show that for any triangle ABC

$$\frac{a^2 + b^2 + c^2}{2abc} = \frac{\cos A}{a} + \frac{\cos B}{b} + \frac{\cos C}{c}$$

10.6
The Law of Sines

The law of cosines cannot be used to solve triangles for which two angles and one side are given. Triangles of this type may be solved using a formula known as the **law of sines**. This formula in conjunction with the law of cosines enables us to solve any triangle for which we are given three parts, or at least to declare that no solution is possible.

Consider either triangle shown in Figure 10.15. By drawing a perpendicular h from the vertex B to side b or its extension, we see from Figure 10.15(a) that

$$h = c \sin A \text{ and } h = a \sin C$$

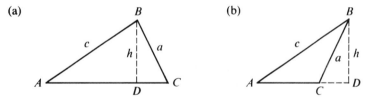

Figure 10.15   Law of sines

Equating these two expressions,

$$c \sin A = a \sin C$$

or, rearranging terms,

$$\frac{a}{\sin A} = \frac{c}{\sin C}$$

In a similar manner we can show that

$$\frac{a}{\sin A} = \frac{b}{\sin B}$$

Hence,

$$(10.4) \qquad \frac{a}{\sin A} = \frac{b}{\sin B} = \frac{c}{\sin C}$$

Equation (10.4) is called the **law of sines**. In words, it states that in any triangle the ratios formed by dividing the sides by the sine of the angle opposite them are equal.

Combinations of any two of the three ratios given in equation (10.4) yield an equation with four parts. Obviously, if we know three of these parts, we can find the fourth.

Example 10.13   Given that $c = 10$, $A = 40°$, and $B = 60°$, find a, b, and C. (See Figure 10.16.)

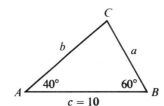

Figure 10.16

Solution   We begin by observing that

$$C = 180° - (A + B) = 180° - (60° + 40°) = 80°$$

Using the law of sines,

$$\frac{a}{\sin 40°} = \frac{10}{\sin 80°} \quad \text{or} \quad a = \frac{10(0.6428)}{0.9848} = 6.53$$

and

$$\frac{b}{\sin 60°} = \frac{10}{\sin 80°} \quad \text{or} \quad b = \frac{10(0.8660)}{0.9848} = 8.79$$

Example 10.14   A surveyor desires to run a straight line from A in the direction AB, as shown in Figure 10.17 but finds that an obstruction interferes with the line of sight. He therefore

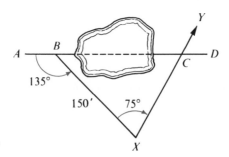

Figure 10.17

298   10 Trigonometric Functions for Any Angle

lays off the line segment $\overline{BX}$ for a distance of 150 feet in such a way that angle $ABX = 135°$ and runs XY at an angle of 75° with $\overline{BX}$. At what distance from X in this line should he take the point C from which to run a line CD in prolongation of AB?

Solution   Since angle $CBX = 45°$, we have from the law of sines,

$$\frac{\overline{CX}}{\sin 45°} = \frac{150'}{\sin 60°}$$

Hence,

$$\overline{CX} = \frac{\sin 45°}{\sin 60°} 150'$$

$$= \frac{\sqrt{2}/2}{\sqrt{3}/2} 150 = \frac{\sqrt{2}}{\sqrt{3}} 150 \approx \frac{1.414}{1.732} 150 = 122.4'$$

The next example involves a triangle in which two sides and an angle opposite one of them is given. Such data may define one, two, or no triangles. In the following example a unique triangle is formed by the given data. The next section presents a discussion of the ambiguous case.

Example 10.15   A satellite traveling in a circular orbit 1000 miles above the earth is due to pass directly over a tracking station at noon. Assume that the satellite takes 2 hours to make an orbit and that the radius of the earth is 4000 miles. If the tracking antenna is aimed 30° above the horizon, at what time will the satellite pass through the beam of the antenna? (See Figure 10.18.)

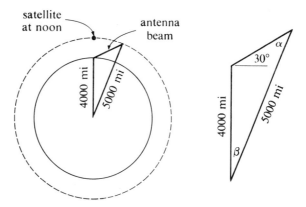

Figure 10.18

Solution   From the law of sines,

$$\frac{\sin \alpha}{4000} = \frac{\sin 120°}{5000}$$

$$\sin \alpha = \frac{4000 \sin 120°}{5000} = 0.693$$

10.6 The Law of Sines

299

Hence,

$$\alpha = 43.9°$$

and

$$\beta = 180° - (120° + 43.9°) = 16.1°$$

Time between $\beta = 16.1°$ and $\beta = 0.0°$ is $(16.1°/360°)(120 \text{ min}) = 5.4$ minutes. Thus, the satellite will pass through the beam of the antenna at $12:00 - 5.4$ minutes, or $11:54.6$ A.M.

Exercises for
Section 10.6

Solve the oblique triangles given in Exercises 1–15.

1. $A = 32°, B = 48°, a = 10$ 2. $A = 60°, B = 45°, b = 3$

3. $A = 45°, a = 8, b = 5$ 4. $A = 75°, a = 20, b = 10$

5. $A = 30°, b = 10, a = 5$ 6. $A = 30°, b = 10, a = 20$

7. $A = 120°, a = 6, b = 5$ 8. $A = 51°10', a = 59.2, b = 53.5$

9. $C = 53°, b = 18.3, c = 30.2$ 10. $C = 58°, c = 83, b = 51$

11. $B = 122°, b = 30, a = 25$ 12. $B = 63°, b = 5, c = 4$

13. $C = 110°, B = 50°, b = 40$ 14. $C = 73.2°, A = 13.7°, c = 20.5$

15. $B = 48°, A = 43.4°, c = 61.3$

16. The crank and connecting rod of an engine, like the one illustrated in the following figure are 12 inches and 40 inches long, respectively. What angle does the crank make with the horizontal when the angle made by the connecting rod is 12°?

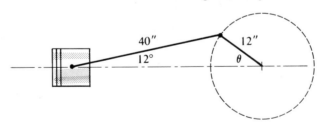

17. From a given position an observer notes that the angle of elevation of the top of an antenna is 45°. After walking 1000 feet toward the base of the antenna up a slope of 30°, he finds the angle of elevation to be 75°. Find the vertical height of the antenna above each point of observation.

18. A satellite traveling in a circular orbit 1500 miles above the earth is due to pass directly over a tracking station at noon. Assume that the satellite takes 90 minutes to make an orbit and that the radius of the earth is 4000 miles. If the tracking antenna is aimed 20° above the horizon, at what time will the satellite pass through the beam of the antenna?

19. Using information in the previous exercise, determine the angle above the horizon that the antenna should be pointed so that its beam will intercept the satellite at 12:05 P.M.

20. Consider a flight from Miami to New York to be along a north-south direction with an airline distance of approximately 1000 miles. A jet having an air speed of 500 mph makes the round trip. With a constant northwest wind of 100 mph, how long will it take for the round trip? What headings will the pilot use for the two parts of the trip?

10.7
The Ambiguous
Case

We now analyze how to solve those triangles for which the measure of two sides and an angle opposite one of them is given. For ease of discussion, suppose that two sides a and b and an angle A are given. As you will see, there may be one, two, or no triangles with these measurements.

$A < 90°$: Perhaps the best way to make the situation clear, when angle A is acute, is to draw a figure. Let us construct a line segment having a length of b units along one side of angle A to locate the vertex C. Then it is obvious from Figure 10.19 that the length of side a determines if there are one, two, or no triangles. In Figure 10.19(a) only one triangle is possible since $a > b$. In Figure 10.19(b) two triangles are possible by swinging an arc of length a from C so that it intersects side c at two points. In Figure 10.19(c) the length of side a is such

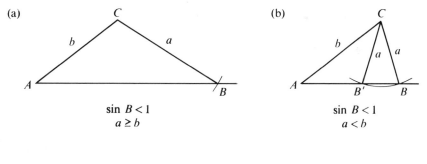

(a)

sin $B < 1$
$a \geq b$

(b)

sin $B < 1$
$a < b$

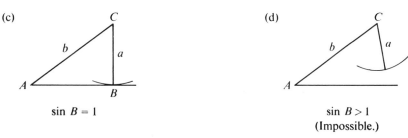

(c)

sin $B = 1$

(d)

sin $B > 1$
(Impossible.)

Figure 10.19 Ambiguous case, $A \leq 90°$

that it intersects side c at one point to form a single right triangle. Finally, in Figure 10.19(d) the length of side a is too short to intersect side c and therefore no triangle can be formed.

The situations described graphically in Figure 10.19 can be stated analytically by solving

$$\frac{a}{\sin A} = \frac{b}{\sin B}$$

for sin B, and noting that

(1) If $a \geq b$, then there is only one triangle.
(2) If $a < b$ and sin $B < 1$, then two angles at B are possible: the acute angle B from the tables and the obtuse angle $B' = 180° - B$.
(3) If $a < b$ and sin $B = 1$, then $B = 90°$, so there is one right triangle.
(4) If $a < b$ and sin $B > 1$, then B cannot exist, so there is no triangle.

$A \geq 90°$: The case in which angle A is greater than or equal to $90°$ is much easier to analyze, as shown in Figure 10.20. As you can see in Figure 10.20(a) if $a \leq b$, there is no triangle. If $a > b$, there is one triangle, as shown in Figure 10.20(b).

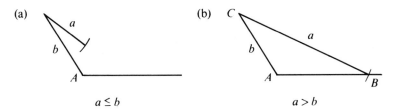

$$a \leq b \qquad\qquad a > b$$

Figure 10.20   Ambiguous case, $A > 90°$

Example 10.16   How many triangles can be formed if $a = 4$, $b = 10$, and $A = 30°$?

Solution   Using the law of sines,

$$\frac{\sin B}{10} = \frac{\sin 30°}{4} \quad\text{or}\quad \sin B = \frac{10(0.5)}{4} = 1.25$$

Since sin $B > 1$, we conclude that no triangle corresponds to this given information. (See Figure 10.21.)

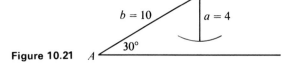

Figure 10.21

Example 10.17   Verify that two triangles can be drawn for $a = 9$, $b = 10$, and $A = 60°$ and then solve each triangle.

Solution   Substituting the given values in the law of sines,

$$\frac{\sin B}{10} = \frac{\sin 60°}{9} \quad \text{or} \quad \sin B = \frac{10(0.8660)}{9} = 0.9622$$

Since $\sin B < 1$ and $a < b$, we conclude that there are two possible solutions. This is shown in Figure 10.22. One triangle is ABC and the other is $AB'C'$. From Table D we find that B is approximately

$$B = 74°10'$$

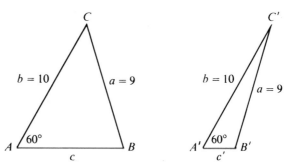

Figure 10.22

Therefore, angle B' is given by

$$B' = 180° - B = 180° - 74°10' = 105°50'$$

To solve triangle ABC, note that angle C is given by

$$C = 180° - (A + B) = 180° - (60° + 74°10') = 45°50'$$

Hence,

$$\frac{c}{\sin 45°50'} = \frac{9}{\sin 60°} \quad \text{or} \quad c = \frac{9(0.7173)}{0.8660} = 7.45$$

Similarly in triangle $AB'C'$,

$$C' = 180° - (A + B') = 180° - (60° + 105°50') = 14°10'$$

So

$$\frac{c'}{\sin 14°10'} = \frac{9}{\sin 60°} \quad \text{or} \quad c' = \frac{9(0.2447)}{0.8660} = 2.54$$

Example 10.18   Verify that only one triangle can be drawn for the case in which $b = 10$, $A = 60°$, and $a = 11$.

Solution   Figure 10.23 depicts the information given. Applying the law of sines,

$$\frac{11}{0.866} = \frac{10}{\sin B}$$

from which $\sin B = 0.7873$. Since the side opposite the given angle is greater than the

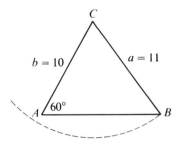

Figure 10.23

side adjacent, there is only one solution. Notice that had we missed the fact that $a > b$, we would get

$$B = 51°55' \quad \text{and} \quad B' = 128°05'$$

However, the "solution" of $B' = 128°05'$ is impossible because a triangle with an angle of 60° and 128°05' cannot exist. Thus, we reach the same conclusion as before.

This last example shows the importance of a continual check that the information being given and calculated is consistent and not producing impossible situations.

Do not memorize the various subcases within the ambiguous case since for any specific problem the ambiguity or nonsolvability becomes evident with an attempted solution. For example, if in the course of solving a triangle, you find that $\sin B > 1$, this will mean that no triangle exists corresponding to the data given. If $\sin B < 1$, two angles exist that satisfy this particular inequality, but watch for the limitation that the sum of the angles is less than 180°.

Exercises for
Section 10.7

In Exercises 1–5 state if the triangle has one solution, two solutions, or no solutions, given that $A = 30°$, $b = 4$, and

1. $a = 1$ **2.** $a = 2$ **3.** $a = 3$ **4.** $a = 4$ **5.** $a = 5$

For the triangles in Exercises 6–17 find all the unknown measurements or show that no such triangle exists.

6. $a = 20$, $b = 10$, $A = 35°40'$ **7.** $a = 2$, $b = 6$, $A = 26°20'$

8. $a = 4$, $b = 8$, $A = 30°$ **9.** $a = 15$, $c = 8$, $A = 150°$

10. $a = 50$, $b = 19$, $B = 22°30'$ **11.** $b = 60$, $c = 74$, $B = 140°$

12. $a = 50$, $c = 10$, $A = 48°$ **13.** $C = 28°$, $a = 20$, $c = 15$

14. $B = 40°$, $a = 12$, $b = 10$ **15.** $A = 30°$, $b = 400$, $a = 300$

16. $B = 41.2°$, $a = 4.2$, $b = 3.2$ **17.** $a = 0.9$, $b = 0.7$, $A = 72°15'$

18. If $b = 12$ and $A = 30°$, for which values of a will two triangles result?

19. If $c = 15$ and $B = 25°$, for which values of b will two triangles result?

10 Trigonometric Functions for Any Angle

Answer true or false for 1–10.

1. If $\theta_1 < \theta_2$ and both θ_1 and θ_2 are in the third quadrant, then $\cos \theta_1 < \cos \theta_2$.

2. $\sin 30° = \sin (180° - 30°)$

3. $\sin (\pi/6) = \cos (-\pi/3)$

4. $\sin (2\pi + \theta) = \sin (2\pi - \theta)$ for any θ.

5. The law of cosines can be used to find the angles of a triangle if all three sides are given.

6. The law of sines can be used to find the angles of a triangle if all three sides are given.

7. If $45° < \theta < 90°$, then $\sin \theta > \cos \theta$.

8. If $0 < \theta < 360°$, and $\sin \theta < \cos \theta$, then $0 < \theta < 45°$.

9. If $0 < \theta < 360°$ and $\tan \theta = 1$, then $\theta = 45°$ or $225°$.

10. In the third quadrant, $\cot \theta < 0$.

11. Find the six trigonometric functions of an angle in standard position whose terminal side passes through $(2, -1)$.

12. Given that $\tan \theta = -3$ and $\sin \theta > 0$, find the values of the other five trigonometric functions.

13. Find $\tan -1030°$.

14. Find $\sin 45$.

15. Solve the triangle ABC with $b = 4$, $c = 5$, and $A = 60°$.

16. Solve the triangle ABC with $b = 5$, $c = 4$ and $B = 60°$.

1. Find the sine and tangent functions of the angle in standard position whose terminal side passes through $(-2, 3)$.

2. Answer true or false:
   (a) $\sin \theta > 0$ in quadrant III
   (b) $\sin \theta < 0$ in quadrant IV
   (c) $\tan \theta < 0$ in quadrant III

3. Given $\tan \theta = -\sqrt{2}$ in quadrant II, find $\cos \theta$ and $\csc \theta$.

4. Evaluate (a) $\sin 206°$, (b) $\cos 495°20'$, (c) $\tan 252°15'$.

5. Find θ, where $0 \le \theta < 2\pi$. (a) $\tan \theta = 1.3957$, (b) $\sin \theta = -0.5666$.

Solve the triangles in Exercises 6–9.

6. $B = 73°20'$, $C = 15°10'$, $c = 25$

7. $a = 15, c = 8, B = 112°16'$

8. $a = 7, b = 3, c = 9$

9. $A = 46°15', a = 20, b = 10$

10. An airplane is flying due east at 190 mph. Find the resultant velocity of the airplane if a 50 mph tail wind blows at an angle of 25° north of east.

11
Analytic
Trigonometry

11.1
Trigonometric
Functions of Real Numbers

In Chapter 9 the domain of the trigonometric functions was defined as the set of all angles, with most of the discussion being limited to the interior angles of a triangle. Because of this restriction, you may think that the trigonometric functions are important only for angles less than 180°. This is far from the case; as a matter of fact, some of the important applications of trigonometry have nothing to do with triangles.

Modern trigonometry consists of two more or less distinct branches. The study of the six ratios and their applications to problems involving triangles is one branch, called *triangle trigonometry*. The other branch is concerned with the general functional behavior of the six ratios, especially with respect to the nature of their variation and their graphs. This branch is often called *analytical trigonometry*.

In analytical trigonometry we consider the six trigonometric functions to be functions of real numbers in addition to being functions of angles. The discussion in this section shows that the extension of the domain of the trigonometric functions to include real numbers is a rather simple matter of matching real numbers with the radian measure of angles.

We begin by locating the unit circle in the rectangular plane with center at the origin and passing through (1, 0) as shown in Figure 11.1(a). The circumference of the unit circle is 2π, or approximately 6.28.

Let L denote a real number line that is parallel to the y-axis with its 0 point at (1, 0). Now if L is wrapped around the unit circle, each point on the line is mapped onto a point on the circle, as in Figure 11.1(b). The positive half line is wound in a counterclockwise direction, whereas the negative half line is wound in a clockwise direction.

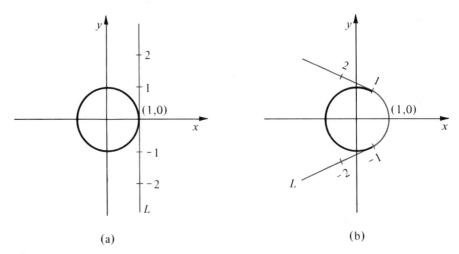

(a)   (b)

Figure 11.1

Each real number u mapped onto the unit circle determines both a point P in the plane and an angle α in standard position, as shown in Figure 11.2. The point P and the angle α are said to be *associated* with the real number u.

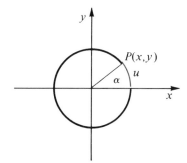

Figure 11.2

To establish a relationship between the number u and the angle α, remember that the radian measure of an angle is the ratio of the length of the arc of a circle subtended by the angle to the radius of the circle; that is,

$$\alpha(\text{radians}) = \frac{u(\text{arc length})}{r(\text{radius})}$$

Since $r = 1$ for the unit circle, the measure of angle α is numerically equal to the arc length u. Symbolically,

$$\alpha(\textbf{radians}) = u$$

Example 11.1 illustrates this fact.

Example 11.1   Sketch the points and angles associated with the real numbers 2, $\sqrt{13}$, $- 3.6$, and 6.

Solution   See Figure 11.3.

Using the natural association of real numbers with angles in standard position, we may define the trigonometric functions for any real number u. If α, in radians, is the angle associated with the real number u, then

$$\sin u = \sin \alpha \quad \cos u = \cos \alpha \quad \tan u = \tan \alpha$$

$$\sec u = \sec \alpha \quad \csc u = \csc \alpha \quad \cot u = \cot \alpha$$

Since it is customary not to write the dimension of radians, it will be impossible (and immaterial) to determine the distinction between an argument of a real number and an argument of an angle in radians. Take care to indicate the correct units of measurements only if the argument is an angle measured in

11.1 Trigonometric Functions of Real Numbers   309

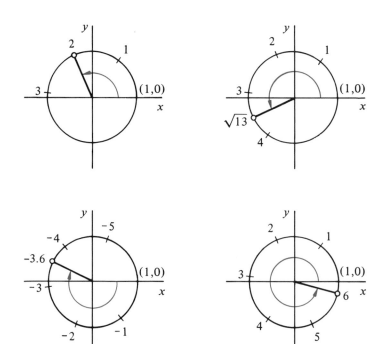

Figure 11.3

degrees, minutes, and seconds. Otherwise, by convention, the argument is an angle measured in radians or is a real number. Thus, sin 30° means the sine of an angle of 30°, but sin 30 means either of the following two concepts, both of which give equal numerical values:

(1) the sine of an angle of 30 radians
(2) the sine of the real number 30

By locating the unit circle in the rectangular plane, the point P associated with the number u has coordinates (x, y). This association defines a function called the **wrapping function**. The domain of this function is the set of real numbers and the range is a set of ordered pairs of real numbers. The wrapping function is denoted and defined by

$$W(u) = (x, y)$$

where u is a real number and (x, y) are the coordinates of the associated unit circle point.

An interesting and important relationship exists between the coordinates of the point associated with u and cos u and sin u. Since we are working on the unit circle,

$$\cos u = \frac{x}{r} = \frac{x}{1} = x$$

$$\sin u = \frac{y}{r} = \frac{y}{1} = y$$

That is, the x- and y-coordinates of the point associated with the real number u are equal to cos u and sin u, respectively. The wrapping function can then be written

$$W(u) = (\cos u, \sin u)$$

Figure 11.4 shows a unit circle with real numbers from 0 to 2π marked off on the circumference. Using this circle, values of cos u and sin u may be approximated for any real number u in the interval $0 \leq u < 2\pi$. For a number u in the interval $2\pi \leq u < 4\pi$, use the fact that there is a number u' in the interval $0 \leq u' < 2\pi$ such that

$$u' = u - 2\pi$$

The number u' is called the **reference number** of the number u and, in general, is given by

$$u' = u \pm 2n\pi$$

where n is an integer.

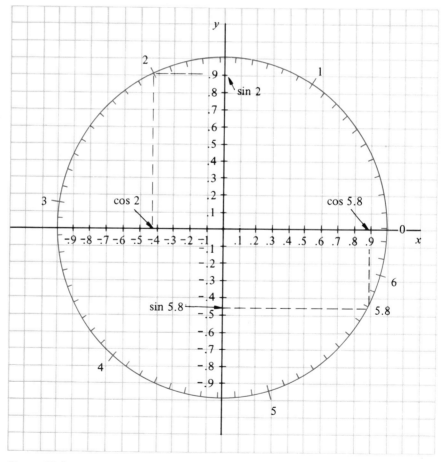

Figure 11.4

11.1 Trigonometric Functions of Real Numbers

311

Since the range values of the wrapping function repeat every 2π units of u, we say that the wrapping function is **periodic** with **period** 2π. This is denoted

$$W(u) = W(u \pm 2n\pi)^*$$

By definition of the wrapping function, it follows that both the sine and cosine functions are periodic with period 2π.

Example 11.2 Using Figure 11.4, find the cosine and sine of (a) 2, (b) 5.8, (c) 8.28, (d) 100, (e) -4.28.

Solution With reference to Figure 11.4 we estimate

(a) $\cos 2 = -0.42$, $\sin 2 = 0.91$

(b) $\cos 5.8 = 0.89$, $\sin 5.8 = -0.46$

(c) To find $\cos 8.28$ and $\sin 8.28$, note that $8.28 = 6.28 + 2$. Thus, $\cos 8.28 = \cos 2 = -0.42$, $\sin 8.28 = \sin 2 = 0.91$

(d) To find $\cos 100$ and $\sin 100$, note that $100 = 15 \times 6.28 + 5.8$. Thus, $\cos 100 = \cos 5.8 = 0.89$, $\sin 100 = 5.8 = -0.46$

(e) To find $\cos -4.28$ and $\sin -4.28$, note that $-4.28 = 2 - 6.28$. Thus, $\cos -4.28 = \cos 2 = -0.42$, $\sin -4.28 = \sin 2 = 0.91$

Using multiples of π to express real numbers in connection with the argument of a trigonometric function is common practice, since it is then easy to determine the associated angle.

Example 11.3 Evaluate $\sin \frac{1}{6}\pi$.

Solution Note that we need not say "$\frac{1}{6}\pi$ what?" For in this case "$\frac{1}{6}\pi$" could mean either $\frac{1}{6}\pi$ radians or merely the real number $\frac{1}{6}\pi$. Either way, the same numerical value is obtained. Hence,

$$\sin \frac{1}{6}\pi = \frac{1}{2}$$

The values of the trigonometric functions for real numbers may be found from Table E in the appendix, by considering the real number as an angle expressed in radians. Table E may be interpreted either as a table of trigonometric functions of angles measured in radians or of trigonometric functions of real numbers.

* More generally, a function f is periodic with period p $(p \neq 0)$ if $f(x + p) = f(x)$ for all x. The smallest such p is called *the* period of the function.

Example 11.4   Find cos 0.5, sin 1.4, tan 0.714.

Solution   From Table E,

$$\cos 0.5 = 0.8776$$

$$\sin 1.4 = 0.9854$$

Tan 0.714 must be approximated by interpolation. From Table E,

$$\tan 0.71 = 0.8595$$

$$\tan 0.72 = 0.8771$$

and thus,

$$\tan 0.714 \approx (0.4)(.0176) + 0.8595 \approx 0.8665$$

Example 11.5   Find the values of x for which $\tan x = 1$.

Solution   Some of the numbers in the solution set are $-7\pi/4$, $-3\pi/4$, $\pi/4$, and $5\pi/4$. Notice that each of these numbers is an integral multiple of $\pi/4$. Using this fact, the desired solution set can be written in the form $(4n + 1)(\pi/4)$, where n is an integer.

The names of the trigonometric functions are the same whether they are used in the sense of ratios or in a wider functional sense. However, by writing $y = \sin x$ or $f(x) = \sin x$, you are obviously emphasizing the functional concept of the sine function. Further, do not be misled into believing that one letter is used conventionally for the argument of the trigonometric functions. Any convenient letter or symbol suffices. Thus, $\sin x$, $\sin u$, $\sin \theta$, or $\sin v$ mean exactly the same thing. Only the application reveals if the argument is to be interpreted as an angle or as a real number.

Exercises for
Section 11.1

1.   Sketch the point on the unit circle associated with each of the real numbers. Find the cosine and sine of each number using Figure 11.4 and check the answer using Table E.

(a) 1   (b) -2 (c) 3   (d) 10

(e) 3π (f) -4 (g) -4π (h) $\frac{1}{3}\pi$

(i) $\frac{1}{3}$ (j) $\frac{1}{2}$ (k) $\sqrt{7}$ (l) 5.15

2.   In calculus the ratio $\sin x / x$ is important. Using Table E, find the values of the ratio for the following values of x.

(a) 0.3   (b) 0.2   (c) 0.1   (d) 0.05   (e) 0.01

What value do you think $\sin x / x$ approaches as x approaches 0?
What is $\sin x / x$ when $x = 0$?

3. If $f(x) = \sin x$ and $g(x) = \cos x$, show that $[f(x)]^2 + [g(x)]^2 = 1$.

If $f(x) = \sin x$, find the values in Exercises 4–10.

4. $f(\tfrac{1}{2}\pi)$ **5.** $f(\pi)$ **6.** $f(50)$ **7.** $f(-10)$

8. $f(3\pi)$ **9.** $f(\tfrac{1}{6}\pi)$ **10.** $f(2\pi)$

If $g(x) = \cos x$, find the values in Exercises 11–17.

11. $g(0)$ **12.** $g(\tfrac{1}{3}\pi)$ **13.** $g(\pi)$ **14.** $g(25)$

15. $g(-10)$ **16.** $g(5\pi)$ **17.** $g(5)$

18. If $f(x) = \sin x$, solve the equation $f(x) = 0$.

19. If $g(x) = \cos x$, solve the equation $g(x) = 0$.

20. For which values of x is $\sin x = 1$?

21. For which values of x is $\cos x = 1$?

22. For which values of x is $\sec x = \tfrac{1}{2}$?

23. Solve the inequality $\cos x \le \sec x$.

24. Solve the inequality $\sin x > \csc x$.

25. Solve the inequality $\sin x \ge 1$.

26. What are the zeros of $\sin x$?

27. What are the zeros of $\cos x$?

28. Which pairs of functions have the same zeros?

11.2
Graphs of the
Sine and Cosine Functions

We now examine the graphs of the sine and cosine functions considered as functions of *real numbers*. These two types of graphs have significance in many unrelated areas, and the job of graphing either the sine or the cosine is almost identical.

We first summarize some of the analytical properties.

(1) Both $\sin x$ and $\cos x$ are *bounded*, above by 1 and below by -1. Thus, the graph of each of the functions lies between the lines $y = 1$ and $y = -1$.

(2) Both $\sin x$ and $\cos x$ are *periodic* with period 2π; that is, the functional values repeat themselves every 2π units. Thus, only one period need be considered when graphing $\sin x$ and $\cos x$.

(3) The sine function is *odd*; that is, $\sin x = -\sin(-x)$. Thus, the graph of $\sin x$ is symmetric about the origin.
The cosine function is *even*; that is, $\cos x = \cos(-x)$. Thus, its graph is symmetric about the y-axis.

(4) Sin $x = 0$ for $x = 0$, $\pm\pi$, $\pm2\pi$, $\pm3\pi$, and so on.
Cos $x = 0$ for $x = \pm\frac{1}{2}\pi$, $\pm\frac{3}{2}\pi$, $\pm\frac{5}{2}\pi$, and so on.
In each case they are the intercepts on the x-axis.

(5) The numerical values of the sine and cosine functions for $0 \le x \le \frac{1}{2}\pi$ correspond to the values of sin x and cos x in the first quadrant. The other three quadrants yield values numerically the same with, at most, a difference in sign.

To obtain the specific graph we need a reasonable number of points for $0 < x < \frac{1}{2}\pi$. Then a smooth curve can be drawn through these points, after which the general properties may be used to obtain the remainder of the curve. Usually we emphasize certain "special" points corresponding to $x = 0$, $\frac{1}{2}\pi$, π, $\frac{3}{2}\pi$, and 2π.

Figure 11.5 displays the graph of one period of the sine function. To the left of the graph is a circle of radius 1. The sine function has values numerically

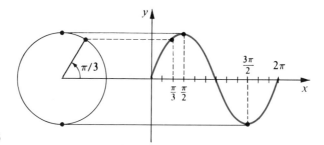

Figure 11.5

equal to the y-coordinates of points on this circle. This figure displays the relationship between points on the unit circle and corresponding points on the graph of the function.

Figure 11.6 shows a graph of several periods of the function $y = \sin x$, and Figure 11.7 shows several periods of the cosine function. The figures show the graphs as having been terminated, but in reality they continue indefinitely. To emphasize this indefinite continuation, a statement of the period is often included with the graph.

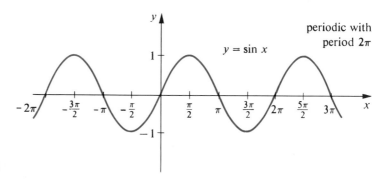

Figure 11.6

11.2 Graphs of the Sine and Cosine Functions

315

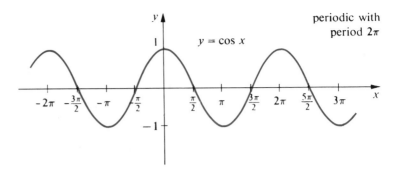

Figure 11.7

The graph of the sine function is sometimes called a **sine wave** or a **sinusoid**. A **cycle** is the shortest segment of the graph that includes one period. The **frequency** of the sinusoid is the reciprocal of the period. It represents the number of cycles of the sine function in each unit interval. The graphs of the sine and cosine functions should clearly demonstrate their boundedness, their periodicity, and their zeros.

The graphs of the sine and cosine functions are quite similar. In fact, to obtain the graph of the cosine function, shift the graph of the sine function $\pi/2$ units to the left.

11.3

More on the

Sine and Cosine Functions

Instead of sin x and cos x, you will frequently encounter such functions as sin $2x$, 4 cos x, or cos $(x + \pi)$. A familiarity with the properties of sin x and cos x makes modified functions of this type easy to graph.

In practice we must deal with the basic trigonometric functions altered in three ways:

(1) multiplication of the function by a constant

(2) multiplication of the argument by a constant

(3) addition of a constant to the argument

We will use $y = \sin x$ to explain each of these cases with the understanding that the results apply also to $y = \cos x$.

(1) Multiplication of the Function by a Constant

We have seen that the values of the sine function oscillate between $+1$ and -1. If we multiply sin x by a positive constant A, we then write $y = A \sin x$. Since

$$-1 \leq \sin x \leq 1$$

it follows that, when multiplying through by A,

$$-A \leq A \sin x \leq A$$

The value of A is called the **amplitude** of the sine wave. If A is greater than 1, the amplitude of the basic sine wave is increased; if A is less than 1, the amplitude is decreased. Sometimes A is called the *maximum*, or *peak*, value of the function. Figure 11.8 shows the graph of $y = A \sin x$ for $A = 1, \frac{1}{2}$, and 2.

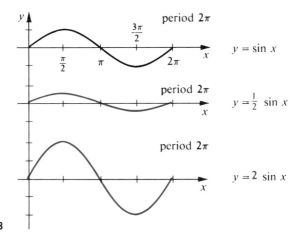

Figure 11.8

(2) Multiplication of the Argument by a Constant

If $\sin x$ has its argument multiplied by a constant B, the function becomes $\sin Bx$. The graph of this function remains sinusoidal in form but since the argument is Bx and since the sine function repeats itself for every increase in the argument of 2π, we can see that one period of $\sin Bx$ is contained in the interval

$$0 \leq Bx \leq 2\pi$$

That is, for

$$0 \leq x \leq \frac{2\pi}{B}$$

Therefore, multiplying the argument by a constant has the effect of altering the period to be $2\pi/B$. Thus, the period of $\sin 2x$ is π. The period of $\sin \frac{1}{2}x$ is 4π. Graphically, increasing B has the effect of squeezing the sine curve together like an accordion. Decreasing B has the effect of pulling it apart. (See Figure 11.9.) On a fundamental interval the sine curve is 0 at $x = 0$, π, and 2π. The curve $y = \sin Bx$ is 0 at $x = 0$, π/B, and $2\pi/B$. The basic sine curve reaches a maximum at $y = \pi/2$. The curve $y = \sin Bx$ reaches a maximum at $y = \pi/(2B)$.

(3) Addition of a Constant to the Argument

The addition of a constant to the argument of $\sin x$ is written $\sin (x + C)$. The constant C has the effect of shifting the graph of the sine function to the right or to the left. Notice that $\sin (x + C)$ is zero when $x + C = 0$, that is for $x = -C$.

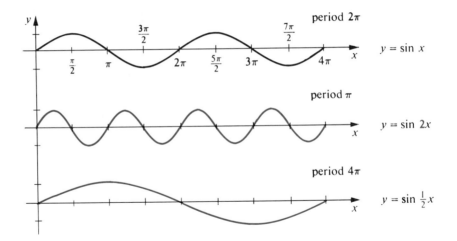

Figure 11.9

This value of x for which the argument of the sine function is zero is called the **phase shift**. If C is positive, the shift is to the left and if C is negative, the shift is to the right. Figure 11.10 shows three sine waves with phase shifts of $0, \frac{1}{4}\pi$, and $-\frac{1}{4}\pi$.

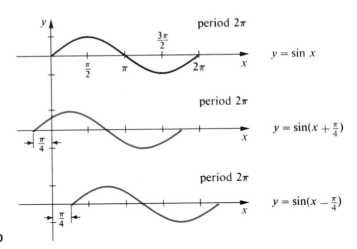

Figure 11.10

   In the more general case, the effects of changes in amplitude, period, and phase shift are all combined. The function

$$y = A \sin (Bx + C)$$

has an amplitude of A, a period of $2\pi/B$, and a phase shift corresponding to the value of x given by $Bx + C = 0$; that is, $x = -C/B$. Figure 11.11 shows a graph of the basic sine curve and the graph of $y = 3 \sin (2x - \frac{1}{3}\pi)$.

11 Analytic Trigonometry

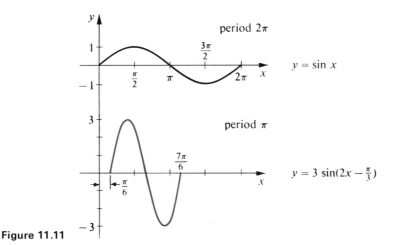

Figure 11.11

Example 11.6   Sketch the graph of $y = 2 \sin\left(\frac{1}{3}x + \frac{1}{9}\pi\right)$.

Solution   The amplitude of the graph is 2, the period is $2\pi/(1/3) = 6\pi$, and the phase shift is $-\frac{1}{3}\pi$. (See Figure 11.12.)

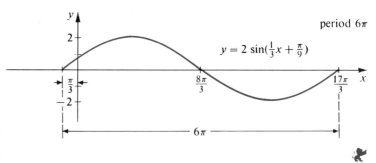

Figure 11.12

In all cases the distinctive shape of the sine curve remains unaltered. This basic shape is expanded or contracted vertically through multiplication by the amplitude constant A, expanded or contracted horizontally by the constant B, and shifted to the right or left by the constant C.

A similar analysis could be made for the cosine function. We do not discuss in detail the function $y = A \cos (Bx + C)$, but the constants A, B, and C alter the basic cosine function in a manner quite similar to that described for the sine function.

Example 11.7   Sketch the graph of $y = 3 \cos\left(\frac{1}{2}x + \frac{1}{4}\pi\right)$.

Solution   The amplitude is 3 since the basic cosine function is multiplied by 3. The period is $2\pi/(\frac{1}{2}) = 4\pi$. The phase shift is found from the equation $\frac{1}{2}x + \frac{1}{4}\pi = 0$, that is $x = -\pi/2$. Hence, the phase shift is $\pi/2$ units to the left. The graph of this function is shown in Figure 11.13.

11.3 More on the Sine and Cosine Functions

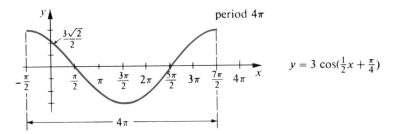

Figure 11.13

If the function is multiplied by a negative constant, use one of the relationships of Section 10.3 to put the expression into a more standard form.

Example 11.8   Sketch $y = -2 \sin (3x + 1)$ by first expressing it in the form $y = A \sin (Bx + C)$, where both A and B are positive.

Solution   By using the fact that $\sin x = -\sin (-x)$,

$$y = 2 \sin (-3x - 1)$$

Then, since $\sin (x + \pi) = \sin (-x)$, (see page 289)

$$y = 2 \sin [(3x + 1) + \pi].$$

See Figure 11.14.

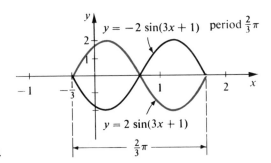

Figure 11.14

Another method of graphing the above function is to initially sketch the function $y = 2 \sin (3x + 1)$ and then reflect that graph in the x-axis.

Exercises for
    Sections 11.2 and 11.3

1.   What are the domain and the range of $\sin x$? $\cos x$?

2.   Sketch one period of $\sin x$ using increments of $\pi/4$.

3. Sketch one period of cos x using increments of $\pi/4$.

4. Sketch sin $2x$ on the interval $0 \le x < 2\pi$ in increments of $\pi/4$.

Sketch the graphs of the functions given in Exercises 5–22. In each case give the amplitude, the period, and the phase shift.

5. $y = 3 \sin x$

6. $y = \frac{1}{2} \sin x$

7. $y = 6 \cos x$

8. $y = \frac{1}{3} \sin x$

9. $y = \sin \frac{2}{3}x$

10. $y = 0.3 \sin 3x$

11. $y = \sin \pi x$

12. $y = \cos 0.1x$

13. $y = \cos \left(x + \frac{1}{3}\pi\right)$

14. $y = 2 \sin \frac{1}{3}x$

15. $y = 2 \cos \left(\frac{1}{2}x - \frac{1}{2}\pi\right)$

16. $y = \sin 2(x + \frac{1}{6}\pi)$

17. $y = \cos (2x + \pi)$

18. $y = 3 \cos (3x - \pi)$

19. $y = 4 \sin \left(\frac{1}{3}x + \frac{\pi}{3}\right)$

20. $y = 0.2 \sin (0.25x - \pi)$

21. $y = \cos \left(\pi x - \frac{\pi}{4}\right)$

22. $y = \sqrt{3} \cos (\pi x + \pi)$

Write the expressions in Exercises 23–27 in the form $A \sin (Bx + C)$, where A and B are positive, and then sketch.

23. $-\sin (x + 1)$

24. $-\sin (-2x + 3)$

25. $-\sin (2\pi x + \frac{1}{2})$

26. $3 \cos (2\pi x + \pi)$

27. $-\cos (\pi x + 1)$

Write the equation of the sinusoids in Exercises 28–31 whose graphs are shown over one period.

28.

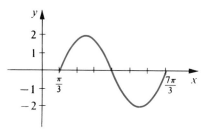

29.

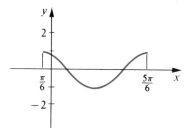

30.

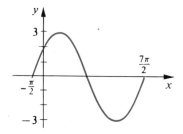

31.

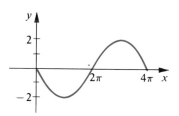

11.3 More on the Sine and Cosine Functions
321

32. The equation for the voltage drop across the terminals of an ordinary electric outlet is given approximately by

$$E = 156 \sin (110\pi t)$$

Sketch the voltage curve for several cycles.

33. If B is small, the equation $y = \sin Bx$ approximates the shape of ocean waves. Sketch several cycles of an ocean wave

$$y = \sin \frac{1}{20} \pi x$$

34. It is always possible to express functions of the type $A \sin (Bx + C)$ and $A \cos (Bx + C)$ in the form $A' \sin (B'x + C')$, where A', B', and C' are positive. Prove this.

35. How are the graphs of $y = \sin (-t)$ and $y = \sin (t)$ related?

36. How are the graphs of $\cos (-t)$ and $\cos (t)$ related?

37. How are the graphs of $\sin (t)$ and $\cos (\frac{1}{2}\pi - t)$ related?

38. Sketch the graphs of $y = \sin x$ and $y = x$ on the same axes and convince yourself that $\sin x < x$ if $x > 0$.

39. Prove the last statement of Section 11.2.

40. The function $f(x) = |\sin x|$ is called the *full wave rectified sine wave*. Make a sketch of its graph. What is its period?

41. Make a sketch of the half wave rectified sine wave defined by

$$f(x) = \sin x, \qquad 0 \le x \le \pi$$
$$= 0, \qquad \pi \le x \le 2\pi$$

and periodic with period 2π.

42. Sketch the graph of the function $f(x) = |\cos x|$.

11.4
Graphs of the
Tangent and Cotangent Functions

The analytical properties of the tangent and cotangent functions discussed previously are summarized here. Each of the properties influences the nature of the graph in a very important manner.

(1) Both $\tan x$ and $\cot x$ are periodic with period π. Thus, only an interval of length π need be analyzed for purposes of graphing the two functions; for example, $-\frac{1}{2}\pi < x < \frac{1}{2}\pi$ or $0 < x < \pi$.

(2) Both $\tan x$ and $\cot x$ are *unbounded*, which means that their values

become arbitrarily large. Tan x becomes unbounded near odd multiples of $\frac{1}{2}\pi$, whereas cot x becomes unbounded near multiples of π.

(3) Both tan x and cot x are odd since they are quotients of an odd function and an even function. Thus, their graphs are symmetric with respect to the origin.

(4) Tan x is zero for $x = 0$, $\pm\pi$, $\pm 2\pi$, and so on. Cot x is zero at $x = \pm\frac{1}{2}\pi$, $\pm\frac{3}{2}\pi$, $\pm\frac{5}{2}\pi$, and so on. At these places the graph crosses the x-axis.

(5) Numerically (ignoring sign), the values of both functions are completely determined in the first quadrant; that is, for $0 < x < \frac{1}{2}\pi$.

Figure 11.15 shows a graph of several periods of the tangent function and of the cotangent function. For purposes of graphing, the places at which the graphs cross the x-axis and the places at which the functions become unbounded are emphasized. The places at which the functions become unbounded are called **vertical asymptotes**. Thus, the asymptotes for tan x are $x = \pm\frac{1}{2}\pi$, $\pm\frac{3}{2}\pi$, $\pm\frac{5}{2}\pi$, and so on. The asymptotes for cot x are $x = 0$, $\pm\pi$, $\pm 2\pi$, $\pm 3\pi$, and so on.

The graphs of the more general functions $y = A \tan (Bx + C)$ and $y = A \cot (Bx + C)$ are analyzed in a manner similar to that of Section 11.3.

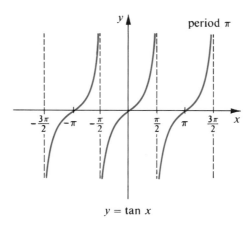

$y = \tan x$

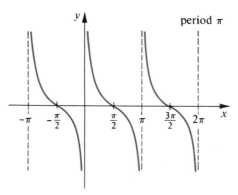

Figure 11.15 $y = \cot x$

11.4 Graphs of the Tangent and Cotangent Functions   323

In the case of $y = A \tan x$, we do not call A the amplitude because this would imply that the function is bounded. The constant A, then, multiplies each functional value but has no other graphical significance.

The period of $\tan Bx$ is π/B. Thus, if $B > 1$, the period is shortened; if $B < 1$, the period is larger than that of the basic tangent function.

The constant C is a phase shift constant and acts to translate the basic function to the right or left.

Example 11.9   Sketch the function $y = \tan(4x - \frac{1}{3}\pi)$.

Solution   The period of this function is $\frac{1}{4}\pi$. The phase shift is located by determining where the argument $4x - \frac{1}{3}\pi$ is equal to zero. Thus, the phase shift is $\frac{1}{12}\pi$. The graph is shown in Figure 11.16.

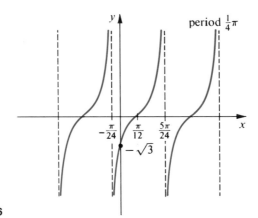

Figure 11.16

11.5
Graphs of the
Secant and Cosecant Functions

The graphs of sec x and csc x can be sketched directly from graphs of the cos x and sin x since they are reciprocals of the respective functions. You should, of course, note their important general properties.

(1)   Both functions are unbounded. In fact, since both sin x and cos x are bounded by ± 1, the graphs of csc x and sec x lie above $y = 1$ and below $y = -1$.

(2)   Both sec x and csc x are periodic with period 2π.

(3)   The secant function is even and the cosecant function is odd.

(4)   Sec x and csc x are never 0.

(5)   Numerically, the functional values are determined for $0 < x < \pi/2$.

Both functions are sketched in Figure 11.17. In each case their reciprocal functions are sketched in dashed lines on the same coordinate system to show the relationship between the two.

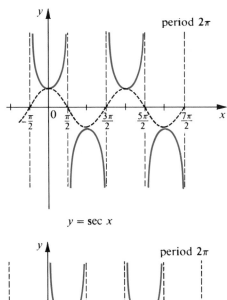

$y = \sec x$

Figure 11.17 $\qquad\qquad\qquad y = \csc x$

The manner of sketching the more general functions $y = A \sec (Bx + C)$ and $y = A \csc (Bx + C)$ is similar to that discussed for the other functions. Suffice it to say that the basic waveforms remain the same, but the constants A and B exert a kind of vertical and horizontal stretching whereas C effects a horizontal translation.

Exercises for
Sections 11.4 and 11.5

Find the period of each of the functions in Exercises 1–8.

1. $\cot \frac{1}{2}x$ **2.** $\csc 3x$ **3.** $\sec \pi x$ **4.** $\tan 3\pi x$

5. $\tan \frac{1}{2}\pi x$ **6.** $\sec \frac{1}{3}x$ **7.** $\cot \frac{5}{6}x$ **8.** $\sec \frac{1}{\pi} x$

Sketch the graphs of the functions in Exercises 9–17 over at least two periods. Give the period and the phase shift. List the asymptotes.

9. $y = \tan 2x$

10. $y = \tan (x + \frac{1}{2}\pi)$

11. $y = \cot (\frac{1}{4}\pi - x)$

12. $y = 2 \sec (x - \frac{1}{2}\pi)$

13. $y = \tan (2x + \frac{1}{3}\pi)$

14. $y = 2 \csc 2x$

15. $y = \csc (2x - 3\pi)$

16. $y = \sec (x + \frac{1}{3}\pi)$

17. $y = -\tan (x - \frac{1}{4}\pi)$

18. Does $\tan x$ exist at its asymptote?

19. How are the graphs of $\tan x$ and $\cot x$ related?

20. How are the graphs of $\sec x$ and $\csc x$ related?

21. How are the zeros of the tangent function related to the asymptotes of the cotangent function?

22. How are the zeros of the sine function and the asymptotes of the cosecant function related?

23. How are the graphs of $y = \tan x$ and $y = \tan (-x)$ related?

24. How are the graphs of $y = \tan x$ and $y = -\tan x$ related?

11.6

Inverse

Trigonometric Functions*

In many applications it is highly desirable to work with one-to-one functions since, given any x, there is a uniquely determined value of y; conversely, given a y, there is a unique value of x paired with it. None of the six trigonometric functions are one-to-one. Therefore, none of the trigonometric functions have an inverse—a fact that causes difficulty in certain applications. To circumvent this difficulty, we limit the domain of each trigonometric function to a set of values, called **principal values**, for which the function is one-to-one. Thus, at least for the principal values, each of the trigonometric functions has an inverse. Table 11.1 indicates the principal values for each of the six trigonometric functions.

Table 11.1 Table of Principal Values of the Trigonometric Functions

$\sin x, \quad -\frac{1}{2}\pi \le x \le \frac{1}{2}\pi$	$\cot x, \quad 0 < x < \pi$
$\cos x, \quad 0 \le x \le \pi$	$\csc x, \quad -\frac{1}{2}\pi \le x \le \frac{1}{2}\pi, x \ne 0$
$\tan x, \quad -\frac{1}{2}\pi < x < \frac{1}{2}\pi$	$\sec x, \quad 0 \le x \le \pi, x \ne \pi/2$

* Before reading this section you may wish to review Section 3.9.

Example 11.10   Find the principal value of x for which

(a) $\cos x = -\frac{1}{2}$

(b) $\sin x = -\frac{1}{2}$.

Solution   Figure 11.18(a) shows the cosine function and 11.18(b) shows the sine function intersecting the line $y = -\frac{1}{2}$. In each case the interval of principal values is

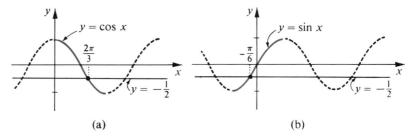

(a)   (b)

Figure 11.18

in color so you can see that only one value of x on that interval satisfies the equation. Thus, the principal value of x for which $\cos x = -\frac{1}{2}$ is $x = \frac{2}{3}\pi$. The principal value of x for which $\sin x = -\frac{1}{2}$ is for $x = -\frac{1}{6}\pi$.

We are now in a position to define functions inverse to the six trigonometric functions on the intervals of principal values. Actually, you need not continually affirm that a particular trigonometric function is limited to its principal values because the only way that its inverse can exist (as a function) is by such a limitation.

The inverse for $y = \sin x$ (where x is limited to the principal values of the sine function) is found by interchanging x and y to get $x = \sin y$ and then solving for y. We cannot algebraically solve $x = \sin y$ for y, but we know that a solution should state that "y is a number or angle whose sine is x." The word "arcsin" traditionally conveys this idea, and, therefore, the inverse to $x = \sin y$ is written $y = \arcsin x$.* This notation is particularly descriptive since you can think of it as meaning "the arc length of the unit circle whose sine is x." Thus, $\arcsin \frac{1}{2}$ is the arc or angle whose sine is $\frac{1}{2}$; that is, $\frac{1}{6}\pi$. Note that only one value for the angle is obtained, and this value *must* be chosen from the set of principal values.

The definition of each of the six inverse trigonometric functions proceeds in a similar manner. The domain of each function is limited to its principal values so that a one-to-one function is obtained, thereby making an inverse function possible.

---

* Another notation used for the inverse to $y = \sin x$ is $y = \sin^{-1} x$, read "the inverse sine of x." This notation is somewhat confusing since it suggests taking the reciprocal of $\sin x$. For this reason we use arcsin to designate the inverse sine function.

The Inverse Trigonometric Functions

$$y = \arcsin x \quad \text{means} \quad x = \sin y, \ -\frac{1}{2}\pi \le y \le \frac{1}{2}\pi$$

$$y = \arccos x \quad \text{means} \quad x = \cos y, \ 0 \le y \le \pi$$

$$y = \arctan x \quad \text{means} \quad x = \tan y, \ -\frac{1}{2}\pi < y < \frac{1}{2}\pi$$

$$y = \text{arccot } x \quad \text{means} \quad x = \cot y, \ 0 < y < \pi$$

$$y = \text{arcsec } x \quad \text{means} \quad x = \sec y, \ 0 \le y \le \pi, \ y \ne \frac{1}{2}\pi$$

$$y = \text{arccsc } x \quad \text{means} \quad x = \csc y, \ -\frac{1}{2}\pi \le y \le \frac{1}{2}\pi, \ y \ne 0$$

Example 11.11   Find arccos $(\frac{1}{3})$.

Solution   Let $y = \arccos(\frac{1}{3})$. Then,

$$\frac{1}{3} = \cos y, \quad \text{where } 0 \le y \le \pi$$

By use of Table E, $y = 1.23$.

Example 11.12   Find arctan (-1) and arccot (-1).

Solution   Let $y = \arctan(-1)$ and $u = \text{arccot}(-1)$. Then,

$$-1 = \tan y, \qquad -\frac{1}{2}\pi < y < \frac{1}{2}\pi$$

and

$$-1 = \cot u, \qquad 0 < u < \pi$$

Thus,

$$y = -\frac{1}{4}\pi \quad \text{and} \quad u = \frac{3}{4}\pi$$

Since the tangent and cotangent are reciprocal functions, you might have expected that the arctan (-1) and arccot (-1) yield the same value. This example shows the necessity of adhering strictly to the definitions of the inverse functions, giving close attention to the principal values.

Example 11.13   Find $\sin\left(\arccos \tfrac{1}{2}\right)$.

Solution   First, let $\theta = \arccos \tfrac{1}{2}$. Then θ is the angle as shown in Figure 11.19, from which it is easy to see that

$$\sin\left(\arccos \frac{1}{2}\right) = \sin \theta = \sqrt{3}/2$$

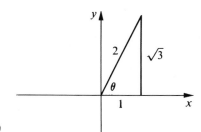

Figure 11.19

Example 11.14   Find $\cos(\arcsin x)$.

Solution   If we let $\theta = \arcsin x$, then we wish to find $\cos \theta$. The expression $\theta = \arcsin x$ can also be written $x = \sin \theta$ and $\cos \theta = \pm\sqrt{1 - \sin^2 \theta}$. Therefore,

$$\cos \theta = \pm\sqrt{1 - \sin^2 \theta} = \pm\sqrt{1 - x^2}$$

or

$$\cos(\arcsin x) = \pm\sqrt{1 - x^2}$$

In passing, note that

$$\sin(\arcsin x) = x$$
$$\cos(\arccos x) = x$$

and so forth, for all six trigonometric functions. This result is a direct consequence of the inverse nature of the functions involved. Also *if x is limited to the principal values of the function,*

$$\arcsin(\sin x) = x$$
$$\arccos(\cos x) = x$$

and so forth.

In closing this section we want to point out that while the choice of principal values is a matter of convention, these particular values are chosen for some important reasons. For example, the reason for defining the principal values of $\cos x$ to be $0 \le x \le \pi$ is so that

$$\arccos x = \frac{1}{2}\pi - \arcsin x$$

11.6 Inverse Trigonometric Functions

329

a relation expressing the fact that the angle whose cosine is x is the complement of the angle whose sine is x. Thus, once the principal values of the sine function are chosen to be between $-\frac{1}{2}\pi$ and $\frac{1}{2}\pi$, this complementary relation automatically means that

$$0 \le \arccos x \le \pi$$

Note, however, that not all writers agree on the specific choices for principal values. For example, the principal values of the secant function are often chosen to be between 0 and $\frac{1}{2}\pi$ when sec x is positive and between $-\pi$ and $-\frac{1}{2}\pi$ when sec x is negative. This latter method has the advantage of simplifying some rather important formulas of calculus but has the disadvantage of failing to satisfy the relation

$$\operatorname{arcsec} x = \arccos \frac{1}{x} \qquad \text{when } x < 0$$

Be aware that the choice of principal values is not dictated by whim, but is a matter of convention.

Exercises for
Section 11.6

Find the exact value of each of Exercises 1–17.

1.	$\arcsin \frac{1}{2}$	**2.**	$\arcsin 1$	**3.**	$\arctan 1$
4.	$\operatorname{arccot}(-\sqrt{3})$	**5.**	$\operatorname{arccot} 0$	**6.**	$\operatorname{arcsec} 1$
7.	$\arctan \sqrt{3}$	**8.**	$\arccos(-1)$	**9.**	$\sin(\arcsin 1)$
10.	$\sec(\arcsin \frac{1}{2})$	**11.**	$\sin(\arctan 2)$	**12.**	$\sec(\arccos \frac{1}{3})$
13.	$\cos(\arcsin \frac{1}{4})$	**14.**	$\tan(\operatorname{arcsec} x)$	**15.**	$\sin(\arccos x^2)$
16.	$\tan(\arcsin x)$	**17.**	$\cos[\arcsin(x-4)]$		

18. Show that the inverse sine function does not have the linearity property by showing that $\arcsin 2x \ne 2 \arcsin x$.

19. Show that the inverse cosine function does not have the linearity property by showing that $\arccos x + \arccos y \ne \arccos(x+y)$.

20. Make a table listing the domain and range of each of the six inverse trigonometric functions.

What function is inverse to (Exercises 21–24)

21.	$\arcsin x$	**22.**	$\arccos 3x$
23.	$3 \arccos x$	**24.**	$\arcsin \sqrt{1+x}$

Sketch the graph of Exercises 25–26.

25.	$\arcsin(\sin x)$	**26.**	$\arcsin(\cos x)$

Simplify Exercises 27–29

27. $\sin (2 \arcsin x)$ **28.** $\cos (\arccos x + \arcsin y)$

29. $\sin (\arcsin x + \arcsin y)$

30. A picture u feet high hangs on a wall, with its base v feet above the level of the observer's eye. If the observer stands x feet from the wall, show that the angle of vision α subtended by the picture is given by

$$\alpha = \text{arccot} \frac{x}{u + v} - \text{arccot} \frac{x}{v}$$

11.7
Graphs of the
Inverse Trigonometric Functions

The graphs of the six inverse trigonometric functions are found by direct appeal to the definition and by a knowledge of the graphs of the trigonometric functions. For example, $y = \arcsin x$ if and only if $x = \sin y$, where $-\frac{1}{2}\pi \leq y \leq \frac{1}{2}\pi$. It follows that $y = \arcsin x$ looks like a piece of the relation $x = \sin y$. In Figure 11.20 we see such a graph.

The other parts of Figure 11.20 show the graphs of $y = \arccos x$ and $y = \arctan x$. In each case, think of the graph of the original function wrapped around the y-axis and then consider the portion that corresponds to the principal values.

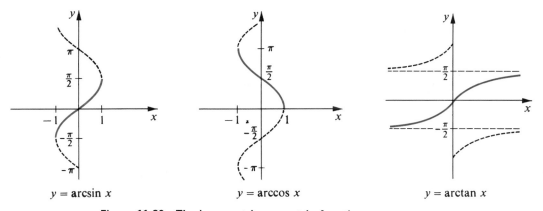

$y = \arcsin x$ $y = \arccos x$ $y = \arctan x$

Figure 11.20   The inverse trigonometric functions

Example 11.15   Sketch the graph of $\arccos 2x$.

Solution   First, let $y = \arccos 2x$. Then by definition of an inverse, we have $2x = \cos y$ or $x = \frac{1}{2} \cos y$, which has a period of 2π and an amplitude of $\frac{1}{2}$. Sketching this cosine wave around the y-axis from 0 to π yields the graph of $y = \arccos 2x$. (See Figure 11.21.)   ✿

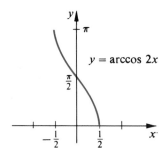

Figure 11.21

Example 11.16   Sketch the graph of 2 arccos x.

Solution   Let $y = 2$ arccos x. Then dividing by 2,

$$\frac{1}{2} y = \text{arccos } x$$

Hence, by definition,

$$x = \cos \frac{1}{2} y$$

This cosine wave has an amplitude of 1 and a period of 4π. The principal values in this case are $0 \le \frac{1}{2} y \le \pi$ or $0 \le y \le 2\pi$. (See Figure 11.22.)

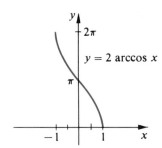

Figure 11.22

Exercises for
Section 11.7

Sketch the graph of each of the functions in Exercises 1–22.

1. arcsin $2x$	**2.** arccos $2x$	**3.** 2 arccos $\frac{1}{2}x$
4. $\frac{1}{2}$ arcsin $\frac{1}{2}x$	**5.** arctan $3x$	**6.** arctan $x + \frac{1}{2}\pi$
7. 2 arcsin x	**8.** $\frac{1}{4}$ arccos x	**9.** arcsin $x + \pi$
10. 3 arctan $2x$	**11.** $\frac{1}{2}$ arcsin $x + \frac{1}{2}\pi$	**12.** $\pi + 2$ arcsin $\frac{1}{2}x$
13. $-$arcsin x	**14.** -2 arccos x	**15.** arcsin $(x + 1)$
16. arccos $(x + 1)$	**17.** arctan $(x - 1)$	**18.** arctan $(x + 1)$

19. $\arcsin (x + \tfrac{1}{2})$ **20.** $\arccos \left(x - \dfrac{\sqrt{3}}{2} \right)$ **21.** $\arcsin (2x - 1)$

22. $\arccos \left(2x - \dfrac{\sqrt{3}}{2} \right)$

Test 1 for
Chapter 11

Answer true or false for 1–10.

1. If x_1 and x_2 are real numbers such that $x_1 < x_2$, then $\sin x_1 < \sin x_2$.

2. The sine and cosine functions are equal to each other twice on $(0, 2\pi)$.

3. The period of $f(x) = \cos 2x$ is 4π.

4. $(\cos x)(\arccos x) = 1$.

5. The graphs of $y = \sin x$ and $y = \cos \left(x - \dfrac{\pi}{2} \right)$ are identical.

6. The zeros of the tangent and cotangent function coincide.

7. $\sin x = \pi/4$ when $x = \sqrt{2}/2$.

8. If $-\pi/6 \le x \le \pi/6$, then $\cos x \ge \tfrac{1}{2}$.

9. If $\tan x \le 1$, then $-\pi/4 < x < \pi/4$.

10. $\sin (\arcsin x) = x$.

11. Sketch the graph of $y = \sqrt{13} \sin(x - \pi/4)$. Determine the amplitude, the phase shift, the intercepts, and the period.

12. Sketch the graph of $y = -\tan 2x$. What is its period?

13. Sketch the graph of $y = -3 \arccos 2x$.

14. Sketch the graph of $y = 2 \cos 3x$.

15. Solve for x: $\arcsin x = \tan 10$.

16. Determine the zeros for $0 \le x \le 2\pi$: $f(x) = \sin (2x + 5)$.

Test 2 for
Chapter 11

1. Evaluate (a) $\cos 2$, (b) $\tan (-1.1)$, (c) $\sec 3$.

2. What are the zeros of $\tan x$? $\sec x$?

Discuss and sketch Exercises 3–8 (indicate period, amplitude, and phase shift).

3. $y = 5 \cos \tfrac{1}{2}x$

4. $y = \sin \left(2x - \dfrac{\pi}{3} \right)$

5. $y = 3 \sec\left(x - \dfrac{\pi}{2}\right)$

6. $y = \frac{1}{3} \arcsin 5x$

7. $y = 2 \tan 0.4x$

8. $y = -\sin(-x + 2)$

9. Evaluate $\tan(1 + \arctan 1)$

10. Graphically solve the following system of equations.

$$y = \cos \frac{1}{3}x, \qquad 3x - 4y = 6$$

12
Equations and Identities

12.1
Fundamental
Trigonometric Relations

Any combination of trigonometric functions, such as $3 \sin x + \cos x$ or $\sec^2 x + \tan^2 x + 2 \sin x$, is called a trigonometric expression. One of the important things you shall learn in this book is how to simplify or alter the form of trigonometric expressions using certain fundamental trigonometric relations.

There are eight *fundamental* relations or identities that you must know. You are already familiar with most of these relations but they are listed here for completeness. The fundamental relations fall into three groups.

The Reciprocal Relations

(12.1) $\qquad \sin \theta = \dfrac{1}{\csc \theta}$

(12.2) $\qquad \cos \theta = \dfrac{1}{\sec \theta}$

(12.3) $\qquad \tan \theta = \dfrac{1}{\cot \theta}$

We establish equation (12.1) by observing that for any angle θ in standard position

$$\sin \theta \csc \theta = \left(\frac{y}{r}\right)\left(\frac{r}{y}\right) = 1$$

Therefore,

$$\sin \theta = \frac{1}{\csc \theta}$$

The other two relations are established in a similar manner.

The Quotient Relations

(12.4) $\qquad \tan \theta = \dfrac{\sin \theta}{\cos \theta}$

(12.5) $\qquad \cot \theta = \dfrac{\cos \theta}{\sin \theta}$

To establish equation (12.4), note that

$$\cos \theta \tan \theta = \left(\frac{x}{r}\right)\left(\frac{y}{x}\right) = \frac{y}{r} = \sin \theta$$

Therefore,

$$\tan \theta = \frac{\sin \theta}{\cos \theta}$$

The Pythagorean Relations

(12.6) $\quad \sin^2 \theta + \cos^2 \theta = 1$

(12.7) $\quad \tan^2 \theta + 1 = \sec^2 \theta$

(12.8) $\quad \cot^2 \theta + 1 = \csc^2 \theta$

We prove equation (12.6) by dividing $x^2 + y^2 = r^2$ by r^2 to get

$$\frac{x^2}{r^2} + \frac{y^2}{r^2} = 1$$

Then, since

$$\sin \theta = \frac{y}{r} \quad \text{and} \quad \cos \theta = \frac{x}{r}$$

we have

$$\cos^2 \theta + \sin^2 \theta = 1$$

Note that equation (12.7) is derived from equation (12.6). Dividing both sides of equation (12.6) by $\cos^2 \theta$ yields

$$\frac{\sin^2 \theta}{\cos^2 \theta} + 1 = \frac{1}{\cos^2 \theta}$$

from which, after using the fact that $\sin \theta / \cos \theta = \tan \theta$ and $1/\cos \theta = \sec \theta$,

$$\tan^2 \theta + 1 = \sec^2 \theta$$

Similarly, equation (12.8) is derived from equation (12.6) by first dividing both sides by $\sin^2 \theta$ and then applying equations (12.1) and (12.5).

These eight relations are called the *fundamental identities* of trigonometry because they are valid for all values of the argument for which the functions in the expression have meaning. Also, as before, the variable (usually letter x) may be regarded as either a real number or an angle, the interpretation being chosen from the context.

Using the fundamental identities you can (sometimes ingeniously) manipulate trigonometric expressions into alternative forms.

Example 12.1   Write the following expression as a single trigonometric term.

$$\frac{\tan x \csc^2 x}{1 + \tan^2 x}$$

Solution From equation (12.7) the denominator may be written as $\sec^2 x$. Thus,

$$\frac{\tan x \csc^2 x}{1 + \tan^2 x} = \frac{\tan x \csc^2 x}{\sec^2 x}$$

We now express $\tan x$, $\csc x$, and $\sec x$ in terms of the sine and cosine functions.

$$\frac{\tan x \csc^2 x}{1 + \tan^2 x} = \frac{\dfrac{\sin x}{\cos x} \cdot \dfrac{1}{\sin^2 x}}{\dfrac{1}{\cos^2 x}}$$

$$= \frac{\cos^2 x \sin x}{\sin^2 x \cos x}$$

$$= \frac{\cos x}{\sin x}$$

$$= \cot x$$

As you can see from this example, a large part of the process is algebraic. The series of steps in the simplification procedure is not unique. For example, we could have initially expressed the complete expression in terms of the sine and cosine functions. Experience with the use of the eight fundamental relations in simplifying trigonometric expression gives some facility in choosing a reasonable approach. Writing the entire expression in terms of the sine and cosine function is often appropriate but not necessarily the most economical.

Example 12.2 Simplify the expression

$$(\sec x + \tan x)(1 - \sin x)$$

Solution Write each of the functions in terms of the sine and cosine functions.

$$(\sec x + \tan x)(1 - \sin x) = \left(\frac{1}{\cos x} + \frac{\sin x}{\cos x}\right)(1 - \sin x)$$

$$= \frac{(1 + \sin x)(1 - \sin x)}{\cos x}$$

$$= \frac{(1 - \sin^2 x)}{\cos x}$$

$$= \frac{\cos^2 x}{\cos x}$$

$$= \cos x$$

(What is the domain of this expression?)

Example 12.3   Simplify the expression

$$(\sin x + \cos x)^2$$

Solution   Note that this is *not* the same expression as $\sin^2 x + \cos^2 x$. By squaring the expression,

$$(\sin x + \cos x)^2 = \sin^2 x + 2 \sin x \cos x + \cos^2 x$$

$$= 1 + 2 \sin x \cos x$$ 🐦

Example 12.4   Simplify the expression

$$\sin^4 x - \cos^4 x + \cos^2 x$$

Solution   Write the expression in a form involving only the cosine function. Thus,

$$\sin^4 x - \cos^4 x + \cos^2 x = (1 - \cos^2 x)^2 - \cos^4 x + \cos^2 x$$

$$= 1 - 2 \cos^2 x + \cos^4 x - \cos^4 x + \cos^2 x$$

$$= 1 - \cos^2 x$$

$$= \sin^2 x$$ 🐦

Certain algebraic expressions encountered in calculus are often transformed into trigonometric expressions in which, after simplification, hard-to-handle terms such as radicals disappear.

Example 12.5   By using the substitution $x = 2 \sin \theta$, simplify the expression $\sqrt{4 - x^2}$ and determine an interval for the variable θ that corresponds to $0 \le x \le 2$ in a one-to-one manner. What is $\tan \theta$?

Solution   Substituting $x = 2 \sin \theta$ into the radical,

$$\sqrt{4 - x^2} = \sqrt{4 - 4 \sin^2 \theta}$$

$$= \sqrt{4(1 - \sin^2 \theta)}$$

$$= |2 \cos \theta| = 2|\cos \theta|$$

When $x = 0$, $\theta = 0$, and when $x = 2$, $\theta = \frac{1}{2}\pi$, so that the interval $0 \le x \le 2$ corresponds to $0 \le \theta \le \frac{1}{2}\pi$. On this interval $\cos \theta \ge 0$ so that $|\cos \theta| = \cos \theta$. Hence,

$$\sqrt{4 - x^2} = 2 \cos \theta \qquad \text{for } 0 \le x \le 2 \text{ and } 0 \le \theta \le \frac{1}{2}\pi$$

Since $\sin \theta = x/2$, the right triangle in Figure 12.1 shows the relations necessary to establish that

$$\tan \theta = \frac{x}{\sqrt{4 - x^2}}$$ 🐦

12.1 Fundamental Trigonometric Relations

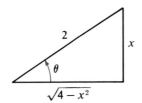

Figure 12.1

$\sqrt{4 - x^2}$

Exercises for
Section 12.1

Simplify the expressions in Exercises 1–20.

1. $\cos \theta + \tan \theta \sin \theta$

2. $\csc \theta - \cot \theta \cos \theta$

3. $\tan x + \cot x$

4. $\dfrac{1 + \cos x}{1 + \sec x}$

5. $\dfrac{(\tan x)(1 + \cot^2 x)}{(1 + \tan^2 x)}$

6. $\sec x - \sin x \tan x$

7. $\cos x \csc x$

8. $\cos x(\tan x + \cot x)$

9. $(\cos^2 x - 1)(\tan^2 x + 1)$

10. $\dfrac{(\sec^2 x - 1)}{\sec^2 x}$

11. $\dfrac{\sec x - \cos x}{\tan x}$

12. $\dfrac{1 + \tan^2 x}{\tan^2 x}$

13. $(\sin^2 x + \cos^2 x)^3$

14. $\dfrac{1 + \sec x}{\tan x + \sin x}$

15. $(\csc x - \cot x)^4(\csc x + \cot x)^4$

16. $\dfrac{\sec x}{(\tan x + \cot x)}$

17. $(\tan x)(\sin x + \cot x \cos x)$

18. $1 + \dfrac{\tan^2 x}{1 + \sec x}$

19. $\dfrac{\tan x \sin x}{(\sec^2 x - 1)}$

20. $(\cos x)(1 + \tan^2 x)$

By using the following substitutions, reduce the given expressions in Exercises 21–24 to one involving only trigonometric functions.

21. $\sqrt{a^2 + x^2}$, let $x = a \tan \theta$. What is $\sin \theta$?

22. $\sqrt{36 + 16x^2}$, let $x = \frac{3}{2} \tan \theta$. What is $\sin \theta$?

23. $\dfrac{\sqrt{x^2 - 4}}{x}$, let $x = 2 \sec \theta$.

24. $x^2\sqrt{4 + 9x^2}$, let $x = \frac{2}{3} \tan \theta$.

12.2 Trigonometric Equations

A **trigonometric equation** is any statement involving a conditional equality of two trigonometric expressions. A **solution** to the trigonometric equation is a value of the variable (within the domain of the function) that makes the statement true. The **solution set** is the set of all values of the variable that are solutions. To solve a trigonometric equation means to find the solution set for some indicated domain. If no domain is specifically mentioned, the domain is assumed to be all values of the independent variable for which the terms of the equation have meaning.

If the solution set is the null set, the equation is said to have no solution. If the solution set is the complete domain of the independent variable for the functions involved, it is called an **identity**. For example, each fundamental relation given by equations (12.1) through (12.8) is an identity because each is true regardless of the value of the argument.

To solve trigonometric equations, proceed in a series of steps until reaching a point that allows an explicit determination of the solution set. Usually, some specific knowledge about certain values of the trigonometric functions is necessary to make this determination.

We say that two trigonometric equations are **equivalent** if they have the same solution sets. Any operation on a given equation is **allowable** if the consequence of the operation is an equivalent equation. It can be shown that the allowable operations are: (1) adding or subtracting the same expression to both sides of an equality, and (2) multiplying or dividing both sides by the same nonzero expression.

The most basic type of trigonometric equation is one that is linear in a single trigonometric function of x. The trigonometric equation in this case is analogous to the linear equation in one variable and can always be put into the form of a trigonometric function equal to a constant. The solution set is then all values of the argument for which the function is equal to this constant.

In most cases trigonometric equations have an infinite number of solutions. However, we shall find the solution set over *one* period unless specified otherwise. The roots on this interval are sufficient since other roots can be obtained by simply adding multiples of the period.

Example 12.6 Solve the equation $\cos x = \frac{1}{2}$.

The period of $\cos x$ is 2π. The only solutions to this equation on the interval $0 \leq x \leq 2\pi$ are $x = \frac{1}{3}\pi$ and $x = \frac{5}{3}\pi$. (Note that the complete solution set is comprised of those values that can be written in the form $\frac{1}{3}\pi + 2n\pi$ and $\frac{5}{3}\pi + 2n\pi$, where n is an integer.) Figure 12.2 illustrates the nature of the solution set as the points of intersection of the curve $y = \cos x$ with the line $y = \frac{1}{2}$.

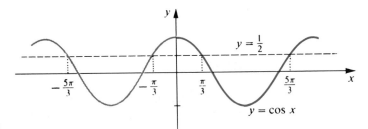

Figure 12.2

Example 12.7   Solve the trigonometric equation $\tan 2x = 1$.

Solution   Since the period of this function is $\frac{1}{2}\pi$, it is sufficient to examine for roots on the interval $0 \leq x \leq \frac{1}{2}\pi$. The value of θ at which $\tan \theta = 1$ is $\theta = \frac{1}{4}\pi$. Hence, $\tan 2x = 1$ has the solution $x = \frac{1}{8}\pi$. Figure 12.3 interprets graphically the solution set as the intersection of the curve $y = \tan 2x$ with the line $y = 1$.

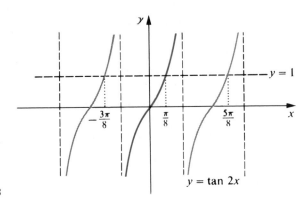

Figure 12.3

Example 12.8   Solve the equation $4 \sin \theta + 1 = 2 \sin \theta$.

Solution

$$4 \sin \theta + 1 = 2 \sin \theta$$

$$2 \sin \theta = -1$$

$$\sin \theta = -\frac{1}{2}$$

The period of $\sin \theta$ is 2π, which means $\theta = \frac{7}{6}\pi$ and $\theta = \frac{11}{6}\pi$ are the desired solutions.

Example 12.9   Find the solution set to the equation $|\sin x| = \frac{1}{2}$.

Solution   Figure 12.4 shows the intersection points of the curve $y = |\sin x|$ with $y = \frac{1}{2}$. Since $|\sin x|$ is periodic with period π, we need only find those values of x for which the equation is true on the interval $0 \leq x \leq \pi$. From your knowledge of the sine function, these values are $x = \frac{1}{6}\pi$ and $x = \frac{5}{6}\pi$.

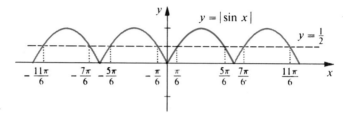

Figure 12.4

Trigonometric equations that are quadratic in one of the functions can be factored into a product of linear factors. The total solution set is the union of the solution sets to each of the resulting linear equations.

Example 12.10   Solve the equation $2 \cos^2 \theta + 3 \cos \theta + 1 = 0$ on $0 \leq \theta \leq 2\pi$.

Solution   This is a quadratic equation in $\cos \theta$ and may be factored as $(2 \cos \theta + 1) \times (\cos \theta + 1) = 0$. The factor $(2 \cos \theta + 1)$ is equal to zero when $\theta = \frac{2}{3}\pi$ and $\theta = \frac{4}{3}\pi$. Likewise, the factor $(\cos \theta + 1)$ is equal to zero when $\theta = \pi$. Hence, the solution set is $\{\frac{2}{3}\pi, \pi, \frac{4}{3}\pi\}$.

If more than one function occurs in the equation, trigonometric identities may be helpful in yielding an equivalent equation involving only one function.

Example 12.11   Solve the equation $2 \cos^2 x - \sin x - 1 = 0$ on the interval $0 \leq x \leq 2\pi$.

Solution   Since $\cos^2 x = 1 - \sin^2 x$,

$$2(1 - \sin^2 x) - \sin x - 1 = 0$$
$$2 - 2 \sin^2 x - \sin x - 1 = 0$$
$$2 \sin^2 x + \sin x - 1 = 0$$

Factoring,

$$(2 \sin x - 1)(\sin x + 1) = 0$$

The solution set of the original equation is given by the union of the solution sets to the two equations.

$$\left\lvert \begin{matrix} 2 \sin x - 1 = 0 \\ \sin x + 1 = 0 \end{matrix} \right\rvert$$

The solution to $2 \sin x - 1 = 0$ is $x = \frac{1}{6}\pi$ and $x = \frac{5}{6}\pi$, and to $\sin x + 1 = 0$ is $\frac{3}{2}\pi$. Hence, the solution set is

$$\left\lvert \frac{1}{6}\pi, \frac{5}{6}\pi, \frac{3}{2}\pi \right\rvert$$

In solving trigonometric equations, the following procedure can be used as a guide.

(1) Gather the entire expression to one side of the equality.

(2) Use the fundamental identities to express this conditional equality in terms of one function, or, failing this, as a product of two expressions each involving one function.

(3) Use some knowledge from algebra, such as the quadratic formula or techniques of factoring, to write as a product of linear factors.

(4) The zeros (if any) of each of the linear factors should be recognizable by inspection. The total solution set is the union of these sets.

Example 12.12   Solve the equation $2 \tan x \sec x - \tan x = 0$ on the interval $[0, 2\pi)$.

Solution   Factoring yields $\tan x(2 \sec x - 1) = 0$, which means that the solution set is given by the union of the solution sets to the two equations $\tan x = 0$ and $2 \sec x - 1 = 0$. The second of these equations has a solution set equal to the null set since $\sec x \geq 1$. On the interval $[0, 2\pi)$, $\tan x$ is zero at $x = 0$ and $x = \pi$. Thus, the solution set is $\{0, \pi\}$.

Note that squaring both sides of an equality is not an allowable operation since it does not necessarily yield an equivalent equation. In practice you need not restrict yourself to allowable operations, but when other operations, such as squaring both sides, are used, be aware that nonequivalent equations may result. For example, if you divide two sides of an equation by $\sin x$, make at least a mental note of the fact that $\sin x = 0$ for values of x of the form $x = n\pi$. Then try these values in the original expression to see if they are members of the solution set.

Example 12.13   Solve the equation $\sin x + \cos x = 1$ on $[0, 2\pi)$.

Solution   Squaring both sides of this equation yields

$$\sin^2 x + 2 \sin x \cos x + \cos^2 x = 1$$

from which, after using the fact that $\sin^2 x + \cos^2 x = 1$,

$$\sin x \cos x = 0$$

The solution set to this equation is the set of values of x for which $\sin x = 0$ (that is, $x = 0$ and π) and the values of x for which $\cos x = 0$ (that is, $x = \frac{1}{2}\pi$ and $\frac{3}{2}\pi$). Hence, the possible solutions are

$$\left\{0, \frac{1}{2}\pi, \pi, \frac{3}{2}\pi\right\}$$

Since the squaring operation does not yield an equivalent equation, check the values in this set to determine if they are truly solutions to the original equation. (You can be sure that the solution set is a *subset* of this set.) It is easy to show that only $x = 0$ and $x = \frac{1}{2}\pi$ are valid solutions. Thus, the solution set to the given equation is

$$\left\{0, \ \frac{1}{2}\pi\right\}$$

Example 12.14 Solve the equation $2 \sin x \cos x = \cos x$ for $0 \le x \le 2\pi$.

Solution Rather than divide both sides by $\cos x$ (which is zero at certain points), transpose $\cos x$ to the left-hand side. Then factor to obtain

$$\cos x(2 \sin x - 1) = 0$$

from which we have the two equations $\cos x = 0$ and $2 \sin x - 1 = 0$. On the interval of interest the solutions to the first of these equations is $x = \frac{1}{2}\pi$ and $x = \frac{3}{2}\pi$. The second equation is valid for $x = \frac{1}{6}\pi$ and $\frac{5}{6}\pi$. Hence, the solution set is

$$\left\{\frac{1}{6}\pi, \ \frac{1}{2}\pi, \ \frac{5}{6}\pi, \ \frac{3}{2}\pi\right\}$$

Exercises for Section 12.2

Solve the equations in Exercises 1–10 over one period of the function. Make a sketch showing the solution set as the intersection of a line with the graph of some trigonometric function.

1. $\sin x = \frac{1}{2}$
2. $\cos 2x = \frac{1}{2}\sqrt{2}$
3. $\tan x = \sqrt{3}$
4. $\cos x = 1$
5. $\sin x = \frac{1}{2}\sqrt{3}$
6. $\cos \left(3x + \frac{1}{6}\pi\right) = \frac{1}{2}$
7. $\sin \left(2x - \frac{1}{4}\pi\right) = \frac{1}{2}\sqrt{3}$
8. $\tan \left(3x - \pi\right) = 1$
9. $\sin \left(\frac{1}{3}x - \frac{1}{12}\pi\right) = -\frac{1}{2}$
10. $\sin \left(\frac{1}{2}x + \frac{1}{8}\pi\right) = -1$

Solve the trigonometric equations in Exercises 11–37 over one period.

11. $2 \sin x + 1 = 0$
12. $\sin 2x + 1 = 0$
13. $\cos 3x = 1$
14. $\tan 2x + 1 = 0$
15. $\cos^2 x + 2 \cos x + 1 = 0$
16. $\tan^2 x - 1 = 0$
17. $2 \sin^2 x = \sin x$
18. $\sec^2 2x = 1$
19. $\sec^2 x + 1 = 0$
20. $\cos^2 x = 2$
21. $\cos x = \sin x$
22. $2 \sec x \tan x + \sec^2 x = 0$
23. $\sec^2 x - 2 = \tan^2 x$
24. $4 \sin^2 x - 1 = 0$
25. $2 \cos^2 x - \sin x = 1$
26. $2 \sec x + 4 = 0$

27. $\sin^2 x - 2 \sin x + 1 = 0$

28. $\cot^2 x - 5 \cot x + 4 = 0$

29. $\tan^2 x - \tan x = 0$

30. $\cos 2x + \sin 2x = 0$

31. $\sin x \tan^2 x = \sin x$

32. $\cos x + 2 \sin^2 x = 1$

33. $\tan x + \sec x = 1$

34. $\tan x + \cot x = \sec x \csc x$

35. $\cos x + 1 = \sin x$

36. $2 \tan x - \sec^2 x = 0$

37. $\csc^5 x - 4 \csc x = 0$

12.3
Trigonometric
Identities

A **trigonometric identity** is a trigonometric equation whose solution set is the set of all permissible values of the independent variable. Thus, every trigonometric identity is a (conditional) equation, but every equation is not an identity.

Example 12.15   The equation $\sin \theta - \cos \theta = 0$ is not an identity since the solution set is $\{\frac{1}{4}\pi + n\pi\}$. The equation $\tan^2 x + 1 = \sec^2 x$ is an identity since it is true for all x except $x = \frac{1}{2}\pi + n\pi$. These values are not in the domain of either the secant or the tangent function.

To show a given trigonometric equation to be an identity, proceed in one of the three following methods:

(1)   By a series of manipulations using other known identities to transform one side of the equation into the form of the other side

(2)   By a series of manipulations using other known identities to transform the left-hand side and the right-hand side into forms that are precisely the same

(3)   By considering the identity to be a conditional equation and then showing that the solution set is the entire set of permissible values of the unknown.

It is incorrect to attempt to establish an identity by beginning with the assumption that it *is* an identity. Sometimes the manipulations that are performed make it seem as though that is the procedure. For example, in using methods (1) or (2) do not use operations (such as transposing) that are valid for conditional equations.

The purpose of verifying rather esoteric identities is to reinforce your knowledge of the more fundamental ones and to give you additional manipulative skill with trigonometric expressions. In this book, in attempting to keep the ultimate purpose in clear perspective, the identities we prove will, hopefully, be reasonable. A review of identities (12.1)–(12.8) is advisable at this point.

While there is no general approach besides the three mentioned, you may find it desirable to express the trigonometric functions in terms of sines and cosines only. This will often enable you to see the manipulations that are necessary to verify a given identity.

Example 12.16   Verify the identity $\cot x + \tan x = \csc x \sec x$.

Solution   Using method (1), express the left-hand side in terms of sines and cosines. Thus,

$$\cot x + \tan x = \frac{\cos x}{\sin x} + \frac{\sin x}{\cos x}$$

$$= \frac{\cos^2 x + \sin^2 x}{\sin x \cos x}$$

$$= \frac{1}{\sin x \cos x}$$

$$= \csc x \sec x$$

Therefore, we have shown that $\cot x + \tan x = \csc x \sec x$.

Example 12.17   Show that $\sin \theta(\csc \theta - \sin \theta) = \cos^2 \theta$ is an identity.

Solution   Here the most expedient approach is to expand the left-hand side. Thus,

$$\sin \theta(\csc \theta - \sin \theta) = \sin \theta \csc \theta - \sin^2 \theta$$

$$= \sin \theta \frac{1}{\sin \theta} - \sin^2 \theta$$

$$= 1 - \sin^2 \theta$$

$$= \cos^2 \theta$$

Example 12.18   Verify the identity

$$\frac{\cos x \cot x}{\cot x - \cos x} = \frac{\cot x + \cos x}{\cos x \cot x}$$

Solution   In this case use method (2) to prove the identity. Expressing the left-hand

12.3 Trigonometric Identities   347 side in terms of sines and cosines,

$$\frac{\cos x \cot x}{\cot x - \cos x} = \frac{\cos x \dfrac{\cos x}{\sin x}}{\dfrac{\cos x}{\sin x} - \cos x}$$

$$= \frac{\dfrac{\cos^2 x}{\sin x}}{\dfrac{\cos x - \cos x \sin x}{\sin x}}$$

$$= \frac{\cos^2 x}{\sin x} \cdot \frac{\sin x}{\cos x(1 - \sin x)}$$

$$= \frac{\cos x}{1 - \sin x}$$

We now manipulate the right-hand side to agree with this expression. Thus,

$$\frac{\cot x + \cos x}{\cos x \cot x} = \frac{\dfrac{\cos x}{\sin x} + \cos x}{\cos x \dfrac{\cos x}{\sin x}}$$

$$= \frac{\dfrac{\cos x + \cos x \sin x}{\sin x}}{\dfrac{\cos^2 x}{\sin x}}$$

$$= \frac{1 + \sin x}{\cos x}$$

Recognizing that

$$(1 + \sin x)(1 - \sin x) = 1 - \sin^2 x = \cos^2 x$$

multiply both numerator and denominator by $1 - \sin x$.

$$\frac{1 + \sin x}{\cos x} \cdot \frac{1 - \sin x}{1 - \sin x} = \frac{1 - \sin^2 x}{\cos x(1 - \sin x)}$$

$$= \frac{\cos^2 x}{\cos x(1 - \sin x)} = \frac{\cos x}{1 - \sin x}$$

Since we have transformed both sides into the same expression, the identity is proved. ✦

Example 12.19   Verify the previous identity using method (3).

Solution   Consider the equation

$$\frac{\cos x \cot x}{\cot x - \cos x} = \frac{\cot x + \cos x}{\cos x \cot x}$$

Cross multiplying yields

$$\cos^2 x \cot^2 x = \cot^2 x - \cos^2 x$$

Dividing both sides by $\cos^2 x$,

$$\cot^2 x = \frac{1}{\sin^2 x} - 1$$

$$= \csc^2 x - 1 = \cot^2 x$$

The solution set to this last equation is $S = \{x \mid x \text{ a real number} \neq n\pi\}$. The set of permissible values of the original expression is the set $D = \{x \mid x \text{ a real number} \neq n\pi/2\}$. Since $D \subseteq S$, the equation is an identity.

Example 12.20 Show that the expression $\log(\csc x - \cot x)$ is identically equal to $-\log(\csc x + \cot x)$.

Solution By an elementary property of logarithms,

$$-\log(\csc x + \cot x) = \log(\csc x + \cot x)^{-1}$$

$$= \log \frac{1}{\csc x + \cot x}$$

Multiplying numerator and denominator of the term inside the logarithm by $\csc x - \cot x$,

$$-\log(\csc x + \cot x) = \log \frac{\csc x - \cot x}{\csc^2 x - \cot^2 x}$$

Since the denominator is identically 1, the verification is completed.

Exercises for Section 12.3

Determine which of the equations in Exercises 1–10 are identities. If one is not an identity, find the solution set on $0 \le x \le 2\pi$.

1. $(\cos x - \sin x)(\cos x + \sin x) = 2 \cos^2 x - 1$

2. $\sin x \sec x = \tan x$ **3.** $\cos x = \cot x$

4. $1 - \cot x = \cot x \tan x - \cot x$ **5.** $1 - \dfrac{2}{\sec^2 x} = \sin^2 x - \cos^2 x$

6. $\cos x + 1 = \sin x$ **7.** $\dfrac{\cos x}{1 - \sin x} = \dfrac{1 + \sin x}{\cos x}$

8. $\sin x \cot x \tan^2 x = \sec x - \sin x \cot x$

9. $\sin x \tan x + \cos x = \sec x$ **10.** $\sin x \tan^2 x = \sin x$

Verify the identities in Exercises 11–26.

11. $\sin^2 x (1 + \cot^2 x) = 1$ **12.** $\csc x - \sin x = \cot x \cos x$

13. $(\sin^2 x - 1)(\cot^2 x + 1) = 1 - \csc^2 x$

14. $\dfrac{2 + \sec x}{\csc x} - 2 \sin x = \tan x$

15. $\dfrac{\sin x}{1 - \cos x} = \csc x + \cot x$

16. $\dfrac{\cot x + 1}{\cot x - 1} = -\dfrac{\tan x + 1}{\tan x - 1}$

17. $\dfrac{1 + \sec x}{\sin x + \tan x} = \csc x$

18. $\dfrac{1 - \sin x}{1 + \sin x} = (\sec x - \tan x)^2$

19. $(\sin^2 x + \cos^2 x)^4 = 1$

20. $\dfrac{\tan x + \cot x}{\tan x - \cot x} = \dfrac{\sec^2 x}{\tan^2 x - 1}$

21. $\dfrac{\sin x}{\csc x(1 + \cot^2 x)} = \sin^4 x$

22. $1 - \tan^4 x = 2 \sec^2 x - \sec^4 x$

23. $\tan x + \cot x = \sec x \csc x$

24. $(\cot x + \csc x)^2 = \dfrac{1 + \cos x}{1 - \cos x}$

25. $\sin^2 x(\csc^2 x - 1) = \cos^2 x$

26. $\sec x \csc x - 2 \cos x \csc x = \tan x - \cot x$

27. Show that $\log(\sec x - \tan x) = -\log(\sec x + \tan x)$

12.4
The Cosine of
the Difference of Two Angles

The formula for cos $(A - B)$ is so basic that it is the only one of the sum and difference formulas that must be derived directly from the definitions of the trigonometric functions.

Let A and B represent angles in standard position superimposed on a circle of radius 1. Figure 12.5(a) is a picture of the general situation. The terminal side of A intersects the unit circle in the point $(x_A, y_A) =$ (cos A, sin A). Similarly, the terminal side of B intersects the circle at $(x_B, y_B) =$ (cos B, sin B). The distance D between these two points is given by

$$D^2 = (x_A - x_B)^2 + (y_A - y_B)^2$$
$$= (\cos A - \cos B)^2 + (\sin A - \sin B)^2$$
$$= (\cos^2 A - 2 \cos A \cos B + \cos^2 B)$$
$$+ (\sin^2 A - 2 \sin A \sin B + \sin^2 B)$$

Using the fact that $\cos^2 A + \sin^2 A = 1$ and $\cos^2 B + \sin^2 B = 1$,

$$D^2 = 2(1 - \cos A \cos B - \sin A \sin B)$$

Now rotate the angle $A - B$ until it is in standard position, as shown in Figure 12.5(b). The coordinates of the point of intersection of the terminal side of the angle $A - B$ and the unit circle are

$$(x_{A-B}, y_{A-B}) = [\cos(A - B), \sin(A - B)]$$

(a)

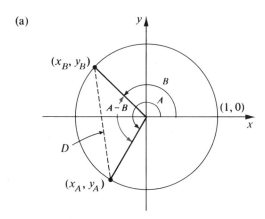

(b)

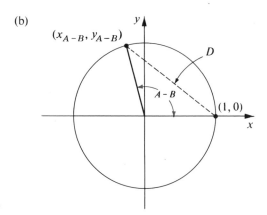

Figure 12.5

D is now the distance connecting $(1, 0)$ to this point. Using the distance formula,

$$D^2 = (x_{A-B} - 1)^2 + (y_{A-B})^2$$
$$= [\cos (A - B) - 1]^2 + \sin^2 (A - B)$$
$$= \cos^2 (A - B) - 2 \cos (A - B) + 1 + \sin^2 (A - B)$$

Since $\cos^2 (A - B) + \sin^2 (A - B) = 1$, we can write D^2 as

$$D^2 = 2[1 - \cos (A - B)]$$

Equating this result to the first expression we derived for D^2, we have

(12.9) $\cos (A - B) = \cos A \cos B + \sin A \sin B$

This is the fundamental formula.

Formula (12.9) was derived under the conditions that $A > B$ and that A and B are between 0 and 2π. However, since

$$\cos (A - B) = \cos (B - A) = \cos (A - B + 2n\pi)$$

12.4 The Cosine of the Difference of Two Angles   351 it follows that the formula is perfectly general. Since it is true for all angles A and B and, consequently for all real numbers, it is an *identity*.

The principal use of this formula is to derive other important relations. However, it can also be used to obtain the value of the cosine function at a particular angle (or real number) if that angle can be expressed as the difference of two angles for which the exact value of the cosine is known.

Example 12.21   Without the use of tables find the exact value of $\cos \frac{1}{12}\pi$.

Solution   First notice that $\frac{1}{12}\pi = \frac{1}{3}\pi - \frac{1}{4}\pi$. Hence,

$$\cos \frac{1}{12}\pi = \cos \left(\frac{1}{3}\pi - \frac{1}{4}\pi \right)$$

$$= \cos \frac{1}{3}\pi \cos \frac{1}{4}\pi + \sin \frac{1}{3}\pi \sin \frac{1}{4}\pi$$

$$= \frac{1}{2}\left(\frac{\sqrt{2}}{2} \right) + \left(\frac{\sqrt{3}}{2} \right)\left(\frac{\sqrt{2}}{2} \right)$$

$$= \frac{\sqrt{2} + \sqrt{6}}{4}$$

If, in formula (12.9) we replace B by $-B$,

$$\cos [A - (-B)] = \cos A \cos (-B) + \sin A \sin (-B)$$

Since the cosine function is even, $\cos (-B) = \cos B$; since the sine function is odd, $\sin (-B) = -\sin B$. Hence,

(12.10) $\cos (A + B) = \cos A \cos B - \sin A \sin B$

Example 12.22   Find the exact value of $\cos 75°$.

Solution   Since $75° = 30° + 45°$,

$$\cos 75° = \cos (30° + 45°)$$

$$= \cos 30° \cos 45° - \sin 30° \sin 45°$$

$$= \frac{\sqrt{3}}{2} \cdot \frac{\sqrt{2}}{2} - \frac{1}{2} \cdot \frac{\sqrt{2}}{2}$$

$$= \frac{\sqrt{6} - \sqrt{2}}{4}$$

Example 12.23   Find the value of $\cos (A - B)$, given that $\sin A = \frac{3}{5}$ in quadrant II and $\tan B = \frac{1}{2}$ in quadrant I.

352   12 Equations and Identities

Solution   From Figure 12.6 we see that $\cos A = -\frac{4}{5}$, $\sin B = 1/\sqrt{5}$, and $\cos B = 2/\sqrt{5}$. Hence,

$$\cos (A - B) = \cos A \cos B + \sin A \sin B$$

$$= \left(-\frac{4}{5}\right)\left(\frac{2}{\sqrt{5}}\right) + \left(\frac{3}{5}\right)\left(\frac{1}{\sqrt{5}}\right)$$

$$= -\frac{5}{5\sqrt{5}} = -\frac{\sqrt{5}}{5}$$

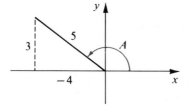 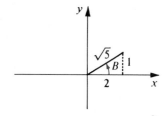

Figure 12.6

In certain applied problems, we encounter functions of the form $c_1 \cos Bx + c_2 \sin Bx$. It is easy to see that this function is periodic with a period of $2\pi/B$; however, in its present form the amplitude and phase shift of the oscillation are not easy to recognize. To obtain these properties, as well as the period, make use of the identity

$$c_1 \cos Bx + c_2 \sin Bx = A \cos (Bx - C)$$

where $A = \sqrt{c_1^2 + c_2^2}$ and $\tan C = c_2/c_1$.

To verify this identity, note that by equation (12.9),

$$A \cos (Bx - C) = A \cos C \cos Bx + A \sin C \sin Bx$$

Therefore,

$$c_1 \cos Bx + c_2 \sin Bx = A \cos C \cos Bx + A \sin C \sin Bx$$

if and only if $c_1 = A \cos C$ and $c_2 = A \sin C$. Squaring c_1 and c_2 and adding,

$$c_1^2 + c_2^2 = A^2 \cos^2 C + A^2 \sin^2 C = A^2(\cos^2 C + \sin^2 C)$$

or

$$A = \sqrt{c_1^2 + c_2^2}$$

Also, the ratio of c_2 to c_1 yields

$$\frac{c_2}{c_1} = \frac{A \sin C}{A \cos C} = \tan C$$

Example 12.24   Express $f(x) = \sin x + \cos x$ as a cosine function and sketch.

12.4 The Cosine of the Difference of Two Angles   353

Solution   Using the above formulas, we have that

$$f(x) = A \cos (x - C) \text{ where } A = \sqrt{1^2 + 1^2} = \sqrt{2} \text{ and } \tan C = 1.$$

Many values of C may be chosen to satisfy $\tan C = 1$, such as $\frac{1}{4}\pi$, $\frac{3}{4}\pi$, or $\frac{7}{4}\pi$. Any of these values is satisfactory, but generally we choose a value between $-\frac{1}{2}\pi$ and $\frac{1}{2}\pi$. Hence, we let $C = \frac{1}{4}\pi$. Therefore,

$$f(x) = \sqrt{2} \cos \left(x - \frac{1}{4}\pi \right)$$

This is a function with amplitude $\sqrt{2}$, period 2π, and phase shift $\frac{1}{4}\pi$. The graph is shown in Figure 12.7 along with the graphs of the sine and cosine functions.

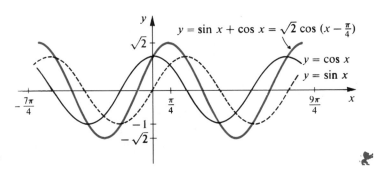

Figure 12.7

Exercises for

Section 12.4

1.   Show that $\sin (x + y) \neq \sin x + \sin y$. (Let $x = \frac{1}{3}\pi$ and $y = \frac{1}{6}\pi$.)

2.   Show that $\tan (x + y) \neq \tan x + \tan y$. (Let $x = \frac{1}{3}\pi$ and $y = \frac{1}{6}\pi$.)

3.   Show that $\sin 2x \neq 2 \sin x$. (Let $x = \frac{1}{4}\pi$.)

4.   Show that $\cos 2x \neq 2 \cos x$. (Let $x = \frac{1}{4}\pi$.)

5.   Show that $\tan 2x \neq 2 \tan x$. (Let $x = \frac{1}{4}\pi$.)

Find the *exact* values of the trigonometric functions in Exercises 6–10.

6. $\cos 105°$ 7. $\cos \frac{1}{12}\pi$ 8. $\cos \frac{11}{12}\pi$ 9. $\cos 195°$

10. $\cos 345°$

Use Equation 12.9 to show that Exercises 11–13 are true.

11. $\cos (\pi - \theta) = -\cos \theta$ 12. $\cos (\frac{1}{2}\pi - \theta) = \sin \theta$

13. $\cos (\frac{1}{2}\pi + \theta) = -\sin \theta$

14.   Using equation (12.9) give a proof that the cosine is an even function.

Verify the identities in Exercises 15–19.

15. $\cos (\frac{1}{3}\pi - x) = \dfrac{\cos x + \sqrt{3} \sin x}{2}$

16. $\cos\left(\frac{1}{4}\pi + \theta\right) = \dfrac{\cos\theta - \sin\theta}{\sqrt{2}}$

17. $\cos\left(\frac{3}{2}\pi + x\right) = \sin x$

18. $\cos(x + y)\cos(x - y) = \cos^2 x - \sin^2 y$

19. $\cos(x + y) + \cos(x - y) = 2\cos x \cos y$

Reduce to a single term Exercises 20–22.

20. $\cos 2x \cos 3x + \sin 2x \sin 3x$

21. $\cos 7x \cos x - \sin 7x \sin x$

22. $\cos \frac{1}{6}x \cos \frac{5}{6}x - \sin \frac{1}{6}x \sin \frac{5}{6}x$

Find the value of $\cos(A + B)$ for the conditions in Exercises 23–26.

23. $\cos A = \frac{1}{3}$, $\sin B = -\frac{1}{2}$, A in quadrant I, B in quadrant IV

24. $\cos A = \frac{3}{5}$, $\tan B = \frac{12}{5}$, both A and B acute

25. $\tan A = \frac{24}{7}$, $\sec B = \frac{5}{3}$, A in quadrant III, B in quadrant I

26. $\sin A = \frac{1}{4}$, $\cos B = \frac{1}{2}$, both A and B in quadrant I

Let both A and B be positive acute angles (Exercises 27–28).

27. Find $\cos A$ if $\cos(A + B) = \frac{5}{6}$ and $\sin B = \frac{1}{3}$.

28. Find $\cos A$ if $\cos(A - B) = \frac{3}{4}$ and $\cos B = \frac{2}{3}$.

Graph the functions in Exercises 29–32. What is the amplitude and phase shift of each?

29. $f(x) = \cos x - \sin x$

30. $f(x) = 2\cos x + 2\sin x$

31. $f(x) = \cos 2x + \sqrt{3}\sin 2x$

32. $f(x) = -\cos 2x + \sqrt{3}\sin 2x$

12.5
Other Addition
Formulas

From the formula for the cosine of the difference it is easy to establish that

$$(12.11) \qquad \cos\left(\frac{1}{2}\pi - \theta\right) = \sin\theta \quad \text{and} \quad \sin\left(\frac{1}{2}\pi - \theta\right) = \cos\theta$$

Note that this is a general statement of the identity relating cofunctions of complementary angles. In Chapter 9 this formula was derived with the condition that the two angles were acute. We now see that this is a general formula, true for all values of the argument.

Example 12.25

$$\cos(-10°) = \cos(90° - 100°) = \sin 100°$$

$$\sin\left(\frac{5}{6}\pi\right) = \sin\left(\frac{1}{2}\pi - \left(-\frac{1}{3}\pi\right)\right) = \cos\left(-\frac{1}{3}\pi\right) = \cos\frac{1}{3}\pi$$

You know that the fundamental Pythagorean relationship states that $\sin^2 x + \cos^2 x = 1$. A formula involving *two* numbers x and y which looks quite similar is also true if x and y have a sum of $\frac{1}{2}\pi$.

Example 12.26   If x and y are complementary numbers (that is, if their sum is $\frac{1}{2}\pi$), show that $\sin^2 x + \sin^2 y = 1$.

Solution   Since $x + y = \frac{1}{2}\pi$, $y = \frac{1}{2}\pi - x$. Therefore, $\sin y = \sin\left(\frac{1}{2}\pi - x\right) = \cos x$. Hence, from the Pythagorean relation,

$$\sin^2 x + \cos^2 x = 1$$

we have, using $\sin y = \cos x$,

$$\sin^2 x + \sin^2 y = 1$$

By letting $\theta = A + B$ in equation 12.11, we can write

$$\sin(A + B) = \cos\left[\frac{1}{2}\pi - (A + B)\right]$$

$$= \cos\left[\left(\frac{1}{2}\pi - A\right) - B\right]$$

$$= \cos\left(\frac{1}{2}\pi - A\right)\cos B + \sin\left(\frac{1}{2}\pi - A\right)\sin B$$

(12.12) $\sin(A + B) = \sin A \cos B + \cos A \sin B$

Similarly, if $\theta = A - B$,

$$\sin(A - B) = \sin A \cos(-B) + \cos A \sin(-B)$$

and since the cosine is an even function and the sine function is odd, this equation becomes

(12.13) $\sin(A - B) = \sin A \cos B - \cos A \sin B$

Example 12.27   Find the exact value of $\sin\left(\frac{1}{12}\pi\right)$.

356   12 Equations and Identities

Solution Since $\frac{1}{12}\pi = \frac{1}{3}\pi - \frac{1}{4}\pi$, we have that

$$\sin\left(\frac{1}{12}\pi\right) = \sin\left(\frac{1}{3}\pi\right)\cos\left(\frac{1}{4}\pi\right) - \cos\left(\frac{1}{3}\pi\right)\sin\left(\frac{1}{4}\pi\right)$$

$$= \frac{\sqrt{3}}{2}\frac{\sqrt{2}}{2} - \frac{1}{2}\frac{\sqrt{2}}{2}$$

$$= \frac{1}{4}(\sqrt{6} - \sqrt{2})$$

Example 12.28 Show that $\sin x + \cos x = \sqrt{2}\sin(x + \frac{1}{4}\pi)$.

Solution If $\sin x + \cos x = A\sin(x + C) = A\sin x\cos C + A\cos x\sin C$, then $A\cos C = 1$ and $A\sin C = 1$. Squaring these two equations and adding the results,

$$A^2\cos^2 C + A^2\sin^2 C = 1^2 + 1^2 = 2$$

or $A = \sqrt{2}$

Also, $\dfrac{A\sin C}{A\cos C} = \dfrac{1}{1}$

so $\tan C = 1$

and $C = \dfrac{1}{4}\pi$

Therefore,

$$\sin x + \cos x = \sqrt{2}\sin\left(x + \frac{1}{4}\pi\right)$$

The sketch of this function is precisely that given in Figure 12.7. Can you verify this sketch?

Sum and difference formulas for the tangent follow directly from those for the sine and the cosine.

$$\tan(A + B) = \frac{\sin(A + B)}{\cos(A + B)}$$

$$= \frac{\sin A\cos B + \cos A\sin B}{\cos A\cos B - \sin A\sin B}$$

Now divide both the numerator and the denominator by $\cos A\cos B$.

$$\tan(A + B) = \frac{\dfrac{\sin A\cos B}{\cos A\cos B} + \dfrac{\cos A\sin B}{\cos A\cos B}}{\dfrac{\cos A\cos B}{\cos A\cos B} - \dfrac{\sin A\sin B}{\cos A\cos B}}$$

Simplifying,

$$(12.14) \qquad \tan (A + B) = \frac{\tan A + \tan B}{1 - \tan A \tan B}$$

Similarly,

$$(12.15) \qquad \tan (A - B) = \frac{\tan A - \tan B}{1 + \tan A \tan B}$$

In summary, the following sum and difference formulas have been derived:

$$\sin (A \pm B) = \sin A \cos B \pm \cos A \sin B$$

$$\cos (A \pm B) = \cos A \cos B \mp \sin A \sin B$$

$$\tan (A \pm B) = \frac{\tan A \pm \tan B}{1 \mp \tan A \tan B}$$

By convention, the symbols $\pm$ and $\mp$ in the same formula mean to use the topmost signs together and the bottommost signs together.

Exercises for
Section 12.5

Find the exact value of Exercises 1–4.

1. $\sin \left(\frac{5}{12}\pi\right)$ 2. $\tan 15°$ 3. $\sin \left(\frac{7}{12}\pi\right)$

4. $\sin (345°)$ 5. $\cot \left(\frac{5}{12}\pi\right)$

Verify the identities in Exercises 6–13.

6. $\sin (A + \frac{1}{4}\pi) = \frac{\sqrt{2}}{2}(\sin A + \cos A)$

7. $\tan (A + \frac{1}{2}\pi) = -\cot A$ 8. $\tan (A + \frac{1}{4}\pi) = \frac{1 + \tan A}{1 - \tan A}$

9. $\cot (A + B) = \frac{\cot A \cot B - 1}{\cot A + \cot B}$ 10. $\frac{\sin (A + B)}{\sin (A - B)} = \frac{\tan A + \tan B}{\tan A - \tan B}$

11. $\sin (A + B) \sin (A - B) = \sin^2 A - \sin^2 B$

12. $\sin (A + B) + \sin (A - B) = 2 \sin A \cos B$

13. $\tan A + \tan B = \frac{\sin (A + B)}{\cos A \cos B}$

Reduce to a single term Exercises 14–17.

14. $\sin 2x \cos 3x + \sin 3x \cos 2x$ 15. $\frac{\tan 3x - \tan 2x}{1 + \tan 3x \tan 2x}$

16. $\sin \frac{1}{3}x \cos \frac{2}{3}x + \sin \frac{2}{3}x \cos \frac{1}{3}x$ **17.** $\dfrac{\tan (x + y) + \tan z}{1 - \tan (x + y) \tan z}$

Find the values of $\sin (A + B)$ and $\tan (A + B)$ if (Exercises 18–20)

18. $\sin A = \frac{3}{5}$, $\cos B = \frac{4}{5}$, both A and B in quadrant I

19. $\tan A = -\frac{7}{24}$, $\tan B = \frac{5}{12}$, A in quadrant II, B in quadrant III

20. $\cos A = \frac{1}{3}$, $\cos B = -\frac{1}{3}$, A in quadrant IV, B in quadrant III

Express as a sine function with a phase shift and sketch (Exercises 21–24).

21. $\sin 2x + \cos 2x$ **22.** $\cos x$

23. $\sqrt{3} \sin \pi x + \cos \pi x$ **24.** $7 \sin 2x - 24 \cos 2x$

12.6
Multiple-Angle
and Half-Angle Formulas

In the two previous sections we have been primarily interested in expanding trigonometric functions whose arguments are $A \pm B$. Now we will derive formulas for functions of $2A$ and $\frac{1}{2}A$. If A represents an angle, the formulas are called the double-angle and half-angle formulas, respectively.

The double-angle formulas are easily proved by choosing $B = A$ in the formulas for the sum of two angles. Thus,

$$\sin 2A = \sin (A + A)$$
$$= \sin A \cos A + \sin A \cos A$$

(12.16) $\sin 2A = 2 \sin A \cos A$

and

$$\cos 2A = \cos (A + A)$$
$$= \cos A \cos A - \sin A \sin A$$

(12.17) $\cos 2A = \cos^2 A - \sin^2 A$

By use of the Pythagorean relationship, this last formula may also be expressed in the equivalent forms

(12.18a) $\cos 2A = 2 \cos^2 A - 1$

and

(12.18b) $\cos 2A = 1 - 2 \sin^2 A$

Similarly,

$$\tan 2A = \frac{\tan A + \tan A}{1 - \tan A \tan A}$$

(12.19) $$\tan 2A = \frac{2 \tan A}{1 - \tan^2 A}$$

Example 12.29   Find $\sin 2A$ if $\sin A = \frac{1}{3}$ and A is in quadrant II.

Solution   Since $\sin A = \frac{1}{3}$, we have from Figure 12.8 that $\cos A = -\frac{1}{3}\sqrt{8}$ and hence,

$$\sin 2A = 2 \sin A \cos A$$

$$= 2\left(\frac{1}{3}\right)\left(\frac{-\sqrt{8}}{3}\right) = \frac{-2\sqrt{8}}{9}$$

Note that $\sin 2A \neq \frac{2}{3}$!

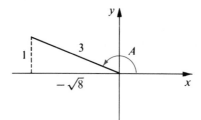

Figure 12.8

Example 12.30   Sketch the graph of $y = \sin x \cos x$. Where does the maximum value of this function occur?

Solution   Initially you might think that you must graph this function by point plotting, but multiplying and dividing the right-hand side by 2 yields

$$y = \frac{2 \sin x \cos x}{2} = \frac{1}{2} \sin 2x$$

Thus, the graph of this function is a sine wave with amplitude $\frac{1}{2}$ and period π.

Its maximum value of $\frac{1}{2}$ occurs at $x = \frac{1}{4}\pi + 2n\pi$. (See Figure 12.9.)

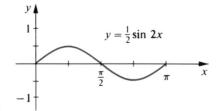

Figure 12.9

The half-angle formulas are direct consequences of the formulas for the cosine of a double angle. Since

$$\cos 2A = 2\cos^2 A - 1$$

we have, upon solving for $\cos A$,

$$\cos A = \pm\sqrt{\frac{1 + \cos 2A}{2}}$$

Using the formula $\cos 2A = 1 - 2\sin^2 A$ and solving for $\sin A$,

$$\sin A = \pm\sqrt{\frac{1 - \cos 2A}{2}}$$

By letting $A = \frac{1}{2}x$ in both of these formulas,

(12.20) $$\cos\frac{1}{2}x = \pm\sqrt{(1 + \cos x)/2}$$

and

(12.21) $$\sin\frac{1}{2}x = \pm\sqrt{(1 - \cos x)/2}$$

To get the formula for $\tan\frac{1}{2}x$, write

$$\tan\frac{1}{2}x = \frac{\sin\frac{1}{2}x}{\cos\frac{1}{2}x}$$

$$= \frac{\sqrt{(1 - \cos x)/2}}{\sqrt{(1 + \cos x)/2}}$$

$$= \sqrt{(1 - \cos x)/(1 + \cos x)}$$

Multiplying numerator and denominator by this expression by $(1 + \cos x)$,

$$\tan\frac{1}{2}x = \sqrt{(1 - \cos^2 x)/(1 + \cos x)^2}$$

$$= \sqrt{\sin^2 x/(1 + \cos x)^2}$$

Therefore,

(12.22) $$\tan\frac{1}{2}x = \frac{\sin x}{1 + \cos x}$$

Example 12.31   If $\tan\theta = -\frac{4}{3}$ and $-\frac{1}{2}\pi < \theta < 0$, find $\sin\frac{1}{2}\theta$ and $\cos\frac{1}{2}\theta$.

Solution Figure 12.10 shows the angle θ in standard position. From this, $\cos\theta = \frac{3}{5}$, and hence,

$$\sin\frac{1}{2}\theta = -\sqrt{\frac{1-(3/5)}{2}} = -\frac{\sqrt{5}}{5}$$

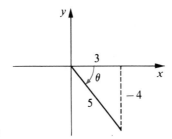

Figure 12.10

(The minus sign is chosen because $\sin\frac{1}{2}\theta$ is negative on the indicated range.) Similarly,

$$\cos\frac{1}{2}\theta = \sqrt{\frac{1+(3/5)}{2}} = \sqrt{4/5} = \frac{2\sqrt{5}}{5}$$

Example 12.31 Find an expression for $\sin 3\theta$ in terms of $\sin\theta$.

Solution

$$\sin 3\theta = \sin(2\theta + \theta)$$
$$= \sin 2\theta \cos\theta + \sin\theta \cos 2\theta$$
$$= 2\sin\theta \cos^2\theta + \sin\theta(1 - 2\sin^2\theta)$$
$$= 2\sin\theta(1 - \sin^2\theta) + \sin\theta(1 - 2\sin^2\theta)$$
$$= 3\sin\theta - 4\sin^3\theta$$

Example 12.32 Solve the equation $\cos 2x = \cos x$ on the interval $0 \le x \le 2\pi$.

Solution First, use the identity for $\cos 2x$ to transform the equation into one involving $\cos x$.

$$2\cos^2 x - 1 = \cos x$$

Transferring $\cos x$ to the left-hand side,

$$2\cos^2 x - \cos x - 1 = 0$$

Factoring,

$$(2\cos x + 1)(\cos x - 1) = 0$$

From this we have the two separate equations,

$$2\cos x + 1 = 0 \quad \text{and} \quad \cos x = 1$$

362   12 Equations and Identities

The solution set to the first of these on $0 \leq x \leq 2\pi$ is $x = \frac{2}{3}\pi$ and $\frac{4}{3}\pi$ and, to the second one, $x = 0$ and $x = 2\pi$. Hence, the complete solution set is

$$\left\{ 0, \frac{2}{3}\pi, \frac{4}{3}\pi, 2\pi \right\}$$

Exercises for Section 12.6

Express each of the functions in Exercises 1–6 as a single trigonometric term.

1. $2 \sin 3x \cos 3x$
2. $6 \sin \frac{1}{2}x \cos \frac{1}{2}x$

3. $\sin^2 4x - \cos^2 4x$
4. $4 \sin^2 x \cos^2 x$

5. $\dfrac{2 \tan \frac{1}{6}x}{1 - \tan^2 \frac{1}{6}x}$
6. $\dfrac{\sin 6x}{1 + \cos 6x}$

7. Sketch the graph of the function $f(x) = \sin 2x \cos 2x$. What is the maximum value of the function? Where does it occur?

8. Sketch the graph of the two functions $f(x) = \cos^2 x - \sin^2 x$ and $g(x) = \cos^2 x + \sin^2 x$. In each case tell what the maximum values are.

9. Sketch the graph of the function $f(x) = \sec x \csc x$. Does this function have a maximum? Where is this function undefined?

10. Sketch the graph of the function $f(x) = (2 \tan x)/(1 + \tan^2 x)$. What is the maximum value of this function? What is the period?

11. Sketch the graph of the function $f(x) = \tan x + \cot x$. Where is this function undefined? What is the period?

12. Sketch the graph of the function $f(x) = \cot x - \tan x$. What are the zeros of this function? Is it bounded or unbounded? What is the period?

Find $\sin 2A$, $\cos 2A$, and $\tan 2A$, given that: (Exercises 13–16)

13. $\sin A = \frac{3}{5}$, A in quadrant I
14. $\cos A = -\frac{12}{13}$, A in quadrant III

15. $\tan A = \frac{7}{24}$, A in quadrant III
16. $\sec A = -\frac{13}{5}$, A in quadrant II

Determine the exact values of Exercises 17–21.

17. $\sin \frac{1}{8}\pi$
18. $\cos \frac{5}{8}\pi$
19. $\tan 157.5°$

20. $\sin 67.5°$
21. $\cos \frac{1}{12}\pi$

Verify the identities in Exercises 22–28.

22. $(\sin x + \cos x)^2 = 1 + \sin 2x$
23. $\cos 3x = 4 \cos^3 x - 3 \cos x$

24. $\sin 4x = 4 \cos x \sin x(1 - 2 \sin^2 x)$
25. $\tan x + \cot x = 2 \csc 2x$

26. $\cos 4x = 8 \cos^4 x - 8 \cos^2 x + 1$
27. $\cot^2 \frac{1}{2}x = \dfrac{\sec x + 1}{\sec x - 1}$

28. $\cos^4 x = \frac{3}{8} + \frac{1}{2} \cos 2x + \frac{1}{8} \cos 4x$

12.6 Multiple-Angle and Half-Angle Formulas 363

Find the functional values in Exercises 29–31.

29. Find $\tan \theta$ if $\sin 2\theta = \frac{5}{13}$.   **30.** Find $\sin \theta$ if $\sin 2\theta = \frac{3}{5}$.

31. Find $\cos \theta$ if $\cos 2\theta = \frac{24}{25}$.

Solve the equations in Exercises 32–40 for those numbers that belong to the interval $0 \leq x \leq 2\pi$.

32. $\sin 2x = \sin x$ **33.** $\sin x = \cos x$

34. $\sin 2x \sin x + \cos x = 0$ **35.** $\tan 2x = \tan x$

36. $\cos x - \sin 2x = 0$ **37.** $\sin 2x + \cos 2x = 0$

38. $\sin 2x - 2 \cos x + \sin x - 1 = 0$

39. $2(\sin^2 2x - \cos^2 2x) = 1$

40. $\sin 2x \cos x - \frac{1}{2} \sin 3x = \frac{1}{2} \sin x$

Simplify the expressions in Exercises 41–45.

41. $(\sin x + \cos x)^2 - \sin 2x$ **42.** $\dfrac{\sin 4x}{1 - \cos 4x}$

43. $\sec^4 x - \tan^4 x - 2 \tan^2 x$ **44.** $\dfrac{\sin 2x}{\sin x} - \dfrac{\cos 2x}{\cos x}$

45. $\cos 2x + \sin 2x \tan x$

12.7
Sums and
Differences of Sines and Cosines

Sometimes you will want to factor a sum of sines and cosines into a product. A scheme based on the addition formulas is shown below.

Example 12.33   Factor $\sin 7x + \sin 3x$.

Solution   Write

$$\sin 7x + \sin 3x = \sin (5x + 2x) + \sin (5x - 2x)$$

$$= \sin 5x \cos 2x + \sin 2x \cos 5x$$

$$+ \sin 5x \cos 2x - \sin 2x \cos 5x$$

$$= 2 \sin 5x \cos 2x$$

The method, illustrated in the preceding example, is called the *average angle method*. In the general case, we can proceed

$$\sin A + \sin B = \sin\left(\frac{A+B}{2} + \frac{A-B}{2}\right) + \sin\left(\frac{A+B}{2} - \frac{A-B}{2}\right)$$

$$= \sin\frac{A+B}{2}\cos\frac{A-B}{2} + \cos\frac{A+B}{2}\sin\frac{A-B}{2}$$

$$+ \sin\frac{A+B}{2}\cos\frac{A-B}{2} - \cos\frac{A+B}{2}\sin\frac{A-B}{2}$$

(12.23) $$\sin A + \sin B = 2\sin\frac{A+B}{2}\cos\frac{A-B}{2}$$

The following formulas are derived analogously. If you followed the technique used in deriving equation 12.23 you will not have to memorize them.

(12.24) $$\sin A - \sin B = 2\cos\frac{A+B}{2}\sin\frac{A-B}{2}$$

(12.25) $$\cos A + \cos B = 2\cos\frac{A+B}{2}\cos\frac{A-B}{2}$$

(12.26) $$\cos A - \cos B = -2\sin\frac{A+B}{2}\sin\frac{A-B}{2}$$

Example 12.34   The difference quotient of a function is defined to be

$$\Delta f = \frac{f(x + \Delta x) - f(x)}{\Delta x}$$

Find the difference quotient for the sine function.

Solution   First, compute $\sin(x + \Delta x) - \sin x$.

$$\sin(x + \Delta x) - \sin x = 2\cos\frac{(x + \Delta x) + x}{2}\sin\frac{(x + \Delta x) - x}{2}$$

$$= 2\sin\frac{\Delta x}{2}\cos\frac{2x + \Delta x}{2}$$

Thus, the difference quotient for the sine function is

$$\frac{\sin(\Delta x/2)}{\Delta x/2}\cos\frac{2x + \Delta x}{2}$$

12.7 Sums and Differences of Sines and Cosines   365

12.8

Product

Formulas

The objective in this section is to find formulas to express products of trigonometric functions as sums of trigonometric functions. The derivations are made from the formulas for the sine and the cosine of the sum and the difference. If we add the formulas for $\sin (A + B)$ and $\sin (A - B)$,

(12.27) $\qquad \sin A \cos B = \dfrac{1}{2}[\sin (A + B) + \sin (A - B)]$

Upon subtracting $\sin (A - B)$ from $\sin (A + B)$ and simplifying,

(12.28) $\qquad \cos A \sin B = \dfrac{1}{2}[\sin (A + B) - \sin (A - B)]$

In like manner, by first adding and then subtracting the formulas for $\cos (A + B)$ and $\cos (A - B)$,

(12.29) $\qquad \cos A \cos B = \dfrac{1}{2}[\cos (A + B) + \cos (A - B)]$

(12.30) $\qquad \sin A \sin B = \dfrac{1}{2}[\cos (A - B) - \cos (A + B)]$

Example 12.34　Express $\sin mx \cos nx$ as a sum of functions.

　　　　Solution　Using equation 12.27 with $A = mx$ and $B = nx$,

$$\sin mx \cos nx = \frac{1}{2}\{\sin (mx + nx) + \sin (mx - nx)\}$$

$$= \frac{1}{2}\{\sin (m + n)x + \sin (m - n)x\}$$

Example 12.35　In the analysis of some types of harmonic motion the governing equation is $y(t) = A(\cos \omega t - \cos \omega_0 t)$, where the difference of ω and ω_0 is considered to be very small. Make a sketch of the graph of this function.

　　　　Solution　By using equation 12.26,

$$y(t) = 2A \sin \frac{\omega_0 - \omega}{2} t \, \sin \frac{\omega_0 + \omega}{2} t$$

If ω is close to ω_0, the resultant oscillation can be interpreted to have a frequency close to $\omega_0/2\pi$ (and of course close to $\omega/2\pi$), with variable amplitude given by

$$2A \sin \frac{\omega_0 - \omega}{2} t$$

which fluctuates with frequency $(\omega - \omega_0)/\pi$.

　　　　Oscillations of this type are called *beats*. (See Figure 12.11.)

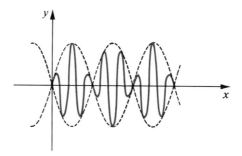

Figure 12.11

Exercises for

Sections 12.7 and 12.8

Express each of Exercises 1–7 as a product.

1. $\sin 3\theta + \sin \theta$

2. $\cos 3\alpha - \cos 8\alpha$

3. $\sin 8x + \sin 2x$

4. $\sin \frac{1}{2}x - \sin \frac{1}{4}x$

5. $\cos 50° - \cos 30°$

6. $\sin \frac{3}{4}\pi - \sin \frac{1}{4}\pi$

7. $\sin \frac{3}{4} - \sin \frac{1}{4}$

Express each of Exercises 8–12 as a sum or difference.

8. $\sin 3x \cos x$

9. $\cos x \sin \frac{1}{2}x$

10. $\cos \frac{1}{3}\pi \sin \frac{2}{3}\pi$

11. $\cos 6x \cos 2x$

12. $\sin \frac{1}{4}\pi \sin \frac{1}{12}\pi$

Verify the identities in Exercises 13–18.

13. $\dfrac{\sin x + \sin y}{\cos x + \cos y} = \tan \frac{1}{2}(x + y)$

14. $\dfrac{\sin x + \sin y}{\sin x - \sin y} = \dfrac{\tan \frac{1}{2}(x + y)}{\tan \frac{1}{2}(x - y)}$

15. $\dfrac{\cos 3x + \cos x}{\sin 3x + \sin x} = \cot 2x$

16. $\cos 7x + \cos 5x + 2 \cos x \cos 2x = 4 \cos 4x \cos 2x \cos x$

17. $\dfrac{\sin 2x + \sin 2y}{\cos 2x + \cos 2y} = \tan (x + y)$

18. $\dfrac{\sin 9x - \sin 5x}{\sin 14x} = \dfrac{\sin 2x}{\sin 7x}$

19. Find the difference quotient for $\cos x$.

Solve the equations in Exercises 20–23 on $0 \leq x \leq \pi$.

20. $\sin 3x + \sin 5x = 0$

21. $\sin x - \sin 5x = 0$

22. $\cos 3x - \cos x = 0$

23. $\cos 2x - \cos 3x = 0$

24. Let $f(x) = \sin (2x + 1) + \sin (2x - 1)$. Make a sketch of the graph of the function. What is the period and the amplitude?

25. Let $f(x) = \cos (3x + 1) + \cos (3x - 1)$. Make a sketch of the graph of this function and give the period and the amplitude.

26. Make a sketch of the graph of the function $f(x) = \cos 99x - \cos 101x$.

12.8 Product Formulas
367

Test 1 for
Chapter 12

Answer true or false for 1–10.

1. $\sin^4 x + \cos^4 x = 1$

2. $\left| \tan^2 420 - \sec^2 420 \right| = 1$

3. $\cos 2x = 2 \cos x$

4. $\sin (x + y) = \sin x + \sin y$

5. $\tan \dfrac{x}{y} = \dfrac{\tan x}{\tan y}$

6. $\cos^2 300 - \sin^2 300 = \cos 600$

7. $\left| \sin 2x \cos 2x \right| \le \frac{1}{2}$

8. $(\sin x + \cos x)^2 = 1$

9. $\tan^2 x = 1$ where $\cos x = \pm \sin x$

10. $\sin x = \cos \left(x + \dfrac{\pi}{2} \right)$

11. Solve the following equation on $(0, 2\pi)$.

    $2 \sin^2 x + 5 \sin^2 x - 3 = 0$

12. Solve the following equation on $(0, 2\pi)$.

    $3 \sin^2 x + \cos^2 x + 4 \sin x = 0$

13. By using the substitution $x = 3 \sin \theta$, reduce the expression

    $(9 - x^2)^{1/2}$

    to one with one trigonometric function. What is $\tan \theta$?

14. Graph the function $f(x) = \tan^2 x - \sec^2 x$.

15. Verify the identity $\cos x \tan x \cot^2 x = \csc x - \cos x \tan x$.

16. Verify the identity $\sin 3x = \sin x(3 \cos^2 x - \sin^2 x)$.

Test 2 for
Chapter 12

1. Compute $\sin 195°$ from the functions of $60°$ and $135°$.

2. Solve $2 \cos \theta + \sqrt{3} = 0, 0 \le \theta < 2\pi$.

3. Solve $2 \sin^2 x + 3 \sin x + 1 = 0, 0 \le x < 2\pi$.

Verify the identities in Exercises 4–7.

4. $\tan 3x \csc 3x = \sec 3x$

5. $\dfrac{\cot^2 x - 1}{1 + \cot^2 x} = 2\cos^2\theta - 1$

6. $\cot 2\phi + \csc 2\phi = \cot \phi$

7. $\tan \frac{1}{2}\theta = \csc \theta - \cot \theta$

8. Sketch the graph of $y = 3\cos 2x + 2\sin 2x$. What is the amplitude, the period, and the phase shift?

9. Find $\sin(A + B)$ if $\cos A = 5/13$, $\sin B = -\sqrt{3}/2$, and A and B are in quadrant IV.

10. Find $\sin 2\theta$ if $\tan \theta = -\frac{3}{4}$ and θ in quadrant II.

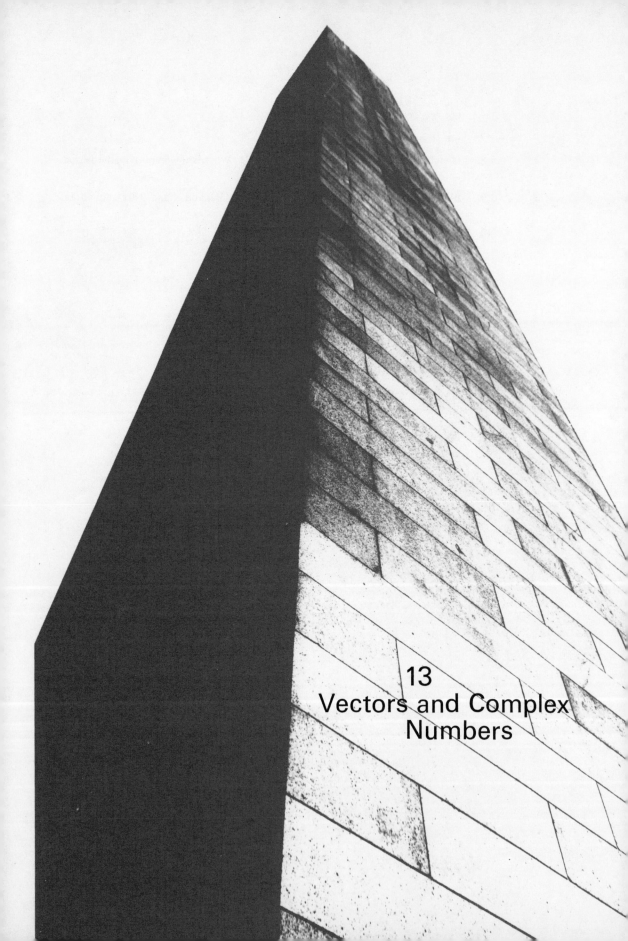

13
Vectors and Complex
Numbers

13.1
Introduction

The idea of a vector was presented briefly in Chapter 9, and that of a complex number was mentioned in Chapter 1. This chapter explores these concepts more completely. Although vectors and complex numbers are conceptually quite different, their mathematical representations exhibit unmistakable similarities.

13.2
Vectors in the
Plane

A description of some physical quantities such as temperature, length, or volume requires one number. These are examples of **scalar** quantities. Other quantities such as velocity, acceleration, or force can only be described by giving both a magnitude and a direction. For example, a velocity of 70 mph to the north is quite different from 70 mph to the south.

To describe quantities that have a magnitude and an associated direction we use (geometric) **vectors**. Usually an arrow represents a vector quantity. Its length corresponds to the magnitude of the quantity and the direction of the arrowhead gives its direction. Thus, in Figure 13.1 one arrow represents a velocity of 100 mph north and the other a velocity of 200 mph northeast.

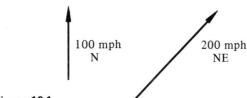

100 mph
N

200 mph
NE

Figure 13.1

Vectors are given in boldface to distinguish them from scalars. The length of a vector **V** is denoted by $|\mathbf{V}|$ and is always a positive quantity. The direction of a vector is given in various ways, depending largely on the application.

For the sake of completeness we shall on occasion need to consider a vector with zero length. Such a vector, called the *zero vector*, is denoted by **0** and has an undefined direction.

For the kind of vectors we will consider, the direction and the length are the complete determining factors. That is, for mathematical purposes two vectors are to be considered the same if they have the same direction and length, regardless of the location of the initial point of the vector. Thus, in Figure 13.2 all the vectors are mathematically equivalent.

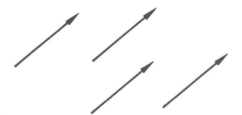

Figure 13.2

Note that this type of vector equality may not always be the kind you need. For example, in Figure 13.3 if **F** is a 10-lb force pointing down, it will certainly make a difference as to which of the three places it is applied. Sometimes vectors for which you may ignore the actual point of application are said to be *free*. The physical situation shown in Figure 13.3 obviously cannot be described using free vectors and hence is not part of this discussion.

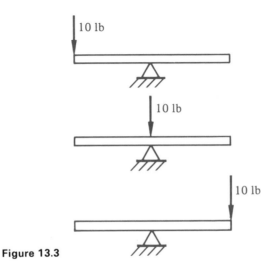

10 lb

10 lb

10 lb

Figure 13.3

By first imposing a coordinate system on the plane, we may move all the vectors in this plane so that their initial points are at the origin. See Figure 13.4. Such vectors are said to be in *standard position*. In effect, a vector at the origin represents all other vectors with the same direction and length, that is, all other vectors equivalent to it.

The technique of referencing any vector to the origin means that the terminal point of a vector will be sufficient to describe it. Thus, the coordinates

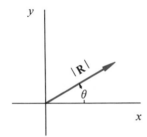

Figure 13.4

13 Vectors and Complex Numbers

of the terminal point completely describe the vector, and conversely, an ordered pair of numbers determines a vector whose initial point is at the origin and whose terminal point is at the point whose coordinates are given by the ordered pair of numbers.

If a vector is placed in standard position, you can find its length from the Pythagorean theorem. The direction of the vector is commonly given as the angle it makes with the positive x-axis.

Example 13.1

Find the magnitude and direction of the vector $\mathbf{V}$ in standard position whose terminal point is at $(2, 1)$.

Solution Figure 13.5 shows the length of the vector to be

$$|\mathbf{V}| = \sqrt{2^2 + 1^2} = \sqrt{5}$$

and the angle θ that $\mathbf{V}$ makes with the positive x-axis

$$\theta = \arctan(0.5) = 26.6°$$

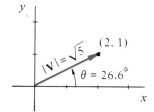

Figure 13.5

Example 13.2 Figure 13.6 shows a vector $\mathbf{V}$ with $|\mathbf{V}| = 12$ and $\theta = 60°$. Find the ordered pair of numbers that determines $\mathbf{V}$.

Solution The ordered pair of real numbers that essentially determines the vector $\mathbf{V}$ is given by the coordinates of the point which is at the tip of $\mathbf{V}$ when $\mathbf{V}$ is in standard position. Thus, in Figure 13.6 the x-coordinate of the tip of $\mathbf{V}$ is given by

$$x = |\mathbf{V}| \cos \theta$$

$$= 12 \cos 60° = 12\left(\frac{1}{2}\right) = 6$$

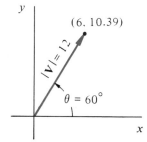

Figure 13.6

13.2 Vectors in the Plane

The y-coordinate is

$$y = |\mathbf{V}| \sin \theta$$

$$= 12 \sin 60° = 12\left(\frac{\sqrt{3}}{2}\right) = 10.39$$

Thus, the ordered pair (6, 10.39) completely determines **V**.

Two vectors in the plane need a special notation. Figure 13.7 shows these two vectors in standard position, one ending at (1, 0), called the **i** vector, and the other ending at (0, 1), called the **j** vector. These two vectors are basic in the sense that every other vector in the plane can be expressed in terms of these two.

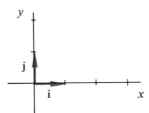

Figure 13.7

Exercises for
Sections 13.1 and 13.2

Draw the vectors in Exercises 1–10 whose initial point is at the origin and whose terminal point is at the indicated point. Calculate the magnitude and direction of each vector.

1. (1, 2) 2. (−3, 2) 3. ($\sqrt{2}$, $\sqrt{7}$) 4. (1, −1)

5. (−4, −4) 6. (5, 8) 7. (4, −3) 8. (−3, −7)

9. (−$\sqrt{3}$, 6) 10. ($\sqrt{5}$, 3)

Find the x- and y-coordinates of the terminal point of the vectors in Exercises 11–20 in standard position.

11. $|\mathbf{V}| = 10, \theta = 50°$ 12. $|\mathbf{V}| = 25, \theta = 75°$

13. $|\mathbf{V}| = 13.7, \theta = 34°10'$ 14. $|\mathbf{V}| = .751, \theta = 56°30'$

15. $|\mathbf{V}| = 158, \theta = 125°$ 16. $|\mathbf{V}| = 875, \theta = 145°$

17. $|\mathbf{V}| = 43.5, \theta = 220°$ 18. $|\mathbf{V}| = 9.41, \theta = 195°$

19. $|\mathbf{V}| = 10.4, \theta = 335°$ 20. $|\mathbf{V}| = 0.05, \theta = 280°$

13.3
Scalar
Multiplication

Given any vector **A**, we may obtain other vectors in the same (or opposite) direction of **A** by multiplying **A** by a real number c. The resulting vector, denoted by $c\mathbf{A}$, is a vector that points in the same direction as **A** if $c > 0$ and opposite to that of **A** if $c < 0$. The magnitude of $c\mathbf{A}$ is $|c|\,|\mathbf{A}|$; that is, it is larger than $|\mathbf{A}|$ if $|c| > 1$ and smaller than $|\mathbf{A}|$ if $|c| < 1$. The vector $c\mathbf{A}$ is called a **scalar multiple** of the vector **A**. Figure 13.8 shows some scalar multiples of a given vector **A**.

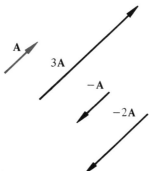

Figure 13.8

The particular scalar multiple of a vector obtained by multiplying a vector **A** by the reciprocal of its magnitude leads to a vector in the direction of **A** whose length is 1. This is the **unit vector** in the direction of **A**, denoted by $\mathbf{u}_A$. Thus,

$$(13.1) \qquad \mathbf{u}_A = \frac{\mathbf{A}}{|\mathbf{A}|}$$

Two important examples of unit vectors are the **i** and **j** vectors in the direction of the x- and y-axes.

13.4
Vector Addition

Two vectors are added by a rule called the **parallelogram rule**.

Rule | To add two vectors **A** and **B**, place both with their initial points together. Then form a parallelogram with these vectors as sides. The vector from the initial point which is the diagonal of the parallelogram is called the *sum* of **A** and **B**. The term **resultant** is often used instead of sum. Figure 13.9 depicts the resultant of two vectors.

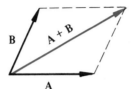

Figure 13.9

Addition of vectors is most frequently used in expressing a vector **A** as the sum of its component vectors, one in the direction of the **i** vector and one in the direction of the **j** vector. Figure 13.10 shows a vector **A** as the sum of $A_x\mathbf{i}$ and $A_y\mathbf{j}$. The quantity A_x is called the **horizontal component** and A_y the **vertical component** of the vector **A**.

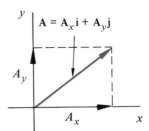

Figure 13.10

The numbers A_x and A_y are equal to, respectively, the x- and y-coordinates of the point at the terminal end of the vector **A**. From the previous discussion, or from Figure 13.10,

(13.2) $\qquad |\mathbf{A}| = \sqrt{A_x^2 + A_y^2}$

(13.3) $\qquad \tan\theta = \dfrac{A_y}{A_x}$

Thus, a vector **A** may ordinarily be expressed in one of the two following equivalent ways:

(1) as the sum $A_x\mathbf{i} + A_y\mathbf{j}$
(2) as the set of ordered pairs (A_x, A_y).

Addition of vectors may be removed from a geometric setting as the directed diagonal of a parallelogram by using the component method of representation. To see this, note that

$$\mathbf{A} = A_x\mathbf{i} + A_y\mathbf{j}$$
$$\mathbf{B} = B_x\mathbf{i} + B_y\mathbf{j}$$

The components A_x, A_y, B_x, and B_y are shown in Figure 13.11. From the figure we see that the horizontal component of **A** + **B** is $A_x + B_x$ and the vertical component is $A_y + B_y$. Thus,

$$\mathbf{A} + \mathbf{B} = (A_x + B_x)\mathbf{i} + (A_y + B_y)\mathbf{j}$$

13 Vectors and Complex Numbers

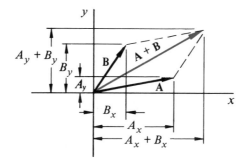

Figure 13.11

In words, the horizontal component of the sum of two vectors is simply the sum of the individual horizontal components, and the vertical component of the sum is the sum of the individual vertical components.

Example 13.3   Add the vectors $\mathbf{A} = \mathbf{i} - 3\mathbf{j}$ and $\mathbf{B} = 5\mathbf{i} + \mathbf{j}$. (See Figure 13.12.)

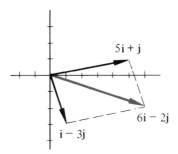

Figure 13.12

Solution $\mathbf{A} + \mathbf{B} = (\mathbf{i} - 3\mathbf{j}) + (5\mathbf{i} + \mathbf{j}) = 6\mathbf{i} - 2\mathbf{j}$

Example 13.4   Find the sum of the two vectors given in Figure 13.13, **A** of magnitude 100 and direction 63° and **B** of magnitude 40 and direction 325°. (See Figure 13.13.)

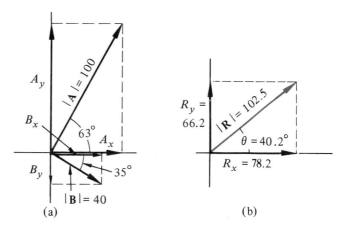

Figure 13.13   (a)   (b)

13.4 Vector Addition   377

Solution

$$A_x = 100 \cos 63° = 100(.4540) = 45.4$$

$$A_y = 100 \sin 63° = 100(.8910) = 89.1$$

$$B_x = 40 \cos 35° = 40(.8192) = 32.8$$

$$B_y = -40 \sin 35° = -40(.5736) = -22.9$$

Let $\mathbf{A} + \mathbf{B} = \mathbf{R}$. Then

$$R_x = A_x + B_x = 45.4 + 32.8 = 78.2$$

$$R_y = A_y + B_y = 89.1 - 22.9 = 66.2$$

Finally,

$$|\mathbf{R}| = \sqrt{R_x^2 + R_y^2} = \sqrt{78.2^2 + 66.2^2} = \sqrt{10498} = 102.5$$

$$\tan \theta = \frac{R_y}{R_x} = \frac{66.2}{78.2} = .8465$$

$$\theta = 40.2°$$

There is an alternate, and sometimes illuminating, definition for the addition of two vectors. Place the initial point of the second arrow at the terminal point of the first. Then the resultant, or sum, is the arrow whose initial point is at the initial point of the first arrow and whose terminal point is at the terminal point of the second. (See Figure 13.14.)

Figure 13.14

It should be easy for you to see that this definition of a sum yields the same vector as the first definition.

Exercises for
Sections 13.3 and 13.4

The vectors in Exercises 1–9 are given in the form $a\mathbf{i} + b\mathbf{j}$. Find the sum of $\mathbf{A}$ and $\mathbf{B}$ by adding the respective vertical and horizontal components. Draw each vector and show the sum graphically.

1. $\mathbf{A} = 2\mathbf{i} + 2\mathbf{j}$
   $\mathbf{B} = 3\mathbf{i} - \mathbf{j}$

2. $\mathbf{A} = \mathbf{i} - \mathbf{j}$
   $\mathbf{B} = 5\mathbf{i} + 3\mathbf{j}$

3. $\mathbf{A} = -2\mathbf{i} + 3\mathbf{j}$
   $\mathbf{B} = -4\mathbf{i} - 5\mathbf{j}$

4.	$A = 7i + 8j$	5.	$A = -i - j$	6.	$A = 6i + 6j$
	$B = 6i - 2j$		$B = 2i - 2j$		$B = 3i - 6j$
7.	$A = -4i - 6j$	8.	$A = 9i + 5j$	9.	$A = 5i - 5j$
	$B = 4i + 2j$		$B = -7i + j$		$B = i - 2j$

The vectors in Exercises 10–17 are defined in terms of a magnitude and a direction. Find the sum of the given vectors.

10.	$|A| = 20, \theta_A = 15°$	11.	$|A| = 16, \theta_A = 25°$
	$|B| = 25, \theta_B = 50°$		$|B| = 22, \theta_B = 70°$
12.	$|A| = 15, \theta_A = 0°$	13.	$|A| = 9.5, \theta_A = 90°$
	$|B| = 26, \theta_B = 60°$		$|B| = 5.1, \theta_B = 40°$
14.	$|A| = 2.5, \theta_A = 35°$	15.	$|A| = 29.2, \theta_A = 15.6°$
	$|B| = 3.0, \theta_B = 120°$		$|B| = 82.6, \theta_B = 150°$
16.	$|A| = 125, \theta_A = 145°$	17.	$|A| = 550, \theta_A = 140°$
	$|B| = 92, \theta_B = 215°$		$|B| = 925, \theta_B = 310°$

18. What are the horizontal and vertical components of the velocity of a ball thrown 100 ft/sec at an angle of 40° with respect to the horizontal?

19. A plane is headed due north at 300 mi/hr. If the wind is from the east at 50 mi/hr, what is the velocity of the plane?

20. Both a vertical force of 50 lb and a horizontal force of 75 lb act through the center of gravity of an object. What single force could replace the two given forces?

21. An object is acted upon by a force of 200 lb at an angle of 35° to the horizontal. What is the horizontal component of the force?

22. An object is thrown vertically downward with a speed of 50 ft/sec from a plane moving horizontally with a speed of 250 ft/sec. What is the velocity of the object as it leaves the plane?

23. A force of 60 lb acts horizontally on an object. Another force of 75 lb acts on the object at an angle of 55° with the horizontal. What is the resultant of these forces?

24. A plane flies due west with an air speed of 150 mph. If the wind is from the southwest at 35 mph, what is the resultant speed of the plane? In what direction is it traveling?

25. A bullet is fired from a plane at an angle of 20° below the horizontal and in the direction the plane is moving. If the bullet leaves the muzzle of the gun with a speed of 1200 ft/sec and the plane is flying 500 ft/sec, what is the resultant speed of the bullet?

26. An object weighing 120 lb hangs at the end of a rope. The object is pulled sideways by a horizontal force of 30 lb. What angle does the rope make with the vertical? (*Hint*: Weight is a vector that is always considered to be acting vertically downward.)

13.5

The Dot Product

of Two Vectors

The **dot product** of two vectors **A** and **B** (denoted by placing a dot between the factors) is defined by

(13.4) $\mathbf{A} \cdot \mathbf{B} = |\mathbf{A}| \, |\mathbf{B}| \, \cos \theta$

where θ is the angle between the two vectors. Notice that a dot product is a scalar quantity since it involves the product of scalars.

The quantity $|\mathbf{B}| \cos \theta$ is called the *component* of **B** along **A**. Numerically, it is equal to the projection of **B** on **A**. (See Figure 13.15.) In words, the

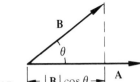

Figure 13.15

dot product of **A** and **B** is equal to the product of $|\mathbf{A}|$ and the component of **B** along **A**. It is also equal to the product of $|\mathbf{B}|$ and the component of **A** along **B**.

If **A** and **B** are perpendicular, $\cos \theta$ is zero, and

$\mathbf{A} \cdot \mathbf{B} = 0$

Conversely, if the dot product is zero, the vectors are perpendicular or else one of the vectors is the zero vector.

If **A** and **B** have the same direction, $\cos \theta$ is equal to 1, and

$\mathbf{A} \cdot \mathbf{B} = |\mathbf{A}| \, |\mathbf{B}|$

In particular,

$\mathbf{A} \cdot \mathbf{A} = |\mathbf{A}| \, |\mathbf{A}| = |\mathbf{A}|^2$

Also, since **i** and **j** are perpendicular unit vectors,

$\mathbf{i} \cdot \mathbf{i} = 1$

$\mathbf{i} \cdot \mathbf{j} = 0$

$\mathbf{j} \cdot \mathbf{j} = 1$

The dot product is distributive over addition, which means that for any three vectors, **A**, **B**, and **C**,

$\mathbf{A} \cdot (\mathbf{B} + \mathbf{C}) = \mathbf{A} \cdot \mathbf{B} + \mathbf{A} \cdot \mathbf{C}$

This law allows for the derivation of a convenient formula for determining the value of the dot product in terms of its components. Let

$$\mathbf{A} = A_x \mathbf{i} + A_y \mathbf{j}$$
$$\mathbf{B} = B_x \mathbf{i} + B_y \mathbf{j}$$

Then

$$\mathbf{A} \cdot \mathbf{B} = (A_x \mathbf{i} + A_y \mathbf{j}) \cdot (B_x \mathbf{i} + B_y \mathbf{j})$$
$$= A_x B_x (\mathbf{i} \cdot \mathbf{i}) + A_x B_y (\mathbf{i} \cdot \mathbf{j}) + A_y B_x (\mathbf{j} \cdot \mathbf{i}) + A_y B_y (\mathbf{j} \cdot \mathbf{j})$$

and, because of the known values of the dot products of the $\mathbf{i}$ and $\mathbf{j}$ vectors,

(13.5) $$\mathbf{A} \cdot \mathbf{B} = A_x B_x + A_y B_y$$

Example 13.5   Find $\mathbf{A} \cdot \mathbf{B}$ if $\mathbf{A} = 4\mathbf{i} - 3\mathbf{j}$ and $\mathbf{B} = 2\mathbf{i} + \mathbf{j}$.

Solution   By equation (13.5),

$$\mathbf{A} \cdot \mathbf{B} = (4)(2) + (-3)(1) = 8 - 3 = 5$$

Notice that with the use of equation (13.5) the angle between $\mathbf{A}$ and $\mathbf{B}$ need not be known. In fact, the cosine of the angle may be calculated if the dot product is known. For example, from the definition of the dot product of $\mathbf{A}$ and $\mathbf{B}$,

$$\cos \theta = \frac{\mathbf{A} \cdot \mathbf{B}}{|\mathbf{A}||\mathbf{B}|}$$

$$= \frac{5}{\sqrt{25}\sqrt{5}}$$

$$= \frac{1}{\sqrt{5}} = 0.447$$

From this the approximate value of θ may be computed to be 63.4°.

Example 13.6   Show that vectors $\mathbf{A}$ and $\mathbf{B}$ are perpendicular if

$$\mathbf{A} = \mathbf{i} - 2\mathbf{j} \quad \text{and} \quad \mathbf{B} = 2\mathbf{i} + \mathbf{j}$$

(See Figure 13.16.)

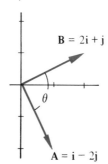

Figure 13.16

13.5 The Dot Product of Two Vectors

Solution   Here $\mathbf{A} \cdot \mathbf{B} = 2 - 2 = 0$, from which we conclude that $\cos \theta = 0$ and hence $\theta = 90°$.

Perhaps the most familiar physical interpretation of a dot product is with regard to mechanical work. When a force $\mathbf{F}$ experiences a displacement (represented in magnitude and direction by the vector $\mathbf{S}$ in Figure 13.17), the work

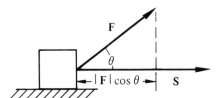

Figure 13.17

done by the force is defined as the product of the displacement by the component of force in the direction of the displacement. Thus,

$$\text{Work} = |\mathbf{S}||\mathbf{F}| \cos \theta = \mathbf{F} \cdot \mathbf{S}$$

As a further result, if $\mathbf{F}_1$ and $\mathbf{F}_2$ are two forces acting at the same point, then the work done by the resultant $\mathbf{F} = \mathbf{F}_1 + \mathbf{F}_2$ is

$$\mathbf{F} \cdot \mathbf{S} = (\mathbf{F}_1 + \mathbf{F}_2) \cdot \mathbf{S} = \mathbf{F}_1 \cdot \mathbf{S} + \mathbf{F}_2 \cdot \mathbf{S}$$

That is, the work of the resultant is equal to the sum of the work done by the separate forces. This is just a restatement of the distributive property of the dot product over addition.

Exercises for
    Section 13.5

Find the dot product for each pair of vectors in Exercises 1–12.

1. $\mathbf{A} = \mathbf{i} + \mathbf{j}$

    $\mathbf{B} = 2\mathbf{i} - \mathbf{j}$

2. $\mathbf{A} = 2\mathbf{i} - 3\mathbf{j}$

    $\mathbf{B} = 3\mathbf{i} + 2\mathbf{j}$

3. $\mathbf{A} = 6\mathbf{i} + \mathbf{j}$

    $\mathbf{B} = 7\mathbf{i} - \mathbf{j}$

4. $\mathbf{A} = 6\mathbf{i} + 2\mathbf{j}$

    $\mathbf{B} = 6\mathbf{i} + 2\mathbf{j}$

5. $\mathbf{A} = \mathbf{i}$

    $\mathbf{B} = \mathbf{i} + 3\mathbf{j}$

6. $\mathbf{A} = 2\mathbf{i} - 3\mathbf{j}$

    $\mathbf{B} = 2\mathbf{j}$

7. $|\mathbf{A}| = 25, \theta_A = 27°$

    $|\mathbf{B}| = 40, \theta_A = 85°$

8. $|\mathbf{A}| = 9.3, \theta_A = 46°$

    $|\mathbf{B}| = 6.5, \theta_B = 105°$

9. $|\mathbf{A}| = 190, \theta_A = 100°$

    $|\mathbf{B}| = 75, \theta_B = 205°$

10. $|\mathbf{A}| = 0.6, \theta_A = 75°$

    $|\mathbf{B}| = 1.3, \theta_B = 180°$

11. $|\mathbf{A}| = 24.3, \theta_A = 245°$ **12.** $|\mathbf{A}| = 975, \theta_A = 135°$

      $|\mathbf{B}| = 16.2, \theta_B = 276°$ $|\mathbf{B}| = 562, \theta_B = 300°$

Find the angle between the vectors in Exercises 13–16 using the definition of dot product.

13. $\mathbf{A} = 5\mathbf{i} + \mathbf{j}$ **14.** $\mathbf{A} = \mathbf{i} - \mathbf{j}$

      $\mathbf{B} = 2\mathbf{i} - \mathbf{j}$ $\mathbf{B} = \mathbf{i} + \mathbf{j}$

15. $\mathbf{A} = -3\mathbf{i} + 4\mathbf{j}$ **16.** $\mathbf{A} = 2\mathbf{i} + 4\mathbf{j}$

      $\mathbf{B} = 2\mathbf{i} - 3\mathbf{j}$ $\mathbf{B} = -3\mathbf{i} - 3\mathbf{j}$

17. A large bookcase is pulled a distance of 20 ft along a level floor by a 30-lb force acting 28° above the horizontal. How much work is done on the bookcase?

18. How much work is done in moving a block of wood a distance of 100 ft if a 75-lb force acting 10° above the horizontal is needed to move it?

19. A horizontal force of 100 lb is applied to a block resting on a plane inclined at 30° to the horizontal. How much work is done in moving the block 5 ft up the incline?

20. What work is done in pulling a sled 50 ft horizontally when a 15-lb force is applied through a rope making an angle of 35° with the ground?

13.6
Complex
Numbers

Complex numbers were defined in Chapter 1 and have been used as needed in this book, particularly when they arose as roots of certain polynomial equations. For instance, in solving the equation $x^2 + 1 = 0$, we wrote the solution as $x = \pm i$. Thus,

$$i^2 = -1 \quad \text{or} \quad i = \sqrt{-1}$$

Numbers of the form bi, where b is a real number, make up the set of **imaginary* numbers**.

Example 13.7   Solve the equation $x^2 + 9 = 0$.

Solution

$$x^2 + 9 = 0$$
$$x^2 = -9$$
$$x = \pm\sqrt{-9} = \pm 3i$$

----

* The word imaginary is, in a sense, an unfortunate choice of words since it could easily lead to the belief that imaginary numbers have a more fictitious character than the real numbers.

In solving an equation such as $x^2 - 2x + 5 = 0$ we found the solution from the quadratic formula to be

$$x = 1 \pm \sqrt{-4} = 1 \pm 2i$$

which is a combination of a real and an imaginary number called a **complex number**. For convenience we reiterate and highlight the definition of a complex number originally given in Chapter 1.

Definition	A **complex number** z is any number of the form $z = a + bi$, where a and b are real numbers and $i = \sqrt{-1}$.

The real number a is called the *real part* of z, whereas the real number b is called the imaginary part of z. By convention, if $b = 1$, the number is written $a + i$. Further, if $b = 0$, the imaginary part is customarily omitted and the number is said to be pure real. If $a = 0$ and $b \neq 0$, the real part is omitted and the number is said to be pure imaginary.

Two complex numbers are equal if, and only if, their real parts are equal and their imaginary parts are equal. Thus, $a + bi$ and $c + di$ are equal if, and only if, $a = c$ and $b = d$.

Combinations of complex numbers obey the ordinary algebraic rules for real numbers. Thus, the sum, the difference, the product, or the quotient of two complex numbers is found in the same manner as the sum, the difference, the product, or the quotient of two real binomials—bearing in mind that $i^2 = -1$.

Example 13.8   Find the sum and difference of $3 + 5i$ and $-9 + 2i$.

Solution

(a) $(3 + 5i) + (-9 + 2i) = (3 - 9) + (5 + 2)i = -6 + 7i$

(b) $(3 + 5i) - (-9 + 2i) = (3 + 9) + (5 - 2)i = 12 + 3i$

Example 13.9   Find the product of $(3 - 2i)(4 + i)$.

Solution

$$(3 - 2i)(4 + i) = 12 + 3i - 8i - 2i^2$$
$$= 12 - 5i + 2$$
$$= 14 - 5i$$

The number $a - bi$ is called the **conjugate** of $a + bi$. To find the quotient of two complex numbers, we use the following scheme: *multiply the numerator and the denominator of the given quotient by the conjugate of the denominator.* Example 13.10 illustrates this technique.

Example 13.10   Find the quotient $(2 + 3i)/(4 - 5i)$.

Solution

$$\frac{2 + 3i}{4 - 5i} = \frac{(2 + 3i)(4 + 5i)}{(4 - 5i)(4 + 5i)}$$

$$= \frac{8 + (12 + 10)i + 15i^2}{16 - 25i^2}$$

$$= \frac{-7 + 22i}{16 + 25}$$

$$= \frac{-7 + 22i}{41}$$

Exercises for
Section 13.6

Perform the indicated operations in Exercises 1–24, expressing all answers in the form $a + bi$.

1. $(3 + 2i) + (4 + 3i)$ 2. $(6 + 3i) + (5 - i)$

3. $(5 - 2i) + (-7 + 5i)$ 4. $(-1 + i) + (2 - i)$

5. $(1 + i) + (3 - i)$ 6. $7 - (5 + 3i)$

7. $(3 + 5i) - 4i$ 8. $(3 + 2i) + (3 - 2i)$

9. $(2 + 3i)(4 + 5i)$ 10. $(7 + 2i)(-1 - i)$

11. $(5 - i)(5 + i)$ 12. $(6 - 3i)(6 + 3i)$

13. $(4 + \sqrt{3}i)^2$ 14. $(5 - 2i)^2$

15. $6i(4 - 3i)$ 16. $3i(-2 - i)$

17. $\dfrac{3 + 2i}{1 + i}$ 18. $\dfrac{4i}{2 + i}$

19. $\dfrac{3}{2 - 3i}$ 20. $\dfrac{7 - 2i}{6 - 5i}$

21. $\dfrac{1}{5i}$ 22. $\dfrac{-3 + i}{-2 - i}$

23. $\dfrac{-1 - 3i}{4 - \sqrt{2}i}$ 24. $\dfrac{i}{2 + \sqrt{5}i}$

25. Show that the sum of a complex number and its conjugate is a real number.

26. Show that the product of a complex number and its conjugate is a real number.

13.7
Graphical
Representation of Complex Numbers

Since complex numbers are ordered pairs of real numbers, some two-dimensional configuration is necessary to represent them graphically. The Cartesian coordinate system is often used for this purpose, in which case it is called the **complex plane**. The x-axis is used to represent the real part of the complex number, and the y-axis to represent the imaginary part. Hence, the axes are called real and imaginary, respectively. Thus, the complex number $x + iy$ is represented by the point whose coordinates are (x, y) as shown in Figure 13.18. For this reason the complex number $z = x + iy$ is said to be written in *rectangular form*.

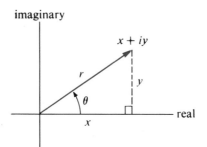

Figure 13.18

It is often convenient to think of a complex number $x + iy$ as representing a vector. With reference to Figure 13.18, the complex number $x + iy$ can be represented by the vector drawn from the origin to the point $x + iy$ with coordinates (x, y).

Example 13.11   Represent $5 + 3i$, $-2 + 4i$, $-1 - 3i$, and $5 - i$ in the complex plane. (See Figure 13.19.)

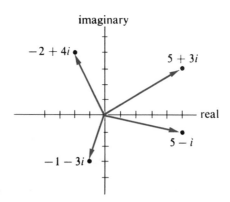

Figure 13.19

13 Vectors and Complex Numbers

It is instructional to show the graphical representation of the sum of two complex numbers. Recalling that the sum of $a + bi$ and $c + di$ is given by

$$(a + bi) + (c + di) = (a + c) + (b + d)i$$

we have represented $a + bi$, $c + di$, and $(a + c) + (b + d)i$ in Figure 13.20. The result is the same as if we had applied the parallelogram law to the vectors representing $a + bi$ and $c + di$. Note that $c + di$ is subtracted from $a + bi$ by plotting $a + bi$ and $-c - di$ and then using the parallelogram law.

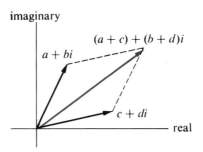

Figure 13.20   Addition of Complex Numbers

Exercises for
Section 13.7

Perform the indicated operations in Exercises 1–16 graphically and check the results algebraically.

1. $(4 + i) + (3 + 5i)$ 2. $(3 + 2i) + (1 - 3i)$

3. $(4 + 3i) + (-2 + i)$ 4. $(-5 - 7i) + (-1 + 3i)$

5. $(2 - 4i) + (-3 + i)$ 6. $i + (3 + 4i)$

7. $(5 + 3i) - 6$ 8. $(3 + 2i) + (3 - 2i)$

9. $(5 - 3i) + (5 + 3i)$ 10. $(6 + 4i) - 2i$

11. $(1 + 3i) - (2 - 5i)$ 12. $(2 - i) - i$

13. $(2 + \sqrt{3}i) - (-1 - i)$ 14. $(\sqrt{5} - i) - (\sqrt{5} + 3i)$

15. $(-3 + 2i) - (-3 - 2i)$ 16. $(10 - 3i) - (10 + 3i)$

On the same coordinate system plot the number, its negative, and its conjugate. (Exercises 17–22).

17. $-3 + 2i$ 18. $4 - 3i$ 19. $-2i$

20. $5 + i$ 21. $-1 - i$ 22. $3 + 5i$

13.7 Graphical Representation of Complex Numbers   387

13.8
Polar
Representation of Complex Numbers

In discussing graphical representations of complex numbers, we indicated the convenience of thinking of a complex number in terms of a vector drawn from the origin to the point in the plane. This conceptual use of vectors to represent complex numbers suggests an alternate method for describing complex numbers. Referring to Figure 13.21, we see that the complex number $a + bi$ can also

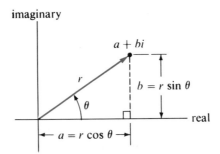

Figure 13.21 Polar form

be located in the plane by giving the length of the vector and the angle that the vector makes with the positive real axis. Also, from Figure 13.21 we observe that $a = r \cos \theta$ and $b = r \sin \theta$. Therefore,

(13.6) $z = a + bi = r(\cos \theta + i \sin \theta)$

The right-hand side of this equation is called the **trigonometric**, or **polar**, form of the complex number $a + bi$. The quantity $(\cos \theta + i \sin \theta)$ is sometimes written *cis* θ, in which case we write

(13.7) $z = r \text{ cis } \theta$

as the polar form of the complex number z. The number r is called the *modulus*, or *magnitude*, of the complex number z and is given by

$$r = \sqrt{a^2 + b^2}$$

The angle θ is called the *argument* of the complex number. Since $\tan \theta = b/a$ in Figure 13.21, it follows that θ is an angle whose tangent is b/a; that is,

$$\theta = \arctan \frac{b}{a}$$

Note that a given complex number has many arguments, all differing by multiples of 2π. Sometimes we limit the argument to some interval of length 2π and thus obtain a *principal value*. In this book, unless we say otherwise, the principal values will be between $-\pi$ and π; that is, between $-180°$ and $180°$.

Example 13.12   Represent $z = 1 + \sqrt{3}\,i$ in polar form. (See Figure 13.22.)

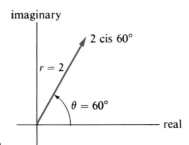

Figure 13.22

Solution   Since

$$r = \sqrt{1^2 + (\sqrt{3})^2} = \sqrt{4} = 2$$

and

$$\theta = \arctan \sqrt{3} = 60°$$

then

$$1 + \sqrt{3}\,i = 2(\cos 60° + i \sin 60°) = 2 \text{ cis } 60°$$

Example 13.13   Express $z = 6(\cos 120° + i \sin 120°)$ in rectangular form. (See Figure 13.23.)

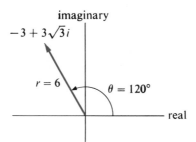

Figure 13.23

Solution   Using the fact that $a = r \cos \theta$ and $b = r \sin \theta$,

$$a = 6 \cos 120° = 6\left(-\frac{1}{2}\right) = -3$$

$$b = 6 \sin 120° = 6\left(\frac{\sqrt{3}}{2}\right) = 3\sqrt{3}$$

Therefore,

$$z = a + bi = -3 + 3\sqrt{3}\,i$$

The polar form of complex numbers makes it easy to give a geometric interpretation to the product of two complex numbers. Thus, if $z_1 = r_1 \text{ cis } \theta_1$

13.8 Polar Representation of Complex Numbers   389 and $z_2 = r_2$ cis θ_2, the product $z_1 z_2$ may be written

$$z_1 z_2 = r_1(\cos \theta_1 + i \sin \theta_1) \cdot r_2(\cos \theta_2 + i \sin \theta_2)$$
$$= r_1 r_2[\cos \theta_1 \cos \theta_2 + i \cos \theta_1 \sin \theta_2$$
$$+ i \sin \theta_1 \cos \theta_2 + i^2 \sin \theta_1 \sin \theta_2]$$
$$= r_1 r_2[(\cos \theta_1 \cos \theta_2 - \sin \theta_1 \sin \theta_2)$$
$$+ i(\cos \theta_1 \sin \theta_2 + \sin \theta_1 \cos \theta_2)]$$

Now, by using the identities for the sine and cosine of the sum of two angles, we have

(13.8) $\qquad z_1 z_2 = r_1 r_2[\cos (\theta_1 + \theta_2) + i \sin (\theta_1 + \theta_2)] = r_1 r_2 \text{ cis } (\theta_1 + \theta_2)$

Therefore, the modulus of the product of two complex numbers is the product of the individual moduli and the argument of the product is the sum of the individual arguments. Graphically, multiplication of z_1 by z_2 results in a rotation of the vector through z_1 by an angle equal to the argument of z_2 and an expansion or a contraction of the modulus depending on whether $|z_2| > 1$ or $|z_2| < 1$. (See Figure 13.24.)

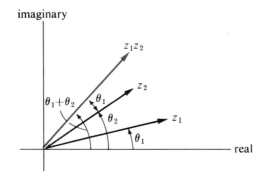

Figure 13.24 Multiplication of Complex Numbers

Example 13.14   Multiply $z_1 = -1 + \sqrt{3}\,i$ and $z_2 = 1 + i$, using the polar form of each.

Solution   Computing the modulus and argument of each complex number yields

$$r_1 = \sqrt{(-1)^2 + (\sqrt{3})^2} = 2, \qquad \theta_1 = \arctan \frac{\sqrt{3}}{-1} = 120°$$

$$r_2 = \sqrt{1^2 + 1^2} = \sqrt{2}, \qquad \theta_2 = \arctan \frac{1}{1} = 45°$$

Therefore,

$$z_1 z_2 = (2 \text{ cis } 120°)(\sqrt{2} \text{ cis } 45°) = 2\sqrt{2} \text{ cis } (120° + 45°)$$
$$= 2\sqrt{2} \text{ cis } 165°$$

In the same manner as in the above discussion, we may show that if $z_1 = r_1 \text{ cis } \theta_1$ and $z_2 = r_2 \text{ cis } \theta_2$, then

(13.9) $\quad \dfrac{z_1}{z_2} = \dfrac{r_1}{r_2} \cos (\theta_1 - \theta_2) + i \sin (\theta_1 - \theta_2) = \dfrac{r_1}{r_2} \text{ cis } (\theta_1 - \theta_2)$

In words, the modulus of the quotient of two complex numbers is the quotient of the individual moduli, and the argument is the difference of the individual arguments.

Example 13.15 Divide $z_1 = 2 \text{ cis } 120°$ by $z_2 = \sqrt{2} \text{ cis } 45°$.

Solution

$$\frac{z_1}{z_2} = \frac{2 \text{ cis } 120°}{\sqrt{2} \text{ cis } 45°} = \frac{2}{\sqrt{2}} \text{ cis } (120° - 45°) = \sqrt{2} \text{ cis } 75°$$

Exercises for
Section 13.8

Plot the complex numbers in Exercises 1–10 and then express them in polar form.

1. $1 - \sqrt{3}\,i$ 2. $3 + 4i$

3. $\sqrt{5} + 2i$ 4. $\sqrt{3} - i$

5. 9 6. $5i$

7. $3 - 4i$ 8. $-1 + i$

9. $5 - 6i$ 10. $-3 - 4i$

Plot the complex numbers in Exercises 11–20, then express them in rectangular form.

11. $2 \text{ cis } 30°$ 12. $4 \text{ cis } 60°$

13. $5 \text{ cis } 135°$ 14. $10 \text{ cis } 90°$

15. $\sqrt{3} \text{ cis } 210°$ 16. $\sqrt{5} \text{ cis } 180°$

17. $3 \text{ cis } 300°$ 18. $7 \text{ cis } 0°$

19. $10 \text{ cis } 20°$ 20. $2 \text{ cis } 100°$

Perform the indicated operations in Exercises 21–36. If the complex numbers are not already in polar form, put them in that form before proceeding.

21. $(4 \text{ cis } 30°)(3 \text{ cis } 60°)$ 22. $(2 \text{ cis } 120°)(\sqrt{5} \text{ cis } 180°)$

23. $(\sqrt{2} \text{ cis } 90°)(\sqrt{2} \text{ cis } 240°)$ 24. $(5 \text{ cis } 180°)(3 \text{ cis } 90°)$

25. $(10 \text{ cis } 35°)(2 \text{ cis } 100°)$ 26. $(3 \text{ cis } 45°)(2 \text{ cis } 120°)$

27. $(3 + 4i)(\sqrt{3} - i)$ 28. $3i(2 - i)$

29. $\dfrac{10 \text{ cis } 30°}{2 \text{ cis } 90°}$ 30. $\dfrac{5 \text{ cis } 29°}{3 \text{ cis } 4°}$

13.8 Polar Representation of Complex Numbers   **391**

31. $\dfrac{4 \text{ cis } 26°40'}{2 \text{ cis } 19°10'}$

32. $\dfrac{12 \text{ cis } 100°}{3 \text{ cis } 23°}$

33. $\dfrac{1 - i}{\sqrt{3} + i}$

34. $\dfrac{\sqrt{3} + i}{\sqrt{3} - i}$

35. $\dfrac{4i}{-1 + i}$

36. $\dfrac{5}{1 + i}$

37. Prove Euler's identities:

$$\cos \theta = \tfrac{1}{2}[\text{cis } \theta + \text{cis } (-\theta)] \quad \text{and} \quad \sin \theta = (1/2i)[\text{cis } \theta - \text{cis } (-\theta)].$$

13.9
DeMoivre's
Theorem

The square of the complex number $z = r \text{ cis } \theta$ is given by

$$z^2 = (r \text{ cis } \theta)(r \text{ cis } \theta)$$
$$= r^2 \text{ cis } 2\theta$$

Likewise,

$$z^3 = z^2 \cdot z = (r^2 \text{ cis } 2\theta) \cdot (r \text{ cis } \theta)$$
$$= r^3 \text{ cis } 3\theta$$

We expect the pattern exhibited for r^2 and r^3 to apply as well to r^4, r^5, r^6, and so forth. As a matter of fact, if $z = r \text{ cis } \theta$, then we have **DeMoivre's theorem**.

(13.10) $\qquad z^n = r^n \text{ cis } n\theta$

The theorem is true for all real values of n, a fact that we shall accept without proof.

Example 13.16 Use DeMoivre's theorem to find $(-2 + 2i)^4$.

Solution Here we have

$$r = \sqrt{2^2 + (-2)^2} = \sqrt{8}, \qquad \theta = 135°$$

Therefore,

$$(-2 + 2i)^4 = [\sqrt{8}(\cos 135° + i \sin 135°)]^4$$
$$= (\sqrt{8})^4[\cos 4(135°) + i \sin 4(135°)]$$
$$= 64[\cos 540° + i \sin 540°]$$
$$= 64[\cos 180° + i \sin 180°]$$
$$= -64$$

In the system of real numbers there is no square root of -1, no fourth root of -81, and so on. However, if we use complex numbers, we can find the nth root of any number by using DeMoivre's theorem.

Recalling that DeMoivre's theorem is valid for all real n, it is possible to evaluate $[r \text{ cis } \theta]^{1/n}$ as

(13.11) $$[r \text{ cis } \theta]^{1/n} = r^{1/n} \text{ cis } \frac{\theta}{n} = \sqrt[n]{r} \text{ cis } \frac{\theta}{n}$$

Since $\cos \theta$ and $\sin \theta$ are periodic functions with a period of $360°$, we can write $\cos \theta = \cos (\theta + k \cdot 360°)$ and $\sin \theta = \sin (\theta + k \cdot 360°)$, where k is an integer. Hence,

(13.12) $$[r \text{ cis } \theta]^{1/n} = \sqrt[n]{r} \text{ cis } \left(\frac{\theta + k \cdot 360°}{n}\right)$$

For a given number n, the right side of this equation takes on n distinct values corresponding to $k = 0, 1, 2, \ldots, n - 1$. For $k > n - 1$ the result is merely a duplication of the first n values.

Example 13.17   Find the square roots of $4i$.

Solution   We first express $4i$ in polar form using

$$r = \sqrt{0^2 + 4^2} = 4 \quad \text{and} \quad \theta = 90°$$

Thus,

$$4i = 4 \text{ cis } 90°$$

and the square roots of $4i$ are given by

$$2 \text{ cis } \left(\frac{90° + k \cdot 360°}{2}\right)$$

Therefore, for $k = 0$,

$$2 \text{ cis } 45° = \sqrt{2} + \sqrt{2}i$$

13.9 DeMoivre's Theorem

393

and for $k = 1$,

$$2 \text{ cis } 225° = -\sqrt{2} - \sqrt{2}\,i$$

It is convenient and informative to plot these values in the complex plane as shown in Figure 13.25. Notice that both roots are located on a circle of radius 2, but 180° apart.

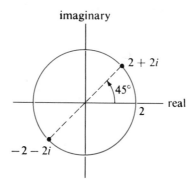

imaginary

Figure 13.25

Example 13.18   Find the three cube roots of unity.

Solution   In polar form the number 1 may be written $1 \text{ cis } 0°$. Thus,

$$\sqrt[3]{1 \text{ cis } 0°} = 1 \text{ cis } \left(\frac{0° + k \cdot 360°}{3} \right)$$

For $k = 0$, $1 \text{ cis } 0° = 1$

For $k = 1$, $1 \text{ cis } 120° = \dfrac{-1 + \sqrt{3}\,i}{2}$

For $k = 2$, $1 \text{ cis } 240° = \dfrac{-1 - \sqrt{3}\,i}{2}$

Figure 13.26 displays these roots. Notice that they are located on a circle of radius 1 at equally spaced intervals of 120°.

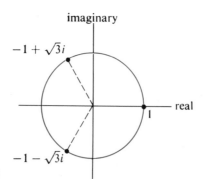

imaginary

Figure 13.26

Example 13.19   Find the fourth roots of $-1 + \sqrt{3}\,i$.

Solution   Writing $-1 + \sqrt{3}\,i$ in polar form,

$$-1 + \sqrt{3}\,i = 2 \text{ cis } 120°$$

Therefore,

$$[-1 + \sqrt{3}\,i]^{1/4} = \sqrt[4]{2} \text{ cis } \frac{120° + k \cdot 360°}{4}$$

The four roots correspond to $k = 0, 1, 2, 3$; that is,

$$\text{for} \quad k = 0, \quad \sqrt[4]{2} \text{ cis } 30° = \sqrt[4]{2}\left(\frac{\sqrt{3}}{2} + \frac{1}{2}i\right)$$

$$\text{for} \quad k = 1, \quad \sqrt[4]{2} \text{ cis } 120° = \sqrt[4]{2}\left(-\frac{1}{2} + \frac{\sqrt{3}}{2}i\right)$$

$$\text{for} \quad k = 2, \quad \sqrt[4]{2} \text{ cis } 210° = \sqrt[4]{2}\left(-\frac{\sqrt{3}}{2} - \frac{1}{2}i\right)$$

$$\text{for} \quad k = 3, \quad \sqrt[4]{2} \text{ cis } 300° = \sqrt[4]{2}\left(\frac{1}{2} - \frac{\sqrt{3}}{2}i\right)$$

Exercises for
Section 13.9

Use DeMoivre's theorem to evaluate powers in Exercises 1–10. Leave the answer in polar form.

1. $(-1 + \sqrt{3}\,i)^3$ 2. $(1 + i)^4$

3. $(\sqrt{3} \text{ cis } 60°)^4$ 4. $(\sqrt{3} - i)^6$

5. $(-2 + 2i)^5$ 6. $(-1 + 3i)^3$

7. $(-\sqrt{3} + i)^7$ 8. $(2 \text{ cis } 20°)^5$

9. $(2 + 5i)^4$ 10. $(3 + 2i)^{10}$

Find the indicated roots in Exercises 11–20 and sketch their location in the complex plane.

11. Fifth roots of 1   12. Cube roots of 64

13. Fourth roots of i 14. Fourth roots of -16

15. Square roots of $1 + i$ 16. Fifth roots of $\sqrt{3} + i$

17. Sixth roots of $-\sqrt{3} + i$ 18. Cube roots of $-1 + i$

19. Fourth roots of $-1 + \sqrt{3}\,i$ 20. Sixth roots of $-i$

21. Obtain an expression for $\cos 2\theta$ and $\sin 2\theta$ in terms of trigonometric functions of θ by making use of DeMoivre's theorem.

22. Find all roots of the equation $x^4 + 81 = 0$.

23. Find all roots of $x^3 + 64 = 0$.

13.9 DeMoivre's Theorem   395

Answer true or false for Exercises 1–10.

1. Vectors that point in the same direction may be added merely by adding their lengths.

2. Two vectors are equal if they have the same length and if they originate from the same point.

3. Ordered pairs of real numbers can describe vectors in the plane.

4. The scalar multiple of a vector **A** always points in the same direction as **A**.

5. To add two vectors, add their magnitudes and their reference angles.

6. The resultant of two vectors is their dot product.

7. The dot product of two vectors is a scalar.

8. The sum of two complex numbers is complex.

9. To multiply two complex numbers, multiply their magnitudes and add their arguments.

10. Complex numbers are added by adding the real part of one to the real part of the other and the imaginary part of one to the imaginary part of the other.

11. Find the x and y components of the vector **V** in standard position if $|\mathbf{V}| = 8$ and $\theta = 35°$.

12. Find the angle between the vectors $\mathbf{A} = 2\mathbf{i} + \mathbf{j}$ and $\mathbf{B} = \mathbf{i} - \mathbf{j}$.

13. Find the quotient of the complex numbers $(2 + 3i)/(4 + i)$ and express it in the form $a + bi$.

14. Multiply $(2 + i) \cdot (6 - \sqrt{2}\,i)$ by first expressing the given numbers in polar form.

15. Use DeMoivre's theorem to find $(1 + 3i)^5$.

16. Find the three cube roots of -1.

1. Find the x- and y-coordinates of $|\mathbf{V}| = 25$, $\theta = 15°28'$.

2. Find the sum $\mathbf{A} + \mathbf{B}$ if $\mathbf{A} = 7\mathbf{i} + 8\mathbf{j}$ and $\mathbf{B} = -3\mathbf{i} + \mathbf{j}$.

3. Find the sum $\mathbf{A} + \mathbf{B}$ if $|\mathbf{A}| = 5.6$, $\theta_A = 19°10'$ and $|\mathbf{B}| = 0.9$, $\theta_B = 95°30'$.

4. Find the dot product $\mathbf{A} \cdot \mathbf{B}$ if $|\mathbf{A}| = 0.5$, $\theta_A = 18°50'$, $|\mathbf{B}| = 0.4$, $\theta_B = 2°20'$.

5. Evaluate: (a) $(3 + 4i) - (5 - 2i)$; (b) $(-2 - i)(-7 + 2i)$.

6. Plot $2 - \sqrt{3}\,i$ and then express it in polar form.

7. Plot $7 \operatorname{cis} 315°$ and then express it in rectangular form.

8. Evaluate $(\sqrt{5} \text{ cis } 120°)(7 \text{ cis } 80°)$.

9. Find the cube roots of $-1 + i$.

10. Find all the roots of $x^5 + 32 = 0$.

14
Arithmetic and
Geometric Sequences

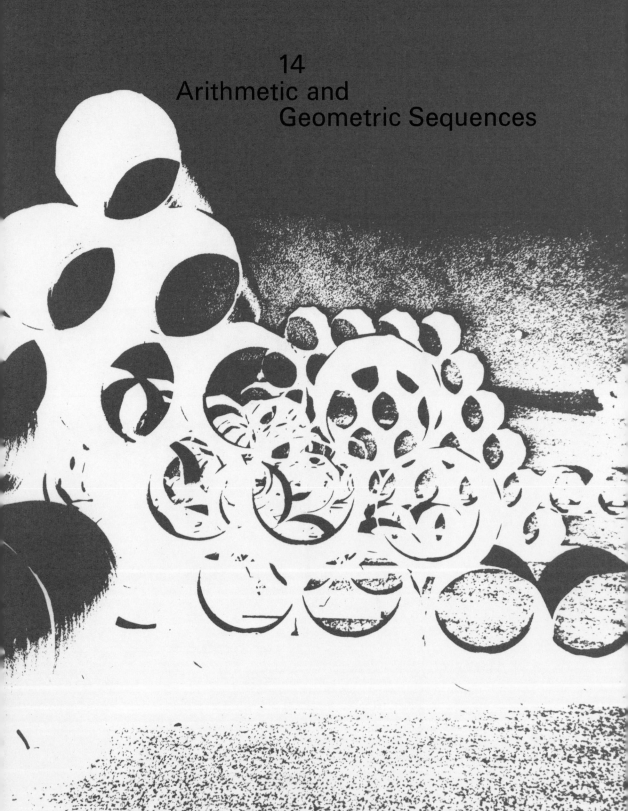

14.1
Sequences in General

A **sequence** is a set of numbers in a fixed order. Each of the numbers is called a *term* of the sequence, and we designate the *general term* by the notation a_n. Using this notation, the entire sequence of numbers is written $\{a_n\}$, where n is a positive integer.

The ordering arrangement allows you to designate the first term a_1, the second term a_2, the third term a_3, and so on, where the subscript determines the position of each term.

Example 14.1   In the sequence of terms 5, 9, 13, 17,

$$a_1 = 5, a_2 = 9, a_3 = 13, a_4 = 17$$

If, as in Example 14.1, a sequence has only finitely many terms, it is called a **finite sequence**; otherwise it is an **infinite sequence**. For finite sequences it is at least theoretically possible to list every term. For infinite sequences (and for some finite ones) the terms are often designated by a formula that gives the value of a_n for any positive integer n.

Example 14.2   The formula $a_n = 2n + 1$ defines the sequence whose first few terms are

$$a_1 = 3, a_2 = 5, a_3 = 7, a_4 = 9, a_5 = 11$$

Another method of giving the terms of a sequence is in a *recursive* (or inductive) manner. We give the first term of the sequence, followed by a recursive formula from which any term can be determined from the preceding one.

Example 14.3   The formula $a_n = a_{n-1} + 2$, along with the fact that $a_1 = 3$, defines the sequence whose first few terms are

$$3, 5, 7, 9, \ldots$$

Whether defined by listing the terms, by giving an explicit formula for the nth term, or by supplying a recursive formula, a sequence may be considered a function whose domain is some subset of the positive integers. In fact, a sequence is sometimes called a **sequence function**. The range values of a sequence are, of course, nothing more than the terms of the sequence.

Example 14.4   What is the range of the sequence function defined by

$$a_n = (-1)^n?$$

Solution   Since $a_1 = -1$, $a_2 = 1$, $a_3 = -1$, and so on, the range values are merely 1 and -1.

Sometimes you are asked to try to find a formula for the nth term of a sequence when several successive terms are known. Example 14.5 illustrates the technique.

Example 14.5   Find a formula for the general term of the sequence

$$5, 9, 13, 17, \ldots$$

Solution   Notice that the rule is "add 4 to each term." Therefore, the general term can be written

$$a_n = 5 + 4(n - 1)$$

In this chapter we examine a few of the important sequences. The following sequences are included for reference with no other details given.

The sequence of natural numbers: 1, 2, 3, 4, 5, ..., n, ...

The sequence of positive even numbers: 2, 4, 6, 8, ..., $2n$, ...

The sequence of positive odd numbers: 1, 3, 5, 7, 9, ..., $2n - 1$, ...

The sequence of squares: 1, 4, 9, 16, 25, ..., n^2, ...

The sequence of cubes: 1, 8, 27, 64, ..., n^3, ...

The sequence of k-powers: 1^k, 2^k, 3^k, 4^k, ..., n^k, ...

The sequence of reciprocals: $1, \dfrac{1}{2}, \dfrac{1}{3}, \dfrac{1}{4}, \dfrac{1}{5}, \ldots, \dfrac{1}{n}, \ldots$

Exercises for Section 14.1

Write the first five terms of the sequences in Exercises 1–15.

1. $a_n = n + 1$

2. $a_n = 2^n$

3. $a_n = 1 - (-1)^n$

4. $a_n = \sin n\pi$

5. $a_n = \cos n\pi$

6. $a_n = \log n$

7. $a_n = \dfrac{n+2}{n+1}$ **8.** $a_n = n - \dfrac{1}{n}$ **9.** $a_n = n^2$

10. $a_n = n(n+1)$ **11.** $a_n = 2n+1$ **12.** $a_n = \dfrac{1}{n}$

13. $a_n = \dfrac{1}{n^2}$ **14.** $a_n = (-1)^{2n+1}$ **15.** $a_n = 5(\tfrac{1}{2})^n$

Find the first five terms of the sequences in Exercises 16–20 given the following recursive information.

16. $a_1 = 2,\ a_n = a_{n-1} + 2$ **17.** $a_1 = 3,\ a_n = a_{n-1}^2$

18. $a_1 = -1,\ a_n = 5a_{n-1}$ **19.** $a_1 = 10,\ a_n = 5 - a_{n-1}$

20. $a_1 = 1,\ a_2 = 1,\ a_n = a_{n-1} + a_{n-2}$

Find a formula for the general term of the sequences in Exercises 21–26.

21. 2, 4, 6, 8, ...   **22.** 1, 3, 7, 15, 31, ...

23. 1, 4, 7, 10, 13, ...   **24.** $\tfrac{1}{2}, \tfrac{2}{3}, \tfrac{3}{4}, \tfrac{4}{5}, \ldots$

25. 1, 4, 9, 16, 25, ...   **26.** 1, 8, 27, 64, ...

27. Suppose that in a year's time an automobile loses one-fourth of the value it had at the beginning of the year. If a car costs \$4000 new, what is its value at the end of 4 years?

28. A certain yeast plant matures in one hour; each hour thereafter it buds off one new plant, which also matures in one hour and starts to produce new plants, and so on. Write the terms of the sequence that describe the total number of plants at any time. This is an example of a *Fibonacci sequence*. Can you write a recursive formula for this sequence? (*Hint*: See Exercise 20.)

14.2
Sequences of
Partial Sums

Corresponding to each sequence $\{a_n\}$ we may form another sequence $\{S_n\}$ by forming sums of the first n terms. Thus, if $a_1, a_2, a_3, \ldots, a_n, \ldots$ are the terms of a sequence, then

$$S_1 = a_1,\ S_2 = a_1 + a_2,\ S_3 = a_1 + a_2 + a_3,$$

$$\ldots, S_n = a_1 + a_2 + a_3 + \cdots + a_n$$

The sequence $\{S_n\}$ is called the **corresponding sequence of partial sums.**

A compact notation often used to express terms of the sequence of sums is called the sigma, or summation, notation. The Greek letter Σ (sigma) means to form the sum of the indicated terms.

14.2 Sequences of Partial Sums

Definition	By $\displaystyle\sum_{k=1}^{n} a_k$ is meant the sum
	$a_1 + a_2 + a_3 + \cdots + a_n$

The subscript k, called the **index of summation**, is often called a "dummy" variable, since its only purpose is to indicate the steps in the summation process. The choice of the letter k for the index is arbitrary—any other symbol would serve as well.

The 1 and the n indicate the range of the index. In the definition, k begins at 1 and increases in steps of 1 until it becomes equal to n.

Writing a sum such as $\displaystyle\sum_{k=2}^{5} k^2$ in the form $4 + 9 + 16 + 25$ is called *expanding* the summation, or writing it in *expanded form*.

Example 14.6   The sum of the first 100 integers may be written $\displaystyle\sum_{k=1}^{100} k$.

Example 14.7   Write $\displaystyle\sum_{k=2}^{4} x^k$ in expanded form.

Solution $\displaystyle\sum_{k=2}^{4} x^k = x^2 + x^3 + x^4$

Example 14.8   Write $\displaystyle\sum_{i=1}^{10} (-1)^{i-1}$ in expanded form and simplify.

Solution $\displaystyle\sum_{i=1}^{10} (-1)^{i-1} = (-1)^0 + (-1)^1 + (-1)^2 + \cdots + (-1)^9 = 0$

Two basic rules govern the use of the summation symbol. The first allows us to factor out a constant coefficient and the second allows us to compute the sum of sums on a term-by-term basis. Together these two properties are called the **linearity properties**.

Property 1 $\displaystyle\sum_{k=1}^{n} ca_k = c \sum_{k=1}^{n} a_k$

Property 2 $\displaystyle\sum_{k=1}^{n} (a_k + b_k) = \sum_{k=1}^{n} a_k + \sum_{k=1}^{n} b_k$

14 Arithmetic and Geometric Sequences

As an example of the use of these properties, the sum

$$\sum_{k=1}^{3} k(5k + 1) = 1(6) + 2(11) + 3(16) = 76$$

can also be written

$$\sum_{k=1}^{3} (5k^2 + k) = 5 \sum_{k=1}^{3} k^2 + \sum_{k=1}^{3} k = 5(1 + 4 + 9) + (1 + 2 + 3) = 76$$

Either way the value is the same.

You should also be aware of the fact that a sum may be represented by more than one summation expression. One such instance is given in the following expression.

Example 14.9 $\qquad \displaystyle\sum_{k=1}^{n} \frac{1}{k} = \sum_{k=0}^{n-1} \frac{1}{k + 1}$

Showing that these two sums are equal is merely a matter of writing them both in expanded form. The index on the left summation ranges from 1 to n and on the right it ranges from 0 to $n - 1$. The second sum is said to be obtained by a *shift of index*.

Example 14.10 $\qquad$ Write the summation $\displaystyle\sum_{k=0}^{n} a_k(k - 1)x^k$ as a summation whose index begins at 2.

Solution $\quad$ Proceeding in a formal manner, let $k = t - 2$. Then when $k = 0$, $t = 2$ and when $k = n$, $t = n + 2$, so that the summation becomes

$$\sum_{t=2}^{n+2} a_{t-2}(t - 3)x^{t-2}$$

Letting $k = t$, this last sum becomes

$$\sum_{k=2}^{n+2} a_{k-2}(k - 3)x^{k-2}$$

Example 14.11 $\qquad$ The sum of the first six terms of the *harmonic* sequence is $1 + \frac{1}{2} + \frac{1}{3} + \frac{1}{4} + \frac{1}{5} + \frac{1}{6}$. The first term can be written as $\frac{1}{1}$ and since the denominator varies from 1 to 6 in steps of 1, the sum can be written in summation notation as

$$\sum_{n=1}^{6} \frac{1}{n}$$

14.2 Sequences of Partial Sums

403

Exercises for
Section 14.2

Write Exercises 1–10 in expanded form and evaluate.

1. $\displaystyle\sum_{m=1}^{5} \frac{1}{m+2}$

2. $\displaystyle\sum_{k=2}^{3} \frac{1-k}{1+k}$

3. $\displaystyle\sum_{n=0}^{5} n^2$

4. $\displaystyle\sum_{k=0}^{3} \left(-\frac{1}{2}\right)^k$

5. $\displaystyle\sum_{j=1}^{5} 3j$

6. $\displaystyle\sum_{k=0}^{5} (-1)^k$

7. $\displaystyle\sum_{k=1}^{5} (1+k)$

8. $\displaystyle\sum_{k=0}^{5} [2 + 3(k-1)]$

9. $\displaystyle\sum_{n=-2}^{2} n^2$

10. $\displaystyle\sum_{k=-1}^{2} (3k-1)$

Write the terms of the summation in Exercises 11 and 12.

11. $\displaystyle\sum_{k=1}^{5} x_k$

12. $\displaystyle\sum_{k=1}^{5} x^k$

Represent the summations in Exercises 13–17 using the sigma notation.

13. $1 + 2 + 3 + 4$

14. $\dfrac{1}{2} + \dfrac{1}{4} + \dfrac{1}{8}$

15. $1 + 4 + 9 + 16$

16. $x_0 + x_1 + x_2 + x_3 + x_4$

17. $2x + 4x + 8x + 16x + 32x$

Which of Exercises 18–23 are true?

18. $\displaystyle\sum_{k=1}^{n} ax_k = a\sum_{k=1}^{n} x_k$

19. $\displaystyle\sum_{i=1}^{n} (x_i + d) = nd + \sum_{i=1}^{n} x_i$

20. $\displaystyle\sum_{k=1}^{n} d = nd$

21. $\displaystyle\sum_{k=2}^{5} a_{k-2} = \sum_{0}^{3} a_k$

22. $\displaystyle\sum_{n=1}^{4} n^2 = \sum_{n=2}^{5} n^2$

23. $\displaystyle\sum_{n=1}^{3} x^n = \sum_{t=2}^{4} x^{t-1}$

Find the sequence whose sequence of sums is given by the formulas in Exercises 24–27.

24. $S_n = \dfrac{n}{n+1}$

25. $S_n = 2$

26. $S_n = n$

27. $S_n = (-1)^n$

28. Find the sum of the first six terms of the Fibonacci sequence defined by $a_1 = 2$, $a_2 = 3$, and $a_n = a_{n-2} + a_{n-1}$.

14.3
Arithmetic
Sequences

A sequence of n equally spaced numbers is called an **arithmetic sequence**. Saying it another way, an arithmetic sequence is one in which each term differs from the preceding term by a constant amount. This constant number is called the **common difference** and is usually denoted by the letter d. Thus, an arithmetic sequence is defined by the following recursive relationship:

$$a_1 = a; \qquad a_n = a_{n-1} + d$$

Like all sequences, arithmetic sequences can be finite or infinite; unless stated otherwise, assume it to be infinite. Perhaps the simplest arithmetic sequence is the sequence of counting numbers, 1, 2, 3, 4, ..., whose general term is $a_n = n$.

Example 14.12   Find the first few terms of the arithmetic sequence with

$$a_1 = 7 \text{ and } d = -3.$$

Solution

$$a_1 = 7, a_2 = 7 - 3 = 4, a_3 = 4 - 3 = 1, a_4 = 1 - 3 = -2,$$
$$a_5 = -2 - 3 = -5, \ldots$$

Example 14.13   When a parachutist jumps from an airplane, the distances, in feet, he falls in successive seconds before pulling the rip cord are

16, 48, 80, 112, 144, ...

These numbers form an arithmetic sequence whose common difference is 32.

To find the general term of any arithmetic sequence with first term a and common difference d, we note that the succeeding terms are $a_2 = a + d$, $a_3 = a + 2d$, $a_4 = a + 3d$, ... Therefore, the general term of an arithmetic sequence is

$$a_n = a + (n - 1)d$$

Example 14.14   Find the hundredth term of the arithmetic sequence whose first term is 3 and whose common difference is 2.

Solution Using the formula for the general term with $a = 3$, $d = 2$, and $n = 100$,

$$a_{100} = 3 + (99)(2) = 201$$

The sequence of partial sums corresponding to an arithmetic sequence is $a_1, a_1 + a_2 = 2a_1 + d, a_1 + a_2 + a_3 = 3a_1 + 3d$, and so on. The formula for the nth term of the sequence of sums is derived by a method made famous by Karl Gauss for computing the sum of the first 100 integers. Gauss recognized the simple but significant fact that the sum is the same regardless of the order in which the terms are written. Thus, for the sum of the first 100 positive integers,

$$S_{100} = 1 + 2 + 3 + \cdots + 98 + 99 + 100$$

and, in reverse order,

$$S_{100} = 100 + 99 + 98 + \cdots + 3 + 2 + 1$$

Adding these two equalities,

$$2S_{100} = 101 + 101 + 101 + \cdots + 101 + 101 + 101$$
$$2S_{100} = (100)(101)$$
$$S_{100} = 5050$$

This technique can be used conveniently to derive a formula for the nth term of the sequence of sums corresponding to *any* arithmetic sequence.

$$
\begin{array}{l}
S_n = a_1 \quad\quad + (a_1 + d) + (a_1 + 2d) + \cdots + (a_n - 2d) + (a_n - d) + a_n \\
S_n = a_n \quad\quad + (a_n - d) + (a_n - 2d) + \cdots + (a_1 + 2d) + (a_1 + d) + a_1 \\
\hline
2S_n = (a_1 + a_n) + (a_1 + a_n) + (a_1 + a_n) + \cdots + (a_1 + a_n) + (a_1 + a_n) + (a_1 + a_n) \\
S_n = \dfrac{n(a_1 + a_n)}{2}
\end{array}
$$

Thus, the sum of n terms of an arithmetic sequence is the average of the first and last terms times the number of terms. Since $a_n = a + (n - 1)d$, we may express this formula in terms of a and d.

$$S_n = \frac{n(a + a + (n - 1)d)}{2} = a \cdot n + \frac{n(n - 1)}{2} d$$

Example 14.15 Find the sum of the first 50 terms of the arithmetic sequence whose first term is 2 and whose common difference is -3.

Solution Here $a_{50} = 2 + (49)(-3) = 2 - 147 = -145$. Hence,

$$S_{50} = 50 \frac{(2 - 145)}{2} = 25(-143) = -3575$$

14 Arithmetic and Geometric Sequences

Example 14.16   Find $\displaystyle\sum_{k=1}^{25} (5k - 3)$.

Solution   This sum can be identified with the sum of the first 25 terms of an arithmetic sequence whose first term is 2 and whose common difference is 5. Thus, the sum is equal to

$$\frac{25}{2}[2 + (24)5] = 1525$$

The concepts of an arithmetic sequence and a linear function are closely related. To see this we sketch the points $(1, a_1)$, $(2, a_2)$, $(3, a_3)$, and so on, in Figure 14.1, and join them by a straight line as if the domain were all real numbers. The equation of the line is

$$\frac{y - a_1}{x - 1} = \frac{a_2 - a_1}{2 - 1} = d$$

Thus,

$$y = a_1 + (x - 1)d$$

which is the arithmetic sequence rule with n replaced by x. In this manner every arithmetic sequence determines a linear function. Conversely, given a linear

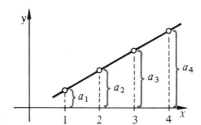

Figure 14.1

function $f(x)$, the terms $f(1)$, $f(2)$, $f(3)$, and so on determine an arithmetic sequence with common difference $f(2) - f(1)$. Note that the common difference, d, is the slope of the line. Thus, an arithmetic sequence is, in reality, a linear function whose domain is restricted to the positive integers.

Exercises for
Section 14.3

Determine which of the sequences in Exercises 1–10 are arithmetic and which are not. For those which are, give the common difference.

1.   1, 2, 3, 4, 5, ...   **2.**   2, 5, 8, 11, ...

3.   2, 4, 6, 8, 10, ...   **4.**   3, 9, 27, 81, ...

5.   3, 6, 9, 12, ...   **6.**   1, $\dfrac{1}{2}$, 0, $-\dfrac{1}{2}$, ...

7. $1, \dfrac{1}{2}, \dfrac{1}{4}, \dfrac{1}{8}, \ldots$

8. $1, -1, 1, 3, 1, 3, 5, 3, \ldots$

9. $\dfrac{1}{2}, \dfrac{1}{3}, \dfrac{1}{4}, \dfrac{1}{5}, \dfrac{1}{6}, \ldots$

10. $4, 14, 24, 34, 44, \ldots$

For Exercises 11–16 suppose that a_n is an arithmetic sequence.

11. If $a_1 = 2$ and $d = 3$, find the general term.

12. If $a_1 = 3$ and $a_7 = 23$, find the common difference.

13. If $a_1 = 2$ and $S_7 = 35$, find the common difference.

14. If $a_1 = -1$ and $d = 3$, find S_8.

15. If $a_2 = 5$ and $d = -4$, find S_{10}.

16. If $d = 3$ and $S_6 = 57$, find a_1.

Find the value of the sums in Exercises 17–22.

17. $\displaystyle\sum_{k=1}^{8} (2k - 3)$

18. $\displaystyle\sum_{k=2}^{7} (k + 4)$

19. $\displaystyle\sum_{k=0}^{4} (7k - 4)$

20. $\displaystyle\sum_{n=1}^{5} \left(\dfrac{1}{2}n + 3\right)$

21. $\displaystyle\sum_{k=0}^{4} 7(k - 4)$

22. $\displaystyle\sum_{k=1}^{5} (2k + 1)$

23. Find a formula for the sum of the first n odd integers.

24. Find a formula for the sum of the first n even integers.

25. Show that the technique for finding the sum of an arithmetic sequence does not work for the sequence of squares.

26. A gasoline company runs a contest in which it sends the winner some money every day for a month. The amounts are $50 the first day, $100 the second day, $150 the third day, and so on. In a 30-day month, how much will the winner collect?

Find the first 5 terms of the arithmetic sequence determined by the linear functions in Exercises 27–32.

27. $f(x) = x + 2$

28. $f(x) = 2x + 1$

29. $f(x) = -x + 2$

30. $f(x) = x$

31. $f(x) = 2x + 5$

32. $f(x) = -2x + 4$

What linear function is defined by the arithmetic sequences?

33. $3, 6, 9, 12, \ldots$

34. $a_n = 2n + 3$

35. $a_1 = 4, d = 3$

36. $a_1 = 2, d = -1$

37. $a_1 = 5, a_8 = 26$

38. $a_1 = 1, d = 2$

14.4
Geometric
Sequences

A number sequence constructed by successively multiplying by the same number is called a **geometric sequence**. The constant multiplier is called the **common ratio** and is usually denoted by r. The recursive definition of a geometric sequence is

$$a_1 = a$$

$$a_n = ra_{n-1}$$

The number sequence giving the number of your ancestors in the preceding generations is 2, 4, 8, 16, ... and is obviously a geometric sequence with common ratio 2.

A geometric sequence is completely determined by its first term a_1 and the common ratio r. If the sequence under consideration is to terminate, that is, be a finite sequence, then some mention should ordinarily be made of this fact. To determine the general term, note that

$$a_1 = a$$

$$a_2 = ar$$

$$a_3 = a_2r = ar^2$$

$$a_4 = a_3r = ar^3$$

$$\vdots$$

$$a_n = a_{n-1}r = ar^{n-1}$$

Example 14.17   What is the tenth term of a geometric sequence whose first term is 1 and whose common ratio is 0.1? Write an expression for the general term.

Solution   Using the formula for the nth term, we have

$$a_{10} = (1)(0.1)^9 = 10^{-9}$$

The general term for this sequence can be written

$$a_n = (1)(0.1)^{n-1} = 10^{1-n}$$

Example 14.18   Find the recursive form for the geometric sequence whose general formula is

$$a_n = 5\left(\frac{1}{3}\right)^{n-3}$$

Solution   From the given formula for a_n,

$$a_1 = 5\left(\frac{1}{3}\right)^{-2} = 45$$

Also,

$$r = \frac{a_n}{a_{n-1}} = \frac{5(\frac{1}{3})^{n-3}}{5(\frac{1}{3})^{n-4}} = \frac{1}{3}$$

Therefore, we have the recursive definition,

$$a_1 = 45, \; a_n = \frac{1}{3} a_{n-1}$$

To find the sequence of partial sums corresponding to the geometric sequence, we proceed as follows. Let

$$S_n = a_1 + a_1 r + \cdots + a_1 r^{n-1}$$

Multiplying both sides of this equation by the common ratio, r, yields

$$rS_n = a_1 r + a_1 r^2 + \cdots + a_1 r^n$$

Subtracting the left side of the second equation from the first equation and equating it to the difference of the right-hand sides of the two equations,

$$S_n(1 - r) = a_1(1 - r^n)$$

from which, if $r \neq 1$,

$$S_n = \frac{1 - r^n}{1 - r} a_1$$

Example 14.19   Find $\sum\limits_{k=1}^{10} (0.1)^k$.

Solution   This sum can be written as the sum of the first ten terms of a geometric sequence whose first term is 0.1 and whose common ratio is 0.1. Thus,

$$S_{10} = \frac{1 - (0.1)^{10}}{1 - 0.1}(0.1) = (1.111111111)(0.1)$$

$$= 0.1111111111$$

Exponential functions of the type $f(x) = ca^x$ can be closely identified with geometric sequences of the type $a_n = ca^n$ in a manner analogous to the identification of arithmetic sequences and linear functions. The sequence is obtained from the function by restricting the domain of the function to the positive integers. Conversely, by sketching terms of the geometric sequence ca^n and connecting the points by a smooth curve, we obtain a distinctively exponential curve whose equation is $f(x) = ca^x$. (See Figure 14.2.)

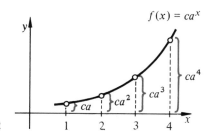

Figure 14.2

Another application of the use of geometric sequences is in computing accumulated interest. Recall that money paid for the use of another person's money is called *interest*. If the interest is computed on the original principal only, it is called **simple interest**. In contrast, if the interest is permitted to accumulate and is paid not only on the original principal but on the accumulated interest as well, the investment is said to earn **compound interest**.

Example 14.20   A principal of $2000 is invested at 8 percent interest for 10 years. Find the accumulated interest if it is compounded (a) annually and (b) semiannually.

Solution   In the case of the annual compounding, at the end of the first year the accumulated total amount is $A_1 = 2000 + .08(2000) = 2000(1.08)$. At the end of the second year $A_2 = A_1 + .08A_1 = 2000(1.08)^2$. Continuing in this manner the accumulated amount at the end of ten years is given by $A_{10} = 2000(1.08)^{10} = 2000(2.1589) = 4318. For the case of semiannual compounding the reasoning is similar, and the accumulated amount at the end of 20 payment periods is

$$B_{20} = 2000(1.04)^{20} = $4382$$

Thus, in the annual compounding case the accumulated interest is $2318 and in the semiannual case, $2382.

Exercises for
Section 14.4

Determine which of Exercises 1–8 are geometric sequences and for those that are, give the value of the common ratio. For each of the geometric sequences find the general term.

1.   4, 12, 36, 108, ...

2.   1, -3, 7, -11, ...

3.   3, 6, 9, 12, ...

4.   2, 4, 16, 256, ...

5. $\dfrac{1}{3}, \dfrac{-2}{3}, \dfrac{4}{3}, -\dfrac{8}{3}, \ldots$

6.   1, -1, 1, -1, ...

7. $\dfrac{1}{2}, \dfrac{1}{4}, \dfrac{1}{8}, \dfrac{1}{16}, \dfrac{1}{32}, \ldots$

8.   6, -6, 6, -6, 6, ...

In Exercises 9–14 assume that a_n is a geometric progression.

9. If $a_1 = 3$ and $r = 5$, find a_4 and S_4.

10. If $a_2 = 2$ and $r = 2$, find S_{10}.

11. If $a_1 = 5$ and $a_5 = 80$, find all possible real values of r and S_5.

12. If $a_3 = \frac{1}{2}$ and $a_7 = \frac{1}{32}$, find a_{20}.

13. If $a_1 = -2$, $r = \frac{2}{3}$, find a_{10}.

14. If $a_4 = 4$ and $a_7 = 32$, find a_1 and r.

Find the value of the sums in Exercises 15–21.

15. $\displaystyle\sum_{n=1}^{5} 2(3)^n$ **16.** $\displaystyle\sum_{k=2}^{6} (3^k + 2k)$ **17.** $\displaystyle\sum_{k=1}^{10} \left[\left(\frac{1}{2}\right)^k + \left(\frac{3}{2}\right)^k \right]$

18. $\displaystyle\sum_{n=1}^{10} 2^n$ **19.** $\displaystyle\sum_{k=1}^{6} 5\left(\frac{1}{2}\right)^k$ **20.** $\displaystyle\sum_{n=1}^{3} \left(\frac{2}{3}\right)^n$

21. $\displaystyle\sum_{n=1}^{3} \left(\frac{1}{4}\right)^n$

22. A certain ball, when dropped from a height, rebounds to three-fourths of the original height. At what bounce will the ball fail to reach one-fourth of the original height?

23. With each stroke a vacuum pump removes one-fifth of the air in a container. After how many strokes will it remove three-fourths of the original air?

Find the exponential function defined by the geometric sequences in Exercises 24–26.

24. $a_1 = 2$, $r = \dfrac{2}{3}$ **25.** $a_3 = 4$, $a_4 = 8$ **26.** $a_1 = 1$, $r = 3$

Give the first five terms of the geometric sequence defined by the given exponential function in Exercises 27–29.

27. $f(x) = 3^x$ **28.** $f(x) = 2(10)^x$ **29.** $f(x) = \left(\dfrac{1}{2}\right)^x$

30. What is the formula for the sum of n terms of a geometric sequence if $r = 1$?

31. The speed of a chemical reaction approximately doubles each time the temperature increases by 10°C. Write a geometric sequence to show how many times faster paper will burn if the temperature rises by 10°, 20°, 30°, and 40°C.

32. Find the amount of an investment of $5,500 at the end of 3 years invested at 8 percent compounded quarterly.

33. What rate of interest, compounded annually, does an investment earn if the principal of $8000 amounts to $12,000 at the end of 6 years?

34. What principal should be invested to amount to $10,000 at the end of 20 years with interest at 8 percent compounded semiannually?

35. A particular substance decays in such a way that it loses half its weight each day. What is its half-life? In how many days will it have lost 90 percent of its initial weight?

36. A binary sequence is defined by the formula $a_n = 2^{n-1}$. Find the formula for the sum of the first n terms of a binary sequence.

14.5
The General
Power of a Binomial

In Section 2.2 we showed that the expanded product of two binomials follows a special pattern. In particular, you were asked to memorize the expansions of the special products of $(x + y)^2$ and $(x + y)^3$ since they are so frequently used. Now we want to show that the general expansion of $(x + y)^n$ follows a recognizable and important formula that will allow the easy expansion of any binomial as well as the determination of any particular term within that expansion.

By actually performing the multiplications for $n = 1$ through 5,

$$(x + y)^1 = x + y$$
$$(x + y)^2 = x^2 + 2xy + y^2$$
$$(x + y)^3 = x^3 + 3x^2y + 3xy^2 + y^3$$
$$(x + y)^4 = x^4 + 4x^3y + 6x^2y^2 + 4xy^3 + y^4$$
$$(x + y)^5 = x^5 + 5x^4y + 10x^3y^2 + 10x^2y^3 + 5xy^4 + y^5$$

Here are some pertinent observations:

(1) There are always $(n + 1)$ terms, the first being $x^n y^0$ and the last, $x^0 y^n$.

(2) Each intermediate term contains a product of $x^j y^k$, where the sum of j and k in every term is n. Thus, the product is of the form $x^{n-k} y^k$.

(3) The exponents of x decrease by 1 from one term to the next, whereas the exponent associated with y increases by 1.

(4) The coefficients follow a symmetric pattern; that is, by starting at either end of the expansion, the coefficients match those obtained by starting at the other end and proceeding in the reverse direction.

(5) The actual formula for the coefficients is more difficult to guess with such limited information. However, note that the coefficient of the second term is $n/1$, the coefficient of the third term is $n(n - 1)/2$, the coefficient of the fourth term is $n(n - 1)(n - 2)/1 \cdot 2 \cdot 3$.

In a more formal treatment of taking the general power of a binomial we would show that the coefficient of $x^j y^k$ in the expansion of $(x + y)^n$ is given by

(14.1) $$C_{n,k} = \frac{n(n - 1)(n - 2) \cdots (n - k + 1)}{1 \cdot 2 \cdot 3 \cdot 4 \cdots k} \qquad \text{if } k \neq 0$$

$$= 1 \qquad\qquad\qquad\qquad \text{if } k = 0$$

Formula (14.1) is known as the **binomial coefficient**. It depends not only upon the order of the expansion n, but also upon the number of the term within that expansion, $(k + 1)$. Thus, the general expansion of a binomial consists of terms of the form $C_{n, k} x^{n-k} y^k$, where $k = 0, 1, 2, \ldots, n$.

The binomial coefficient $C_{n, k}$ may be considerably shortened and thereby made easier to learn with use of **factorial notation**, a mathematical abbreviation for the product of integers 1 through n. The symbol $n!$ is read "n factorial" and is defined to be

(14.2) $n! = n(n - 1)(n - 2)(n - 3) \cdots 3 \cdot 2 \cdot 1$

The number $0!$ does not quite fit into this definition but in order to make most mathematical formulas read simpler, we define $0!$ to be 1.

Example 14.21 $5! = 5 \cdot 4 \cdot 3 \cdot 2 \cdot 1 = 120$

$10! = 10 \cdot 9 \cdot 8 \cdot 7 \cdot 6 \cdot 5! = 30{,}240 \cdot 120 = 3{,}628{,}800$

$\dfrac{10!}{5!} = 30{,}240$

Most modern slide rule calculators can rapidly compute the product given by a factorial. For example, using a calculator you can obtain $60! = 8.320987112 \cdot 10^{81}$.

Here is how the factorial symbol simplifies the form of $C_{n, k}$. Note that the numerator being the product of integers that begins at n and ends at $(n - k + 1)$ may be written as $n!/(n - k)!$ The denominator is the product of integers from k to 1 and, hence, is simply $k!$ Thus, the binomial coefficient is given by

(14.3) $C_{n, k} = \dfrac{n!}{(n - k)! k!}$

The general term of the expansion of $(x + y)^n$ is then

$$\frac{n!}{(n - k)! k!} x^{n-k} y^k$$

Notice that the numerator is the factorial of the power of the binomial and the denominator is the product of the factorials of each of the exponents of the $(k + 1)$th term of the expansion. Thus, the sixth term (that is, $k = 5$) of the binomial $(x + y)^9$ is

$$\frac{9!}{4! 5!} x^4 y^5 = 126 x^4 y^5$$

Example 14.22   Find the coefficient of $x^9 y^7$ in the expansion of $(2x^3 - y)^{10}$.

Solution   The term of the expansion is

$$C_{10,\,7}(2x^3)^3 y^7 = \frac{10!}{7!\,3!}(2x^3)^3 y^7$$

$$= 120 \cdot 8x^9 y^7 = 960x^9 y^7$$

The desired coefficient is therefore 960.

The binomial coefficients $C_{n,\,k}$ have many interesting properties. Perhaps the best device for memorizing the pattern of the coefficients is through a triangular display called **Pascal's triangle**. Write $C_{n,\,k}$ for $k = 0, 1, 2, 3, \ldots$ on successive lines to obtain

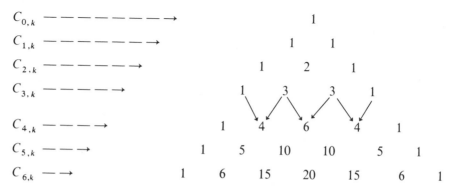

$C_{0,\,k}$	$------\to$				1				
$C_{1,\,k}$	$-----\to$			1		1			
$C_{2,\,k}$	$----\to$		1		2		1		
$C_{3,\,k}$	$---\to$	1		3		3		1	
$C_{4,\,k}$	$--\to$	1	4		6		4		1
$C_{5,\,k}$	$-\to$	1	5	10		10		5	1
$C_{6,k}$	$\to$	1	6	15	20		15		6	1

Each number *within* the triangle is found by adding the pair of numbers directly above it. For example, look at the interior numbers in the fifth row $(C_{n,\,4})$: $4 = 1 + 3$, $6 = 3 + 3$, and $4 = 3 + 1$. This observation suggests the following formula:

$$C_{n+1,\,k+1} = C_{n,\,k+1} + C_{n,\,k}$$

which is easily proven using the formula for $C_{n,\,k}$ directly.

The first two terms of a binomial expansion are often used to give a rough approximation to powers of numbers.

Example 14.23   By using the first two terms of the binomial expansion, approximate the value of $(1.01)^{50}$.

Solution   Letting $x = 1$ and $y = .01$ in the binomial, we have

$$(1.01)^{50} = (1 + .01)^{50} = 1^{50} + 50(1^{49})(.01)$$

$$= 1 + 50(.01) = 1.5$$

In fact, we have shown that $(1.01)^{50} > 1.5$.

14.5 The General Power of a Binomial

We have arrived at the results of this section in an intuitive manner. They can all be formally proven. Many books choose to prove these results under the heading of the **binomial theorem**. In calculus we show that this theorem can be generalized to include expansions of $(1 + x)^n$, where n is not an integer if $|x| < 1$. This generalized binomial expansion continues without end but very often we are interested in only the first few terms. In the use of the generalized form of the binomial theorem, the binomial coefficient cannot be computed from equation (14.3) since the factorial of a fraction is undefined. In this case use equation (14.1).

Example 14.24   By using the first three terms of the generalized binomial expansion, approximate the value of $\sqrt[3]{5}$.

Solution $\sqrt[3]{5} = (5)^{1/3} = (8 - 3)^{1/3} = 8^{1/3}\left(1 - \frac{3}{8}\right)^{1/3} = 2\left(1 - \frac{3}{8}\right)^{1/3} = 2(1 - .375)^{1/3}$

Using the first three terms of the generalized binomial expansion for $(1 - .375)^{1/3}$,

$$\sqrt[3]{5} = 2(1 - .375)^{1/3} = 2\left[1 + \frac{1}{3}(-.375) + \frac{(\frac{1}{3})(-\frac{2}{3})}{1 \cdot 2}(-.375)^2\right]$$

$$= 2[1 - .125 - .015625]$$

$$= 1.7188$$

Exercises for
Section 14.5

Expand and simplify Exercises 1–16, using the binomial formula.

1. $(x - y)^6$ 2. $(x + 7y)^4$

3. $(3x - y)^5$ 4. $(x - .1)^5$

5. $\left(x + \frac{1}{x}\right)^5$ 6. $\left(x + \frac{1}{3x^2}\right)^4$

7. $(y^2 + 3x)^3$ 8. $(\sqrt{x} + x)^5$

9. $(\sqrt{x} + \sqrt{y})^6$ 10. $\left(yx^2 + \frac{2}{y}\right)^4$

11. $(x^{1/3} + x^{-3/4})^4$ 12. $(2y^{1/5} - 3z^{1/3})^4$

13. $(2 + .1)^4$ 14. $(x^{-1} + y^{-1})^5$

15. $(x^{-3/4} - x^{3/4})^3$ 16. $(2x^5 + 5y^{-3})^4$

17.   Find the 4th term in the expansion of $(\sqrt{x} + \sqrt{y})^{10}$.

18.   Find the 8th term in the expansion of $(1 + .1)^{20}$.

19.   Find the 12th term in the expansion of $(3x^3 - 7y^{1/3})^{20}$.

20.   Find the 15th term in the expansion of $(2y^3 - 3x^4)^{20}$.

21. Find the coefficient of $x^{12}y^2$ in the expansion of $(x^3 - 2y^2)^5$.

22. Find the coefficient of $(x/y)^5$ in the expansion of $(2x + 3y^{-1})^{10}$.

23. Find the coefficient of the constant term in the expansion of $[x + (1/3x)]^8$.

24. Find the coefficient of the x term in the expansion of $(2x^{1/3} - 7)^9$.

By using the first two terms of an appropriate binomial expansion, approximate Exercises 25–30.

25. $(2.3)^6$ **26.** $(1.99)^5$ **27.** $(3.99)^3$

28. $(.99)^{100}$ **29.** $(1.01)^{500}$ **30.** 99^4

By using the first three terms of the generalized binomial expansion, approximate Exercises 31–40.

31. $\sqrt{24}$ **32.** $\sqrt{13}$ **33.** $\sqrt[3]{7}$ **34.** $\sqrt{66}$ **35.** $\sqrt[3]{30}$

36. $\sqrt{5}$ **37.** $\sqrt[4]{80}$ **38.** $\sqrt[5]{31}$ **39.** $\sqrt{98}$ **40.** $\sqrt[3]{120}$

Use a slide rule calculator to compute Exercises 41–44.

41. $40!/30!$ **42.** $50!$ **43.** $(35 - 5)!$ **44.** $54!$

45. Using the formula for $C_{n,k}$, show that $\sum_{k=0}^{n} C_{n,k} = 2^n$. Notice that this formula represents the sum of the numbers in the nth row of Pascal's triangle.

46. Using the formula for $C_{n,k}$, show that $C_{n+1,k+1} = C_{n,k+1} + C_{n,k}$.

14.6
Permutations and Combinations

Some applications of mathematics, particularly those involving statistics, require some systematic approach to counting. Typically, the things we count are called objects, or *decisions*, and we attempt to simplify the counting process by considering independent successive decisions using *the fundamental principle of counting*.

To find the number of ways of making several decisions in succession, multiply the number of choices that can be made in each of the individual decisions.

Example 14.25   In how many different patterns can you answer a true-false test consisting of 10 questions?

Solution   Assuming each answer to be independent of the others, there are 2 possible choices for each answer. Hence, the total is

$$2 \cdot 2 \cdot 2 \cdot 2 \cdot 2 \cdot 2 \cdot 2 \cdot 2 \cdot 2 \cdot 2 = 2^{10} = 1024$$

Example 14.26   How many different numbers can be written with the digits 1, 2, 3, 4, and 5 if none are to be repeated?

Solution   There are 5 successive independent decisions. The first can be made in 5 ways after which 4 digits remain. Hence, the second choice can be made in one of 4 ways. Continuing in this manner, the total number is

$$5 \cdot 4 \cdot 3 \cdot 2 \cdot 1 = 5! = 120 \text{ ways}$$

This last example is an application of the fundamental counting principle, which is important enough to analyze more generally. The question to answer is, "Given n distinct objects, in how many ways can we arrange them in a definite order?" Each such ordered arrangement is called a **permutation**.

To determine the number of permutations of n objects, apply the fundamental principle, noting that there are n choices for the first object, $(n-1)$ for the second, $(n-2)$ for the third, and so forth. Therefore, the total number is given by the product $n(n-1)(n-2) \cdots 3 \cdot 2 \cdot 1 = n!$

There are $n!$ permutations of n objects.

Often we wish to choose only a part of the set to make the arrangements. The next example illustrates the point.

Example 14.27   If 9 horses enter a race, in how many ways can the first 3 places be won?

Solution   Note that the answer is *not* 9! since we are not concerned with the total number of possible finishes of all 9 horses. There are 9 possible winning horses, after which 8 possible horses could finish in second place and finally 7 who could finish third. Using the fundamental counting principle, there would be

$$9 \cdot 8 \cdot 7 = 504$$

possible ways for the top 3 to be chosen.

The foregoing example is typical of picking k objects at a time from n objects. The totality of these possible choices for fixed k and n is called **permutations of n objects taken k at a time** and is denoted by $P_{n,k}$. To find the value of $P_{n,k}$ note that the first object may be chosen in n ways, the second in $(n-1)$ ways, and so on for the k choices. Thus,

$$P_{n,k} = \underbrace{n(n-1) \cdots (n-k+2)(n-k+1)}_{k \text{ numbers}}$$

In terms of factorial notation,

$$P_{n,k} = \frac{n!}{(n-k)!}$$

Example 14.28   The number of ways to deal 5 cards from a pack of 52 cards is

$$\frac{52!}{(52-5)!} = 52 \cdot 51 \cdot 50 \cdot 49 \cdot 48 = 311{,}875{,}200$$

Note that this number is *not* the number of distinct poker hands because a poker player holding a hand of 5 cards ordinarily disregards the order. 🐦

The distinction between an ordered arrangement as in the previous example and one for which order is immaterial leads to the idea of choosing a **combination** of k objects from n objects. Instead of deriving the formula for the number N of combinations directly, we will see how this number is related to $P_{n,k}$.

An ordered selection of k objects taken from n objects may be thought of as the following two-step procedure:

(1)   Choose k objects from the n. (We have called this number N.)
(2)   Permute these k objects. ($P_{k,k} = k!$)

By the fundamental counting principle, $P_{n,k}$ is the product of N and $k!$. Thus,

$$P_{n,k} = N \cdot k!$$

and

$$N = \frac{P_{n,k}}{k!} = \frac{n!}{(n-k)!\,k!}$$

which we recognize as the binomial coefficient, $C_{n,k}$. Thus, the number of combinations of n objects taken k at a time is

$$C_{n,k} = \frac{n!}{k!\,(n-k)!}$$

Example 14.29
(a)   The number of combinations taken 5 at a time from a set of 10 is $C_{10,5} = 10!/(5!)(5!) = 252$.
(b)   The number of possible single bridge hands consisting of 13 cards is $C_{52,13} = 52!/(13!)(39!)$. 🐦

Now we can use the fundamental counting principle along with our knowledge of combinations.

Example 14.30   A baseball team has 3 catchers, 9 pitchers, 6 infielders, and 7 outfielders. In how many ways can a team of 9 be chosen?

Solution   The number of ways of choosing a catcher = 3.
The number of ways of choosing a pitcher = 9.
The number of ways of choosing an infielder = $C_{6, 4} = 15$
The number of ways of choosing an outfielder = $C_{7, 3} = 35$

Hence, by the fundamental counting principle, the total number of distinct teams = $3 \cdot 9 \cdot 15 \cdot 35 = 14{,}175$

Exercises for
Section 14.6

1. Find the value of $P_{7, 4}$, of $C_{7, 4}$.

2. Given that $P_{n, 2} = 56$, find n.

3. Given $P_{n, 3} = 9P_{n, 2}$, find n.

4. Show that $P_{20, 2} = 19P_{5, 2}$.

5. Show that $\sum_{k=1}^{4} P_{4, k} = 4^3$.

6. Show that $\sum_{k=1}^{4} (C_{4, k})^2 = C_{8, 4} - 1$.

7. From a committee of 8 people how many subcommittees of 3 people are possible?

8. In how many ways can 10 people line up at a box office?

9. In how many ways can 4 candidates for public office be listed on the ballot?

10. How many ways are there of arranging the letters of the word MATH?

11. In how many ways can you arrange the digits in a 7-digit number, assuming there are no zeros and no repetitions?

12. In poker in how many ways can you get a flush (all of the same suit)?

13. In poker in how many ways can you get a full house (3 of a kind and a pair)?

14. Four persons enter a room in which there are 7 chairs. In how many ways can they select their chairs?

15. How many 4-letter words ending in a vowel can be constructed from the word VOWEL?

16. A building has 5 entrances. In how many ways can you enter the building and leave by a different entrance?

17. How many committees of 4 women can be selected from 10 women if two certain women refuse to serve on a committee together?

14.7
Mathematical
Induction

Proving a mathematical generalization from a given set of hypotheses and axioms, is called **deduction**. You are probably most familiar with this process from your plane geometry course.

Another way of proving a generalization is to observe a specific event and then assume that these observations are true in general. Scientific laws are for the most part established by this process of **incomplete induction**. While incomplete induction is adequate in the physical sciences, it fails in mathematics. To see why, consider this generalization: $n^2 - n + 41$ is prime if n is a positive integer. For the first 40 positive integers this formula yields a prime number. The formula seems to work well until this point. However, in continuing the process you will find that it fails when $n = 41$. Therefore, we *cannot* generalize in mathematics using incomplete induction because the " next " case may be the one that fails.

Example 14.31   Reasoning by example (experimentally), we might conclude that all integers are less than 1,000,000,000—unless we just happen to use an example greater than 1,000,000,000.

In mathematics a process called complete induction or **mathematical induction** proceeds from the particular to the general without the obvious problems of incomplete induction. Mathematical induction is a precise procedure for proving the validity of a generalization concerning some sort of sequential statement.

Example 14.32   We would use mathematical induction to *prove*, not derive, the formula

$$\sum_{k=1}^{n} k^2 = \frac{1}{6}n(n + 1)(2n + 1)$$

The method of mathematical induction consists of two parts.

(1)   **Verification.** The given proposition must be shown to be true for the smallest integral value of n for which the proposition holds. (Ordinarily, this step is carried out for many more than just the one case, since showing the statement true for several cases will at least make the given proposition plausible.)

14.7 Mathematical Induction   421

(2) **Implication.** Demonstrate that if the proposition is true for $n = k$, then it must hold for $n = k + 1$. The assumption that the proposition is true for $n = k$ is sometimes called the *inductive hypothesis*.

If the conditions of both the verification and implication steps have been met, then the statement is true for all positive integers greater than or equal to that number used in the verification step.

The logic behind a proof by mathematical induction is similar to knocking over a row of dominoes by pushing the first one and letting each domino knock over the one immediately following it. (See Figure 14.3.) If the first domino cannot be knocked over or if the dominoes are not close enough (that is, the kth one will not push over the $k + 1$st), then all the dominoes will not fall.

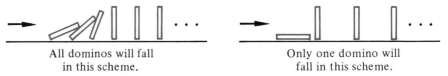

| All dominos will fall in this scheme. | Only one domino will fall in this scheme. |

Figure 14.3

Example 14.33 Prove by mathematical induction that the sum of the first n integers is given by the formula $S_n = n(n + 1)/2$.

Solution

(1) Verification. Verify that when $k = 1$, $S_1 = 1$. Substituting 1 into the proposed formula, we get $S_1 = 1(1 + 1)/2 = 1$.

(2) Implication. We assume the formula true for $n = k$; that is, $S_k = k(k + 1)/2$. Then we must show that $S_{k+1} = (k + 1)(k + 2)/2$. By definition,

$$S_{k+1} = S_k + (k + 1)$$

Using the inductive hypothesis,

$$S_{k+1} = \frac{k(k + 1)}{2} + (k + 1)$$

$$= \frac{(k + 1)(k + 2)}{2}$$

Hence, since both steps have been validated, the given statement is true for all positive integers. ✦

Both parts of the method of mathematical induction are absolutely necessary. The next two examples emphasize this fact.

Example 14.34   Consider the "formula" that the sum of the first n integers is given by $A_n = n^2 - n + 1$. Note that $A_1 = 1$, which verifies the formula for $k = 1$. Assuming that $A_k = k^2 - k + 1$, we must show that $A_{k+1} = (k + 1)^2 - (k + 1) + 1 = k^2 + k + 1$. However, by definition,

$$A_{k+1} = A_k + (k + 1) = (k^2 - k + 1) + (k + 1) = k^2 + 2$$

and since $k^2 + k + 1 \neq k^2 + 2$ (except for $k = 1$), the implication step is unproved.

Example 14.35   Suppose we try to show that the sum of the first n integers is given by the formula $n(n + 1)/2 + 1$. Then the implication step is to assume $B_k = k(k + 1)/2 + 1$ and to attempt to show $B_{k+1} = (k + 1)(k + 2)/2 + 1$. By definition,

$$B_{k+1} = B_k + (k + 1) = \frac{k(k + 1)}{2} + 1 + (k + 1)$$

$$= \frac{(k + 1)(k + 2)}{2} + 1$$

which proves this step. However, $B_1 = 2$, which is *not* the first integer. In fact, B_n does not represent the sum for any value of n. This example illustrates the importance of checking both parts of the induction process.

Example 14.36   Show that if n is a positive integer and $x \neq y$, then $x^n - y^n$ is always divisible by $x - y$.

Solution   Since $x^n - y^n = x - y$ when $n = 1$, the verification step is trivial. Now assume that $x^n - y^n$ is divisible by $x - y$ if $n = k$. Thus, assume that

$$\frac{x^k - y^k}{x - y} = q(x)$$

where the division process yields no remainder. Then,

$$\frac{x^{k+1} - y^{k+1}}{x - y} = \frac{x^{k+1} - xy^k + xy^k - y^{k+1}}{x - y}$$

$$= \frac{x(x^k - y^k) + y^k(x - y)}{x - y}$$

$$= \frac{x(x^k - y^k)}{x - y} + y^k$$

$$= xq(x) + y^k$$

which means that for $n = k + 1$ the division process does not yield a remainder. Because the verification and implication steps are validated, we conclude that $x^n - y^n$ is divisible by $x - y$ for all n.

14.7 Mathematical Induction   423

Exercises for
Section 14.7

Using mathematical induction, prove the statements in Ex. 1–10 valid for all $n \geq 1$.

1. $\displaystyle\sum_{k=1}^{n} 2k = n(n+1)$

2. $\displaystyle\sum_{k=1}^{n} 2^k = 2^{n+1} - 2$

3. $\displaystyle\sum_{k=1}^{n} (3k-2) = \frac{n(3n-1)}{2}$

4. $\displaystyle\sum_{k=1}^{n} (3k-1) = \frac{n(3n+1)}{2}$

5. $\displaystyle\sum_{k=1}^{n} k(k+1) = \frac{n(n+1)(n+2)}{3}$

6. $\displaystyle\sum_{k=1}^{n} (2k-1) = n^2$

7. $\displaystyle\sum_{k=1}^{n} k^2 = \frac{n(n+1)(2n+1)}{6}$

8. $\displaystyle\sum_{k=1}^{n} k^3 = \frac{n^2(n+1)^2}{4}$

9. $\displaystyle\sum_{k=1}^{n} r^{k-1} = \frac{1-r^n}{1-r}, \qquad r \neq 1$

10. $\displaystyle\sum_{k=1}^{n} \frac{1}{k(k+1)} = \frac{n}{n+1}$

11. $n(n+1)(n+2)$ is a multiple of 6 for all $n \geq 1$.

12. $x^{2n-1} + y^{2n-1}$ is divisible by $x + y$ for all $n \geq 1$.

13. $\displaystyle\sum_{k=1}^{n+1} \frac{1}{n+k} \leq \frac{5}{6}$

Test 1 for
Chapter 14

Answer true or false for Exercises 1–10.

1. No term of the sequence whose nth term is $n/(n+1)$ ever exceeds 1.

2. $\displaystyle\sum_{k=2}^{2} 2^k = 2$

3. If $\displaystyle\sum_{k=1}^{n} a_k = \frac{n}{n+1}$, then $a_n = \frac{1}{n(n+1)}$.

4. For any sequence $\displaystyle\sum_{k=1}^{n} a_k < \sum_{k=1}^{n+1} a_k$.

5. $\displaystyle\sum_{k=1}^{20} i^k = 0, \ (i = \sqrt{-1})$.

6. $(2n)!/n! = 2!$

7. The constant term in the expansion of $[x - (1/x)]^{10}$ is $C_{10,5}$.

8. The number of ways to answer a 20-question, true-false test is $20!$

9. The principle of mathematical induction can be used to prove $\displaystyle\sum_{k=1}^{n} k = n(n+1)/2$.

10. $\displaystyle\sum_{k=2}^{10} (k+1)(k+2) = \sum_{k=0}^{8} (k+3)(k+4)$.

11. Consider the sequence 3, 9, 15, 21, ...

(a) Find a formula for the general term.

(b) Find the sum of the first 60 terms.

12. Prove the following formula by mathematical induction: $\sum\limits_{k=1}^{n} (2k + 1) = n(n + 2)$.

13. By using the first two terms of the generalized binomial expansion, approximate $(1.01)^{100}$.

14. Find and simplify the coefficient of $x^{12}y^6$ in the expansion of $(2x^2 - 3y)^{12}$.

15. Find the amount of an investment of $4500 at the end of 5 years at 8 percent compounded quarterly.

Test 2 for
Chapter 14

1. Find a formula for the general term of the sequence 1, 3, 5, 7, 9, ...

2. Write in expanded form and evaluate $\sum\limits_{i=1}^{4} i(i + 2)$.

3. Write the general term and find the sum of the first 99 terms of 2, 4, 6, 8, ...

4. Write the general term and write the sum of the first 10 terms of $\frac{2}{3}, \frac{2}{9}, \frac{2}{27}, \ldots$.

5. Use the binomial theorem to expand $(x + 5)^6$.

6. Use the first two terms of the binomial expansion to approximate $\sqrt{7}$.

7. How many ways can 10 people be arranged in teams of three?

8. Calculate: (a) $P_{5, 2}$; (b) $C_{8, 3}$.

9. A business firm wants to hire 6 men and 3 women. If 10 men and 7 women apply for the positions, in how many ways can they make the selections?

10. Use mathematical induction to prove $4 + 7 + 10 + \cdots + (3n + 1) = \frac{1}{2}n(3n + 5)$.

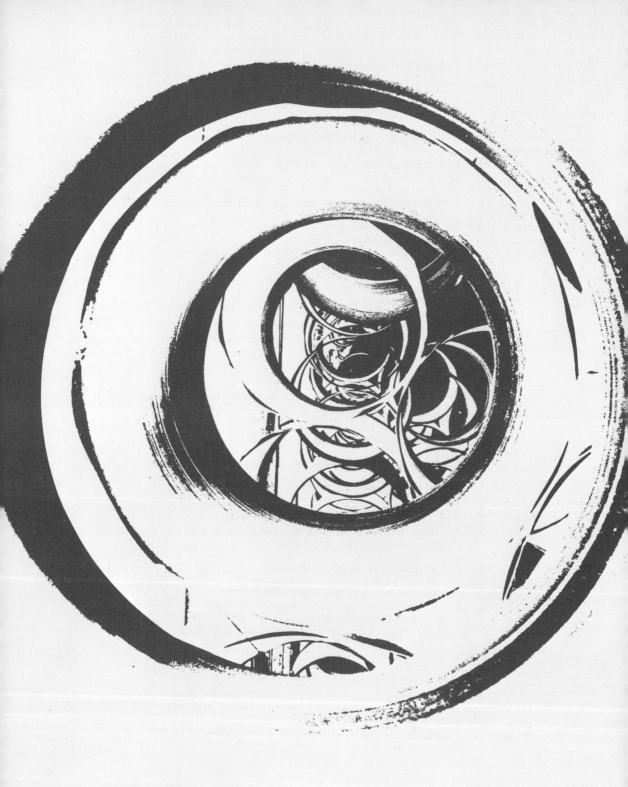

15
Plane Analytic
Geometry

15.1
Introduction

Analytic geometry is a branch of mathematics in which we study the geometry of curves using algebraic equations. Except for some special cases (such as the unit circle with equation $x^2 + y^2 = r^2$), we have so far restricted our discussion of graphs to functional type equations. Analytic geometry poses two fundamental problems.

(1) To associate with an equation involving x and y a curve in the rectangular plane.

(2) To associate with a curve in the rectangular plane a relation between x and y called the **equation** of the curve.

Of these two fundamental problems, the first is at least theoretically easy to solve. All we need do is assign values of x (or y) and find corresponding values of y (or x). Under the assumption that we can solve for y, the totality of ordered pairs (x, y) yields the curve corresponding to the given equation. This procedure is certainly not new, since you have used it at several different places in this book. In its most basic form it is called point plotting and is usually supplemented with some analysis to allow for a more global approach. This analysis is summarily discussed in Section 15.2.

The second problem of analytic geometry is usually substantially more difficult. To write the equation of a curve you must know the rule governing the construction of the curve. So far in this book the only curve whose equation is specifically derived from its construction is that of a straight line. In this chapter we will describe some general procedures and then particularize the discussion to curves called the conic sections.

15.2
Basic Curve
Sketching

Any equation involving real numbers and variables will yield a set of points in the rectangular plane through which the curve of the equation may be drawn. This process of plotting points is time-consuming and tedious so we look for ways to shorten the work. This may be done by making some analytical observations about the nature of the defining equation before plotting any points. The basic properties used in curve plotting are *intercepts, symmetry, excluded values, behavior for large values of the variables, and factorability of the equation.*

Intercepts

The intercepts of a curve are the points at which the curve crosses the x- and y-axes. To find the x-intercepts, let $y = 0$ and solve for x. To find the y-

intercepts, let $x = 0$ and solve for y. For example, the curve $x^2 - y^2 = 4$ has x-intercepts $x = \pm 2$ and has no y-intercepts.

Symmetry

Curves may be symmetric with respect to many different points and lines. However, we are interested in symmetry only with respect to the origin or the two axes, since this type of symmetry is easy to check. (See Figure 15.1.)

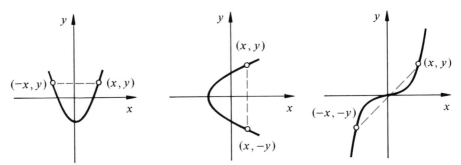

Symmetry about the y–axis   Symmetry about the x–axis   Symmetry about the origin

Figure 15.1

(1)   A curve is symmetric with respect to the y-axis if both the points (x, y) and $(-x, y)$ are on the curve. Hence, the simple test for symmetry with respect to the y-axis is: *If the equation remains unchanged when x is changed to $-x$, then the curve is symmetric with respect to the y-axis.* For example, the curve $y + x^2 - 2 = 0$ is symmetric with respect to the y-axis since $y + (-x)^2 - 2 = y + x^2 - 2$.

(2)   A curve is symmetric with respect to the x-axis if both (x, y) and $(x, -y)$ are on the curve. Hence, *if the equation remains unchanged when y is changed to $-y$, then the curve is symmetric with respect to the x-axis.* For example, the graph of $x^2 + 2x + y^2 = 7$ is symmetric with respect to the x-axis since $x^2 + 2x + (-y)^2 = x^2 + 2x + y^2$.

(3)   A curve is symmetric with respect to the origin if both (x, y) and $(-x, -y)$ are on the curve. *A simple test for this kind of symmetry is to change x to $-x$ and y to $-y$. If the equation remains unchanged, the curve is symmetric with respect to the origin.* The equation $y = x^3 + 4x$ is symmetric with respect to the origin since $-y = (-x)^3 + 4(-x)$ simplifies to the original equation.

Excluded Values

By noticing which values of the variable are not permitted, the curve may be restricted to certain portions of the rectangular plane. Values of x and y must be excluded for which the other variable would be nonreal. For example, the equation $x^2 + 2y^2 = 1$ implies that $x^2 = 1 - 2y^2$. Hence, since $1 - 2y^2$ must be greater than or equal to 0, it follows that y is limited by the values $-1/\sqrt{2} \le$

$y \leq 1/\sqrt{2}$. Likewise, since $y^2 = \frac{1}{2}(1 - x^2)$, x is limited to the values $-1 \leq x \leq 1$.

For many functions, portions of the x-y plane may be excluded merely by noticing where the value of y is positive and negative.

Example 15.1   Determine where the graph of $y = (x - 1)/(x + 2)$ is above and below the x-axis.

Solution   To find where the graph is above the x-axis, solve the inequality $(x - 1)/(x + 2) > 0$. Note that $x - 1$ is positive for $x > 1$ and negative for $x < 1$. The factor $x + 2$ is positive for $x > -2$ and negative for $x < -2$. The following schematic represents the sign of the factors.

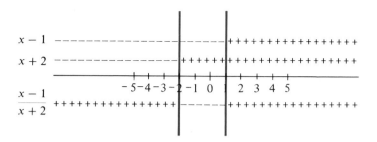

Hence, the graph is above the x-axis for $x < -2$ and for $x > 1$, since the quotient is positive there. The graph is below the x-axis between -2 and 1, since the quotient is negative for this interval.

Behavior for Large Values of the Variables

Sometimes when x and y become large, the given equation may be approximated by a far simpler equation. For example, the equation $y_1 = x^2 + (1/x)$ tends to behave like $y_2 = x^2$ as x becomes large. The curves representing y_1 and y_2 are said to be *asymptotic*. Chapter 7 introduced a particular kind of asymptotic behavior in which y (or x) approaches a finite value as x (or y) becomes large. Such asymptotes are either horizontal or vertical lines. A more general analysis of asymptotic behavior is particularly useful for sketching some curves.

Example 15.2   Sketch the graph of $y = x^2 + (1/x)$.

Solution   Notice that for large positive x, the graph approaches $y = x^2$ from above, while for large negative x, the graph approaches $y = x^2$ from below. Thus, the desired graph is asymptotic to $y = x^2$ for large $|x|$. As x approaches zero through positive values, the value of y becomes arbitrarily large. Similarly, the value of y becomes arbitrarily large but negative as x approaches zero through negative values. Hence, the line $x = 0$ is a vertical asymptote. The point $(-1, 0)$ is obviously the only intercept. Figure 15.2 shows the graph using this information.

15.2 Basic Curve Sketching   429

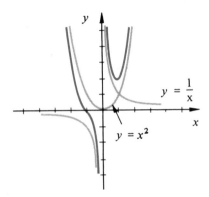

Figure 15.2

Asymptotic behavior is usually not obvious without some preliminary algebraic manipulation.

Example 15.3   Locate the vertical and horizontal asymptotes for the curve whose equation is $xy - y - 2x + 3 = 0$. Sketch the graph.

Solution   Solving the given equation for y,

$$y = \frac{2x - 3}{x - 1}$$

In this form we see that as x approaches 1, the value of y becomes arbitrarily large. Hence, $x = 1$ is a vertical asymptote. Solving the original equation for x,

$$x = \frac{y - 3}{y - 2}$$

From this we see that there is a horizontal asymptote at $y = 2$. With the aid of a couple of additional facts we may easily draw the graph of the equation. From the first equation, the y-intercept is $y = 3$ and from the second equation the x-intercept is $x = \frac{3}{2}$.

Finally, the first equation shows that y is positive for $x > \frac{3}{2}$ and $x < 1$ and negative for $1 < x < \frac{3}{2}$. Therefore, the curve is below the x-axis for $1 < x < \frac{3}{2}$ and above otherwise. Figure 15.3 shows the sketch of the curve.

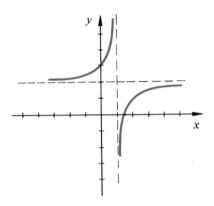

Figure 15.3

Factorable Equations

If an equation in x and y can be factored into two or more factors, it is evident that those values of (x, y) that satisfy either one of the resulting equations will satisfy the total equation and hence determine a point on the curve. Thus, the total graph is made up of the graphs of the two separate factors.

Example 15.4   Graph $x^2y - xy^2 - x + y = 0$.

Solution   The expression $x^2y - xy^2 - x + y$ may be factored into $(xy - 1)(x - y)$. Therefore, the required graph is the union of the graph of $xy - 1 = 0$ and the graph of $x - y = 0$. Figure 15.4 displays the desired graph.

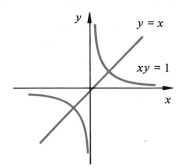

Figure 15.4

Exercises for
Sections 15.1 and 15.2

Discuss and draw the graphs of the equations in Exercises 1–25. In each case determine intercepts, excluded regions, and asymptotic behavior.

1. $x^2 - 3y = 9$

2. $y^2 - x^2 = 16$

3. $y^2 - x^2 = 0$

4. $y^3 = x + 4y$

5. $y^2 = x(x - 4)^2$

6. $y = x^3 - 4x$

7. $y^2 - 4y - x + 3 = 0$

8. $xy = 0$

9. $x^2y^2 = 2xy$

10. $x^2 + y^2 = 1 - 2xy$

11. $y = \dfrac{5}{x - 1}$

12. $y = \dfrac{x - 1}{3 - x}$

13. $y = \dfrac{x^2 - 2x}{x^2 - 2x - 3}$

14. $y = \dfrac{x^2 - 1}{x^2 + 1}$

15. $y^2(x - 1) = x$

16. $x^2 + 2xy + y^2 + 1 = 0$

17. $y^2 = x^2(x - 3)$

18. $x^2y^2 = 4 - x^2$

19. $x^2y + xy^2 - x - y = 0$ (Hint: It factors)

20. $y(1 - x) = x + 4$

21. $y^2(1 - x) = x + 4$

22. $y = x + \dfrac{1}{x}$

23. $y = x - \dfrac{1}{x}$ **24.** $y = x^2 - \dfrac{1}{x}$

25. $y = x^2 - \dfrac{1}{x^2}$

15.3
The Equation of a Curve

To write the algebraic equation of a curve you must know how the curve is constructed. The method of finding an equation corresponding to a given curve varies from problem to problem but will generally embrace the following components.

(1)   Choose a suitable set of axes. The best selection of axes and origin is one that gives the simplest equation.

(2)   Locate a point (x, y) that satisfies the given conditions and draw any auxiliary conditions suggested by the given conditions.

(3)   From this figure obtain an equation involving the coordinates of the general point (x, y). Relations involving distances, slopes, and sides of right triangles are some of the possibilities for writing the desired equation.

Example   15.5   A point moves so that the difference of its distances from the points $(3, 5)$ and $(1, -1)$ is 3. Find the equation of the curve that the point traces.

Solution   In this case the coordinate system is fixed by the problem, so a choice is not possible. Figure 15.5 shows a sketch of the conditions of the problem. The distance of (x, y) from $(3, 5)$ is $\sqrt{(x - 3)^2 + (y - 5)^2}$ and the distance of (x, y) from $(1, -1)$ is $\sqrt{(x - 1)^2 + (y + 1)^2}$. Hence, the equation of the curve in unsimplified form is

$$\left| \sqrt{(x - 3)^2 + (y - 5)^2} - \sqrt{(x - 1)^2 + (y + 1)^2} \right| = 3$$

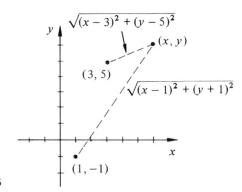

Figure 15.5

15 Plane Analytic Geometry

After considerable effort, this can be written

$$20x^2 - 96xy - 108y^2 + 112x + 624y - 457 = 0$$

In the remainder of this chapter we examine some curves of particular mathematical interest. The procedure is to define the given curve and then derive the equation. In this section we define and discuss the circle.

Definition A circle is a curve consisting of a set of points in a plane equidistant from a fixed point.

The fixed point is called the **center** and the given distance is called the **radius** of the circle.

We obtain the equation of the circle by locating in the plane a fixed point (h, k) and a general point (x, y). Then, as shown in Figure 15.6, the equation of the circle with center at (h, k) and radius r is

$$(x - h)^2 + (y - k)^2 = r^2$$

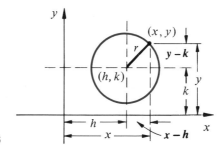

Figure 15.6

If (h, k) is chosen to be the origin, the equation becomes

$$x^2 + y^2 = r^2$$

This is called the standard form of a circle with center at the origin and radius r. For example, the equation of the circle centered at the origin with radius 4 is

$$x^2 + y^2 = 16$$

By expanding the standard form of a circle with center at (h, k), we obtain $x^2 - 2hx + y^2 - 2ky + h^2 + k^2 - r^2 = 0$. Letting $-2h = C$, $-2k = D$, and $h^2 + k^2 - r^2 = E$, the equation of a circle becomes

$$x^2 + y^2 + Cx + Dy + E = 0$$

In this form neither the center nor the radius is obvious, but by completing the square, first on the x terms and then on the y terms, these values may be obtained. The next example shows the technique.

15.3 The Equation of a Curve

Example 15.6   Find the center and radius of the circle whose equation is

$$x^2 + y^2 + 3x - 8y = 0$$

Solution   Rewriting this equation,

$$x^2 + 3x + (\quad) + y^2 - 8y + (\quad) = 0$$

To complete the square on the x term add $(\frac{3}{2})^2$ to both sides of the equation. To complete the square on the y term add 4^2 to both sides. Hence,

$$x^2 + 3x + \left(\frac{3}{2}\right)^2 + y^2 - 8y + 4^2 = \frac{9}{4} + 16$$

or

$$\left(x + \frac{3}{2}\right)^2 + (y - 4)^2 = \frac{73}{4}$$

This form of the given equation shows that the circle is centered at $(-\frac{3}{2}, 4)$ and has a radius of $\sqrt{73}/2$. (See Figure 15.7.)

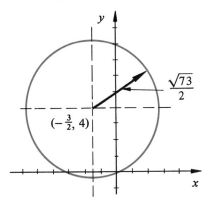

Example 15.7   A point on a curve is always three times as far from one end of a line segment as from the other. The line segment is 8 units long. Find the equation of the curve.

Solution   Choose the origin as the midpoint of the line segment. (See Figure 15.8.) Then the coordinates of the endpoints are $(-4, 0)$ and $(4, 0)$. By the conditions of the problem,

$$\sqrt{(x + 4)^2 + y^2} = 3\sqrt{(x - 4)^2 + y^2}$$

Figure 15.8

434   15 Plane Analytic Geometry

Squaring and reducing, this equation may be written

$$x^2 + y^2 - 10x + 16 = 0$$

which is the equation of a circle. Completing the square on the x term,

$$x^2 - 10x + 25 + y^2 = -16 + 25$$

or $\qquad (x - 5)^2 + y^2 = 9$

Therefore, the curve is a circle with center at $(5, 0)$ and radius 3.

Exercises for
Section 15.3

1. Find the equation of the curve each of whose points is equidistant from $(3, 4)$ and $(-1, 6)$.

2. A point moves so that the sum of the squares of its distances from the ends of the hypotenuse of a right isosceles triangle is twice the square of its distance from the vertex of the right angle. Show that its path is along the extended hypotenuse of the triangle.

3. A point moves so that the sum of the squares of its distances from two vertices of an equilateral triangle is equal to twice the square of its distance from the third vertex. Show that its graph is a straight line parallel to a side of the triangle and passing through the point of intersection of the medians.

4. A point moves so that the difference of its distances from $(4, 1)$ and $(-3, 2)$ is 5. Find the equation of its graph.

5. Find the equation of the locus of points the sum of whose distances from $(5, 1)$ and $(5, -1)$ is 6.

Find the center and the radius of each of the circles in Exercises 6–13. Sketch.

6. $x^2 + y^2 - y = 0$ 7. $2x^2 + 2y^2 - 5x + y = 3$

8. $x^2 + y^2 + 2x - 6y = 15$ 9. $3x^2 + 3y^2 + 7x - y - 9 = 0$

10. $x^2 + y^2 + 4x - 4y = 17$ 11. $x^2 + y^2 + 8x - 10y - 8 = 0$

12. $x^2 + y^2 - 6x + 7 = 0$ 13. $x^2 + y^2 - 5y = 0$

Find the equation of each of the circles in Exercises 14–22.

14. With center at the origin and radius 8.

15. With center at the origin and passing through $(1, 5)$.

16. With center at $(1, 5)$ and passing through the origin.

17. With ends of diameter at $(-6, 1)$ and $(4, 3)$.

18. With center at $(1, 3)$ and touching the x-axis.

19. With center at $(-2, 5)$ and radius $\sqrt{3}$.

20. With center at $(-1, -2)$ and radius 5.

21. With center at $(2, 1)$ and passing through $(5, 3)$.

22. With center at $(0, 4)$ and passing through $(1, -1)$.

15.4
Conic Sections:
The Parabola

Curves that can be formed by cutting a right circular cone with a plane are called **conic sections**. Greek mathematicians in 300 B.C. discovered that they could obtain four distinct curves by cutting a right circular cone with a plane: the circle, the ellipse, the hyperbola, and the parabola. The properties of the conics discovered by the Greeks include those that we use as definitions in this chapter.

If two right circular cones are placed vertex to vertex with a common axis, the resulting figure is referred to as a cone with two *nappes*. To see how the four conics can be generated from a cone with two nappes, refer to Figure 15.9.

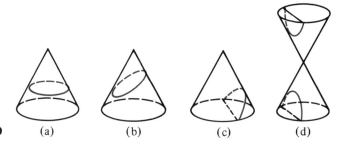

Figure 15.9   (a)   (b)   (c)   (d)

(a) A **circle** is obtained when the cutting plane is perpendicular to the axis, provided it does not pass through the vertex.

(b) An **ellipse** is obtained when the cutting plane is inclined so as to cut entirely through one nappe of the cone without cutting the other nappe.

(c) A **parabola** is obtained when the cutting plane is parallel to one element in the side of the cone.

(d) A **hyperbola** is obtained when the cutting plane is inclined so that it cuts through both nappes.

Recalling that analytic geometry is the study of the relationship between algebra and geometry, we wish to establish the algebraic representation of the four conic sections. The circle, which is the simplest of the conic sections, was defined and discussed in the previous section. In this section we define and discuss the **parabola**.

A parabola is the set of all points in a plane that are equidistant from a fixed point and a fixed line.

The fixed point is called the **focus** and the fixed line, the **directrix** of the parabola. The line through the focus and perpendicular to the directrix is called the **axis** of the parabola. By definition, the midpoint between the focus and the directrix is a point on the parabola and is known as the **vertex**. Recall from Chapter 6 that the shape of the graph of a quadratic function is a parabola whose axis is vertical.

In Figure 15.10 is a parabola with vertex located at the origin, focus at $F(a, 0)$, and directrix perpendicular to the x-axis at $D(-a, 0)$. Observe that a is

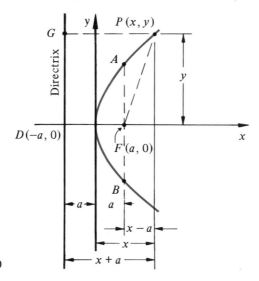

Figure 15.10

the distance from the vertex to the focus, sometimes referred to as the **focal distance**.

To find the algebraic equation of this parabola, consider a point $P(x, y)$ on the parabola. Then, by definition,

(15.1) $\overline{GP} = \overline{FP}$

But from Figure 15.10 we see that

$\overline{GP} = x + a$

and $\overline{FP} = \sqrt{(x - a)^2 + y^2}$

Substituting these expressions in equation (15.1), yields

$x + a = \sqrt{(x - a)^2 + y^2}$

or, squaring both sides,

$(x + a)^2 = (x - a)^2 + y^2$

15.4 Conic Sections: The Parabola   437

Expanding and collecting like terms, the equation of the parabola becomes

(15.2) $y^2 = 4ax$

Equation (15.2) is referred to as the **standard form** of the equation of a parabola with vertex at the origin and focus on the x-axis. It is clearly symmetric about its axis. The focus is at $(a, 0)$ if the coefficient of x is positive. In this case the parabola opens to the right. If the coefficient of x is negative, the focus is at $(-a, 0)$ and the parabola opens to the left.

The chord AB through the focus and perpendicular to the axis is called the **right chord**, or frequently, the latus rectum. The length of the right chord is found by letting $x = a$ in equation (15.2). Making this substitution,

$$y^2 = 4a^2$$

from which

$$y = \pm 2a$$

The length of the right chord is, therefore, equal numerically to $4a$. This fact is useful because it helps to define the shape of the parabola by giving us an idea of the "opening" of the parabola.

The standard form of a parabola with vertex at the origin and focus on the y-axis is

(15.3) $x^2 = 4ay$

The derivation of this formula, which parallels that of equation (15.2), is left for you to do. The parabola represented by equation (15.3) is symmetric about the y-axis. It opens upward if the coefficient of y is positive and downward if it is negative.

The equation of a parabola is characterized by one variable being linear and the other being squared. *The linear variable indicates the direction of the axis of the parabola.*

A unique physical property of the parabola is that it will reflect any rays emitted from the focus such that they travel parallel to the axis of the parabola. This feature makes the parabola a particularly desirable shape for reflectors in spotlights and reflecting telescopes and also for radar antennas.

A rough sketch of the parabola can be drawn if the location of the vertex and the extremities of the right chord are known. As you will see in the following examples, all of this information can be obtained from the standard form of the equation.

Example 15.8   Discuss and sketch the graph of the equation $x^2 = 8y$.

Solution   This equation has the form of equation (15.3) with $4a = 8$ or $a = 2$. The y-axis is the axis of the parabola, the focus is at $(0, 2)$, and the directrix is the line

$y = -2$. The endpoints of the right chord are then $(-4, 2)$ and $(4, 2)$. Figure 15.11 shows the parabola.

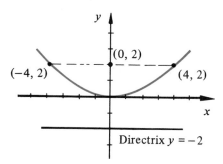

Figure 15.11

Example 15.9   Find the equation of the parabola with focus at $(-1, 0)$ and directrix $x = 1$ and sketch the curve.

Solution   The focus lies on the x-axis to the left of the directrix, so the parabola opens to the left. The desired equation is then the form in equation (15.2) with $a = -1$; that is,

$$y^2 = -4x$$

To sketch the parabola, note that the length of the right chord is $\overline{AB} = 4$. Its extremities are therefore $(-1, 2)$ and $(-1, -2)$. The curve appears in Figure 15.12.

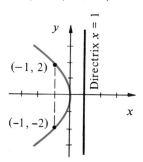

Figure 15.12

Example 15.10   A parabolic reflector is to be built with a focal distance of 2.25 ft. What is the diameter of the reflector if it is to be 1 ft deep at its axis?

Solution   To solve this problem we need the equation of the parabola used to generate the reflector. Referring to Figure 15.13, the vertex is located at the origin and the

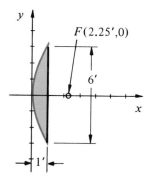

Figure 15.13

15.4 Conic Sections: The Parabola

439

focus on the x-axis. (We could have just as well placed the focus on the y-axis.) Then using equation (15.2) with $a = 2.25$ yields the equation

$$y^2 = 4(2.25)x = 9x$$

The diameter of the reflector can now be found by substituting $x = 1$ into this equation. Thus,

$$y^2 = 9 \quad \text{and} \quad y = \pm 3$$

which means that the diameter of the reflector is 6 ft.

Exercises for
Section 15.4

In Exercises 1–10 find the coordinates of the focus, the endpoints of the right chord, and the equation of the directrix of each of the parabolas. Sketch the graph of each parabola.

1. $y^2 = -8x$
2. $x^2 = 12y$
3. $2x^2 = 12y$
4. $x^2 = -24y$
5. $y^2 + 16x = 0$
6. $y + 2x^2 = 0$
7. $y^2 = 3x$
8. $3x^2 = 4y$
9. $y^2 = -2x$
10. $y^2 = 10x$

In Exercises 11–18, find the equation of the parabolas having the given properties. Sketch each curve.

11. Focus at $(0, 2)$, directrix $y = -2$.
12. Focus at $(0, -\frac{1}{2})$, directrix $y = \frac{1}{2}$.
13. Focus at $(\frac{3}{2}, 0)$, directrix $x = -\frac{3}{2}$.
14. Focus at $(-10, 0)$, directrix $x = 10$.
15. Endpoints of right chord $(2, -1)$ and $(-2, -1)$, vertex at $(0, 0)$.
16. Endpoints of right chord $(3, 6)$ and $(3, -6)$, vertex at $(0, 0)$.
17. Vertex at $(0, 0)$, vertical axis, one point of the curve $(2, 4)$.
18. Vertex at $(0, 0)$, horizontal axis, one point of the curve $(2, 4)$.

In Exercises 19–22 solve the given system of equations graphically.

19. $2x + 4y = 0$
    $x^2 - 4y = 0$
20. $y = e^x$
    $y^2 = -3x$
21. $y^2 = 12x$
    $y = \log x$
22. $y = x^3$
    $x^2 = 8y$

23. The supporting cable of a suspension bridge hangs in the shape of a parabola. Find the equation of a cable hanging from two 400-ft-high supports that are

1000 ft apart, if the lowest point of the cable is 250 ft below the top of the supports. Choose the origin in the most convenient location.

24. A parabolic antenna is to be constructed by revolving the parabola $y^2 = 24x$. Sketch the cross-section of the antenna if the diameter of the circular front is to be 12 ft. Locate the focus.

15.5
The Ellipse

An **ellipse** can be constructed from a loop of string in the following way. Place two pins at F and F', as shown in Figure 15.14 and place the loop of string over them. Pull the string taut with the point of a pencil and then move the pencil,

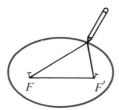

Figure 15.14

keeping the string taut. The figure generated is an ellipse. From this construction observe that the sum of the distances from the two fixed points to the point P is always the same since the loop of string is kept taut. This property characterizes the ellipse.

Definition

> An ellipse is the set of all points in a plane the sum of whose distances from two fixed points in the plane is constant.

The fixed points are called the **foci** of the ellipse. The midpoint of a line through the foci is called the **center** of the ellipse. We use the center of the ellipse to locate the ellipse in the plane in the same way we used the vertex to locate the parabola.

To obtain the equation of an ellipse, consider an ellipse with foci located on the x-axis such that the origin is midway between them, as in Figure 15.15. Letting the foci be the points $F(c, 0)$ and $F'(-c, 0)$ and letting the sum of the distances from a point $P(x, y)$ of the ellipse to the foci be $2a$, where $a > c$, we have

$$PF + PF' = 2a$$

From Figure 15.15 it is clear that

$$PF = \sqrt{(x - c)^2 + y^2}$$

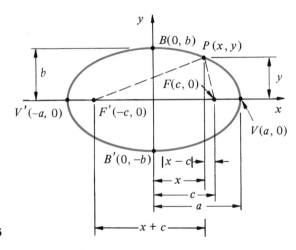

Figure 15.15

and

$$PF' = \sqrt{(x+c)^2 + y^2}$$

so that

$$\sqrt{(x-c)^2 + y^2} + \sqrt{(x+c)^2 + y^2} = 2a$$

Transposing the first radical and squaring,

$$(x+c)^2 + y^2 = 4a^2 - 4a\sqrt{(x-c)^2 + y^2} + (x-c)^2 + y^2$$

Expanding and collecting like terms,

$$a\sqrt{(x-c)^2 + y^2} = a^2 - cx$$

Squaring again and simplifying,

$$(a^2 - c^2)x^2 + a^2y^2 = a^2(a^2 - c^2)$$

Substituting $b^2 = a^2 - c^2$, this equation becomes

$$b^2x^2 + a^2y^2 = a^2b^2$$

Finally, dividing through by the nonzero quantity a^2b^2 we can write the equation of an ellipse with its center at the origin and its foci on the x-axis as

(15.4) $$\frac{x^2}{a^2} + \frac{y^2}{b^2} = 1$$

Equation (15.4) is clearly symmetric about both axes and the origin. By letting $y = 0$ in equation (15.4), we see that the x-intercepts of the ellipse are $(a, 0)$ and $(-a, 0)$. The segment of the line through the foci from $(a, 0)$ to $(-a, 0)$ is called the **major axis** of the ellipse. Clearly the length of the major axis is $2a$, which is also the value chosen for the sum of the distances PF and

PF'. The length a is then known as the **semi-major axis** and the endpoints of the major axis as the **vertices** of the ellipse.

The y-intercepts of the ellipse are found to be $(0, b)$ and $(0, -b)$ by letting $x = 0$ in equation (15.4). The segment of the line perpendicular to the major axis from $(0, b)$ to $(0, -b)$ is called the **minor axis**. Since the length of the minor axis is $2b$, the length of the **semi-minor axis** is b. The graph of an ellipse can readily be sketched once the semi-major and semi-minor axes are known. In this book, **the semi-major axis is represented by the letter a and the semi-minor axis by the letter b.**

The foci of an ellipse are located by solving the equation $b^2 = a^2 - c^2$ for the focal distance c. Thus,

$$c = \sqrt{a^2 - b^2}$$

is the desired equation.

A similar derivation will show that

(15.5) $$\frac{x^2}{b^2} + \frac{y^2}{a^2} = 1$$

is the equation of an ellipse with its center at the origin and its foci on the y-axis. (Note that the letter a is again being used to represent the semi-major axis.)

Example 15.11   Find the equation of an ellipse centered at the origin with foci on the x-axis if the major axis is 10 and the minor axis is 4.

Solution   In this case the major axis is on the x-axis. The semi-major axis is $a = 5$ and the semi-minor axis is $b = 2$. Substituting these values into equation (15.4),

$$\frac{x^2}{5^2} + \frac{y^2}{2^2} = 1$$

or $$\frac{x^2}{25} + \frac{y^2}{4} = 1$$

is the required equation.

Example 15.12   Find the equation of the ellipse with vertices at $(0, 5)$ and $(0, -5)$ and foci at $(0, 4)$ and $(0, -4)$.

Solution   From the given information we are able to conclude that the foci are on the y-axis, the center of the ellipse is at the origin, and the semi-major axis is $a = 5$. To find the semi-minor axis, use the relation $b^2 = a^2 - c^2$. Thus, $b = \sqrt{25 - 16} = \sqrt{9} = 3$. Substituting $a = 5$ and $b = 3$ into equation (15.5), yields

$$\frac{x^2}{9} + \frac{y^2}{25} = 1$$

The ellipse is sketched in Figure 15.16.

15.5 The Ellipse

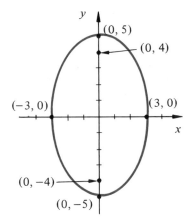

Figure 15.16

Example 15.13 Sketch the graph of the ellipse $4x^2 + 16y^2 = 64$.

Solution The given equation divided by 64 can be written in the form

$$\frac{x^2}{16} + \frac{y^2}{4} = 1$$

The major axis lies along the x-axis since the denominator of the x term in the equation is larger than the denominator of the y term. Consequently, the semi-major axis is $a = 4$ and the semi-minor axis is $b = 2$. The vertices are then $(4, 0)$ and $(-4, 0)$ and the endpoints of the minor axis are $(0, 2)$ and $(0, -2)$. The ellipse is sketched in Figure 15.17.

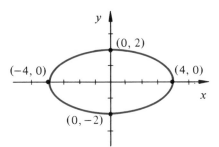

Figure 15.17

One of the first scientific applications of the ellipse was in astronomy. The astronomer Kepler (c. 1600) discovered that the planets moved in elliptical orbits about the sun with the sun at one focus. Artificial satellites also move in elliptical orbits about the earth. Another application is in the design of machines, in which elliptic gears are used to obtain a slow, powerful movement with a quick return. A third application of the ellipse is found in electricity, in which the magnetic field of a single-phase induction motor is elliptical under normal operating conditions.

15 Plane Analytic Geometry

Exercises for
Section 15.5

In Exercises 1–10 discuss each of the given equations and sketch their graphs.

1. $5x^2 + y^2 = 25$ **2.** $4x^2 + 9y^2 = 36$

3. $16x^2 + 4y^2 = 16$ **4.** $3x^2 + 9y^2 = 27$

5. $3x^2 + y^2 = 9$ **6.** $25x^2 + 4y^2 = 100$

7. $2x^2 + 3y^2 - 24 = 0$ **8.** $5x^2 + 20y^2 = 20$

9. $9x^2 + 4y^2 = 4$ **10.** $4x^2 + y^2 = 25$

In Exercises 11–20 find the equation of the ellipses having the given properties. Sketch each curve.

11. Vertices at $(\pm 4, 0)$, minor axis 6.

12. Vertices at $(0, \pm 1)$, minor axis 1.

13. Vertices at $(0, \pm 5)$, semiminor axis $\frac{3}{2}$.

14. Vertices at $(\pm 6, 0)$, semiminor axis 2.

15. Major axis 10, foci at $(\pm 4, 0)$.

16. Major axis 10, foci at $(0, \pm 3)$.

17. Foci at $(\pm 1, 0)$, semimajor axis 4.

18. Vertices at $(0, \pm 7)$, foci at $(0, \pm \sqrt{28})$.

19. Vertices at $(\pm \frac{5}{2}, 0)$, one point of the curve at $(1, 1)$.

20. Vertices at $(\pm 3, 0)$, one point of the curve at $(\sqrt{3}, 2)$.

In Exercises 21–24 solve the given system of equations graphically.

21. $\dfrac{x^2}{4} + y^2 = 4$
$2y + 3x = 0$

22. $\dfrac{x^2}{9} + \dfrac{y^2}{9} = 1$
$y = e^{x+2}$

23. $y = x^2$
$x^2 + 4y^2 = 4$

24. $y^2 - 12x = 0$
$y^2 + 9x^2 = 9$

25. An elliptical cam with a horizontal major axis of 10 in. and a minor axis of 3 in. is to be machined by a numerically controlled vertical mill. Find the equation of the ellipse to be used in programming the control device.

26. An elliptical cam having the equation $9x^2 + y^2 = 81$ revolves against a push rod. What is the maximum travel of the push rod?

15.5 The Ellipse   **445**

15.6

The Hyperbola

The final conic that we consider is the hyperbola.

Definition
A hyperbola is the set of all points in a plane the difference of whose distances from two fixed points in the plane is constant.

In Figure 15.18 we have drawn a hyperbola with foci at $F(c, 0)$ and $F'(-c, 0)$. The origin is then at the midpoint between the foci, which corresponds to the

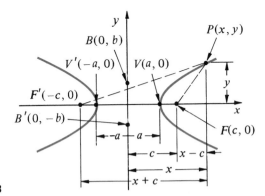

Figure 15.18

center of the hyperbola. The points $V(a, 0)$ and $V'(-a, 0)$ are called the **vertices**, and the segment $\overline{VV'}$ is called the **transverse axis** of the hyperbola. Clearly, the length of the transverse axis is $2a$. The segment BB', which is perpendicular to the transverse axis at the center of the hyperbola, is called the **conjugate axis** and has a length of $2b$. The conjugate axis has an important relation to the curve even though it does not intersect the curve.

To find the algebraic equation of a hyperbola, consider a point $P(x, y)$ on the hyperbola. Then, by definition,

$$\overline{F'P} - \overline{FP} = 2a$$

which in turn can be written

(15.7) $\sqrt{(x + c)^2 + y^2} - \sqrt{(x - c)^2 + y^2} = 2a$

Using the same procedure here that we used for the ellipse, equation (15.7) can be reduced to

$$\frac{x^2}{a^2} - \frac{y^2}{c^2 - a^2} = 1$$

Or, letting $b^2 = c^2 - a^2$, the equation of the hyperbola becomes

(15.8) $\dfrac{x^2}{a^2} - \dfrac{y^2}{b^2} = 1$

which, like the ellipse, is symmetric about both axes and the origin. Letting $y = 0$, the x-intercepts of equation (15.8) are found to be $x = \pm a$. Additional information regarding the shape of the hyperbola can be obtained by solving equation (15.8) for y. Performing the necessary algebraic operations yields

$$y = \pm \frac{b}{a}\sqrt{x^2 - a^2}$$

from which it is evident that the curve does not exist for $x^2 < a^2$. Consequently, the hyperbola consists of two separate curves, or *branches*—one to the right of $x = a$ and a similar one to the left of $x = -a$.

The shape of the hyperbola is constrained by two straight lines called the *asymptotes* of the hyperbola. The asymptotes of a hyperbola are the extended diagonals of the rectangle formed by drawing lines parallel to the coordinate axes through the endpoints of both the transverse axis and the conjugate axis. Referring to Figure 15.19, we see that the slope of the diagonals of this rectangle are

$$m = \pm \frac{y}{x} = \pm \frac{2b}{2a} = \pm \frac{b}{a}$$

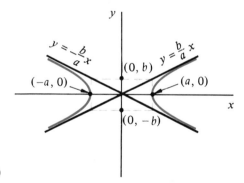

Figure 15.19

and, therefore, the asymptotes are given by the lines

$$y = \pm \frac{b}{a}x$$

We now want to show that these lines are asymptotes of the hyperbola; that is, we want to show that the hyperbola approaches arbitrarily close to the lines as x increases without bound. Solving equation (15.8) for y^2, we can write it in the form

$$y^2 = \frac{b^2 x^2}{a^2}\left(1 - \frac{a^2}{x^2}\right)$$

15.6 The Hyperbola

447

or, taking the square root of both sides,

(15.9) $$y = \pm \frac{b}{a} x \sqrt{1 - \frac{a^2}{x^2}}$$

Now consider the value of the right member as x becomes large. The quantity a^2/x^2 becomes small and, therefore,

$$\pm \frac{b}{a} x \sqrt{1 - \frac{a^2}{x^2}}$$

approaches $\pm(b/a)x$, which means that the hyperbola $(x^2/a^2) - (y^2/b^2) = 1$ is asymptotic to the lines $y = \pm(b/a)x$.

If we begin with the foci of the hyperbola on the y-axis and the center at the origin, the standard form of the equation of a hyperbola becomes

(15.10) $$\frac{y^2}{a^2} - \frac{x^2}{b^2} = 1$$

The vertices of this hyperbola are on the y-axis; **the positive term always indicates the direction of the transverse axis.** Notice that the standard form of the hyperbola, like that for the ellipse, demands that the coefficients of x^2 and y^2 be in the denominator and that the number of the righthand side be 1. In the case of the hyperbola the sign of the term, *not* the magnitude of the denominator, determines the transverse axis.

To sketch the hyperbola, first draw the rectangle through the extremities of the transverse and conjugate axes and extend the diagonals of the rectangle. Then draw the hyperbola so that it passes through the vertex and comes closer to the extended diagonals as x moves away from the origin.

Example 15.14   Discuss and sketch the graph of $4x^2 - y^2 = 16$.

Solution   Dividing by 16, we have

$$\frac{x^2}{4} - \frac{y^2}{16} = 1$$

which is the equation of a hyperbola with center at the origin and foci on the x-axis. It has vertices at $(\pm 2, 0)$ and its conjugate axis extends from $(0, 4)$ to $(0, -4)$. The foci are found from the equation $b^2 = c^2 - a^2$. Thus,

$$c = \sqrt{a^2 + b^2} = \sqrt{4 + 16} = \sqrt{20} = 2\sqrt{5}$$

and the foci are located at $(\pm 2\sqrt{5}, 0)$. Plotting these points and drawing the rectangle and its extended diagonals, the hyperbola shown in Figure 15.20 is obtained.

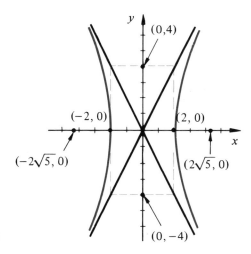

Figure 15.20

Example 15.15   Discuss and sketch the graph of $\dfrac{y^2}{13} - \dfrac{x^2}{9} = 1$.

Solution   This hyperbola has a vertical transverse axis with vertices at $(0, \sqrt{13})$ and $(0, -\sqrt{13})$. The extremes of the conjugate axis are then $(3, 0)$ and $(-3, 0)$. The foci are located at $(0, \sqrt{22})$ and $(0, -\sqrt{22})$. This information is used to sketch the hyperbola in Figure 15.21.

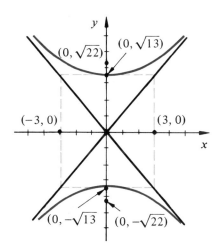

Figure 15.21

Example 15.16   Determine the equation of the hyperbola centered at the origin with foci at $(\pm 6, 0)$ and a transverse axis 8 units long.

Solution   Here $a = 4$ and $c = 6$. Since $c^2 = a^2 + b^2$, we have $b^2 = c^2 - a^2 = 36 - 16 = 20$. Substituting $a^2 = 16$ and $b^2 = 20$ into equation (15.8),

$$\frac{x^2}{16} - \frac{y^2}{20} = 1$$

15.6 The Hyperbola   449

In Exercises 1–10 discuss the properties of the graph of each of the given equations and then sketch the graph.

1. $x^2 - y^2 = 16$ 2. $y^2 - x^2 = 9$

3. $4x^2 - 9y^2 = 36$ 4. $9x^2 - y^2 = 9$

5. $4y^2 - 25x^2 = 100$ 6. $3x^2 - 3y^2 = 9$

7. $4x^2 - 16y^2 = 25$ 8. $4y^2 - x^2 = 9$

9. $y^2 + 1 = x^2$ 10. $x^2 - 25 = 5y^2$

In Exercises 11–20 find the equation of the hyperbolas having the given properties. Sketch each curve.

11. Vertices at $(\pm 4, 0)$, foci at $(\pm 5, 0)$.

12. Vertices at $(0, \pm 3)$, foci at $(0, \pm 5)$.

13. Conjugate axis 4, vertices at $(0, \pm 1)$.

14. Conjugate axis 1, vertices at $(\pm 4, 0)$.

15. Transverse axis 6, foci at $(\pm \frac{7}{2}, 0)$.

16. Transverse axis 3, foci at $(\pm 2, 0)$.

17. Vertices at $(0, \pm 4)$, asymptotes $y = \pm (\frac{1}{2})x$.

18. Vertices at $(\pm 3, 0)$, asymptotes $y = \pm 2x$.

19. Vertices at $(0, \pm 3)$, one point of the curve $(2, 7)$.

20. Vertices at $(\pm 3, 0)$, one point of the curve $(7, 2)$.

15.7
Translation of
Axes

As we have seen, the equation of a circle centered at the origin has the form $x^2 + y^2 = r^2$, whereas if its center is at (h, k), the equation is $(x - h)^2 + (y - k)^2 = r^2$. If the conic sections are referenced to some point (h, k) other than the origin, the same scheme is used. This change of origin, which is called a **translation**, may be interpreted as a change of axes. This section shows how such a translation affects the standard equations of the conic sections.

Consider a point $P(x, y)$ in the xy-coordinate plane. Suppose that we wish to use a $x'y'$-coordinate system whose origin is at the point (h, k) in the original coordinate system. In order to transform a pair of coordinates (x, y)

into (x', y'), notice that Figure 15.22 establishes the relation between the two coordinate systems as

$$x = x' + h \qquad x' = x - h$$

or

$$y = y' + k \qquad y' = y - k$$

These equations are called the *equations of translation.*

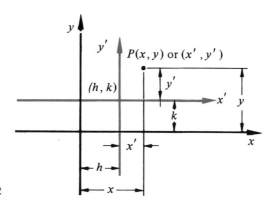

Figure 15.22

To see how to use the equations of translation to write the equations of conics not in standard position, consider the parabola whose vertex is at (h, k). In terms of $x'y'$-coordinates its equation is $(x')^2 = 4ay'$. Using the translation equations, the equation of a parabola with vertex at (h, k) and vertical axis is

$$(15.14) \qquad (x - h)^2 = 4a(y - k)$$

Similarly, the parabola with a horizontal axis and vertex at (h, k) is given by

$$(15.15) \qquad (y - k)^2 = 4a(x - h)$$

By a similar procedure, the standard equations of an ellipse centered at a point (h, k) are seen to be

$$(15.16) \qquad \frac{(x - h)^2}{a^2} + \frac{(y - k)^2}{b^2} = 1$$

if the major axis is horizontal and

$$(15.17) \qquad \frac{(x - h)^2}{b^2} + \frac{(y - k)^2}{a^2} = 1$$

if it is vertical.

Finally, the standard equations of the hyperbola centered at a point (h, k) are seen to be

$$(15.18) \qquad \frac{(x - h)^2}{a^2} - \frac{(y - k)^2}{b^2} = 1$$

if the transverse axis is horizontal and

$$(15.19) \qquad \frac{(y - k)^2}{a^2} - \frac{(x - h)^2}{b^2} = 1$$

if it is vertical.

Example 15.17   Write the equation of the ellipse centered at $(2, -3)$ with horizontal axis 10 units and vertical axis 4 units. (See Figure 15.23.)

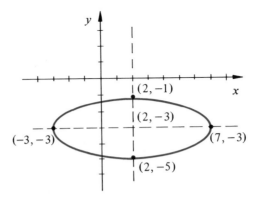

Figure 15.23

Solution   Since the longer of the two axes is the horizontal axis, use form (15.16) with $a = 5$ and $b = 2$. Also, $h = 2$ and $k = -3$. Making these substitutions, we have

$$\frac{(x - 2)^2}{25} + \frac{(y + 3)^2}{4} = 1$$

as the equation of the ellipse.

Example 15.18   Write the equation of the parabola whose directrix is the line $y = -2$ and whose vertex is located at $(3, 1)$.

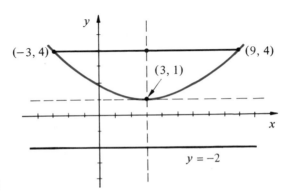

Figure 15.24

Solution The parabola has a vertical axis and opens upward since the directrix is horizontal and lies below the vertex. The vertex lies midway between the focus and the directrix so that $a = 3$. Letting $h = 3$, $k = 1$, and $a = 3$ in equation (15.14), the equation of the parabola is

$$(x - 3)^2 = 12(y - 1)$$

Example 15.19   Discuss and sketch the graph of the hyperbola

$$\frac{(x + 5)^2}{16} - \frac{(y - 2)^2}{9} = 1$$

Solution   The hyperbola is centered at $(-5, 2)$. By equation (15.18) it has a horizontal transverse axis with vertices at $(-9, 2)$ and $(-1, 2)$. The endpoints of the conjugate axis are located at $(-5, 5)$ and $(-5, -1)$. Also the foci are $(-10, 2)$ and $(0, 2)$ since $c = \sqrt{9 + 16} = 5$. The graph appears in Figure 15.25.

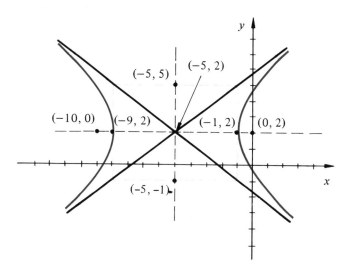

Figure 15.25

Exercises for
    Section 15.7

In Exercises 1–6, write the equations of the *parabolas* having the given properties. Sketch each graph.

1.   Vertex at $(3, 1)$, focus at $(5, 1)$.

2.   Vertex at $(-2, 3)$, focus at $(-2, 0)$.

3.   Directrix $y = 2$, vertex at $(1, -1)$.

4.   Directrix at $x = -1$, vertex at $(0, 4)$.

5.   Endpoints of right chord $(2, 4)$ and $(2, 0)$, opening to the right.

6.   Endpoints of right chord $(-1, -1)$ and $(5, -1)$, opening upward.

15.7 Translation of Axes   453

In Exercises 7–12 write the equations of the *ellipses* having the given properties. Sketch each graph.

7. Major axis 8, foci at $(5, 1)$ and $(-1, 1)$.

8. Minor axis 6, vertices at $(2, -1)$ and $(10, -1)$.

9. Minor axis 2, vertices at $(\frac{1}{2}, 0)$ and $(\frac{1}{2}, -8)$.

10. Semi-major axis $\frac{3}{2}$, foci at $(1, 1)$ and $(1, -1)$.

11. Vertices at $(-6, 3)$ and $(-2, 3)$, foci at $(-5, 3)$ and $(-3, 3)$.

12. Center at $(1, -3)$, major axis 10, minor axis 6, vertical axis.

In Exercises 13–18 write the equations of the *hyperbolas* having the given properties. Sketch each graph.

13. Center at $(-1, 2)$, transverse axis 7, conjugate axis 8, vertical axis.

14. Center at $(3, 0)$, transverse axis 6, conjugate axis 2, horizontal axis.

15. Vertices at $(5, 1)$ and $(-1, 1)$, foci at $(6, 1)$ and $(-2, 1)$.

16. Vertices at $(2, \pm 4)$, conjugate axis 2.

17. Vertices at $(-4, -2)$ and $(0, -2)$, asymptotes $m = \pm\frac{1}{2}$.

18. Vertices at $(3, 3)$ and $(5, 3)$, asymptotes $m = \pm 3$.

Write the equation of the family of curves indicated in Exercises 19–24.

19. Circles with center on the x-axis.

20. Parabolas with vertical axis and vertex on the x-axis.

21. Parabolas with vertex and focus on the x-axis.

22. Ellipses with center on the y-axis and horizontal major axis.

23. Circles passing through the origin with center on the x-axis.

24. Circles tangent to the x-axis.

15.8
Rotation of Axes

In the previous section we saw how an analytic representation of a curve can be considerably simplified by moving the origin of the Cartesian coordinate system. This section shows how to rotate the axes to yield a new rectangular system of coordinates.

Figure 15.26 shows two rectangular coordinate systems with the $x'y'$-axes at an angle θ with the xy-axes. We say that the coordinates of a point (x, y) are *transformed* into the coordinates (x', y') by rotating the axes through an angle θ.

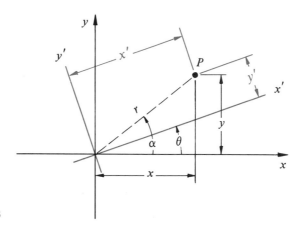

Figure 15.26

The equations of rotation are obtained by expressing (x', y') in terms of (x, y) and the rotation angle θ. From Figure 15.25.

$$(15.20) \quad \begin{aligned} x' &= r \cos (\alpha - \theta) \\ y' &= r \sin (\alpha - \theta) \end{aligned}$$

where α is the angle made by the x-axis and the line drawn from the origin to the point P. Using the trigonometric identities for the cosine and sine of the difference of two angles, equations (15.20) may be written

$$(15.21) \quad \begin{aligned} x' &= r \cos \alpha \cos \theta + r \sin \alpha \sin \theta \\ y' &= r \sin \alpha \cos \theta - r \cos \alpha \sin \theta \end{aligned}$$

From Figure 15.26 $x = r \cos \alpha$ and $y = r \sin \alpha$, and hence, the required relationship between the two coordinate systems is given by

$$(15.22) \quad \begin{aligned} x' &= x \cos \theta + y \sin \theta \\ y' &= -x \sin \theta + y \cos \theta \end{aligned}$$

Solving these equations for x and y in terms of x', y' and θ (using, say, Cramer's rule), we obtain the *equations of the inverse transformation.*

$$(15.23) \quad \begin{aligned} x &= x' \cos \theta - y' \sin \theta \\ y &= x' \sin \theta + y' \cos \theta \end{aligned}$$

Equations (15.22) are used to find the coordinates of any point in the rotated system if you know the coordinates in the original system.

Example 15.20   If the coordinates of a point in a coordinate system are $x = 4$, $y = 3$, find the coordinates of the same point in a rectangular system whose axes are rotated at 30° to the original.

15.8 Rotation of Axes   455

Solution Using the equations of rotation,

$$x' = 4 \cos 30° + 3 \sin 30°$$

$$y' = -4 \sin 30° + 3 \cos 30°$$

from which, $x' = 2\sqrt{3} + \frac{3}{2}$ and $y' = -2 + (3\sqrt{3})/2$.

To express an equation of a curve given in xy-coordinates in terms of $x'y'$-coordinates, merely use the rotation equations in the form (15.23) to substitute for x and y in terms of x', y', and θ.

Example 15.21 Find the equation of the straight line $x + y = 1$ in $x'y'$-coordinates if the prime coordinate system is rotated at 45° to the xy-system.

Solution From (15.23) the expressions for x and y in terms of x' and y' are

$$x = x'\frac{\sqrt{2}}{2} - y'\frac{\sqrt{2}}{2}$$

$$y = x'\frac{\sqrt{2}}{2} + y'\frac{\sqrt{2}}{2}$$

and hence, the equation $x + y = 1$ becomes

$$\frac{\sqrt{2}}{2}(x' - y') + \frac{\sqrt{2}}{2}(x' + y') = 1$$

After simplification this equation becomes

$$\sqrt{2}\,x' = 1$$

The foregoing example is typical of the actual use of rotation of coordinates; that is, the resulting equation should be in a simpler form. In the case of Example 15.21 the straight line is parallel to the y'-coordinate axes, which, at least in some circumstances, can be considered a simplification. Sometimes the curve itself becomes recognizable only after rotation. This simplification is done by judiciously choosing the rotation angle.

Example 15.22 Consider the equation $x^2 + xy + y^2 = 1$. Choose a rotated coordinate system in which the "product term" (that is, the product of the coordinates) is not present. Identify and sketch the curve that the equation represents.

Solution Using the equations of rotation in form (15.23) and substituing into the given equation,

$$(x' \cos \theta - y' \sin \theta)^2 + (x' \cos \theta - y' \sin \theta)(x' \sin \theta + y' \cos \theta)$$
$$+ (x' \sin \theta + y' \cos \theta)^2 = 1$$

Simplifying,

$$(x')^2(1 + \sin \theta \cos \theta) + (\cos^2 \theta - \sin^2 \theta)x'y'$$
$$+ (1 - \sin \theta \cos \theta)(y')^2 = 1$$

Note that the coefficient of $x'y'$ vanishes if $\cos^2 \theta = \sin^2 \theta$, so that we choose $\theta = 45°$ and the equation of the curve becomes

$$\left(1 + \frac{\sqrt{2}}{2}\frac{\sqrt{2}}{2}\right)(x')^2 + \left(1 - \frac{\sqrt{2}}{2}\frac{\sqrt{2}}{2}\right)(y')^2 = 1$$

or
$$\frac{(x')^2}{\frac{2}{3}} + \frac{(y')^2}{2} = 1$$

Hence, the equation represents an ellipse whose axes are at 45° to the xy-axes. Figure 15.27 displays the graph.

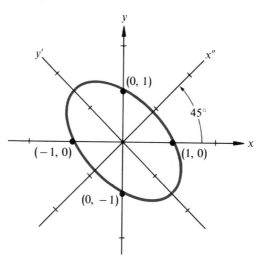

Figure 15.27

Exercises for
Section 15.8

Find the coordinates of the points in Exercises 1–5 in a coordinate system rotated at 30° from the x, y coordinate system.

1. $(3, 1)$ **2.** $(-5, 3)$ **3.** $(-1, -1)$ **4.** $(2, 1)$ **5.** $(2, -1)$

6. Find the equations of rotation for a system rotated first through 30° and then 45°. Compare to the equations obtained by one rotation of 75°.

15.8 Rotation of Axes   457

Find the equation of the curves in Exercises 7–13 after the given rotation.

7. The line $y = 2x$ after a 45° rotation.

8. The line $y = x + 5$ after a 45° rotation.

9. The line $2x + 7y = 3$ after a 60° rotation.

10. The circle $x^2 + y^2 = 4$ after a rotation of any angle θ.

11. The ellipse $x^2 + 4y^2 = 4$ after a rotation of 90°.

12. The parabola $y = x^2$ after a rotation of 30°.

13. The circle $x^2 + 2x + y^2 = 0$ after a rotation of 30°.

14. What is the slope of the line $y = mx$ in a system of coordinates rotated at 45° from the x, y system?

15. Given the transformation equations

$$x' = 0.6x + 0.8y$$

$$y' = -0.8x + 0.6y$$

what is the angle of rotation?

16. Consider the curve $(x - y)^2 - (x + y) = 0$. Rotate the coordinate system 45° and identify the curve.

17. Consider the curve $3x^2 - 2xy + 3y^2 = 2$. Rotate the coordinate system 45° and identify the curve.

Eliminate the product term in Exercises 18–21 by using a proper rotation and then sketch.

18. $xy = 1$ 19. $x^2 + xy = 1$ 20. $y - xy = 1$ 21. $x^2 - xy + y^2 = 1$

22. What is the form of the equation of the hyperbola whose equation is $x^2 - y^2 = a^2$ in a system rotated 45°?

15.9
The General
Second Degree Equation

The general second-degree equation is of the form

(15.24) $Ax^2 + Bxy + Cy^2 + Dx + Ey + F = 0$

where A, B, C, D, E, and F are constants. Each conic described in Sections 15.3 through 15.7 can be expressed in the form of equation (15.24) with $B = 0$. This is seen by expanding the standard form of each conic in a manner similar to that of Section 15.3. Assuming that $B = 0$, the following statements are easy to show.

- If $A = C = 1$, equation (15.24) represents a circle.

- If $A \neq C$ and A and C have the same numerical sign, equation (15.24) represents an ellipse.

- If A and C have different numerical signs, equation (15.24) represents a hyperbola.

- If A or $C = 0$ (but not both), then equation (15.24) represents a parabola.

- Special cases such as a single point or no graph may result.

If $B = 0$, the general form of a conic can be reduced to one of the standard forms by completing the square on x and y. Several examples of this technique follow.

Example 15.23   Discuss and sketch the graph of $x^2 - 4y^2 + 6x + 24y - 43 = 0$.

Solution   This is the equation of a hyperbola since the coefficients of the x^2 and y^2 terms have unlike signs. In order to sketch the hyperbola, reduce the given equation to standard form by rearranging the terms and completing the square on the x-terms and the y-terms. Thus,

$$x^2 - 4y^2 + 6x + 24y - 43 = 0$$

may be written

$$(x^2 + 6x \quad) - 4(y^2 - 6y \quad) = 43$$

Completing the square on each variable,

$$(x^2 + 6x + 9) - 4(y^2 - 6y + 9) = 43 + 9 - 36$$

$$(x + 3)^2 - 4(y - 3)^2 = 16$$

$$\frac{(x + 3)^2}{16} - \frac{(y - 3)^2}{4} = 1$$

The center of the hyperbola is the point $(-3, 3)$. The transverse axis is horizontal with vertices at $(1, 3)$ and $(-7, 3)$. The endpoints of the conjugate axis are located at $(-3, 5)$ and $(-3, 1)$. Finally, the foci are at $(-3 + 2\sqrt{5}, 3)$ and $(-3 - 2\sqrt{5}, 3)$ since $c = \sqrt{16 + 4} = 2\sqrt{5}$. The graph appears in Figure 15.28.

Example 15.24   Discuss and sketch the graph of $2y^2 + 3x - 8y + 9 = 0$.

Solution   By completing the square on the y-variable, this equation can be reduced to the form of equation (15.15). Thus,

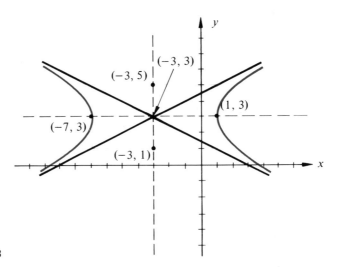

Figure 15.28

$$2y^2 + 3x - 8y + 9 = 0$$

$$2(y^2 - 4y \quad) = -3x - 9$$

$$2(y^2 - 4y + 4) = -3x - 9 + 8$$

$$2(y - 2)^2 = -3x - 1$$

$$2(y - 2)^2 = -3\left(x + \frac{1}{3}\right)$$

$$(y - 2)^2 = -\frac{3}{2}\left(x + \frac{1}{3}\right)$$

This is the standard form of the equation of a parabola with horizontal axis and vertex at $\left(-\frac{1}{3}, 2\right)$. We see that $4a = -\frac{3}{2}$, so $a = -\frac{3}{8}$. Therefore, the focus is at $\left(-\frac{17}{24}, 2\right)$ and the endpoints of the right chord are $\left(-\frac{17}{24}, \frac{11}{4}\right)$ and $\left(-\frac{17}{24}, \frac{5}{4}\right)$. The parabola, which opens to the left, is shown in Figure 15.29.

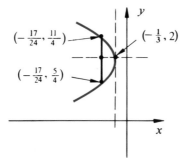

Figure 15.29

If the axis of the conic is not parallel to one of the coordinate axes, then a product term is present, $B \neq 0$, and the nature of the conic is not immediately obvious. By properly choosing θ, this product may be removed in a rotated $x'y'$-system and the problem reduces essentially to the case of $B = 0$.

By substituting the general rotation equations into equation (15.24) we may show that the product term may be made to vanish by choosing a rotation angle θ so that

$$\cot 2\theta = \frac{A - C}{B}$$

Unfortunately, this formula does not give the angle of rotation directly but requires a little unraveling using familiar trigonometric identities. (See Example 15.25.)

Example 15.25   Eliminate the xy term in $3x^2 - 4xy = 20$ and sketch the graph.

Solution   Here $A = 3$, $B = -4$, and $C = 0$. Hence,

$$\cot 2\theta = \frac{3 - 0}{-4} = -\frac{3}{4}$$

which implies the angle shown in Figure 15.30. Assuming that 2θ lies in the second quadrant and noting that $\sin \theta = \sqrt{(1 - \cos 2\theta)/2}$ and $\cos \theta = \sqrt{(1 + \cos 2\theta)/2}$,

$$\sin \theta = \sqrt{\frac{1 + \frac{3}{5}}{2}} = \frac{2\sqrt{5}}{5}$$

$$\cos \theta = \sqrt{\frac{1 - \frac{3}{5}}{2}} = \frac{\sqrt{5}}{5}$$

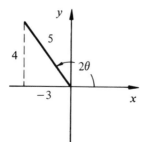

Figure 15.30

Substituting these values into the rotation equations, (15.23)

$$x = \frac{\sqrt{5}}{5}x' - \frac{2\sqrt{5}}{5}y'$$

$$y = \frac{2\sqrt{5}}{5}x' + \frac{\sqrt{5}}{5}y'$$

The equation $3x^2 - 4xy = 20$ can then be written

$$3\left(\frac{\sqrt{5}}{5}x' - \frac{2\sqrt{5}}{5}y'\right)^2 - 4\left(\frac{\sqrt{5}}{5}x' - \frac{2\sqrt{5}}{5}y'\right)\left(\frac{2\sqrt{5}}{5}x' + \frac{\sqrt{5}}{5}y'\right) = 20$$

15.9 The General Second-Degree Equation

This equation reduces (with some effort) to

$$20y'^2 - 5x'^2 = 100$$

or $\quad \dfrac{y'^2}{5} - \dfrac{x'^2}{20} = 1$

which is a hyperbola in standard form with respect to the $x'y'$-coordinate system. (See Figure 15.31.) The rotation angle, θ, is given by

$$\theta = \sin^{-1}\left(\frac{2\sqrt{5}}{5}\right) = 63.4°.$$

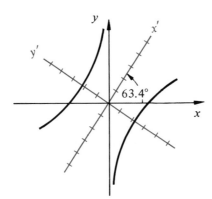

Figure 15.31

The asymptotes are

$$y' = \pm \frac{1}{2}x'$$

or, in terms of the original coordinates,

$$x = 0 \quad \text{(the } y \text{ axis)} \quad \text{and} \quad y = \frac{3}{4}x.$$

Exercises for
Section 15.9

Transform each of the equations in Exercises 1–20 into standard form and sketch their graphs.

1. $x^2 + y^2 + 4x + 6y + 4 = 0$

2. $x^2 - 2x - 8y + 25 = 0$

3. $9x^2 + 4y^2 + 18x + 8y - 23 = 0$

4. $2x^2 + 2y^2 - 4x - 16 = 0$

5. $x^2 - y^2 - 4x - 21 = 0$

6. $y^2 + 4y + 6x - 8 = 0$

7. $x^2 - 6x - 3y = 0$

8. $x^2 + 4y^2 + 8x = 0$

9. $2y^2 - 2y + x - 1 = 0$

10. $3x^2 + 4y^2 - 18x + 8y + 19 = 0$

11. $4x^2 - y^2 + 8x + 2y - 1 = 0$

12. $y^2 - 2x - 4y + 10 = 0$

13. $9x^2 + 4y^2 - 18x + 16y - 11 = 0$

14. $y^2 - 25x^2 + 50x - 50 = 0$

15 Plane Analytic Geometry

15. $x^2 - 2y^2 + 2y = 0$ **16.** $y^2 - y - \frac{1}{2}x + \frac{1}{4} = 0$

17. $x(x + 4) = y^2 + 3$ **18.** $x^2 + y(4 + 2y) = 0$

19. $y = x^2 + 5x + 7$ **20.** $y = 2x^2 + 10x$

Use rotation of axes to identify and sketch the conics in Exercises 21–24.

21. $5x^2 + 12xy = 9$

22. $5x^2 + 3xy + 5y^2 = 7$

23. $5x^2 + 24xy - 2y^2 = 44$

24. $x^2 + 2xy + y^2 = 1$

Test 1 for Chapter 15

Answer true or false for Exercises 1–10.

1. The coordinates of every point (x, y) on a curve satisfy the equation of the curve.

2. The curve $y = x^2$ is symmetric with respect to the origin.

3. The line $y_1 = x$ and the curve $y_2 = x - \dfrac{1}{x}$ are asymptotic.

4. The graph of $x^2 - y^2 = 0$ is a hyperbola.

5. The circle $x^2 + y^2 = 4$ has radius 2.

6. The ellipse $2x^2 + y^2 = 1$ has a major axis of length $\sqrt{2}$.

7. The equation of an ellipse centered at the origin is of the form $ax^2 + by^2 = 1$ where a and b are both > 0.

8. The hyperbola has four branches.

9. The hyperbola $y^2 = 1 + x^2$ has two y-intercepts, ± 1.

10. The curve $y = \dfrac{x - 1}{x + 1}$ is above the x-axis between -1 and 1.

11. Sketch the graph of $x^2 + y^2 + 4y = 0$.

12. Write the equation of the curve determined by a point (x, y) which moves such that its distance from $(3, 2)$ is equal to that from $(-1, 1)$. Sketch the curve.

13. Sketch the graph of $x^2 + 4y^2 = 4$. Locate the foci.

14. Sketch the graph of $2x^2 + x + y^2 + 2y = 1$. Determine the translation which will place the center of the curve at a new origin.

15. Sketch $x^2 - 4y^2 = 4$, being sure to give the oblique asymptotes both graphically and analytically.

16. Sketch the graph of $y = \dfrac{x^2 - 1}{x^2 - 4}$.

Test 2 for
Chapter 15

1. Sketch the graph of $y = \dfrac{3}{x^2 + 2x - 3}$.

2. Find the equation of the parabola with focus at $(-2, 1)$ and directrix $x = 3$.

3. Find the equation of the ellipse with center at $(0, 5)$, a vertical major axis of 6 and a minor axis of 3.

4. Find the equation of the hyperbola with center at the origin, vertices at $(\pm 3, 0)$ and foci at $(\pm 4, 0)$.

5. Find the equation of the circle with center at $(-2, -3)$ and passing through $(0, 2)$.

6. Explain how each of the conic sections is obtained from a right circular cone.

Discuss and sketch the graph of Exercises 7–10.

7. $x^2 + y^2 - y = 0$

8. $y = (x + 3)(x - 2)$

9. $x(x + 8) = y^2$

10. $x^2 + 3y^2 + x - y = 0$

Table A Exponential Functions

x	e^x	e^{-x}	x	e^x	e^{-x}
0.00	1.0000	1.0000	2.5	12.182	0.0821
0.05	1.0513	0.9512	2.6	13.464	0.0743
0.10	1.1052	0.9048	2.7	14.880	0.0672
0.15	1.1618	0.8607	2.8	16.445	0.0608
0.20	1.2214	0.8187	2.9	18.174	0.0550
0.25	1.2840	0.7788	3.0	20.086	0.0498
0.30	1.3499	0.7408	3.1	22.198	0.0450
0.35	1.4191	0.7047	3.2	24.533	0.0408
0.40	1.4918	0.6703	3.3	27.113	0.0369
0.45	1.5683	0.6376	3.4	29.964	0.0334
0.50	1.6487	0.6065	3.5	33.115	0.0302
0.55	1.7333	0.5769	3.6	36.598	0.0273
0.60	1.8221	0.5488	3.7	40.447	0.0247
0.65	1.9155	0.5220	3.8	44.701	0.0224
0.70	2.0138	0.4966	3.9	49.402	0.0202
0.75	2.1170	0.4724	4.0	54.598	0.0183
0.80	2.2255	0.4493	4.1	60.340	0.0166
0.85	2.3396	0.4274	4.2	66.686	0.0150
0.90	2.4596	0.4066	4.3	73.700	0.0136
0.95	2.5857	0.3867	4.4	81.451	0.0123
1.0	2.7183	0.3679	4.5	90.017	0.0111
1.1	3.0042	0.3329	4.6	99.484	0.0101
1.2	3.3201	0.3012	4.7	109.95	0.0091
1.3	3.6693	0.2725	4.8	121.51	0.0082
1.4	4.0552	0.2466	4.9	134.29	0.0074
1.5	4.4817	0.2231	5	148.41	0.0067
1.6	4.9530	0.2019	6	403.43	0.0025
1.7	5.4739	0.1827	7	1096.6	0.0009
1.8	6.0496	0.1653	8	2981.0	0.0003
1.9	6.6859	0.1496	9	8103.1	0.0001
2.0	7.3891	0.1353	10	22026	0.00005
2.1	8.1662	0.1225			
2.2	9.0250	0.1108			
2.3	9.9742	0.1003			
2.4	11.023	0.0907			

Table B   Four-Place Logarithms of Numbers from 1 to 10

n	0	1	2	3	4	5	6	7	8	9
1.0	0.0000	0043	0086	0128	0170	0212	0253	0294	0334	0374
1.1	.0414	0453	0492	0531	0569	0607	0645	0682	0719	0755
1.2	.0792	0828	0864	0899	0934	0969	1004	1038	1072	1106
1.3	.1139	1173	1206	1239	1271	1303	1335	1367	1399	1430
1.4	.1461	1492	1523	1553	1584	1614	1644	1673	1703	1732
1.5	.1761	1790	1818	1847	1875	1903	1931	1959	1987	2014
1.6	.2041	2068	2095	2122	2148	2175	2201	2227	2253	2279
1.7	.2304	2330	2355	2380	2405	2430	2455	2480	2504	2529
1.8	.2553	2577	2601	2625	2648	2672	2695	2718	2742	2765
1.9	.2788	2810	2833	2856	2878	2900	2923	2945	2967	2989
2.0	.3010	3032	3054	3075	3096	3118	3139	3160	3181	3201
2.1	.3222	3243	3263	3284	3304	3324	3345	3365	3385	3404
2.2	.3424	3444	3464	3483	3502	3522	3541	3560	3579	3598
2.3	.3617	3636	3655	3674	3692	3711	3729	3747	3766	3784
2.4	.3802	3820	3838	3856	3874	3892	3909	3927	3945	3962
2.5	.3979	3997	4014	4031	4048	4065	4082	4099	4116	4133
2.6	.4150	4166	4183	4200	4216	4232	4249	4265	4281	4298
2.7	.4314	4330	4346	4362	4378	4393	4409	4425	4440	4456
2.8	.4472	4487	4502	4518	4533	4548	4564	4579	4594	4609
2.9	.4624	4639	4654	4669	4683	4698	4713	4728	4742	4757
3.0	.4771	4786	4800	4814	4829	4843	4857	4871	4886	4900
3.1	.4914	4928	4942	4955	4969	4983	4997	5011	5024	5038
3.2	.5051	5065	5079	5092	5105	5119	5132	5145	5159	5172
3.3	.5185	5198	5211	5224	5237	5250	5263	5276	5289	5302
3.4	.5315	5328	5340	5353	5366	5378	5391	5403	5416	5428
3.5	.5441	5453	5465	5478	5490	5502	5514	5527	5539	5551
3.6	.5563	5575	5587	5599	5611	5623	5635	5647	5658	5670
3.7	.5682	5694	5705	5717	5729	5740	5752	5763	5775	5786
3.8	.5798	5809	5821	5832	5843	5855	5866	5877	5888	5899
3.9	.5911	5922	5933	5944	5955	5966	5977	5988	5999	6010
4.0	.6021	6031	6042	6053	6064	6075	6085	6096	6107	6117
4.1	.6128	6138	6149	6160	6170	6180	6191	6201	6212	6222
4.2	.6232	6243	6253	6263	6274	6284	6294	6304	6314	6325
4.3	.6335	6345	6355	6365	6375	6385	6395	6405	6415	6425
4.4	.6435	6444	6454	6464	6474	6484	6493	6503	6513	6522
4.5	.6532	6542	6551	6561	6571	6580	6590	6599	6609	6618
4.6	.6628	6637	6646	6656	6665	6675	6684	6693	6702	6712
4.7	.6721	6730	6739	6749	6758	6767	6776	6785	6794	6803
4.8	.6812	6821	6830	6839	6848	6857	6866	6875	6884	6893
4.9	.6902	6911	6920	6928	6937	6946	6955	6964	6972	6981
5.0	.6990	6998	7007	7016	7024	7033	7042	7050	7059	7067
5.1	.7076	7084	7093	7101	7110	7118	7126	7135	7143	7152
5.2	.7160	7168	7177	7185	7193	7202	7210	7218	7226	7235
5.3	.7243	7251	7259	7267	7275	7284	7292	7300	7308	7316
5.4	.7324	7332	7340	7348	7356	7364	7372	7380	7388	7396

n	0	1	2	3	4	5	6	7	8	9
5.5	.7404	7412	7419	7427	7435	7443	7451	7459	7466	7474
5.6	.7482	7490	7497	7505	7513	7520	7528	7536	7543	7551
5.7	.7559	7566	7574	7582	7589	7597	7604	7612	7619	7627
5.8	.7634	7642	7649	7657	7664	7672	7679	7686	7694	7701
5.9	.7709	7716	7723	7731	7738	7745	7752	7760	7767	7774
6.0	.7782	7789	7796	7803	7810	7818	7825	7832	7839	7846
6.1	.7853	7860	7868	7875	7882	7889	7896	7903	7910	7917
6.2	.7924	7931	7938	7945	7952	7959	7966	7973	7980	7987
6.3	.7993	8000	8007	8014	8021	8028	8035	8041	8048	8055
6.4	.8062	8069	8075	8082	8089	8096	8102	8109	8116	8122
6.5	.8129	8136	8142	8149	8156	8162	8169	8176	8182	8189
6.6	.8195	8202	8209	8215	8222	8228	8235	8241	8248	8254
6.7	.8261	8267	8274	8280	8287	8293	8299	8306	8312	8319
6.8	.8325	8331	8338	8344	8351	8357	8363	8370	8376	8382
6.9	.8388	8395	8401	8407	8414	8420	8426	8432	8439	8445
7.0	.8451	8457	8463	8470	8476	8482	8488	8494	8500	8506
7.1	.8513	8519	8525	8531	8537	8543	8549	8555	8561	8567
7.2	.8573	8579	8585	8591	8597	8603	8609	8615	8621	8627
7.3	.8633	8639	8645	8651	8657	8663	8669	8675	8681	8686
7.4	.8692	8698	8704	8710	8716	8722	8727	8733	8739	8745
7.5	.8751	8756	8762	8768	8774	8779	8785	8791	8797	8802
7.6	.8808	8814	8820	8825	8831	8837	8842	8848	8854	8859
7.7	.8865	8871	8876	8882	8887	8893	8899	8904	8910	8915
7.8	.8921	8927	8932	8938	8943	8949	8954	8960	8965	8971
7.9	.8976	8982	8987	8993	8998	9004	9009	9015	9020	9025
8.0	.9031	9036	9042	9047	9053	9058	9063	9069	9074	9079
8.1	.9085	9090	9096	9101	9106	9112	9117	9122	9128	9133
8.2	.9138	9143	9149	9154	9159	9165	9170	9175	9180	9186
8.3	.9191	9196	9201	9206	9212	9217	9222	9227	9232	9238
8.4	.9243	9248	9253	9258	9263	9269	9274	9279	9284	9289
8.5	.9294	9299	9304	9309	9315	9320	9325	9330	9335	9340
8.6	.9345	9350	9355	9360	9365	9370	9375	9380	9385	9390
8.7	.9395	9400	9405	9410	9415	9420	9425	9430	9435	9440
8.8	.9445	9450	9455	9460	9465	9469	9474	9479	9484	9489
8.9	.9494	9499	9504	9509	9513	9518	9523	9528	9533	9538
9.0	.9542	9547	9552	9557	9562	9566	9571	9576	9581	9586
9.1	.9590	9595	9600	9605	9609	9614	9619	9624	9628	9633
9.2	.9638	9643	9647	9652	9657	9661	9666	9671	9675	9680
9.3	.9685	9689	9694	9699	9703	9708	9713	9717	9722	9727
9.4	.9731	9736	9741	9745	9750	9754	9759	9763	9768	9773
9.5	.9777	9782	9786	9791	9795	9800	9805	9809	9814	9818
9.6	.9823	9827	9832	9836	9841	9845	9850	9854	9859	9863
9.7	.9868	9872	9877	9881	9886	9890	9894	9899	9903	9908
9.8	.9912	9917	9921	9926	9930	9934	9939	9943	9948	9952
9.9	.9956	9961	9965	9969	9974	9978	9983	9987	9991	9996

Table C   Powers and Roots

n	n^2	$\sqrt{n}$	n^3	$\sqrt[3]{n}$	n	n^2	$\sqrt{n}$	n^3	$\sqrt[3]{n}$
1	1	1.000	1	1.000	51	2,601	7.141	132,651	3.708
2	4	1.414	8	1.260	52	2,704	7.211	140,608	3.733
3	9	1.732	27	1.442	53	2,809	7.280	148,877	3.756
4	16	2.000	64	1.587	54	2,916	7.348	157,464	3.780
5	25	2.236	125	1.710	55	3,025	7.416	166,375	3.803
6	36	2.449	216	1.817	56	3,136	7.483	175,616	3.826
7	49	2.646	343	1.913	57	3,249	7.550	185,193	3.849
8	64	2.828	512	2.000	58	3,364	7.616	195,112	3.871
9	81	3.000	729	2.080	59	3,481	7.681	205,379	3.893
10	100	3.162	1,000	2.154	60	3,600	7.746	216,000	3.915
11	121	3.317	1,331	2.224	61	3,721	7.810	226,981	3.936
12	144	3.464	1,728	2.289	62	3,844	7.874	238,328	3.958
13	169	3.606	2,197	2.351	63	3,969	7.937	250,047	3.979
14	196	3.742	2,744	2.410	64	4,096	8.000	262,144	4.000
15	225	3.873	3,375	2.466	65	4,225	8.062	274,625	4.021
16	256	4.000	4,096	2.520	66	4,356	8.124	287,496	4.041
17	289	4.123	4,913	2.571	67	4,489	8.185	300,763	4.062
18	324	4.243	5,832	2.621	68	4,624	8.246	314,432	4.082
19	361	4.359	6,859	2.668	69	4,761	8.307	328,509	4.102
20	400	4.472	8,000	2.714	70	4,900	8.367	343,000	4.121
21	441	4.583	9,261	2.759	71	5,041	8.426	357,911	4.141
22	484	4.690	10,648	2.802	72	5,184	8.485	373,248	4.160
23	529	4.796	12,167	2.844	73	5,329	8.544	389,017	4.179
24	576	4.899	13,824	2.884	74	5,476	8.602	405,224	4.198
25	625	5.000	15,625	2.924	75	5,625	8.660	421,875	4.217
26	676	5.099	17,576	2.962	76	5,776	8.718	438,976	4.236
27	729	5.196	19,683	3.000	77	5,929	8.775	456,533	4.254
28	784	5.292	21,952	3.037	78	6,084	8.832	474,552	4.273
29	841	5.385	24,389	3.072	79	6,241	8.888	493,039	4.291
30	900	5.477	27,000	3.107	80	6,400	8.944	512,000	4.309
31	961	5.568	29,791	3.141	81	6,561	9.000	531,441	4.327
32	1,024	5.657	32,768	3.175	82	6,724	9.055	551,368	4.344
33	1,089	5.745	35,937	3.208	83	6,889	9.110	571,787	4.362
34	1,156	5.831	39,304	3.240	84	7,056	9.165	592,704	4.380
35	1,225	5.916	42,875	3.271	85	7,225	9.220	614,125	4.397
36	1,296	6.000	46,656	3.302	86	7,396	9.274	636,056	4.414
37	1,369	6.083	50,653	3.332	87	7,569	9.327	658,503	4.431
38	1,444	6.164	54,872	3.362	88	7,744	9.381	681,472	4.448
39	1,521	6.245	59,319	3.391	89	7,921	9.434	704,969	4.465
40	1,600	6.325	64,000	3.420	90	8,100	9.487	729,000	4.481
41	1,681	6.403	68,921	3.448	91	8,281	9.539	753,571	4.498
42	1,764	6.481	74,088	3.476	92	8,464	9.592	778,688	4.514
43	1,849	6.557	79,507	3.503	93	8,649	9.644	804,357	4.531
44	1,936	6.633	85,184	3.530	94	8,836	9.695	830,584	4.547
45	2,025	6.708	91,125	3.557	95	9,025	9.747	857,375	4.563
46	2,116	6.782	97,336	3.583	96	9,216	9.798	884,736	4.579
47	2,209	6.856	103,823	3.609	97	9,409	9.849	912,673	4.595
48	2,304	6.928	110,592	3.634	98	9,604	9.899	941,192	4.610
49	2,401	7.000	117,649	3.659	99	9,801	9.950	970,299	4.626
50	2,500	7.071	125,000	3.684	100	10,000	10.000	1,000,000	4.642

x	$\sin x$	$\cos x$	$\tan x$	$\cot x$	$\sec x$	$\csc x$	
0° 0′	.00000	1.0000	.00000	...	1.0000	...	90° 0′
10′	.00291	1.0000	.00291	343.77	1.0000	343.78	50′
20′	.00582	1.0000	.00582	171.88	1.0000	171.89	40′
30′	.00873	1.0000	.00873	114.59	1.0000	114.59	30′
40′	.01164	.9999	.01164	85.940	1.0001	85.946	20′
50′	.01454	.9999	.01455	68.750	1.0001	68.757	10′
1° 0′	.01745	.9998	.01746	57.290	1.0002	57.299	89° 0′
10′	.02036	.9998	.02036	49.104	1.0002	49.114	50′
20′	.02327	.9997	.02328	42.964	1.0003	42.976	40′
30′	.02618	.9997	.02619	38.188	1.0003	38.202	30′
40′	.02908	.9996	.02910	34.368	1.0004	34.382	20′
50′	.03199	.9995	.03201	31.242	1.0005	31.258	10′
2° 0′	.03490	.9994	.03492	28.6363	1.0006	28.654	88° 0′
10′	.03781	.9993	.03783	26.4316	1.0007	26.451	50′
20′	.04071	.9992	.04075	24.5418	1.0008	24.562	40′
30′	.04362	.9990	.04366	22.9038	1.0010	22.926	30′
40′	.04653	.9989	.04658	21.4704	1.0011	21.494	20′
50′	.04943	.9988	.04949	20.2056	1.0012	20.230	10′
3° 0′	.05234	.9986	.05241	19.0811	1.0014	19.107	87° 0′
10′	.05524	.9985	.05533	18.0750	1.0015	18.103	50′
20′	.05814	.9983	.05824	17.1693	1.0017	17.198	40′
30′	.06105	.9981	.06116	16.3499	1.0019	16.380	30′
40′	.06395	.9980	.06408	15.6048	1.0021	15.637	20′
50′	.06685	.9978	.06700	14.9244	1.0022	14.958	10′
4° 0′	.06976	.9976	.06993	14.3007	1.0024	14.336	86° 0′
10′	.07266	.9974	.07285	13.7267	1.0027	13.763	50′
20′	.07556	.9971	.07578	13.1969	1.0029	13.235	40′
30′	.07846	.9969	.07870	12.7062	1.0031	12.746	30′
40′	.08136	.9967	.08163	12.2505	1.0033	12.291	20′
50′	.08426	.9964	.08456	11.8262	1.0036	11.868	10′
5° 0′	.08716	.9962	.08749	11.4301	1.0038	11.474	85° 0′
10′	.09005	.9959	.09042	11.0594	1.0041	11.105	50′
20′	.09295	.9957	.09335	10.7119	1.0044	10.758	40′
30′	.09585	.9954	.09629	10.3854	1.0046	10.433	30′
40′	.09874	.9951	.09923	10.0780	1.0049	10.128	20′
50′	.10164	.9948	.10216	9.7882	1.0052	9.839	10′
6° 0′	.10453	.9945	.10510	9.5144	1.0055	9.5668	84° 0′
	$\cos x$	$\sin x$	$\cot x$	$\tan x$	$\csc x$	$\sec x$	x

Table D   Trigonometric Functions for Degrees (continued)

x	sin x	cos x	tan x	cot x	sec x	csc x	
6° 0′	.1045	.9945	.10510	9.5144	1.0055	9.5668	84° 0′
10′	.1074	.9942	.10805	9.2553	1.0058	9.3092	50′
20′	.1103	.9939	.11099	9.0098	1.0061	9.0652	40′
30′	.1132	.9936	.11394	8.7769	1.0065	8.8337	30′
40′	.1161	.9932	.11688	8.5555	1.0068	8.6138	20′
50′	.1190	.9929	.11983	8.3450	1.0072	8.4647	10′
7° 0′	.1219	.9925	.12278	8.1443	1.0075	8.2055	83° 0′
10′	.1248	.9922	.12574	7.9530	1.0079	8.0157	50′
20′	.1276	.9918	.12869	7.7704	1.0083	7.8344	40′
30′	.1305	.9914	.13165	7.5958	1.0086	7.6613	30′
40′	.1334	.9911	.1346	7.4287	1.0090	7.4957	20′
50′	.1363	.9907	.1376	7.2687	1.0094	7.3372	10′
8° 0′	.1392	.9903	.1405	7.1154	1.0098	7.1853	82° 0′
10′	.1421	.9899	.1435	6.9682	1.0102	7.0396	50′
20′	.1449	.9894	.1465	6.8269	1.0107	6.8998	40′
30′	.1478	.9890	.1495	6.6912	1.0111	6.7655	30′
40′	.1507	.9886	.1524	6.5606	1.0116	6.6363	20′
50′	.1536	.9881	.1554	6.4348	1.0120	6.5121	10′
9° 0′	.1564	.9877	.1584	6.3138	1.0125	6.3925	81° 0′
10′	.1593	.9872	.1614	6.1970	1.0129	6.2772	50′
20′	.1622	.9868	.1644	6.0844	1.0134	6.1661	40′
30′	.1650	.9863	.1673	5.9758	1.0139	6.0589	30′
40′	.1679	.9858	.1703	5.8708	1.0144	5.9554	20′
50′	.1708	.9853	.1733	5.7694	1.0149	5.8554	10′
10° 0′	.1736	.9848	.1763	5.6713	1.0154	5.7588	80° 0′
10′	.1765	.9843	.1793	5.5764	1.0160	5.6653	50′
20′	.1794	.9838	.1823	5.4845	1.0165	5.5749	40′
30′	.1822	.9833	.1853	5.3955	1.0170	5.4874	30′
40′	.1851	.9827	.1883	5.3093	1.0176	5.4026	20′
50′	.1880	.9822	.1914	5.2257	1.0182	5.3205	10′
11° 0′	.1908	.9816	.1944	5.1446	1.0187	5.2408	79° 0′
10′	.1937	.9811	.1974	5.0658	1.0193	5.1636	50′
20′	.1965	.9805	.2004	4.9894	1.0199	5.0886	40′
30′	.1994	.9799	.2035	4.9152	1.0205	5.0159	30′
40′	.2022	.9793	.2065	4.430	1.0211	4.9452	20′
50′	.2051	.9787	.2095	4.7729	1.0217	4.8765	10′
12° 0′	.2079	.9781	.2126	4.7046	1.0223	4.8097	78° 0′
	cos x	sin x	cot x	tan x	csc x	sec x	x

x	$\sin x$	$\cos x$	$\tan x$	$\cot x$	$\sec x$	$\csc x$	
12° 0′	.2079	.9781	.2126	4.7046	1.0223	4.8097	78° 0′
10′	.2108	.9775	.2156	4.6382	1.0230	4.7448	50′
20′	.2136	.9769	.2186	4.5736	1.0236	4.6817	40′
30′	.2164	.9763	.2217	4.5107	1.0243	4.6202	30′
40′	.2193	.9757	.2247	4.4494	1.0249	4.5604	20′
50′	.2221	.9750	.2278	4.3897	1.0256	4.5022	10′
13° 0′	.2250	.9744	.2309	4.3315	1.0263	4.4454	77° 0′
10′	.2278	.9737	.2339	4.2747	1.0270	4.3901	50′
20′	.2306	.9730	.2370	4.2193	1.0277	4.3362	40′
30′	.2334	.9724	.2401	4.1653	1.0284	4.2837	30′
40′	.2363	.9717	.2432	4.1126	1.0291	4.2324	20′
50′	.2391	.9710	.2462	4.0611	1.0299	4.1824	10′
14° 0′	.2419	.9703	.2493	4.0108	1.0306	4.1336	76° 0′
10′	.2447	.9696	.2524	3.9617	1.0314	4.0859	50′
20′	.2476	.9689	.2555	3.9136	1.0321	4.0394	40′
30′	.2504	.9681	.2586	3.8667	1.0329	3.9939	30′
40′	.2532	.9674	.2617	3.8208	1.0337	3.9495	20′
50′	.2560	.9667	.2648	3.7760	1.0345	3.9061	10′
15° 0′	.2588	.9659	.2679	3.7321	1.0353	3.8637	75° 0′
10′	.2616	.9652	.2711	3.6891	1.0361	3.8222	50′
20′	.2644	.9644	.2742	3.6470	1.0369	3.7817	40′
30′	.2672	.9636	.2773	3.6059	1.0377	3.7420	30′
40′	.2700	.9628	.2805	3.5656	1.0386	3.7032	20′
50′	.2728	.9621	.2836	3.5261	1.0394	3.6652	10′
16° 0′	.2756	.9613	.2867	3.4874	1.0403	3.6280	74° 0′
10′	.2784	.9605	.2899	3.4495	1.0412	3.5915	50′
20′	.2812	9596	.2931	3.4124	1.0421	3.5559	40′
30′	.2840	.9588	.2962	3.3759	1.0430	3.5209	30′
40′	.2868	.9580	.2994	3.3402	1.0439	3.4867	20′
50′	.2896	.9572	.3026	3.3052	1.0448	3.4532	10′
17° 0′	.2924	.9563	.3057	3.2709	1.0457	3.4203	73° 0′
10′	.2952	.9555	.3089	3.2371	1.0466	3.3881	50′
20′	.2979	.9546	.3121	3.2041	1.0476	3.3565	40′
30′	.3007	.9537	.3153	3.1716	1.0485	3.3255	30′
40′	.3035	.9528	.3185	3.1397	1.0495	3.2951	20′
50′	.3062	.9520	.3217	3.1084	1.0505	3.2653	10′
18° 0′	.3090	.9511	.3249	3.0777	1.0515	3.2361	72° 0′
	$\cos x$	$\sin x$	$\cot x$	$\tan x$	$\csc x$	$\sec x$	x

x	sin x	cos x	tan x	cot x	sec x	csc x	
18° 0′	.3090	.9511	.3249	3.0777	1.0515	3.2361	72° 0′
10′	.3118	.9502	.3281	3.0475	1.0525	3.2074	50′
20′	.3145	.9492	.3314	3.0178	1.0535	3.1792	40′
30′	.3173	.9483	.3346	2.9887	1.0545	3.1516	30′
40′	.3201	.9474	.3378	2.9600	1.0555	3.1244	20′
50′	.3228	.9465	.3411	2.9319	1.0566	3.0977	10′
19° 0′	.3256	.9455	.3443	2.9042	1.0576	3.0716	71° 0′
10′	.3283	.9446	.3476	2.8770	1.0587	3.0458	50′
20′	.3311	.9436	.3508	2.8502	1.0598	3.0206	40′
30′	.3338	.9426	.3541	2.8239	1.0609	2.9957	30′
40′	.3365	.9417	.3574	2.7980	1.0620	2.9714	20′
50′	.3393	.9407	.3607	2.7725	1.0631	2.9474	10′
20° 0′	.3420	.9397	.3640	2.7475	1.0642	2.9238	70° 0′
10′	.3448	.9387	.3673	2.7228	1.0653	2.9006	50′
20′	.3475	.9377	.3706	2.6985	1.0665	2.8779	40′
30′	.3502	.9367	.3739	2.6746	1.0676	2.8555	30′
40′	.3529	.9356	.3772	2.6511	1.0688	2.8334	20′
50′	.3557	.9346	.3805	2.6279	1.0700	2.8118	10′
21° 0′	.3584	.9336	.3839	2.6051	1.0712	2.7904	69° 0′
10′	.3611	.9325	.3872	2.5826	1.0724	2.7695	50′
20′	.3638	.9315	.3906	2.5605	1.0736	2.7488	40′
30′	.3665	.9304	.3939	2.5386	1.0748	2.7285	30′
40′	.3692	.9293	.3973	2.5172	1.0760	2.7085	20′
50′	.3719	.9283	.4006	2.4960	1.0773	2.6888	10′
22° 0′	.3746	.9272	.4040	2.4751	1.0785	2.6695	68° 0′
10′	.3773	.9261	.4074	2.4545	1.0798	2.6504	50′
20′	.3800	.9250	.4108	2.4342	1.0811	2.6316	40′
30′	.3827	.9239	.4142	2.4142	1.0824	2.6131	30′
40′	.3854	.9228	.4176	2.3945	1.0837	2.5949	20′
50′	.3881	.9216	.4210	2.3750	1.0850	2.5770	10′
23° 0′	.3907	.9205	.4245	2.3559	1.0864	2.5593	67° 0′
10′	.3934	.9194	.4279	2.3369	1.0877	2.5419	50′
20′	.3961	.9182	.4314	2.3183	1.0891	2.5247	40′
30′	.3987	.9171	.4348	2.2998	1.0904	2.5078	30′
40′	.4014	.9159	.4383	2.2817	1.0918	2.4912	20′
50′	.4041	.9147	.4417	2.2637	1.0932	2.4748	10′
24° 0′	.4067	.9135	.4452	2.2460	1.0946	2.4586	66° 0′
	cos x	sin x	cot x	tan x	csc x	sec x	x

x	$\sin x$	$\cos x$	$\tan x$	$\cot x$	$\sec x$	$\csc x$	
24° 0′	.4067	.9135	.4452	2.2460	1.0946	2.4586	66° 0′
10′	.4094	.9124	.4487	2.2286	1.0961	2.4426	50′
20′	.4120	.9112	.4522	2.2113	1.0975	2.4269	40′
30′	.4147	.9100	.4557	2.1943	1.0990	2.4114	30′
40′	.4173	.9088	.4592	2.1775	1.1004	2.3961	20′
50′	.4200	.9075	.4628	2.1609	1.1019	2.3811	10′
25° 0′	.4226	.9063	.4663	2.1445	1.1034	2.3662	65° 0′
10′	.4253	.9051	.4699	2.1283	1.1049	2.3515	50′
20′	.4279	.9038	.4734	2.1123	1.1064	2.3371	40′
30′	.4305	.9026	.4770	2.0965	1.1079	2.3228	30′
40′	.4331	.9013	.4806	2.0809	1.1095	2.3088	20′
50′	.4358	.9001	.4841	2.0655	1.1110	2.2949	10′
26° 0′	.4384	.8988	.4877	2.0503	1.1126	2.2812	64° 0′
10′	.4410	.8975	.4913	2.0353	1.1142	2.2677	50′
20′	.4436	.8962	.4950	2.0204	1.1158	2.2543	40′
30′	.4462	.8949	.4986	2.0057	1.1174	2.2412	30′
40′	.4488	.8936	.5022	1.9912	1.1190	2.2282	20′
50′	.4514	.8923	.5059	1.9768	1.1207	2.2154	10′
27° 0′	.4540	.8910	.5095	1.9626	1.1223	2.2027	63° 0′
10′	.4566	.8897	.5132	1.9486	1.1240	2.1902	50′
20′	.4592	.8884	.5169	1.9347	1.1257	2.1779	40′
30′	.4617	.8870	.5206	1.9210	1.1274	2.1657	30′
40′	.4643	.8857	.5243	1.9074	1.1291	2.1537	20′
50′	.4669	.8843	.5280	1.8940	1.1308	2.1418	10′
28° 0′	.4695	.8829	.5317	1.8807	1.1326	2.1301	62° 0′
10′	.4720	.8816	.5354	1.8676	1.1343	2.1185	50′
20′	.4746	.8802	.5392	1.8546	1.1361	2.1070	40′
30′	.4772	.8788	.5430	1.8418	1.1379	2.0957	30′
40′	.4797	.8774	.5467	1.8291	1.1397	2.0846	20′
50′	.4823	.8760	.5505	1.8165	1.1415	2.0736	10′
29° 0′	.4848	.8746	.5543	1.8040	1.1434	2.0627	61° 0′
10′	.4874	.8732	.5581	1.7917	1.1452	2.0519	50′
20′	.4899	.8718	.5619	1.7796	1.1471	2.0413	40′
30′	.4924	.8704	.5658	1.7675	1.1490	2.0308	30′
40′	.4950	.8689	.5696	1.7556	1.1509	2.0204	20′
50′	.4975	.8675	.5735	1.7437	1.1528	2.0101	10′
30° 0′	.5000	.8660	.5774	1.7321	1.1547	2.0000	60° 0′
	$\cos x$	$\sin x$	$\cot x$	$\tan x$	$\csc x$	$\sec x$	x

x	$\sin x$	$\cos x$	$\tan x$	$\cot x$	$\sec x$	$\csc x$	
30° 0′	.5000	.8660	.5774	1.7321	1.1547	2.0000	60° 0′
10′	.5025	.8646	.5812	1.7205	1.1567	1.9900	50′
20′	.5050	.8631	.5851	1.7090	1.1586	1.9801	40′
30′	.5075	.8616	.5890	1.6977	1.1606	1.9703	30′
40′	.5100	.8601	.5930	1.6864	1.1626	1.9606	20′
50′	.5125	.8587	.5969	1.6753	1.1646	1.9511	10′
31° 0′	.5150	.8572	.6009	1.6643	1.1666	1.9416	59° 0′
10′	.5175	.8557	.6048	1.6534	1.1687	1.9323	50′
20′	.5200	.8542	.6088	1.6426	1.1708	1.9230	40′
30′	.5225	.8526	.6128	1.6319	1.1728	1.9139	30′
40′	.5250	.8511	.6168	1.6212	1.1749	1.9049	20′
50′	.5275	.8496	.6208	1.6107	1.1770	1.8959	10′
32° 0′	.5299	.8480	.6249	1.6003	1.1792	1.8871	58° 0′
10′	.5324	.8465	.6289	1.5900	1.1813	1.8783	50′
20′	.5348	.8450	.6330	1.5798	1.1835	1.8699	40′
30′	.5373	.8434	.6371	1.5697	1.1857	1.8612	30′
40′	.5398	.8418	.6412	1.5597	1.1879	1.8527	20′
50′	.5422	.8403	.6453	1.5497	1.1901	1.8444	10′
33° 0′	.5446	.8387	.6494	1.5399	1.1924	1.8361	57° 0′
10′	.5471	.8371	.6536	1.5301	1.1946	1.8279	50′
20′	.5495	.8355	.6577	1.5204	1.1969	1.8198	40′
30′	.5519	.8339	.6619	1.5108	1.1992	1.8118	30′
40′	.5544	.8323	.6661	1.5013	1.2015	1.8039	20′
50′	.5568	.8307	.6703	1.4919	1.2039	1.7960	10′
34° 0′	.5592	.8290	.6745	1.4826	1.2062	1.7883	56° 0′
10′	.5616	.8274	.6787	1.4733	1.2086	1.7806	50′
20′	.5640	.8258	.6830	1.4641	1.2110	1.7730	40′
30′	.5664	.8241	.6873	1.4550	1.2134	1.7655	30′
40′	.5688	.8225	.6916	1.4460	1.2158	1.7581	20′
50′	.5712	.8208	.6959	1.4370	1.2183	1.7507	10′
35° 0′	.5736	.8192	.7002	1.4281	1.2208	1.7435	55° 0′
10′	.5760	.8175	.7046	1.4193	1.2233	1.7362	50′
20′	.5783	.8158	.7089	1.4106	1.2258	1.7291	40′
30′	.5807	.8141	.7133	1.4019	1.2283	1.7221	30′
40′	.5831	.8124	.7177	1.3934	1.2309	1.7151	20′
50′	.5854	.8107	.7221	1.3848	1.2335	1.7082	10′
36° 0′	.5878	.8090	.7265	1.3764	1.2361	1.7013	54° 0′
	$\cos x$	$\sin x$	$\cot x$	$\tan x$	$\csc x$	$\sec x$	x

x	$\sin x$	$\cos x$	$\tan x$	$\cot x$	$\sec x$	$\csc x$	
36° 0′	.5878	.8090	.7265	1.3764	1.2361	1.7013	54° 0′
10′	.5901	.8073	.7310	1.3680	1.2387	1.6945	50′
20′	.5925	.8056	.7355	1.3597	1.2413	1.6878	40′
30′	.5948	.8039	.7400	1.3514	1.2440	1.6812	30′
40′	.5972	.8021	.7445	1.3432	1.2467	1.6746	20′
50′	.5995	.8004	.7490	1.3351	1.2494	1.6681	10′
37° 0′	.6018	.7986	.7536	1.3270	1.2521	1.6616	53° 0′
10′	.6041	.7969	.7581	1.3190	1.2549	1.6553	50′
20′	.6065	.7951	.7627	1.3111	1.2577	1.6489	40′
30′	.6088	.7934	.7673	1.3032	1.2605	1.6427	30′
40′	.6111	.7916	.7720	1.2954	1.2633	1.6365	20′
50′	.6134	.7898	.7766	1.2876	1.2662	1.6304	10′
38° 0′	.6157	.7880	.7813	1.2799	1.2690	1.6243	52° 0′
10′	.6180	.7862	.7860	1.2723	1.2719	1.6183	50′
20′	.6202	.7844	.7907	1.2647	1.2748	1.6123	40′
30′	.6225	.7826	.7954	1.2572	1.2779	1.6064	30′
40′	.6248	.7808	.8002	1.2497	1.2808	1.6005	20′
50′	.6271	.7790	.8050	1.2423	1.2837	1.5948	10′
39° 0′	.6293	.7771	.8098	1.2349	1.2868	1.5890	51° 0′
10′	.6316	.7753	.8146	1.2276	1.2898	1.5833	50′
20′	.6338	.7735	.8195	1.2203	1.2929	1.5777	40′
30′	.6361	.7716	.8243	1.2131	1.2960	1.5721	30′
40′	.6383	.7698	.8292	1.2059	1.2991	1.5666	20′
50′	.6406	.7679	.8342	1.1988	1.3022	1.5611	10′
40° 0′	.6428	.7660	.8391	1.1918	1.3054	1.5557	50° 0′
10′	.6450	.7642	.8441	1.1847	1.3086	1.5504	50′
20′	.6472	.7623	.8491	1.1778	1.3118	1.5450	40′
30′	.6494	.7604	.8541	1.1708	1.3151	1.5398	30′
40′	.6517	.7585	.8591	1.1640	1.3184	1.5346	20′
50′	.6539	.7566	.8642	1.1571	1.3217	1.5294	10′
41° 0′	.6561	.7547	.8693	1.1504	1.3250	1.5243	49° 0′
10′	.6583	.7528	.8744	1.1436	1.3284	1.5192	50′
20′	.6604	.7509	.8796	1.1369	1.3318	1.5142	40′
30′	.6626	.7490	.8847	1.1303	1.3352	1.5092	30′
40′	.6648	.7470	.8899	1.1237	1.3386	1.5042	20′
50′	.6670	.7451	.8952	1.1171	1.3421	1.4993	10′
42° 0′	.6691	.7431	.9004	1.1106	1.3456	1.4945	48° 0′
	$\cos x$	$\sin x$	$\cot x$	$\tan x$	$\csc x$	$\sec x$	x

x	$\sin x$	$\cos x$	$\tan x$	$\cot x$	$\sec x$	$\csc x$	
42° 0′	.6691	.7431	.9004	1.1106	1.3456	1.4945	48° 0′
10′	.6713	.7412	.9057	1.1041	1.3492	1.4897	50′
20′	.6734	.7392	.9110	1.0977	1.3527	1.4849	40′
30′	.6756	.7373	.9163	1.0913	1.3563	1.4802	30′
40′	.6777	.7353	.9217	1.0850	1.3600	1.4755	20′
50′	.6799	.7333	.9271	1.0786	1.3636	1.4709	10′
43° 0′	.6820	.7314	.9325	1.0724	1.3673	1.4663	47° 0′
10′	.6841	.7294	.9380	1.0661	1.3711	1.4617	50′
20′	.6862	.7274	.9435	1.0599	1.3748	1.4572	40′
30′	.6884	.7254	.9490	1.0538	1.3786	1.4527	30′
40′	.6905	.7234	.9545	1.0477	1.3824	1.4483	20′
50′	.6926	.7214	.9601	1.0416	1.3863	1.4439	10′
44° 0′	.6947	.7193	.9657	1.0355	1.3902	1.4396	46° 0′
10′	.6967	.7173	.9713	1.0295	1.3941	1.4352	50′
20′	.6988	.7153	.9770	1.0235	1.3980	1.4310	40′
30′	.7009	.7133	.9827	1.0176	1.4020	1.4267	30′
40′	.7030	.7112	.9884	1.0117	1.4061	1.4225	20′
50′	.7050	.7092	.9942	1.0058	1.4101	1.4184	10′
45° 0′	.7071	.7071	1.0000	1.0000	1.4142	1.4142	45° 0′
	$\cos x$	$\sin x$	$\cot x$	$\tan x$	$\csc x$	$\sec x$	x

t	sin t	cos t	tan t	cot t	sec t	csc t
.00	.0000	1.0000	.0000	......	1.000	......
.01	.0100	1.0000	.0100	99.997	1.000	100.00
.02	.0200	.9998	.0200	49.993	1.000	50.00
.03	.0300	.9996	.0300	33.323	1.000	33.34
.04	.0400	.9992	.0400	24.987	1.001	25.01
.05	.0500	.9988	.0500	19.983	1.001	20.01
.06	.0600	.9982	.0601	16.647	1.002	16.68
.07	.0699	.9976	.0701	14.262	1.002	14.30
.08	.0799	.9968	.0802	12.473	1.003	12.51
.09	.0899	.9960	.0902	11.081	1.004	11.13
.10	.0998	.9950	.1003	9.967	1.005	10.02
.11	.1098	.9940	.1104	9.054	1.006	9.109
.12	.1197	.9928	.1206	8.293	1.007	8.353
.13	.1296	.9916	.1307	7.649	1.009	7.714
.14	.1395	.9902	.1409	7.096	1.010	7.166
.15	.1494	.9888	.1511	6.617	1.011	6.692
.16	.1593	.9872	.1614	6.197	1.013	6.277
.17	.1692	.9856	.1717	5.826	1.015	5.911
.18	.1790	.9838	.1820	5.495	1.016	5.586
.19	.1889	.9820	.1923	5.200	1.018	5.295
.20	.1987	.9801	.2027	4.933	1.020	5.033
.21	.2085	.9780	.2131	4.692	1.022	4.797
.22	.2182	.9759	.2236	4.472	1.025	4.582
.23	.2280	.9737	.2341	4.271	1.027	4.386
.24	.2377	.9713	.2447	4.086	1.030	4.207
.25	.2474	.9689	.2553	3.916	1.032	4.042
.26	.2571	.9664	.2660	3.759	1.035	3.890
.27	.2667	.9638	.2768	3.613	1.038	3.749
.28	.2764	.9611	.2876	3.478	1.041	3.619
.29	.2860	.9582	.2984	3.351	1.044	3.497
.30	.2955	.9553	.3093	3.233	1.047	3.384
.31	.3051	.9523	.3203	3.122	1.050	3.278
.32	.3146	.9492	.3314	3.018	1.053	3.179
.33	.3240	.9460	.3425	2.920	1.057	3.086
.34	.3335	.9428	.3537	2.827	1.061	2.999
.35	.3429	.9394	.3650	2.740	1.065	2.916
.36	.3523	.9359	.3764	2.657	1.068	2.839
.37	.3616	.9323	.3879	2.578	1.073	2.765
.38	.3709	.9287	.3994	2.504	1.077	2.696
.39	.3802	.9249	.4111	2.433	1.081	2.630

Table E   The Trigonometric Functions for Radians and Real Numbers (continued)

t	$\sin t$	$\cos t$	$\tan t$	$\cot t$	$\sec t$	$\csc t$
.40	.3894	.9211	.4228	2.365	1.086	2.568
.41	.3986	.9171	.4346	2.301	1.090	2.509
.42	.4078	.9131	.4466	2.239	1.095	2.452
.43	.4169	.9090	.4586	2.180	1.100	2.399
.44	.4259	.9048	.4708	2.124	1.105	2.348
.45	.4350	.9004	.4831	2.070	1.111	2.299
.46	.4439	.8961	.4954	2.018	1.116	2.253
.47	.4529	.8916	.5080	1.969	1.122	2.208
.48	.4618	.8870	.5206	1.921	1.127	2.166
.49	.4706	.8823	.5334	1.875	1.133	2.125
.50	.4794	.8776	.5463	1.830	1.139	2.086
.51	.4882	.8727	.5594	1.788	1.146	2.048
.52	.4969	.8678	.5726	1.747	1.152	2.013
.53	.5055	.8628	.5859	1.707	1.159	1.978
.54	.5141	.8577	.5994	1.668	1.166	1.945
.55	.5227	.8525	.6131	1.631	1.173	1.913
.56	.5312	.8473	.6269	1.595	1.180	1.883
.57	.5396	.8419	.6410	1.560	1.188	1.853
.58	.5480	.8365	.6552	1.526	1.196	1.825
.59	.5564	.8309	.6696	1.494	1.203	1.797
.60	.5646	.8253	.6841	1.462	1.212	1.771
.61	.5729	.8196	.6989	1.431	1.220	1.746
.62	.5810	.8139	.7139	1.401	1.229	1.721
.63	.5891	.8080	.7291	1.372	1.238	1.697
.64	.5972	.8021	.7445	1.343	1.247	1.674
.65	.6052	.7961	.7602	1.315	1.256	1.652
.66	.6131	.7900	.7761	1.288	1.266	1.631
.67	.6210	.7838	.7923	1.262	1.276	1.610
.68	.6288	.7776	.8087	1.237	1.286	1.590
.69	.6365	.7712	.8253	1.212	1.297	1.571
.70	.6442	.7648	.8423	1.187	1.307	1.552
.71	.6518	.7584	.8595	1.163	1.319	1.534
.72	.6594	.7518	.8771	1.140	1.330	1.517
.73	.6669	.7452	.8949	1.117	1.342	1.500
.74	.6743	.7385	.9131	1.095	1.354	1.483
.75	.6816	.7317	.9316	1.073	1.367	1.467
.76	.6889	.7248	.9505	1.052	1.380	1.452
.77	.6961	.7179	.9697	1.031	1.393	1.437
.78	.7033	.7109	.9893	1.011	1.407	1.422
.79	.7104	.7038	1.009	.9908	1.421	1.408

t	sin t	cos t	tan t	cot t	sec t	csc t
.80	.7174	.6967	1.030	.9712	1.435	1.394
.81	.7243	.6895	1.050	.9520	1.450	1.381
.82	.7311	.6822	1.072	.9331	1.466	1.368
.83	.7379	.6749	1.093	.9146	1.482	1.355
.84	.7446	.6675	1.116	.8964	1.498	1.343
.85	.7513	.6600	1.138	.8785	1.515	1.331
.86	.7578	.6524	1.162	.8609	1.533	1.320
.87	.7643	.6448	1.185	.8437	1.551	1.308
.88	.7707	.6372	1.210	.8267	1.569	1.297
.89	.7771	.6294	1.235	.8100	1.589	1.287
.90	.7833	.6216	1.260	.7936	1.609	1.277
.91	.7895	.6137	1.286	.7774	1.629	1.267
.92	.7956	.6058	1.313	.7615	1.651	1.257
.93	.8016	.5978	1.341	.7458	1.673	1.247
.94	.8076	.5898	1.369	.7303	1.696	1.238
.95	.8134	.5817	1.398	.7151	1.719	1.229
.96	.8192	.5735	1.428	.7001	1.744	1.221
.97	.8249	.5653	1.459	.6853	1.769	1.212
.98	.8305	.5570	1.491	.6707	1.795	1.204
.99	.8360	.5487	1.524	.6563	1.823	1.196
1.00	.8415	.5403	1.557	.6421	1.851	1.188
1.01	.8468	.5319	1.592	.6281	1.880	1.181
1.02	.8521	.5234	1.628	.6142	1.911	1.174
1.03	.8573	.5148	1.665	.6005	1.942	1.166
1.04	.8624	.5062	1.704	.5870	1.975	1.160
1.05	.8674	.4976	1.743	.5736	2.010	1.153
1.06	.8724	.4889	1.784	.5604	2.046	1.146
1.07	.8772	.4801	1.827	.5473	2.083	1.140
1.08	.8820	.4713	1.871	.5344	2.122	1.134
1.09	.8866	.4625	1.917	.5216	2.162	1.128
1.10	.8912	.4536	1.965	.5090	2.205	1.122
1.11	.8957	.4447	2.014	.4964	2.249	1.116
1.12	.9001	.4357	2.066	.4840	2.295	1.111
1.13	.9044	.4267	2.120	.4718	2.344	1.106
1.14	.9086	.4176	2.176	.4596	2.395	1.101
1.15	.9128	.4085	2.234	.4475	2.448	1.096
1.16	.9168	.3993	2.296	.4356	2.504	1.091
1.17	.9208	.3902	2.360	.4237	2.563	1.086
1.18	.9246	.3809	2.427	.4120	2.625	1.082
1.19	.9284	.3717	2.498	.4003	2.691	1.077

t	$\sin t$	$\cos t$	$\tan t$	$\cot t$	$\sec t$	$\csc t$
1.20	.9320	.3624	2.572	.3888	2.760	1.073
1.21	.9356	.3530	2.650	.3773	2.833	1.069
1.22	.9391	.3436	2.733	.3659	2.910	1.065
1.23	.9425	.3342	2.820	.3546	2.992	1.061
1.24	.9458	.3248	2.912	.3434	3.079	1.057
1.25	.9490	.3153	3.010	.3323	3.171	1.054
1.26	.9521	.3058	3.113	.3212	3.270	1.050
1.27	.9551	.2963	3.224	.3102	3.375	1.047
1.28	.9580	.2867	3.341	.2993	3.488	1.044
1.29	.9608	.2771	3.467	.2884	3.609	1.041
1.30	.9636	.2675	3.602	.2776	3.738	1.038
1.31	.9662	.2579	3.747	.2669	3.878	1.035
1.32	.9687	.2482	3.903	.2562	4.029	1.032
1.33	.9711	.2385	4.072	.2456	4.193	1.030
1.34	.9735	.2288	4.256	.2350	4.372	1.027
1.35	.9757	.2190	4.455	.2245	4.566	1.025
1.36	.9779	.2092	4.673	.2140	4.779	1.023
1.37	.9799	.1994	4.913	.2035	5.014	1.021
1.38	.9819	.1896	5.177	.1931	5.273	1.018
1.39	.9837	.1798	5.471	.1828	5.561	1.017
1.40	.9854	.1700	5.798	.1725	5.883	1.015
1.41	.9871	.1601	6.165	.1622	6.246	1.013
1.42	.9887	.1502	6.581	.1519	6.657	1.011
1.43	.9901	.1403	7.055	.1417	7.126	1.010
1.44	.9915	.1304	7.602	.1315	7.667	1.009
1.45	.9927	.1205	8.238	.1214	8.299	1.007
1.46	.9939	.1106	8.989	.1113	9.044	1.006
1.47	.9949	.1006	9.887	.1011	9.938	1.005
1.48	.9959	.0907	10.983	.0910	11.029	1.004
1.49	.9967	.0807	12.350	.0810	12.390	1.003
1.50	.9975	.0707	14.101	.0709	14.137	1.003
1.51	.9982	.0608	16.428	.0609	16.458	1.002
1.52	.9987	.0508	19.670	.0508	19.695	1.001
1.53	.9992	.0408	24.498	.0408	24.519	1.001
1.54	.9995	.0308	32.461	.0308	32.476	1.000
1.55	.9998	.0208	48.078	.0208	48.089	1.000
1.56	.9999	.0108	92.620	.0108	92.626	1.000
1.57	1.0000	.0008	1255.8	.0008	1255.8	1.000

Answers to Odd-Numbered Exercises

Section 1.1 (page 5)

1. $A = \frac{1}{2}bh$ **3.** $P = 4s$ **5.** $a = v/t$ **7.** $x - 8$ **9.** $5(x + 3)$
11. $0.20(x - 12000)$ **13.** $\frac{1}{3}(x + y + z)$ **15.** $I = PR$ **17.** $2(x + y)$
19. $A = 6s^2$ **21.** a, e, and g are true.
23. a. $\{x \mid x$ greater than or equal to 40$\}$
     b. $\{x \mid x$ is air-conditioned cars in New York City$\}$
     e. $\{x \mid x$ is people in U.S. who own color TV's$\}$
25. a. $\{2, 4, 6, 8, 10\}$ b. $\{6, 7, 8, 9, 10\}$ c. $\{1, 5, 6, 7, 8, 9, 10\}$
27. $\{1, 2, 3, 5, 6, 7, 8\}$ **29.** $\{1, 3, 8\}$ **31.** $\{1, 2, 3, 5, 7, 8\}$
33. $\{1, 2, 3, 5, 8\}$ **35.** $\{1, 2, 3, 4, 5, 8\}$ **37.** True
39. False   **41.** True

Sections 1.2 through 1.4 (page 15)

1. a. $0.\overline{142857}$ b. $3.\overline{142857}$ c. 0.375 d. $0.\overline{54}$

3. $\frac{241}{99}$ **5.** 10 **7.** 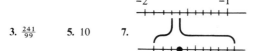   **9.**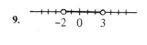

11. 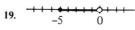   **13.**

15.   **17.**

19.   **21.** $\varnothing$ **23.**

25.   **27.** $[0, \infty)$ **29.** $(-\infty, 4]$

31. Yes. It is a subset of $[a, b]$ but does not include the endpoints a and b.
33. a. 5   b. 3   c. 15   **35.** $(-1.5, 1.5)$ **37.** $(-\infty, -4] \cup [4, \infty)$
39. $|x| < 10$ **41.** $|x| \geq 1$ **43.** Try $x = 2, y = -3.$ **45.** False
47. False   **49.** False   **51.** True

Section 1.5 (page 19)

1. -1 **3.** 4   **5.** -6 **7.** -432 **9.** -8 **11.** 13
13. -12 **15.** 28   **17.** $\frac{10}{21}$ **19.** $\frac{1}{4}$ **21.** $\frac{18}{35}$
23. $\frac{2}{3}$ **25.** $-\frac{11}{12}$ **27.** $\frac{13}{6}$ **29.** $-\frac{3}{8}$ **31.** $-\frac{1}{4}$
33. $\frac{7}{36}$ **35.** $\frac{10}{9}$ **37.** $\frac{1}{2}$ **39.** $\frac{9}{25}$

Section 2.1 (page 26)

1. $x^5 + 2x^2$ **3.** $x^5 - 5x^4$ **5.** $x^2 - 4y^2$ **7.** $x^4 - 1$
9. $x^4 - 2x^3 + 2x^2 - 2x + 1$ **11.** $x^2y^2 - 1$ **13.** $x^3 + 3x^2y^2 + 3xy^4 + y^6$
15. $x^4 - x^2y^2 - x^2y + y^3$ **17.** $x^2 + y^2 + z^2 + 2xy + 2xz + 2yz$
19. $6x^2 - 12y^2 - xy - 2xz + 3yz$ **21.** $x^2 + 8x + 16$ **23.** $x^2 + 30x + 225$
25. $b^2 - 144$ **27.** $4x^2 + 20x + 25$ **29.** $81y^2 - 36y + 4$ **31.** $16x^2 - 25$
33. $x^3 + 6x^2 + 12x + 8$ **35.** $125a^3 + 75a^2b + 15ab^2 + b^3$
37. $8x^3 - 60x^2 + 150x - 125$ **39.** $x^3 + 8$ **41.** $x^3 - 27$ **43.** $8x^3 + 1$
45. $x^2 + 14x + 45$ **47.** $6x^2 - 14x - 40$ **49.** $2y^2 + 9y + 10$
51. $2x^2 + 5xy - 12y^2$ **53.** $36x^2 - 111x + 40$

Section 2.2 (page 28)

1. $x(3x^2 - 5x + 15)$ **3.** $y^3(13y^4 - 27)$ **5.** $(z - 12)^2$ **7.** $(3x + 1)^2$
9. $(\frac{1}{2}x + 1)^2$ **11.** $(x + 13)(x - 13)$ **13.** $4(m + 4)(m - 4)$
15. $(x + 2y)(x - 2y)$ **17.** $(\frac{1}{2}x + \frac{1}{3})(\frac{1}{2}x - \frac{1}{3})$ **19.** $(3x + 2)^2$
21. $\frac{1}{9}(x + 1)^2$ **23.** $(x - 4)(x + 3)$ **25.** $(y + 6)(y + 7)$
27. $(x - 9)(x + 6)$ **29.** $(2x + 1)(x + 3)$ **31.** $(5x - 3)(x - 5)$
33. $(6m - 5)(m - 1)$ **35.** $(3x - 5y)(x + 3y)$ **37.** $(3x + 2y)(x - 2y)$
39. $4(2x - y)(x - 2y)$ **41.** $(x + 4)(x^2 - 4x + 16)$ **43.** $(2x + 1)(4x^2 - 2x + 1)$
45. $(a + \frac{1}{2})(a^2 - \frac{1}{2}a + \frac{1}{4})$ **47.** $(y - 3)^3$ **49.** $(2x + 1)^3$ **51.** $(3x + 2)^3$

Section 2.3 (page 33)

1. $\dfrac{5c}{12a^2b^2}$ **3.** $\dfrac{1}{6x^3y^2}$ **5.** $\dfrac{6a^4}{b^2c^2}$ **7.** $\dfrac{x - 3}{2}$ **9.** $\dfrac{6y}{5x(2x - 3)}$

11. $\dfrac{x(x - 2)}{y(x - 1)}$ **13.** $\dfrac{2y + 1}{y + 2}$ **15.** $\dfrac{x(2x + 3)}{x + 6}$ **17.** $\dfrac{(s + 1)^2}{s + 3}$ **19.** 1

21. $-(2y + 1)(y + 4)$ **23.** $-\dfrac{(a + 100)(a + 400)}{2(a + 40)}$ **25.** $\dfrac{2ac + ab - 3bc}{abc}$

27. $\dfrac{2t - 3s + 1}{3st}$ **29.** $\dfrac{3 + 2y^2 - 3xy}{xy^2}$ **31.** $\dfrac{5x - 7}{(x + 1)(x - 3)}$

33. $\dfrac{x^2 + 5x - 10}{(x - 5)(x + 3)}$ **35.** $\dfrac{x + 5}{x(x + 2)}$ **37.** $\dfrac{7a + 4}{a(2a + 3)}$ **39.** $\dfrac{3x + 32}{3x + 4}$

41. $\dfrac{p^2 + 5p + 2}{p(p + 1)^2}$ **43.** $\dfrac{x - 4}{(x + 1)(x - 2)(x + 3)}$ **45.** $\dfrac{5x^2 - x - 3}{(x + 3)(x - 2)^2}$

47. $\dfrac{x^2 + 2x - 15}{(x - 3)(x - 2)(x - 4)}$ **49.** $x + 1$ **51.** $\dfrac{x + 2}{x - 1}$ **53.** $\dfrac{(x + 2)(x - 3)}{(x - 4)(x + 1)}$

55. $\dfrac{2t^3 + 3t^2 - 15}{6t^3}$ **57.** $\dfrac{5s + 9}{s(s + 3)(s + 1)}$

Section 2.4 (page 39)

1. 64   **3.** 256   **5.** $1/a^2$ **7.** 3   **9.** a^3/b^3x^3 **11.** $-\frac{1}{8}$
13. $\frac{3}{2}$ **15.** 1   **17.** $1/(x + y)$ **19.** 1   **21.** $x/(x^3 + 1)$
23. $x/(1 + xy)$ **25.** $1/(a + b)$ **27.** $\frac{1}{256}$ **29.** $(2x^2 + 2x + 11)/7$

31. 8.2344×10^9 **33.** 5.2×10^{-11} **35.** 4.6×10^{39}
37. $3,485,200,000$ **39.** 0.0000009385 **41.** 0.02222 **43.** 3×10^{10}
45. $1,500,000$ **47.** False   **49.** False   **51.** False   **53.** False

Section 2.5 (page 44)

1. $x^{1/3}$ **3.** $(x/y)^{1/4}$ **5.** $x^{2/3}$ **7.** $x^{5/12}$ **9.** $\sqrt[5]{x^3}$
11. $\sqrt[8]{a^3}$ **13.** $\sqrt[3]{a+b}$ **15.** $5\sqrt{5}$ **17.** $5x^2y^3$
19. $3\sqrt[3]{x^2y}$ **21.** $\sqrt[3]{2}$ **23.** $\sqrt{5}/5$ **25.** $\sqrt{x(x+y)}/(x+y)$
27. $-(\sqrt{3} - \sqrt{5})/2$ **29.** $x(\sqrt{x} - \sqrt{y})/(x-y)$ **31.** $(\sqrt{a} + \sqrt{b})^2/(a-b)$
33. 8 **35.** 27 **37.** $\frac{1}{8}$ **39.** $x^{7/6}$ **41.** $y^{5/6}$ **43.** $5ab^3$

45. $3x^{1/3}$ **47.** $\dfrac{2y^{1/2} + 3x^{1/2}}{x^{1/2}y^{1/2}}$ **49.** $a + 2a^{1/2}b^{1/2} + b$

51. $\dfrac{y^2 + 2y + 1}{y}$ **53.** $(2x+1)(x-2)^{1/2}/(x-2)$ **55.** $13\sqrt{3}$ **57.** $10\sqrt{5}$

59. $2\sqrt{2}$ **61.** No   **63.** 358.364 **65.** 36.462 **67.** False   **69.** False

Sections 3.1 and 3.2 (page 56)

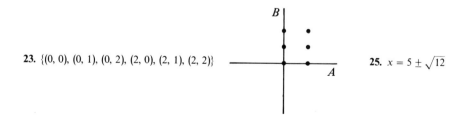

1, 3, 5.   **7.** I, IV   **9.** III   **11.** 0

13. $\sqrt{2}$ **15.** $\frac{5}{4}$ **17.** 8.2 **19.** 4.8

21. $\{(1, -1), (1, 1)\}$

23. $\{(0, 0), (0, 1), (0, 2), (2, 0), (2, 1), (2, 2)\}$ **25.** $x = 5 \pm \sqrt{12}$

27. $2|x|$ **29.** $x = 2$ **31.** The y-axis

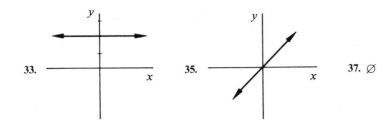

33. 35. 37. $\varnothing$

Section 3.3 (page 60)

1. 252 mi   **3.** 62.5 lb sodium, 37.5 lb chlorine   **5.** 4.44 and 3.56 ft
7. 400 lb/in.^{2} **9.** 0.15   **11.** $y = 6$ **13.** $z = 1$ **15.** 64 ft/sec
17. $C = 28.3¢$ **19.** $I = 1$ ft-cand.   **21.** $P = 200$ watts
23. 1 amp   **25.** $2300
27. (a) directly proportional to t^2 (b) constant   (c) directly proportional to t

Section 3.4 (page 67)

1. Function   **3.** Function   **5.** Function   **7.** Not a function
9. Function   **11.** Not a function   **13.** (a) and (b)
15. D: all reals. R: all reals   **17.** D: $x \geq 0$. R: $F(x) \geq 0$
19. D: all reals. R: all reals   **21.** D: $x \leq 0$. R: $f(x) \geq 0$
23. D: $x \geq 1$. R: $f(x) \geq 0$ **25.** D: $x \geq 0$, $x \neq 1$. R: all reals
27. D: all reals except $x = \pm 1$. R: all reals
29. a. 10   b. $3\pi + 1$ c. $3z + 1$ d. $3(x - h) + 1$ e. 3   f. All reals
   g. 31   h. 13   i. 3
31. a. 3   b. -3 c. undefined   d. $\{-3, 3, 9\}$ e. $\{2, 5, 7\}$
   f. $H(2 + 5) = -3$; $H(2) + H(5) = 12$

33. $2x + h$ **35.** $\dfrac{-2x - h}{x^2(x + h)^2}$ **37.** 0

39. (a) x_2/x_1 (b) $f(1/x) = kx$; $1/f(x) = x/k$ (c) $f(x^2) = k/x^2$; $[f(x)]^2 = k^2/x^2$
   (d) $-k/x(x + h)$ (e) $f(x) + 1 = (x + k)/x$; $f(x + 1) = k/(x + 1)$
   (f) $f(x_1 + x_2) = k/(x_1 + x_2)$; $f(x_1) + f(x_2) = k(x_1 + x_2)/x_1 x_2$
   (g) $af(x) = ak/x$; $f(ax) = k/ax$
41. In general, none are equal.

Sections 3.5 and 3.6 (page 75)

1. Function   **3.** Not a function   **5.** Not a function

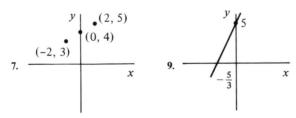

7.

9.

11.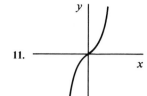

13.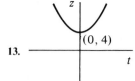

15.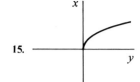

17.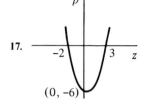

19.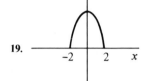

21.

23.

25.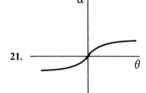

27.

29.

31.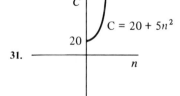

33.

35.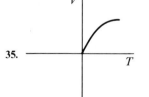

Section 3.7 (page 80)

1.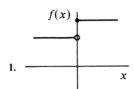

3.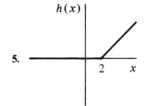

5.

7.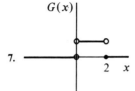

9.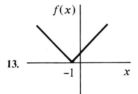

11.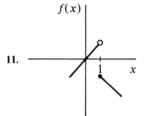

13.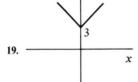

15.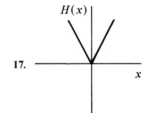

17.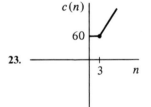

19.

21.

23.

25. Let $x = z$, $y = -3$.

27.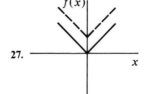

Section 3.8 (page 86)

1. $\frac{3}{2}$ 3. $\frac{5}{2}$ 5. 3, None   7. {(7, 3), (9, 5), (3, 7), (5, 9)}
9. No inverse function   11. {(3, −2), (4, −1), (0, 0)}

13. No inverse function **15.** Inverse functions **17.** Not inverse functions
19. Inverse functions **21.** Inverse functions **23.** a, c, and d have inverses.
25. $6x + 4; 6x + 8$ **27.** $x^2; x^2$ **29.** $x - 1; (x^3 - 1)^{1/3}$
37. $f^{-1}(x) = x + 3$ **39.** $f^{-1}(x) = (1 - x)/x$ **41.** $f^{-1}(x) = (1 + x)/(1 - x)$

Section 4.1 (page 95)

1. $x = -\frac{3}{2}$ **3.** $x = \frac{2}{3}$ **5.** $x = 13$ **7.** $a = \frac{18}{25}$ **9.** $x = 7$
11. $C = \frac{1}{2}$ **13.** $x = -20$ **15.** $y = \frac{1}{3}$ **17.** $x = 6$ **19.** $m = 2$
21. 102, 104, 106 **23.** 133 mph **25.** .5 hr **27.** $x = 4$
29. 9 and 11 amps **31.** No solution **33.** $x = \frac{1}{2}$ **35.** No solution
37. No solution **39.** $x = -\frac{9}{5}, 1$

Section 4.2 (page 102)

1. 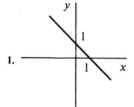   **3.** 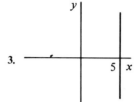   **5.**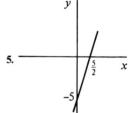

7.    **9.** 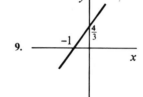   **11.**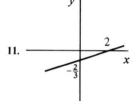

13. $m = \frac{1}{2}$ **15.** $m = -\frac{5}{4}$ **17.** $m = \frac{4}{3}$ **19.** $m = 0$

21. 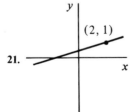   **23.**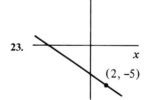

25. $m = \sqrt{481}/12 \approx 1.83$ **27.** $m = 2$ **29.**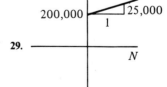

Answers to Odd-Numbered Exercises   487

Section 4.3 (page 107)

1. $x - 2y = -8$ **3.** $7x + y = 33$ **5.** $x + 5y = 16$ **7.** $2y - 3x = 1$
9. $5y - 2x = 10$ **11.** $m = \frac{2}{3}, b = -\frac{5}{3}$ **13.** $m = -1, b = 2$
15. $m = \frac{1}{2}, b = -2$ **17.** $m = \frac{1}{2}, b = \frac{5}{2}$ **19.** $m = 0, b = 5$
21. $m = \frac{1}{5}, b = \frac{7}{5}$ **23.** $2x - 3y = -4$ **25.** $x + y = 8$ **27.** $I = V/12$
29. \$225   **31.** \$151.11 per mo.

33.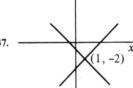

35.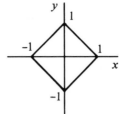

37.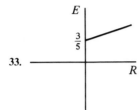

39.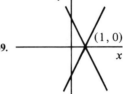

41.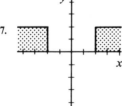

43.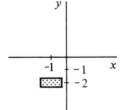

Section 4.4 (page 113)

1. $x > -\frac{5}{2}$ **3.** $x \geq (\sqrt{2} - 1)/(1 + \sqrt{3})$ **5.** $x > \frac{70}{11}$ **7.** $x > -13$
9. $x \geq \frac{2}{5}$ **11.** $x > 0$ **13.** $x > \frac{4}{3}$ **15.** $(-1, 5)$
17. $(-7, 3)$ **19.** $(-\infty, 4) \cup (6, \infty)$ **21.** $[-4, 16]$ **23.** $[\frac{1}{2}, \frac{5}{2}]$
25. $|x - 4| < 2$ **27.** $|x - 3| < 13$ **29.** $|x| > 2$ **31.** $|2x - 9| \leq 5$
33. $|2x - 5| \geq 5$ **35.** $(-3, \frac{3}{2})$ **37.** $(0, 3)$ **39.** $(-1, 2)$
41. $x \geq -\frac{1}{2}$ **43.** $x > 8$ **45.** $-\frac{1}{5} < x < \frac{11}{7}$

47.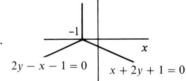

49.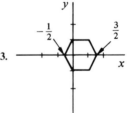

488   Answers to Odd-Numbered Exercises

51. All reals except $x = 0$. **53.** $x \geq -\frac{3}{2}$ **55.** $[-3, 1]$ **57.** $\varnothing$

Section 4.5 (page 117)

1.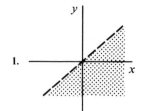

3.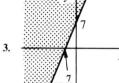

5.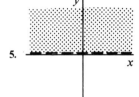

7.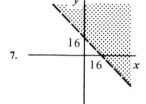

9.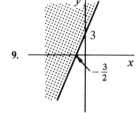

11.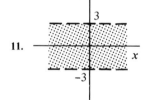

13.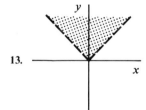

15.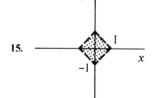

17. $C < -\frac{160}{9}$

19.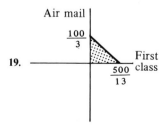

Sections 5.1 and 5.2 (page 124)

1. $(-2.6, -1.1)$ **3.** $(5, 2)$ **5.** Dependent **7.** Inconsistent
9. $(1.6, 2.8)$ **11.** $(\frac{1}{4}, -\frac{3}{4})$ **13.** $(1.1, 0.8)$ **15.** $(1.7, -2.7)$
17. $(\pm 1, 0)$ **19.** $(\pm 0.4, \pm 0.4)$ **21.** $(1.28, 0.79), (-1.28, -0.79)$
23. None **25.** None **29.** $(15, 15)$

Section 5.3 (page 131)

1. $(4, 1)$ **3.** Inconsistent **5.** $(-5, 4)$ **7.** $w = 3, z = 4$
9. $(-2, -2)$ **11.** $(0, \pm 2)$ **13.** None **15.** $r = 1, s = -2$ **17.** Inconsistent
19. $(3, 1)$ **21.** $(-4, 2)$ **23.** Dependent **25.** $(\pm 1, \pm 2)$
27. $(-13, -6)$ **29.** $(\pm 2, 6)$ **31.** None **33.** $a = 0, b = \frac{1}{2}$
35. $a = \frac{1}{18}, K = \frac{220}{9}$ **37.** $\frac{5}{3}$ hr **39.** $30, \frac{15}{2}$

Section 5.4 (page 135)

1. $(7, 3, -2)$ **3.** $(\frac{5}{2}, \frac{1}{2}, \frac{5}{2})$ **5.** Inconsistent **7.** $(0, 0, 0)$
9. $a = 1, b = 2, c = -2$ **11.** $(\frac{2}{3}, \frac{3}{4}, -1)$ **13.** $(\frac{1}{11}, -\frac{7}{11}, \frac{5}{11})$
15. $(\frac{13}{3}, -\frac{10}{3}, -\frac{7}{3})$ **17.** $(\frac{160}{29}, \frac{66}{29}, \frac{64}{29})$
19. $n = 246, d = 226, q = 428$ **21.** $l_1 = 15, l_2 = 17, l_3 = 13$

Sections 5.5 and 5.6 (page 144)

1. $(2, 4)$ **3.** $(2, 1)$ **5.** $(-\frac{3}{4}, 2, 3)$ **7.** $(8, 5, 6)$
9. $(6, \frac{5}{3}, 2)$ **11.** -2 **13.** -2 **15.** 24 **17.** 0
29. $x = \pm 1$ **31.** -70 **33.** $x = -3$ **35.** -5

Section 5.7 (page 150)

1. $(2, 0)$ **3.** $(5, 2)$ **5.** Dependent **7.** Inconsistent **9.** $(\frac{8}{5}, \frac{14}{5})$
11. $(-1, -4)$ **13.** $(7, 3, -2)$ **15.** $r = 3, s = -3, t = 4$

17. $(-135, -101, -7)$ **19.** $(0, 0, 0)$ **21.** $\left(\dfrac{497}{636}, -\dfrac{291}{636}, -\dfrac{270}{636}\right)$

23. $a = \frac{1}{5}, b = \frac{3}{5}$ **25.** 5 sec **27.** 8 dimes
29. $l_1 = \frac{65}{3}, l_2 = \frac{50}{3}, l_3 = \frac{35}{3}$
31. $u' = FQ_2/(R_1 Q_2 - R_2 Q_1); v' = -FR_2/(R_1 Q_2 - R_2 Q_1)$

Sections 5.8 and 5.9 (page 157)

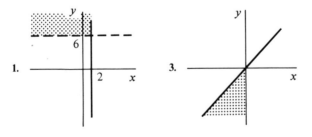

Answers to Odd-Numbered Exercises

5.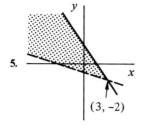

(3, −2)

7.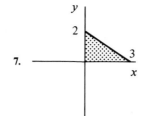

9.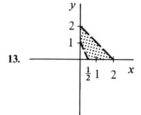

(−3, 0) (3, 2) (2, 0)

11.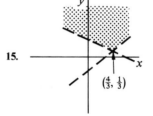

13.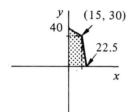

15.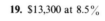

$\left(\frac{4}{3}, \frac{1}{3}\right)$

17. $x = 15, y = 30$

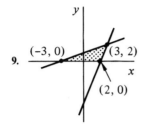

(15, 30)

40

22.5

19. \$13,300 at 8.5%

6,700 at 7.0%

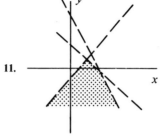

13,300

6700

20,000

Section 6.1 (page 167)

1.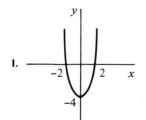

−2   2

−4

3.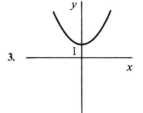

1

5.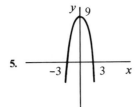

7.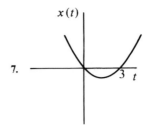

9.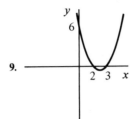

11. $y = x^2 - 2x$

13. $y = x^2 - 2x + 1$ **15.** Symmetric with respect to the x-axis

17.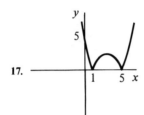

19.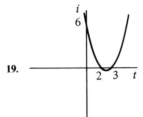

21. $x = 0, 2$ **23.** $x = -1, 2$ **25.** $x = -2, 3$ **27.** $z = -5, 2$
29. $x = -4, \frac{3}{2}$ **31.** $w = -\frac{1}{3}, 2$ **33.** $v = 0, \frac{1}{5}$
35. $t = -2, 5$ **37.** $x = -\frac{6}{7}, \frac{4}{5}$ **39.** $x^2 - 3x + 2$ **41.** $x^2 - 5x$
43. $x^2 + 2x - 24$ **45.** $3x^2 + 2x - 8$ **47.** $2x^2 - 11x + 15$
49. $(-1, -2)$ and $(2, 1)$ **51.** $a = 2, b = 0$ **53.** $c = 2, d = 2$
$\qquad\qquad\qquad\qquad\qquad a = 3, b = 1 \qquad\qquad c = -2, d = -2$
55. $5, 12$ **57.** $t = 3$ **59.** 56×42

Section 6.2 (page 171)

1. $\{-1, -5\}$ **3.** $\{-3, 4\}$ **5.** $\{(3 \pm \sqrt{17})/2\}$ **7.** $\{1, \frac{2}{3}\}$
9. $\{\frac{3}{2}, -4\}$ **11.** $\{(-1 \pm i\sqrt{3})/2\}$ **13.** $\{(3 \pm \sqrt{3})/3\}$
15. $\{(-1 \pm i\sqrt{11})/6\}$ **17.** $R = (3 + \sqrt{5})/2 = 2.62$
$\qquad\qquad\qquad\qquad\qquad\quad R = (3 - \sqrt{5})/2 = 0.38$
19. $T = 87.4°$. $T = 12.6°$ is unrealistic since water freezes at $32°F$.
21. $(-14 + \sqrt{356})/2 = 2.43$ cm   **23.** 30

Section 6.3 (page 176)

1. $\{\frac{2}{3}, -2\}$ **3.** $\{-1, \frac{3}{5}\}$ **5.** $\{(1 \pm \sqrt{17})/4\}$ **7.** $\{(1 \pm \sqrt{33})/4\}$
9. $\{(5 \pm \sqrt{5})/2\}$ **11.** $\{(-6 \pm \sqrt{6})/5\}$ **13.** $\{(1 \pm i\sqrt{5})/3\}$
15. $\{(1 \pm 3i)/2\}$ **17.** $k = 3/\pi$ **19.** $k \le \frac{1}{32}$ **21.** $k = 4, -4$ and others

23. $k = 2$ **25.** $-4 < k < 0$

27. x-intercept: -1 and $\frac{5}{2}$ **29.** x-intercept: $(1 \pm \sqrt{13})/2$
  y-intercept: -5 y-intercept: 3
  vertex $(\frac{3}{4}, -\frac{49}{8})$ vertex $(\frac{1}{2}, \frac{13}{4})$

31. No x-intercept   **33.** No x-intercept   **35.** $x = 2$ mph
  y-intercept: 1 y-intercept: 4
  vertex $(-\frac{1}{2}, \frac{3}{4})$ vertex $(-1, 3)$

37. $(-15 + \sqrt{285})/2 = 0.94$ **39.** 40 hr   **41.** 11, 12, 13

43. $r = (10 - \sqrt{60})/2 = 1.13$

Section 6.4 (page 180)

1. $\{\pm 2, \pm i\sqrt{3}\}$ **3.** $\{\pm i\sqrt{2}, \pm 2\sqrt{2}\}$ **5.** $\{\pm i, \pm 2\sqrt{2}i\}$ **7.** $\{-2, \frac{1}{3}\}$

9. $\{-\frac{3}{2}, \frac{1}{2}\}$ **11.** $\{-4, 2\}$ **13.** $\{\pm i\sqrt{13}, \pm i\sqrt{3}\}$

15. $\{(141 \pm i\sqrt{139})/70\}$ **17.** $\{\pm 1, \pm i\sqrt{5}/2\}$ **19.** $\{15\}$ **21.** $\{11\}$

23. $\{-5, 5\}$ **25.** $\varnothing$ **27.** $\{3\}$ **29.** $\{2\}$ **31.** $\varnothing$ **33.** $\{18\}$

35. $\{0, 1\}$ **37.** 30   **39.** $h = \sqrt{s^2 - \pi^2 r^4}/\pi r$ **41.** $t = 2$

Section 6.5 (page 185)

1. $-3 < x < 1$ **3.** $(7 - \sqrt{89})/2 < x < (7 + \sqrt{89})/2$ **5.** $x < 0$ or $x > 1$
            $-1.2 < x < 8.2$

7. $\varnothing$ **9.** $(10 - \sqrt{44})/2 < x < (10 + \sqrt{44})/2$ **11.** $x \le -3$ or $x \ge 1$
            $1.7 < x < 8.3$

13. $x < -\frac{1}{3}$ or $x > 2$ **15.** $-\frac{3}{2} \le x \le \frac{5}{2}$ **17.** All x

19. $x < (1 - \sqrt{33})/2 = -2.37$ **21.** $x < -5, -4 < x < -1$
  $x > (1 + \sqrt{33})/2 = 3.37$

23. $x \le -2$ or $x > -\frac{3}{2}$ **25.** $-2 < x \le -1, 1 \le x < 2$

27. All x **29.** $(-1 - \sqrt{5})/2 < x < (-1 + \sqrt{5})/2$ or $x \ge 2$

31. $x \le (1 - \sqrt{21})/2 \left.\begin{array}{l} \\ \\ \end{array}\right\}$ $x \le -1.79$ **33.** $k \ge \sqrt{48}$ or $k \le -\sqrt{48}$
  $-\sqrt{3} < x < \sqrt{3}$ $-1.73 < x < 1.73$
  $x \ge (1 + \sqrt{21})/2$ $x \ge 2.79$

35. $k = -\frac{1}{2}, \frac{1}{2}$ **37.** $0 < t < 5$ **39.** $10 < T < 20$

Sections 7.1 and 7.2 (page 192)

1.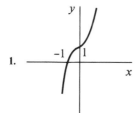

3.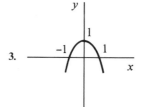

5.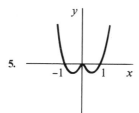

7.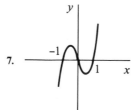

9.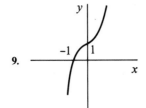

11.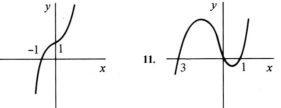

13.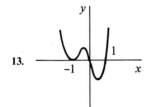

15.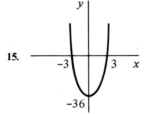

17.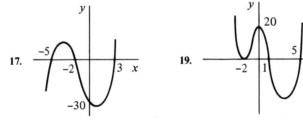

19.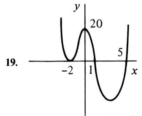

Section 7.3 (page 195)

1. $x - 5 - \dfrac{3}{x - 1}$ **3.** $x^2 + x - 4 + \dfrac{8}{x + 1}$ **5.** $2x^2 - 8x + 17 - \dfrac{35}{x + 2}$

7. $3x^3 - 6x^2 + 8x - 16 + \dfrac{17}{x + 1}$ **9.** $x^3 - 2x^2 + 2x - 1$ **11.** Factor

13. Not a factor   **15.** Factor   **17.** Not a factor

19. Factor   **21.** Factor   **23.** $y = -(x + 1)(x - 1)(x - 2)$

25. $y = \frac{3}{4}(x - 1)^2(x - 2)^2$ **27.** $y = \dfrac{-\sqrt{2}}{5}(x - \sqrt{2})(x^2 - 4x + 5)$

Sections 7.4 and 7.5 (page 201)

1. $x - 1$ **3.** $x^2 + 3 + \dfrac{5}{x - 2}$ **5.** $x^2 - \dfrac{1}{2}x - \dfrac{11}{4} + \dfrac{83}{8(x + \frac{1}{2})}$

7. $x^3 + 2x^2 + 8x + 24$ **9.** $-3x^4 - 6x^3 - 12x^2 - 24x - 41 - \dfrac{74}{x - 2}$

11. $3x^2 - 21x + 30$ **13.** 28   **15.** $-\frac{1}{8}$ **17.** -1.9506

19. 36   **21.** -6665 **23.** 61.8832

Sections 7.6 and 7.7 (page 203)

1. $1, -1, -2$ **3.** $-2, \pm i$ **5.** $-\frac{5}{2}, 1 \pm \sqrt{5}$ **7.** $-1, -2, 2, 3$
9. $\frac{1}{3}, (3 \pm i\sqrt{3})/2$ **11.** $-1, -1, -1, 3$ **13.** $-\frac{2}{3}, (1 \pm i\sqrt{2})/3$
15. $\frac{1}{2}, (1 \pm i\sqrt{7})/2$ **17.** $-1, 1, 2, -1 \pm i\sqrt{3}$ **19.** 23

Section 7.8 (page 206)

1. $\frac{1}{2}$ **3.** $-1.88, 0.35, 1.53$ **5.** $-2.08, 0.47, 3.12$
7. $-2, -0.41, 1, 2.41$ **9.** $-0.5, 0.25$ **11.** $-3.41, -0.59, 1.5$
13. $-1.3, 2.3$ **15.** $-2.59, 1.61$ **17.** -1 **19.** -2.41
21. No real roots   **23.** 1

Section 7.9 (page 211)

1.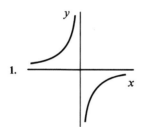

3.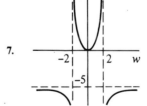

5.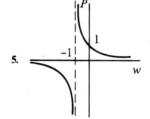

7.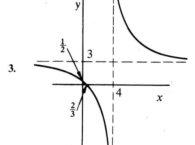

9.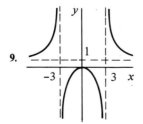

11.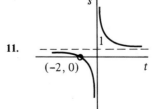

Answers to Odd-Numbered Exercises

13.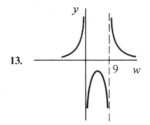

15.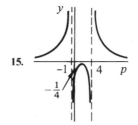

17.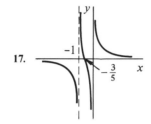

19.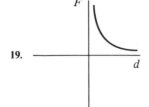

21.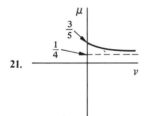

Sections 8.1 and 8.2 (page 222)

1.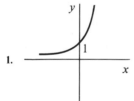

3.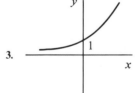

5.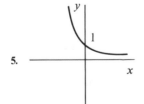

7.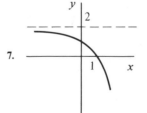

9.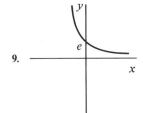

11.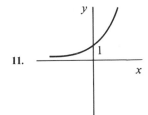

13.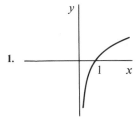

(0.45, 1.55)

15.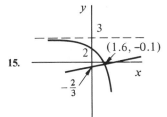

3

(1.6, −0.1)

2

$-\frac{2}{3}$

17. (a) 2.7   (b) 8.8   (c) 2.8   (d) 0.35   (e) 1.3   **19.** $y = 1$ for all x
21. Reflection in the x-axis   **23.** The same curve
25. The same curve shifted 3 units in the negative x direction.
27. 7 days   **29.** \$1276.28

Section 8.3 (page 225)

1. $\log_2 x = 3$ **3.** $\log_5 M = -3$ **5.** $\log_7 L = 2$ **7.** 2
9. 10   **11.** 10,000   **13.** 10   **15.** 4   **17.** 9
19. 2   **21.** a **23.** 8   **25.** 36   **27.** 6   **29.** $-\frac{5}{2}$
31. $-1 < x < 8$ **33.** $4 \leq x \leq 8$ **35.** 2, −3, 4   **37.** $t = 2 - \frac{1}{3}\log_2 P$

Section 8.4 (page 228)

1.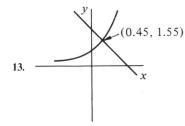

3.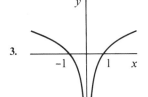

5.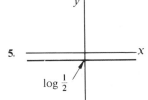

$\log \frac{1}{2}$

7.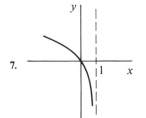

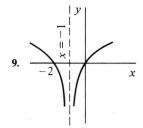

9.

11. Reflection in the x-axis

13. Negative portion reflected in the x-axis
15. Curve moved 3 units in the negative x direction.
17. Reflections of each other in the line $y = x$
19. 2   **21.** 10   **23.** $(1, 0)$

Section 8.5 (page 230)

1. 9   **3.** $\frac{1}{2}$ **5.** 6   **7.** 24   **9.** 0.1761
11. 1.0791   **13.** 1.9542   **15.** 0.3495   **17.** 3.3801

19. -2.8539 **21.** $\log_2 x$ **23.** 0   **25.** $\log \dfrac{5t(t^2 - 4)^2}{\sqrt{t + 3}}$

27. $\log \dfrac{u^3}{(u + 1)^2(u - 1)^5}$

31. The same for $x > 0$. For $x < 0$ $\log x^2$ is defined, $2 \log x$ is not.
33. Both are -2.
35. (a) Multiply each ordinate value by p.   (b) Move curve up $\log p$ units.
    (c) Move curve p units to the left.   (d) Move curve down $\log p$ units.

Section 8.6 (page 234)

1. (a) 0.7332   (b) 3.7332   (c) $7.7332 - 10$
3. (a) 0.9557   (b) $6.9557 - 10$ (c) 5.9557
5. (a) 1.2825   (b) 0.1578
7. (a) 1.3390   (b) $7.4740 - 10$
9. (a) 5.9763   (b) $8.8469 - 10$
11. (a) 1,820   (b) 1.82   (c) 0.0182
13. (a) 15.2   (b) 0.000000152   (c) 1,520,000
15. (a) 4.03   (b) 0.00403   (c) 0.403
17. $x = 1.3979$ **19.** $x = 0.6505$ **21.** $x = 7.990$
23. $x = 1.758$ **25.** $x = -3.398$ **27.** $x = -8.908$

Section 8.7 (page 238)

1. 0.3731   **3.** $7.9811 - 10$ **5.** 0.4343   **7.** 5.8077   **9.** 3.0022
11. 0.4321   **13.** $8.7991 - 10$ **15.** $7.8867 - 10$ **17.** 0.01344
19. 2595   **21.** 3.162   **23.** 2.155   **25.** 7.218×10^{-4}
27. 0.4972   **29.** -0.8413 **31.** 2.115   **33.** 22.46
35. 2.734   **37.** 2.6 (low)

Section 8.8 (page 240)

1. 0.2700 **3.** 10.41 **5.** 1.501 **7.** 70.46 **9.** 3001
11. 5739 **13.** 0.08172 **15.** 1.095 **17.** 1.651
19. -0.6414 **21.** 1.737 **23.** 3.860 **25.** 0.9606 **27.** -1.123

Section 8.9 (page 243)

1. 1.553 **3.** $x = 0, x = \log 2 = 0.301$ **5.** 0.5850 **7.** $x = 10$
9. $x = 1, 10^4$ **11.** $x = 1$ **13.** $x = 1.17$
$$x = 10^{\sqrt{3}} = 53.96$$
$$x = 10^{-\sqrt{3}} = 0.0185$$
15. $x = 2 + \sqrt{5} = 4.236$ **17.** $x = \ln(2 + \sqrt{3}) = 1.317$
$$x = \ln(2 - \sqrt{3}) = -1.317$$
19. The logarithm is a 1-1 function. **21.** $k = 0.02476$
23. 173.3 **25.** 52.5 hr

Section 9.1 (page 253)

1. A multiple of 2π **3.** $75°15', 15°5'$ **5.** $109°10', 8°1'20''$
7. $130°55'15'', -10°34'45''$ **9.** $574°10'54'', -92°39'34''$
11. $-121°1'10'', 39°35'16''$ **13.** $30°, \pi/6$ **15.** $45°, \pi/4$
17. $135°, -5\pi/4$ **19.** $-70°, 29\pi/18$ **21.** $0°, 4\pi$ **23.** $120°, 14\pi/3$
25. $45°, 33\pi/4$ **27.** $-25°, -5\pi/36$ **29.** $1, 57.3°$ **31.** $\pi, 180°$
33. $\pi, -540°$ **35.** $-0.48, 5729.58°$ **37.** $0, 18,000°$
39. $2.618 = (5\pi/6)$ feet.

Section 9.2 (page 257)

(In 1, 3, 5, 7, 9 the trigonometric functions are listed in this order: sine, cosine, tangent, cotangent, secant, cosecant.)
1. $\frac{4}{5}, \frac{3}{5}, \frac{4}{3}, \frac{3}{4}, \frac{5}{3}, \frac{5}{4}$ **3.** $\frac{12}{13}, \frac{5}{13}, \frac{12}{5}, \frac{5}{12}, \frac{13}{5}, \frac{13}{12}$
5. $2/\sqrt{5}, 1/\sqrt{5}, 2, \frac{1}{2}, \sqrt{5}, \sqrt{5}/2$ **7.** $1/\sqrt{5}, 2/\sqrt{5}, \frac{1}{2}, 2, \sqrt{5}/2, \sqrt{5}$
9. $\sqrt{2}/2, \sqrt{2}/2, 1, 1, \sqrt{2}, \sqrt{2}$ **11.** 0.6265, 0.7794, 0.8038, 1.244, 1.283, 1.596
13. 0.5400, 0.8416, 0.6417, 1.558, 1.188, 1.852 **15.** 0.5812, 0.8137, 0.7143, 1.400, 1.229,
1.720 **17.** 1.5 **19.** 0.3536 **21.** 0.957

Sections 9.3 and 9.4 (page 261)

(The trigonometric functions are listed in this order: sine, cosine, tangent, cotangent, secant, cosecant.)

1. $\frac{4}{5}, \frac{3}{5}, \frac{4}{3}, \frac{3}{4}, \frac{5}{3}, \frac{5}{4}$ **3.** $\frac{1}{3}, \frac{\sqrt{8}}{3}, 1/\sqrt{8}, \sqrt{8}, 3/\sqrt{8}, 3$ **5.** $\frac{\sqrt{3}}{2}, \frac{1}{2}, \sqrt{3}, \frac{\sqrt{3}}{2}, 2, 2/\sqrt{3}$

7. $u/v, \sqrt{v^2 - u^2}/v, u/\sqrt{v^2 - u^2}, \sqrt{v^2 - u^2}/u, v/\sqrt{v^2 - u^2}, v/u$
9. $\sqrt{1 - u^2}, u, \sqrt{1 - u^2}/u, u/\sqrt{1 - u^2}, 1/u, 1/\sqrt{1 - u^2}$

11. $\frac{1}{2}, \frac{\sqrt{3}}{2}, \frac{\sqrt{3}}{2}, \sqrt{3}, 2/\sqrt{3}, 2$ **13.** $\frac{\sqrt{2}}{2}, \frac{\sqrt{2}}{2}, 1, 1, \sqrt{2}, \sqrt{2}$

15. $5/\sqrt{26}, 1/\sqrt{26}, 5, \frac{1}{5}, \sqrt{26}, \frac{\sqrt{26}}{5}$

17. $1/\sqrt{1 + t^2}, t/\sqrt{1 + t^2}, 1/t, t, \sqrt{1 + t^2}/t, \sqrt{1 + t^2}$
19. $\sqrt{t^2 - 1}/t, 1/t, \sqrt{t^2 - 1}, 1/\sqrt{t^2 - 1}, t, t/\sqrt{t^2 - 1}$ **21.** $\sin \theta = \frac{\sqrt{2}}{3}$

Section 9.5 (page 265)

1. 0.2250 **3.** 0.3153 **5.** 1.0041 **7.** 3.1084 **9.** 0.9681
11. 0.1736 **13.** 0.2476 **15.** 2.3515 **17.** 0.6412
19. 2.820 **21.** 0.6421 **23.** 1.011 **25.** 27°30′
27. 75° **29.** 56°10′ **31.** 1.00 **33.** 1.33 **35.** 0.56

Section 9.6 (page 267)

1. 0.6243 **3.** 0.8916 **5.** 1.2460 **7.** 0.9095 **9.** 1.2225
11. 0.3827 **13.** 0.6478 **15.** 0.8543 **17.** 0.9999 **19.** 50°54′
21. 54°28′ **23.** 59°17′ **25.** 26°34′ **27.** 56°15′ **29.** 14°29′
31. 0.137 **33.** 0.384 **35.** 1.167 **37.** 0.713 **39.** 0.105 **41.** 0.795

Section 9.7 (page 271)

1. $A = 29°45′, B = 60°15′, c = 8.07$ **3.** $A = 36°52′, B = 53°8′, b = 16$
5. $B = 80°35′, b = 30.15, c = 30.56$ **7.** 1.36 miles **9.** 8 A.M.
11. 55°, 35° **13.** 67°40′, 22°20′ **15.** 38°56′
17. $X = 52, \theta = 60°$ **19.** $Z = 225, \theta = 26°34′$ **21.** $R = 43.3, Z = 50$

Section 9.8 (page 276)

1. $F_x = 17.63, F_y = 17.73$ **3.** $F_x = 0.0197, F_y = 0.0032$
5. $F_x = 14.52, F_y = 8.249$ **7.** 25, 36°52′ **9.** 71.47, 75°50′
11. 0.153, 31°36′ **13.** 948.7 mph **15.** 5.84 mph, 59°2′ with shoreline
17. 50% **19.** 110.3 ft **21.** 13.46 lb

Sections 10.1 and 10.2 (page 285)

(The trigonometric functions are listed in this order: sine, cosine, tangent, cotangent, secant, cosecant.)
1. $2/\sqrt{5}, 1/\sqrt{5}, 2, 1/2, \sqrt{5}, \sqrt{5}/2$
3. $16/\sqrt{337}, -9/\sqrt{337}, -16/9, -9/16, -\sqrt{337}/9, \sqrt{337}/16$
5. $-7/\sqrt{53}, 2/\sqrt{53}, -7/2, -2/7, \sqrt{53}/2, -\sqrt{53}/7$
7. $-1/\sqrt{10}, 3/\sqrt{10}, -1/3, -3, \sqrt{10}/3, -\sqrt{10}$
9. $-1/2, -\sqrt{3}/2, \sqrt{3}/3, \sqrt{3}, -2\sqrt{3}/3, -2$
11. I, II; I, IV; I, III **15.** $-1, 0$, undefined, 0, undefined, -1
17. 3/5, 4/5, 3/4, 4/3, 5/4, 5/3 **19.** $-3/5, -4/5, 3/4, 4/3, -5/4, -5/3$
21. 0, -1, 0, undefined, -1, undefined
23. 0, 1, 0, undefined, 1, undefined and 0, -1, 0, undefined, -1, undefined
25. QIII: $-1/2, -\sqrt{3}/2, \sqrt{3}/3, \sqrt{3}, -2/\sqrt{3}, -2$; QIV: $-1/2, \sqrt{3}/2, -\sqrt{3}/3, -\sqrt{3},$ $2/\sqrt{3}, -2$
27. $10/\sqrt{101}, 1/\sqrt{101}, 10, 1/10, \sqrt{101}, \sqrt{101}/10$
29. QI: 5/13, 12/13, 5/12, 12/5, 13/12, 13/5; QIV: $-5/13, 12/13, -5/12, -12/5, 13/12, -13/5$
31. QII: $0.9529, -0.3033, -\pi, -1/\pi, -3.297, 1.049$; QIV: $-.9529, .3033, -\pi, -1/\pi, 3.2970,$ 1.0494

Section 10.3 (page 290)

1. $-\cos 55°$ **3.** $-\sin 45°$ **5.** $-\tan 17°$ **7.** $-\sec 0.58$
9. $\cos 1.04$ **11.** 0.4384 **13.** -9.5144 **15.** -1.0439
17. 0.2728 **19.** -0.9245 **21.** -0.4618 **23.** -0.8820 **25.** 1.091

27. 0.2403 **29.** -0.9916 **31.** $\dfrac{\sqrt{3}}{2}$ **33.** Undefined   **35.** $\sqrt{3}$
37. 0 **39.** $-2/\sqrt{3}$ **41.** 5.617 **43.** 3.978 **45.** 5.215
47. $334°50'$ **49.** $198°15'$ **51.** $98°20'$

Sections 10.4 and 10.5 (page 295)

1. $c = 39.7$ **3.** $c = 45.8$ **5.** $a = 73.9$ **7.** $C = 75°30'$
9. $A = 95°44'$ **11.** $B = 118°4'$ **13.** $A = 141°11', B = 8°49', c = 3.19$
15. $A = 37°47', B = 47°48', c = 195.2$ **17.** $A = 28°57', B = 46°34', C = 104°29'$
19. $30°45'$ **21.** $A = 66°35', C = 53°25', \overline{AC} = 3{,}775$ feet   **23.** 346.4 feet

Section 10.6 (page 300)

1. $C = 100°, b = 14.02, c = 18.58$ **3.** $B = 26°14', C = 108°46', c = 10.71$
5. $B = 90°, C = 60°, c = 8.66$ **7.** $B = 46°12', C = 13°48', c = 1.65$
9. $B = 28°57', A = 98°3', a = 37.4$ **11.** $A = 44°58', C = 13°2', c = 7.98$
13. $A = 20°, a = 17.9, c = 49.1$ **15.** $C = 88.6°, a = 42.13, b = 45.57$
17. $h_1 = 500, h_2 = 1000$ **19.** $\theta = 20°$

Section 10.7 (page 304)

1. No solution   **3.** Two solutions   **5.** One solution   **7.** No solution
9. $B = 14°32', C = 15°28', b = 7.53$ **11.** No solution
13. $A = 38°45', B = 113°15', b = 29.4$ **15.** $B = 41°48', C = 108°12', c = 570$
     $A = 141°15', B = 10°45', b = 5.95$ $B = 138°12', C = 11°48', c = 1227$
17. $B = 47°48', C = 59°57', c = 0.818$ **19.** $15 \sin 25° < b < 15$

Section 11.1 (page 313)

1. (a) $\cos 1 = 0.54, \sin 1 = 0.84$ (b) $\cos (-2) = -0.42, \sin (-2) = -0.91$
     (c) $\cos 3 = -0.99, \sin 3 = 0.14$ (d) $\cos 10 = -0.84, \sin 10 = -.54$
     (e) $\cos 3\pi = -1, \sin 3\pi = 0$ (f) $\cos (-4) = -0.65, \sin (-4) = 0.76$
     (g) $\cos (-4\pi) = 1, \sin (-4\pi) = 0$ (h) $\cos (\pi/3) = 0.5, \sin (\pi/3) = .87$
     (i) $\cos (\frac{1}{3}) = 0.95, \sin (\frac{1}{3}) = 0.33$ (j) $\cos (\frac{1}{2}) = 0.88, \sin (\frac{1}{2}) = 0.48$
     (k) $\cos \sqrt{7} = -0.88, \sin \sqrt{7} = 0.48$ (l) $\cos 5.15 = 0.42, \sin 5.15 = -0.91$
5. 0 **7.** 0.5480 **9.** 0.5 **11.** 1 **13.** -1 **15.** -0.8365
17. 0.2867 **19.** $(2n + 1)\pi/2$ **21.** $2n\pi$
23. $-\pi/2 < x < \pi/2, 3\pi/2 < x < 5\pi/2$, etc.   **25.** $x = (4n + 1)\pi/2$
27. $x = (2n + 1)\pi/2$

Sections 11.2 and 11.3 (page 320)

1. Domain of both: all reals.
Range of both: $-1 \le y \le 1$.

3.

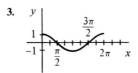

5. $A = 3$, ps $= 0$, per. $= 2\pi$

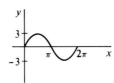

7. $A = 6$, ps $= 0$, per. $= 2\pi$

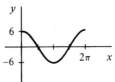

9. $A = 1$, ps $= 0$, per. $= 3\pi$

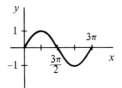

11. $A = 1$, ps $= 0$, per. $= 2$

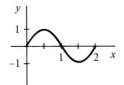

13. $A = 1$, ps $= -\pi/3$, per. $= 2\pi$

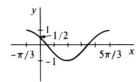

15. $A = 2$, ps $= \pi$, per. $= 4\pi$

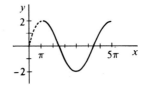

17. $A = 1$, ps $= -\pi/2$, per. $= \pi$

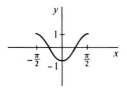

19. $A = 4$, ps $= -\pi$, per. $= 6\pi$

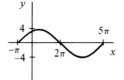

21. $A = 1$, ps $= \frac{1}{4}$, per. $= 2$

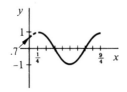

23.

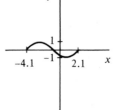

25.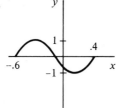

27.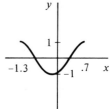

29. $y = \cos 2\left(x + \frac{1}{6}\pi\right)$

31. $y = -2 \sin \frac{1}{2}x$

33.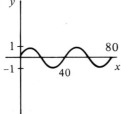

35. They are mirror images in the *t*-axis.

37. They are the same.

41.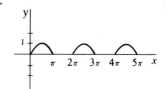

Sections 11.4 and 11.5 (page 325)

1. 2π **3.** 2   **5.** 2   **7.** $12\pi/5$

9. Period $\pi/2$,
phase shift 0

11. Period π,
phase shift $\pi/4$

13. Period $\pi/2$,
phase shift $-\pi/6$

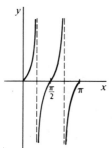

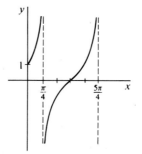

15. Period π, phase shift $3\pi/2$ **17.** Period π, phase shift $\pi/4$

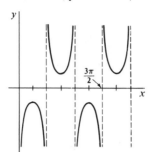   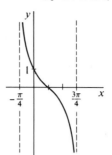

19. $\tan x = -\cot (x + \pi/2)$

21. They are the same.   **23.** They are mirror reflections in the y-axis.

Section 11.6 (page 330)

1. $\pi/6$ **3.** $\pi/4$ **5.** $\pi/2$ **7.** $\pi/3$ **9.** 1   **11.** $2/\sqrt{5}$ **13.** $\sqrt{15}/4$
15. $\sqrt{1 - x^4}$ **17.** $\pm\sqrt{1 - (x - 4)^2}$ **21.** $\sin x$ **23.** $\cos (x/3)$
25.

27. $\pm 2x\sqrt{1 - x^2}$ **29.** $x\sqrt{1 - y^2} + y\sqrt{1 - x^2}$

Section 11.7 (page 332)

1.

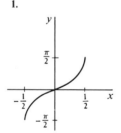

3.

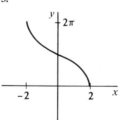

5.

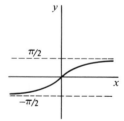

7.

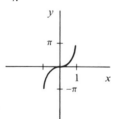

9.

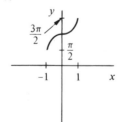

11.

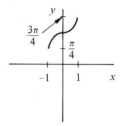

13.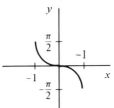

15.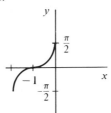

17.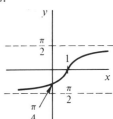

19.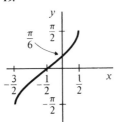

21.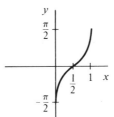

Section 12.1 (page 340)

1. $\sec \theta$ **3.** $\sec x \csc x$ **5.** $\cot x$ **7.** $\cot x$ **9.** $-\tan^2 x$
11. $\sin x$ **13.** 1 **15.** 1 **17.** $\sec x$ **19.** $\cos x$
21. $a \sec \theta, x/\sqrt{a^2 + x^2}$ **23.** $\sin \theta$

Section 12.2 (page 345)

1. $\pi/6, 5\pi/6$ **3.** $\pi/3$ **5.** $\pi/3, 2\pi/3$

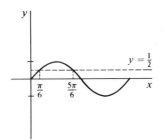

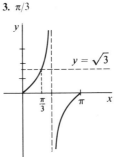

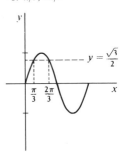

7. $7\pi/24, 11\pi/24$ **9.** $15\pi/4, 23\pi/4$

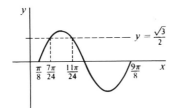

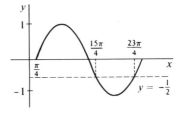

11. $7\pi/6, 11\pi/6$ **13.** $0, 2\pi/3$ **15.** π **17.** $0, \pi, \pi/6, 5\pi/6$ **19.** No solution
21. $\pi/4, 5\pi/4$ **23.** No solution   **25.** $\pi/6, 5\pi/6, 3\pi/2$ **27.** $\pi/2$
29. $0, \pi/4, \pi, 5\pi/4$ **31.** $0, \pi, \pi/4, 3\pi/4, 5\pi/4, 7\pi/4$ **33.** $0, 3\pi/2$ **35.** $\pi/2, \pi$
37. $\pi/4, 3\pi/4, 5\pi/4, 7\pi/4$

Section 12.3 (page 349)

1. Identity   **3.** $\pi/2, 3\pi/2$ **5.** Identity   **7.** Identity   **9.** Identity

Section 12.4 (page 354)

7. $\dfrac{\sqrt{2}}{4}(1 + \sqrt{3})$ **9.** $\dfrac{-\sqrt{2}}{4}(1 + \sqrt{3})$ **21.** $\cos 8x$

23. $(\sqrt{3} + \sqrt{8})/6$ **25.** $\frac{3}{5}$ **27.** $(5\sqrt{8} + \sqrt{11})/18$

29. Amplitude $= \sqrt{2}$,   **31.** Amplitude $= 2$,
     phase shift $= -\pi/4$ phase shift $= \pi/6$

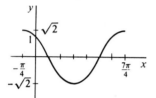 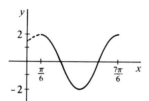

Section 12.5 (page 358)

1. $\dfrac{\sqrt{2}}{4}(1 + \sqrt{3})$ **3.** $\dfrac{\sqrt{2}}{4}(\sqrt{3} + 1)$ **5.** $\dfrac{\sqrt{3} - 1}{\sqrt{3} + 1}$ **15.** $\tan x$

17. $\tan (x + y + z)$ **19.** $36/325, 36/323$
21. $\sqrt{2} \sin (2x + \frac{1}{4}\pi)$ **23.** $2 \sin (\pi x + \frac{1}{6}\pi)$

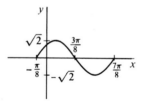 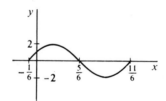

Section 12.6 (page 363)

1. $\sin 6x$ **3.** $-\cos 8x$ **5.** $\tan \frac{1}{3}x$
7. Max. $= \frac{1}{2}$ at $\pi/8$ **9.** Max. $= -2$ at $3\pi/4$, undefined at $0, \pi/2, \pi$

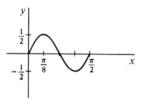 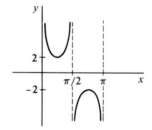

11. Undefined at $x = 0, \pi/2, \pi$. Period $= \pi$
13. 24/25, 7/25, 24/7   **15.** 336/625, 527/625, 336/527
17. $\sqrt{2 - \sqrt{2}}/2$ **19.** $-\sqrt{2}/(2 + \sqrt{2})$ **21.** $2 + \sqrt{3}/2$ **29.** 1/5
31. $7/5\sqrt{2}$ **33.** $\pi/4, 5\pi/4$ **35.** $0, \pi, 2\pi$ **37.** $\pi/4, 5\pi/4$
39. $\pi/6, \pi/3, 2\pi/3, 5\pi/6, 4\pi/3, 7\pi/6, 5\pi/3, 11\pi/6$ **41.** 1   **43.** 1   **45.** 1

Sections 12.7 and 12.8 (page 367)

1. $2 \sin 2\theta \cos \theta$ **3.** $2 \sin 5x \cos 3x$ **5.** $-2 \sin 40° \sin 10°$
7. $2 \cos \frac{1}{2} \sin \frac{1}{4}$ **9.** $\frac{1}{2}[\sin (\frac{3}{2}x) - \sin (\frac{1}{2}x)]$ **11.** $\frac{1}{2}(\cos 8x + \cos 4x)$

19. $\dfrac{-2 \sin \frac{1}{2}(2x + \Delta x) \cos \frac{1}{2} \Delta x}{\Delta x}$ **21.** $0, \pi/6, \pi/2, 5\pi/6, \pi$ **23.** $0, 2\pi/5, 4\pi/5$

25. Amplitude $= 2 \cos 1$, period $= 2\pi/3$

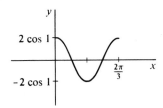

Sections 13.1 and 13.2 (page 374)

1. 2.24, 63.4°   **3.** 3.00, 61.9°   **5.** 5.66, $-135°$ **7.** 5, $-36.9°$
9. 6.24, 106.1°   **11.** (6.43, 7.66)   **13.** (11.34, 7.69)
15. $(-90.63, 129.43)$ **17.** $(-33.33, -27.96)$ **19.** $(9.43, -4.40)$

Sections 13.3 and 13.4 (page 378)

1. $5i + j$ **3.** $-6i - 2j$ **5.** $i - 3j$ **7.** $-4j$ **9.** $6i - 7j$
11. 35.19, 51.2°   **13.** 13.36, 73.0°   **15.** 65.58, 131.4°
17. 395.1, $-64.0°$ **19.** 304 mph, 80.5°N of W   **21.** 163.8 lb
23. 119.9 lb, 30.8°   **25.** 1678.6 fps, 142° below the horizontal

Section 13.5 (page 382)

1. 1   **3.** 41   **5.** 1   **7.** 529.9   **9.** -3688 **11.** 337.4
13. 37.87°   **15.** 176.8°   **17.** 529.8 ft-lb   **19.** 433 ft-lb

Section 13.6 (page 385)

1. $7 + 5i$ **3.** $-2 + 3i$ **5.** 4   **7.** $3 + i$ **9.** $-7 + 22i$ **11.** 26
13. $13 + 8\sqrt{3}i$ **15.** $18 + 24i$ **17.** $(5 - i)/2$ **19.** $(6 + 9i)/13$

21. $-i/5$ **23.** $\dfrac{(-4 + 3\sqrt{2}) - (12 + \sqrt{2})i}{18}$

Section 13.7 (page 387)

1. $7 + 6i$ **3.** $2 + 4i$ **5.** $-1 - 3i$ **7.** $-1 + 3i$ **9.** 10

11. $-1 + 8i$ **13.** $3 + (\sqrt{3} + 1)i$ **15.** $4i$

17.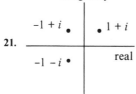

19.

21.

imaginary

$-1 + i$ •   • $1 + i$

real

$-1 - i$ •

Section 13.8 (page 391)

1. $2 \text{ cis } (-60°)$ **3.** $3 \text{ cis } 41°49'$ **5.** $9 \text{ cis } 0°$ **7.** $5 \text{ cis } (-53°8')$

9. $\sqrt{61} \text{ cis } (-50°12')$ **11.** $\sqrt{3} + i$ **13.** $\dfrac{5\sqrt{2}}{2}(-1 + i)$ **15.** $\dfrac{-3 - \sqrt{3}\,i}{2}$

17. $\dfrac{3 - 3\sqrt{3}\,i}{2}$ **19.** $9.397 + 3.420i$ **21.** $12 \text{ cis } 90°$ **23.** $2 \text{ cis } 330°$

25. $20 \text{ cis } 135°$ **27.** $10 \text{ cis } 23°8'$ **29.** $5 \text{ cis } (-60°)$ **31.** $2 \text{ cis } 7°30'$

33. $\dfrac{\sqrt{2}}{2} \text{ cis } (-75°)$ **35.** $\dfrac{4}{\sqrt{2}} \text{ cis } (-45°)$

Section 13.9 (page 395)

1. $8 \text{ cis } 0°$ **3.** $9 \text{ cis } 240°$ **5.** $128\sqrt{2} \text{ cis } 315°$ **7.** $128 \text{ cis } 330°$

9. $841 \text{ cis } 272°48'$

11. $1 \text{ cis } 0° = 1$
$1 \text{ cis } 72° = .3090 + .9511i$
$1 \text{ cis } 144° = -.8090 + .5878i$
$1 \text{ cis } 216° = -.8090 - .5878i$
$1 \text{ cis } 288° = .3090 - .9511i$

13. $1 \text{ cis } 22°30' = .9238 + .3827i$
$1 \text{ cis } 112°30' = -.3827 + .9239i$
$1 \text{ cis } 202°30' = -.9238 - .3827i$
$1 \text{ cis } 292°30' = .3827 - .9239i$

15. $\sqrt[4]{2} \text{ cis } 22°30'$
$\sqrt[4]{2} \text{ cis } 202°30'$